Analysis of Scattering and Decay

Documents on Modern Physics

Edited by

ELLIOTT W. MONTROLL, *University of Rochester*
GEORGE H. VINEYARD, *Brookhaven National Laboratory*
MAURICE LÉVY, *Université de Paris*

A. ABRAGAM L'Effet Mössbauer
K. G. BUDDEN Lectures on Magnetoionic Theory
J. W. CHAMBERLAIN Motion of Charged Particles in the Earth's Magnetic Field
S. CHAPMAN Solar Plasma, Geomagnetism and Aurora
H.-Y. CHIU Neutrino Astrophysics
A. H. COTTRELL Theory of Crystal Dislocations
J. DANON Lectures on the Mössbauer Effect
B. S. DE WITT Dynamical Theory of Groups and Fields
R. H. DICKE The Theoretical Significance of Experimental Relativity
M. GOURDIN Lagrangian Formalism and Symmetry Laws
D. HESTENES Space–Time Algebra
J. G. KIRKWOOD Dielectrics—Intermolecular Forces—Optical Rotation
J. G. KIRKWOOD Macromolecules
J. G. KIRKWOOD Proteins
J, G. KIRKWOOD Quantum Statistics and Cooperative Phenomena
J. G. KIRKWOOD Selected Topics in Statistical Mechanics
J. G. KIRKWOOD Shock and Detonation Waves
J. G. KIRKWOOD Theory of Liquids
J. G. KIRKWOOD Theory of Solutions
V. KOURGANOFF Introduction to the General Theory of Particle Transfer
R. LATTÈS Methods of Resolutions of Selected Boundary Problems in Mathematical Physics
J. LEQUEUX Structure and Evolution of Galaxies
F. E. LOW Symmetries and Elementary Particles
P. H. E. MEIJER Quantum Statistical Mechanics
M. MOSHINSKY Group Theory and the Many-body Problem
M. NIKOLIĆ Analysis of Scattering and Decay
M. NIKOLIĆ Kinematics and Multiparticle Systems
A. B. PIPPARD The Dynamics of Conduction Electrons
H. REEVES Stellar Evolution and Nucleosynthesis
L. SCHWARTZ Application of Distributions to the Theory of Elementary Particles in Quantum Mechanics
J. SCHWINGER and D. SAXON Discontinuities in Waveguides
M. TINKHAM Superconductivity

Foreword

This volume contains selected articles from the first (1965) and second (1966) sessions of the Herceg-Novi International School of Elementary Particle Physics, as well as two articles from the CERN 1964 Easter School, concerning the question of analysis of scattering and decay.

The Organizing Committee of the Herceg-Novi school expresses its gratitude to the European Organization for Nuclear Research, CERN, Geneva, for permission to include in this volume the new version of the lectures of Dr. G. Costa "Topics on Elementary Theory of Scattering" and of W. Koch "Some Methods of Spin Analysis in Elementary Particle Physics", which were first delivered at the CERN 1964 school.

P. Cüer

Chairman of the
Organizing Committee

PROCEEDINGS OF THE INTERNATIONAL SCHOOL OF ELEMENTARY PARTICLE PHYSICS, HERCEG-NOVI (Yugoslavia)

Published by Gordon and Breach Science Publishers Inc.

Methods in Subnuclear Physics, Volume I (1965 lectures)

Methods in Subnuclear Physics, Volume II (1966 lectures)

Methods in Subnuclear Physics, Volume III (1967 lectures)

Kinematics and Multiparticle Systems (selected from CERN 1964 and from the 1965 and 1966 lectures)

Analysis of Scattering and Decay (selected from CERN 1964 and from the 1965 and 1966 lectures)

Organizing Committee of the Herceg-Novi International School

P. CÜER, Chairman of the Committee
H. BRAUN
M. JURIĆ, Secretary of the Committee
Z. MARIĆ
M. NIKOLIĆ, Secretary of the Committee
R. OMNÈS
T. FABERGÉ, Secretary of the School

Contributors to this Volume

G. COSTA
U. NGUYEN-KHAC
W. KOCH
P. MOUSSA
J. SIX
R. STORA
P. WALOSCHEK

Contents

Preface v

Foreword vii

Contributors to this Volume ix

Topics on Elementary Theory of Scattering (G. COSTA) 1

Phase Shift Analysis (P. WALOSCHEK) 37

Angular Analysis of Elementary Particle Reactions (P. MOUSSA and R. STORA) 101

Applications of Invariance Principles in the Physics of Elementary Particles (U. NGUYEN-KHAC and J. SIX) 177

Some Methods of Spin Analysis in Elementary Particle Physics (W. KOCH) 229

Topics on Elementary Theory of Scattering

GIOVANNI COSTA

Istituto di Fisica dell'Università, Padova, Italy

CONTENTS

I. SCATTERING BY A CENTRAL POTENTIAL 3

I.1 Phase shift analysis 3
I.2 Determination of the phase shifts 4
I.3 Resonance scattering 5
I.4 Graphical representation 6

II. SCATTERING OF PARTICLES WITH SPIN 7

II.1 Scattering of a spin-0 particle by a spin-$\frac{1}{2}$particle 7
II.2 Polarization of spin $\frac{1}{2}$ particles 10

III. INELASTIC COLLISIONS 11

III.1 Elastic and inelastic cross-sections 11
III.2 Effective range approximation 13
III.3 Scattering by a black sphere 14

IV. MULTI-CHANNEL FORMALISM 16

IV.1 The scattering matrix 16
IV.2 The scattering amplitude and the reaction matrix 19
IV.3 The reduced reaction matrix 23
IV.4 Resonances in a multi-channel system 24
IV.5 Graphical representation 26

V. REGGE POLES 29

V.1 Regge poles in potential scattering 29
V.2 High energy behaviour of scattering cross-sections 32

REFERENCES 35

I. SCATTERING BY A CENTRAL POTENTIAL

I.1. Phase Shift Analysis

In this section we give a short review of the scattering of a particle by a fixed centre of force described by a potential $V(r)$. (For a more detailed account see e.g. ref. 1).

The problem of elastic collisions between two particles (with masses m_1, m_2) in the center of mass system can be treated as the scattering of a single particle (with reduced mass $\mu = m_1 m_2/(m_1 + m_2)$) by a central potential $V(r)$.

The incident particle (moving along the z axis in the positive direction) is described by a plane wave e^{ikz}; the scattered particle is described, at a great distance from the scattering centre, by an outgoing spherical wave

$$f(\vartheta)\frac{e^{ikr}}{r},$$

where $f(\vartheta)$ is the *scattering amplitude* (ϑ is the angle between the z axis and the direction of motion of the scattered particle; r is the distance of the particle from the scattering centre); thus, the complete solution of the stationary Schrödinger equation

$$-\frac{\hbar^2}{2\mu}\nabla^2\psi + V(r)\,\psi = E\psi \tag{1}$$

is represented, at large distances from the scattering centre, by the asymptotic form

$$\psi(r, \vartheta) \to e^{ikz} + f(\vartheta)\frac{e^{ikr}}{r}. \tag{2}$$

The solution of Eq. (1) can be expanded in terms of the Legendre polynomials $P_l(\cos\vartheta)$:

$$\psi(r, \vartheta) = \frac{1}{r}\sum_{l=0}^{\infty} u_l(r)\, P_l(\cos\vartheta) \tag{3}$$

where $u_l(r)$ is the solution of the radial Schrödinger equation

$$\frac{d^2}{dr^2}u_l + \left[k^2 - U(r) - \frac{l(l+1)}{r^2}\right]u_l = 0 \tag{4}$$

with

$$k^2 = \frac{2\mu E}{\hbar^2}, \quad U(r) = \frac{2\mu V(r)}{\hbar^2}.$$

In the case of a potential with a finite range R, the u_l's have the asymptotic behaviour (for $r \gg R$):

$$u_l(r) \to A_l\frac{1}{k}\sin\left(kr - \frac{1}{2}\pi + \delta_l\right) \tag{5}$$

where the quantity δ_l (which depends, in general, on the energy E) is the *phase shift* for the scattering in the state of angular momentum l. The general asymptotic form of the solution of Eq. (4) can then be written as

$$\psi(r, \vartheta) \to \frac{1}{kr} \sum_{l=0}^{\infty} A_l \sin\left(kr - \frac{1}{2} l\pi + \delta_l\right) P_l(\cos\vartheta). \tag{6}$$

We have now to chose the quantities a_l in such a way that the two expressions Eqs. (2) and (6) coincide. Using the expansion

$$e^{ikz} = \frac{1}{kr} \sum_{l=0}^{\infty} i^l(2l+1) \sin\left(kr - \frac{1}{2} l\pi\right) P_l(\cos\vartheta) \tag{7}$$

one can easily obtain the following relations:

$$A_l = i^l(2l+1)\, e^{i\delta_l} \tag{8}$$

$$f(\vartheta) = \frac{1}{2ik} \sum_{l=0}^{\infty} (2l+1)\,(e^{2i\delta_l} - 1)\, P_l(\cos\vartheta). \tag{9}$$

For future reference we rewrite explicitly Eq. (6) in terms of (8):

$$\psi(r, \vartheta) \to \frac{1}{2ikr} \sum_l i^l(2l+1)[e^{2i\delta_l}\, e^{i(kr-\frac{1}{2}l\pi)} - e^{-i(kr-\frac{1}{2}l\pi)}] \tag{6'}$$

The formula Eq. (9) solves the problem of expressing the scattering amplitude in terms of the phase shifts δ_l. We shall sometimes use the notation

$$f(\vartheta) = \sum_{l=0}^{\infty} (2l+1) f_l(k)\, P_l\,(\cos\vartheta) \tag{10}$$

where

$$f_l(k) = \frac{e^{2i\delta_l} - 1}{2ik} \equiv \frac{e^{i\delta_l}\sin\delta_l}{k} \equiv \frac{1}{k(\cot\delta_l - i)} \tag{11}$$

represents the scattering amplitude of the l-th partial wave.

The *differential cross-section* is obtained by dividing the flux of particles scattered per unit solid angle in the direction (ϑ, φ) by the incident flux:

$$\frac{d\sigma}{d\Omega} = |f(\vartheta)|^2 \tag{12}$$

and the *total cross-section* is given by integration over all the angles:

$$\sigma(k) = 2\pi \int_0^{\pi} |f(\vartheta)|^2 \sin\vartheta\, d\vartheta = \frac{4\pi}{k^2} \sum_{l=0}^{\infty} (2l+1) \sin^2\delta_l. \tag{13}$$

It is easy to derive from Eqs. (10) and (13) the following relation between the total cross-section and the forward scattering amplitude:

$$\operatorname{Im} f(0) = \frac{k}{4\pi}\,\sigma(k), \tag{14}$$

which is known as "optical theorem". It is a consequence of the conservation of probability and it holds in much more general conditions than in the present case.

I.2. Determination of the Phase Shifts

The determination of the phase shifts depends on the specific form of the potential $V(r)$. However, we are interested here in the general properties of the phase shifts valid for a potential of finite range R.

The radial solution of Eq. (4) for $r > R$ (in this region $V(r) = 0$) can be written as:

$$u_l(r > R) = \cos \delta_l \cdot j_l(kr) - \sin \delta_l \cdot \eta_l(kr) \tag{15}$$

where j_l and η_l are the spherical Bessel and Neuman functions. The phase shifts are determined by joining at the boundary $r = R$ the wave function $\chi_l = (1/r)\, u_l$ and its first derivative, i.e. by joining the logarithmic derivative of the wave function. We write:

$$g_l(k) = R\left(\frac{\chi_l'}{\chi_l}\right)_{r=R} \tag{16}$$

where the quantity $g_l(k)$ is R times the logarithmic derivative of the wave function, valid inside the potential region, evaluated at $r = R$. Clearly g_l depends on the form of the potential; but we shall consider it here as a given parameter.

Suppose now that $kR \ll 1$; in this case we can use the asymptotic expansions

$$j_l(x) \approx \frac{x^l}{(2l+1)!!}; \quad \eta_l(x) \approx -\frac{(2l-1)!!}{x^{l+1}} \quad (x \ll 1) \tag{17}$$

in the above relations Eqs. (15) and (16). We obtain in this way:

$$\operatorname{tg} \delta_l = \beta_l \frac{(kR)^{2l+1}}{(2l+1)!!\,(2l-1)!!} \tag{18}$$

with

$$\beta_l = \frac{l - g_l}{l + 1 + g_l}. \tag{19}$$

For a regular behaviour of β_l, $\operatorname{tg} \delta_l$ decreases strongly with the increasing angular momentum l. For very small values of kR, we may neglect all the terms except the first. In this approximation (equivalent to keep only the S wave) one gets:

$$\operatorname{tg} \delta_0 \approx \delta_0 \approx \beta_0 kR \tag{20}$$

and

$$f(\vartheta) \approx \beta_0 R; \quad \sigma \approx 4\pi\beta_0^2 R^2. \tag{21}$$

Then, for small velocity, the scattering is *isotropic*, and the cross-section is independent of the energy.

I.3. Resonance Scattering

We have assumed, in the previous section, that for very small kR the quantities β_l are also small. This is obviously not true in the special case

$$g_l(k_R) = -(l+1). \tag{22}$$

In this case $\tan\delta_l$ goes to infinity and $\delta_l = \pi/2$ at the value $k = k_R$.

We can expand $g_l(k)$ for values of k close to k_R (or equivalently for values of the energy E close to $E_R = \hbar^2 k_R^2/2\mu$):

$$g_l(E) \simeq -(l+1) + (E_R - E)\left(-\frac{dg_l}{dE}\right)_{E=E_R}. \tag{23}$$

We can then re-write Eq. (18) as

$$\operatorname{tg}\delta_l = \frac{\Gamma_l/2}{E_R - E} \tag{24}$$

with

$$\Gamma_l = \frac{2(kR)^{2l+1}}{\left(-\frac{dg_l}{dE}\right)_{E_R}[(2l-1)!!]^2}. \tag{25}$$

In general, this corresponds to expand $\cot\delta_l$ near its zero at $E = E_R$ by a Taylor's series:

$$\cot\delta_l = (E_R - E)\left[-\frac{d}{dE}\cot\delta_l\right]_{E=E_R} + \cdots \tag{26}$$

with

$$\Gamma_l(E_R) = 2\left[-\frac{d}{dE}\cot\delta_l\right]_{E=E_R}.$$

This behaviour of the phase shift corresponds to a *resonance* which occurs in the scattering of the l partial wave at the energy E_R; Γ_l is the *width* of the resonance. The scattering amplitude (11) becomes near the resonance:

$$f_l(k) = \frac{1}{k}\frac{\Gamma_l/2}{(E_R - E) - i\Gamma_l/2}. \tag{27}$$

The resonant behaviour is shown in Fig. 1, where the quantities $k \operatorname{Re} f_l(k)$ and $k \operatorname{Im} f_l(k)$ are represented versus $(E - E_R)/\Gamma_l$.

The l term σ_l of the total crossection, corresponding to keeping only f_l. in (13), becomes:

$$\sigma_l(E) = \frac{4\pi}{k^2}(2l+1)\frac{(\Gamma_l/2)^2}{(E_R - E)^2 + (\Gamma_l/2)^2}. \tag{28}$$

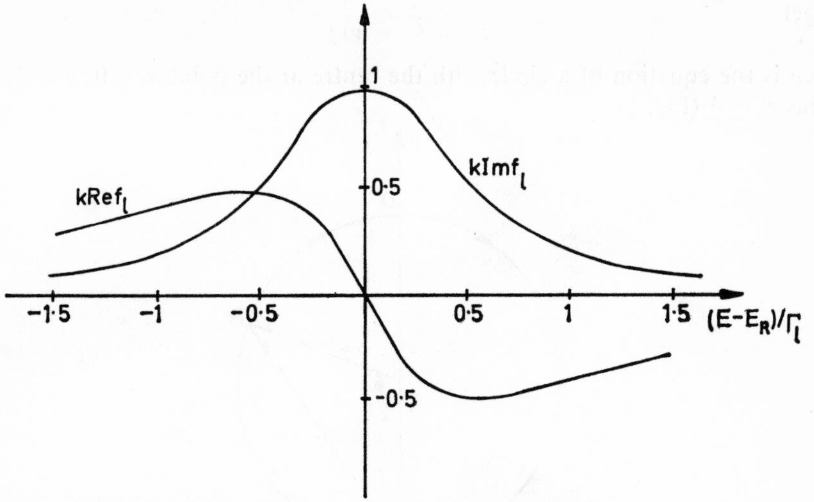

Fig. 1. Real and imaginary parts of elastic scattering amplitude near a resonance.

This is the Breit-Wigner formula for the elastic resonant cross-section. The maximum value compatible with unitarity (*geometrical value*)

$$\sigma_l^{(\max)} = \frac{4\pi}{k^2}(2l + 1) \tag{29}$$

is reached by $\sigma_l(E)$ at $E = E_R\,(k = k_R)$.

I.4. Graphical Representation

A useful graphical representation for the scattering amplitude given by (11) is obtained in the complex plane $x = k \operatorname{Re} f_l$, $y = k \operatorname{Im} f_l$.
We can write

$$kf_l(k) = \frac{1}{\varepsilon - i} \tag{30}$$

with

$$\varepsilon = \cot \delta_l.$$

Then, from

$$\begin{aligned} x &= \frac{1}{2}\sin 2\delta_l = \frac{\varepsilon}{\varepsilon^2 + 1} \\ y &= \sin^2 \delta_l = \frac{1}{\varepsilon^2 + 1}, \end{aligned} \tag{31}$$

we get

$$x^2 = (1 - y)\, y$$

which is the equation of a circle with the centre at the point $x = 0$, $y = \frac{1}{2}$, and radius $R = \frac{1}{2}$ (Fig. 2).

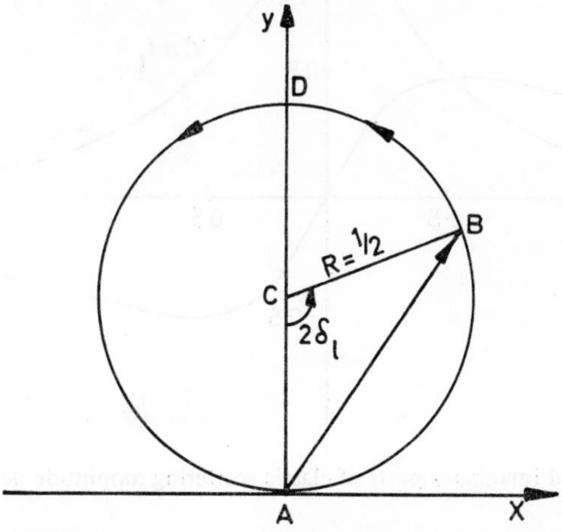

Fig. 2. Graphical representation of elastic scattering amplitude.

The complex quantity $kf_l(k)$ is then represented in Fig. 2 by the vector AB. One gets immediately from (31): $\widehat{ACB} = 2\delta_l$. The end point B moves, by varying the energy, on the circle. It is important to remark that it moves, with increasing energy, in *counter-clockwise* sense. This is a consequence of causality that demands the minus sign in the denominator of Eq. (30), which is equivalent to

$$k \,\mathrm{Im}\, f_l^{-1} = -1. \tag{32}$$

A simple argument was given by Wigner (Ref. 2): it can be easily shown that, if the interaction region is characterized by a radius R, causality requires the condition

$$\frac{d\delta}{dk} \geqq -R. \tag{33}$$

This means that the phase shift cannot decrease with increasing energy faster than a certain amount. There is no limitation on its rate of increase which, in fact, is rather large near a resonance.

II. SCATTERING OF PARTICLES WITH SPIN

II.1. Scattering of a Spin-0 Particle by a Spin-$\frac{1}{2}$ Particle

We generalize here the previous results to the case in which the particles have spins different from zero, and the potential depends on the spin orientation, as in the case of the spin-orbit potential.

In this case the solution of the Schrödinger equation can be expanded in terms of the eigenstates $Y^M_{JlS}(\vartheta, \varphi)$ of J, M, l, S (J is the total angular momentum and M is its component along the z axis, S the total spin):

$$\psi(r, \vartheta, \varphi) = \frac{1}{r} \sum_{J,l} u_{JlS}(r)\, Y^M_{JlS}(\vartheta, \varphi). \tag{34}$$

The Y^M_{JlS} are expressed in terms of the spherical harmonics Y^m_l, and the spin eigenfunctions $\chi^{m_s}_S$:

$$Y^M_{JlS}(\vartheta, \varphi) = \sum_{m,m_s} C_{lS}(J, M; m, m_s)\, \chi^{m_s}_S Y^m_l(\vartheta, \varphi) \tag{35}$$

where the C_{lS}'s are the Clebsch-Gordan coefficients (m, m_s are the z components of l and S). Due to the orthogonality properties of the C_{lS}, the eigenfunctions Y^M_{JlS} form an orthonormal set, as the Y^m_l do (Ref. 3).

The radial Schrödinger equation is now

$$\frac{d^2}{dr^2} u_{JlS} + \left[k^2 - U_{JlS}(r) - \frac{l(l+1)}{r^2}\right] u_{JlS} = 0. \tag{36}$$

We consider the simple case of the scattering of a spin zero particle by a spin $\frac{1}{2}$ particle; for a given value of l, the total angular momentum J can have the two values $J = l \pm \frac{1}{2}$ and the potential splits into two terms (we assume $U_{l+\frac{1}{2},l} \neq U_{l-\frac{1}{2},l}$; clearly, if the potential does not depent on J, the results of the preceding sections remain unchanged).

Since for the incident wave along the z-axis, it is $m = 0$ (there is symmetry around the z axis), the z component of the total angular momentum is $M = m_s = \pm\frac{1}{2}$ in the initial state, and then it will be always $M = \pm\frac{1}{2}$. On the other hand, if the incident particle has a given $m_s = +\frac{1}{2}$, the outgoing particle can have both values $m_s' = +\frac{1}{2}$, $m_s' = -\frac{1}{2}$.

The asymptotic wave function can then be written as follows:

$$\psi_{\pm\frac{1}{2}}(\vartheta\varphi) \to \begin{pmatrix}\alpha\\ \beta\end{pmatrix} e^{ikz} + \left\{\begin{pmatrix}\alpha\\ \beta\end{pmatrix} f(\vartheta, \varphi) \pm \begin{pmatrix}\beta\\ \alpha\end{pmatrix} g_{\pm}(\vartheta, \varphi)\right\} \frac{e^{ikr}}{r} \tag{37}$$

where we have used the notation $\alpha = \chi^{\frac{1}{2}}_{\frac{1}{2}}$, $\beta = \chi^{-\frac{1}{2}}_{\frac{1}{2}}$. The quantity $g_\pm$ is called *spin-flip* amplitude, and f *non spin-flip* amplitude.

The asymptotic form of the general solution is given by Eq. (34) with

$$u_{J,l}(r) \to \frac{1}{k} A_{J,l} \sin\left(kr - \frac{1}{2} l\pi + \delta_{J,l}\right), \quad \left(J = l \pm \frac{1}{2}\right). \tag{38}$$

In this specific case we give the explicit expressions for the Y^M_{JlS}:

$$Y^{\frac{1}{2}}_{l+\frac{1}{2}} = \sqrt{\frac{l+1}{2l+1}}\,\alpha Y^0_l + \sqrt{\frac{l}{2l+1}}\,\beta Y^{-1}_l$$

$$Y^{\frac{1}{2}}_{l-\frac{1}{2}} = -\sqrt{\frac{l}{2l+1}}\,\alpha Y^0_l + \sqrt{\frac{l+1}{2l+1}}\,\beta Y^1_l.$$

Using again the expansion Eq. (7), written in the form

$$e^{ikz} = \frac{1}{kr}\sum_l \sqrt{4\pi(2l+1)}\, i^l \sin\left(kr - \frac{1}{2}l\pi\right) Y_l^0, \tag{39}$$

one obtains by comparison of Eqs. (37) and (34):

$$\begin{aligned} A_{l+\frac{1}{2},l} &= \sqrt{\frac{4\pi}{l+1}}\, i^l e^{i\delta_{l-\frac{1}{2},l}} \\ A_{l-\frac{1}{2},l} &= -\sqrt{4\pi l}\, i^l e^{i\delta_{l-\frac{1}{2},l}} \end{aligned} \tag{40}$$

and

$$f(\vartheta, \varphi) = \sum_l \sqrt{\frac{4\pi}{2l+1}}\, [(l+1) f_{l+\frac{1}{2}} + l f_{l-\frac{1}{2}}]\, Y_l^0(\vartheta)$$

$$g_+(\vartheta, \varphi) \equiv g(\vartheta, \varphi) = \sum_l \sqrt{\frac{4\pi}{2l+1}} \sqrt{l(l+1)}\, [f_{l+\frac{1}{2}} - f_{l-\frac{1}{2}}]\, Y_l^1(\vartheta, \varphi) \tag{41}$$

$$g_-(\vartheta, \varphi) = -g(\vartheta, \varphi)\, e^{-2i\varphi}$$

where

$$f_{l\pm\frac{1}{2}} = \frac{e^{2i\delta_{l\pm\frac{1}{2}}} - 1}{2ik} = \frac{1}{k} e^{i\delta_{l\pm\frac{1}{2}}} \sin \delta_{l\pm\frac{1}{2}}. \tag{42}$$

The *unpolarized* differential cross-section is given by

$$\frac{d\sigma}{d\Omega} = |f(\vartheta, \varphi)|^2 + |g(\vartheta, \varphi)|^2 \tag{43}$$

after summing over the directions of the spin of the final particle, and averaging the spin orientations of the initial particle. By integration over the angles, one obtains the total cross-section

$$\begin{aligned} \sigma &= \frac{4\pi}{k^2} \sum_{l=0}^{\infty} [(l+1)\sin^2 \delta_{l+\frac{1}{2}} + l \sin^2 \delta_{l-\frac{1}{2}}] \\ &= \frac{4\pi}{k^2} \sum_{J=\frac{1}{2}}^{\infty} \sum_{l=J-\frac{1}{2}}^{J+\frac{1}{2}} (J+\tfrac{1}{2}) \sin^2 \delta_{J,l}. \end{aligned} \tag{44}$$

It is clear that $d\sigma/d\Omega$ is invariant under the interchange of f with g, and under the change of the sign of either f or g. These properties can be expressed directly as ambiguities on the phase shifts, which are called respectively Minami and Yang ambiguity (a detailed discussion can be found in Ref. 4).

General expressions for the cross-sections for higher spin case will be given in Section IV.1.

II.2. Polarization of Spin 1/2 Particles

The ambiguities of the Yang and Minami kind can be resolved by considering the polarization P of the final particle, which is defined by:

$$\frac{d\sigma}{d\Omega}P = \frac{d\sigma_+}{d\Omega} - \frac{d\sigma_-}{d\Omega} \tag{45}$$

where $d\sigma/d\Omega$ is the unpolarized cross-section given in Eq. (43), and $d\sigma_\pm/d\Omega$ are the cross-sections of the scattering leading to a given value of the spin component m' of the final particle.

Let us consider first, as in the previous section, the z-axis as polarization axis, and suppose that the initial spin $\frac{1}{2}$ particle is completely polarized ($m = +\frac{1}{2}$). From (37) and (45) we get:

$$\frac{d\sigma}{d\Omega}P_{||} = |f|^2 - |g|^2. \tag{46}$$

However, if the initial particle is not polarized, we have to take the average over the initial spin orientations ($m = \pm\frac{1}{2}$), and we get $P_{||} = 0$, i.e. no polarization is observed along the direction of motion of the incident particle. This is part of a general result: conservation of parity in the scattering process requires no polarization, from unpolarized target, in the scattering plane.

The situation is different if we analize the polarization along a direction $\boldsymbol{n}$ perpendicular to the scattering plane. The spin eigenstates along the direction $\boldsymbol{n}$ can be written as:

$$\alpha' = \sqrt{\frac{1}{2}}(\alpha + i\beta)$$

$$\beta' = \sqrt{\frac{1}{2}}(\alpha - i\beta)$$

so that the scattering amplitude, i.e. the factor multiplying e^{ikr}/r in Eq. (37), becomes:

$$\begin{aligned} F_+ &= \sqrt{\frac{1}{2}}(f - ig)\,\alpha' + \sqrt{\frac{1}{2}}(f + ig)\,\beta' \\ F_- &= -\sqrt{\frac{1}{2}}i(f - ig)\,\alpha' + \sqrt{\frac{1}{2}}i(f + ig)\,\beta' \end{aligned} \tag{47}$$

where we have put $\varphi = 0$, by chosing a convenient orientation for the co-ordinate system. Taking the average over the initial spin orientations, one gets:

$$\frac{d\sigma_\pm}{d\Omega} = \frac{1}{2}|f \mp ig|^2, \tag{48}$$

from which the transverse polarization $P_\perp$ becomes:

$$\frac{d\sigma}{d\Omega} P_\perp = 2\,\mathrm{Im}\, f^* g. \tag{49}$$

We see that the polarization $P_\perp$ changes its sign under each of the transformations $f \leftrightarrow g$, $f \leftrightarrow -f$, $g \leftrightarrow -g$, so that the ambiguities mentioned in the previous section can be eliminated by the knowledge of $P_\perp$.

III. INELASTIC COLLISIONS

III.1. Elastic and Inelastic Cross-sections

We call *inelastic* a collision which produces a change in the nature or in the number of the colliding particles. Examples of inelastic collisions between elementary particles are the following: $K^- + p \to \Sigma^- + \pi^+, \pi^- + p \to p + \pi^- + \pi^0$. In general, several final status are possible for a given initial state. For example, considering only two particle states, the initial system $K^- + p$ can go even at threshold into the final states: $K^- + p$, $\Lambda^0 + \pi^0$, $\Sigma^- + \pi^+$, $\Sigma^0 + \pi^0$. Each different state is called a different *channel.*

The asymptotic form of the wave function of the system of the two colliding particles will be a sum of different terms, each representing a possible channel. Amongst these terms there is always, in particular, a term corresponding to the elastic scattering. In addition there is, of course, a term describing the particles before the collisions.

For the moment we consider only the global effect of the inelastic processes, specifically on the elastic scattering, and devote Section IV to the study of separate inelastic channels. We consider, for the sake of simplicity, spin-zero particles.

The asymptotic expressions of the radial functions $u_l(r)$ are now modified with respect to the pure elastic case. The expression (5) can be considered as the sum of an incident and outgoing wavex with the same amplitudes. In the present case, since several channels are present in the final states, the intensity of the outgoing wave must be less than that of the ingoing wave. We write then:

$$u_l(r) \simeq \frac{a_l\, \mathrm{e}^{i(kr - \frac{1}{2}l\pi)} - \mathrm{e}^{-i(kr - \frac{1}{2}l\pi)}}{2ik} \tag{50}$$

where a_l is in general a complex quantity, with modulus less than unity; it can be written as: $a_l = e^{2i\alpha_l} = \eta_l e^{2i\delta_l}(\delta_l = \mathrm{Re}\,\alpha_l, \eta_l = \exp[-2\,\mathrm{Im}\,\alpha_l])$.

The asymptotic expression of the wave function $\psi(r, \vartheta)$ is then given by:

$$\psi(r, \vartheta) \to \sum_l i^l (2l+1) \frac{a_l\, \mathrm{e}^{i(kr - \frac{1}{2}l\pi)} - \mathrm{e}^{-i(kr - \frac{1}{2}l\pi)}}{2ikr} P_l(\cos\vartheta). \tag{51}$$

Using the same procedure of Section I.1, one can find by comparison of Eqs. (2) and (51):

$$f(\vartheta) = \sum_l (2l + 1) f_l(k) P_l(\cos \vartheta)$$

with

$$f_l(k) = \frac{a_l - 1}{2ik} = \frac{\eta_l e^{2i\delta_l} - 1}{2ik}. \tag{52}$$

The total elastic cross-section is given by:

$$\sigma_{el} = \frac{\pi}{k^2} \sum_l (2l + 1) |1 - a_l|^2 = \frac{4\pi}{k^2} \sum_l (2l + 1) \left| \frac{\eta_l e^{2i\delta_l} - 1}{2i} \right|^2. \tag{53}$$

The total inelastic cross-section (for all possible inelastic final states) represents the amount of incident particles which disappear from the incident beam. It can be obtained by taking the difference between the intensities of the initial particles entering and leaving the scattering region. For each value of l the intensity of the outgoing wave is reduced by the ratio $|a_l|^2 < 1$ with respect to the intensity of the ingoing wave. This reduction is entirely due to inelastic scattering:

$$\sigma_{in} = \frac{\pi}{k^2} \sum_l (2l + 1)(1 - |a_l|^2) = \frac{\pi}{k^2} \sum_l (2l + 1)(1 - \eta_l^2). \tag{54}$$

Obviously, for $\eta_l = 1$, σ_{el} becomes idential to Eq. (13), and σ_{in} vanishes.

We note that only σ_{el} contains the complex term a_l while σ_{in} contains only the modulus $|a_l|$: this corresponds to the fact that in the elastic scattering the incident and outgoing waves are *coherent*.

It is easy to check that the optical theorem expressed by Eq. (14) can be generalized to the present case:

$$\operatorname{Im} f(0) = \frac{k}{4\pi} \sigma_{tot} \tag{55}$$

in terms of the total (complete) cross-section

$$\sigma_{tot} = \sigma_{el} + \sigma_{in}. \tag{56}$$

Let us denote by $\sigma_l^{(el)}$, $\sigma_l^{(in)}$ the partial wave terms in Eqs. (53), (54), and define:

$$R_{el} = \frac{\sigma_l^{(el)}}{\sigma_l^{(max)}} = \frac{1}{4} |\eta_l e^{2i\delta_l} - 1|^2$$
$$R_{in} = \frac{\sigma_l^{(in)}}{\sigma_l^{(max)}} = \frac{1}{4} (1 - \eta_l^2) \tag{57}$$

where $\sigma_l^{(max)}$ is the geometrical value (29). For a given value of δ_l, R_{el} can be expressed in terms of R_{in}. We plot in Fig. 3 R_{el} versus R_{in}, for a few given values of δ_l.

The boundary ($\delta_l = 0$, $\delta_l = \pi/2$) corresponds to the minimum and maximum values of the elastic cross-section, as function of the inelastic one. At $\eta_l = 1 (R_{\text{in}} = 0)$, R_{el} reaches the maximum value $|e^{2i\delta_l} - 1|^2$ (pure elastic scattering). The maximum

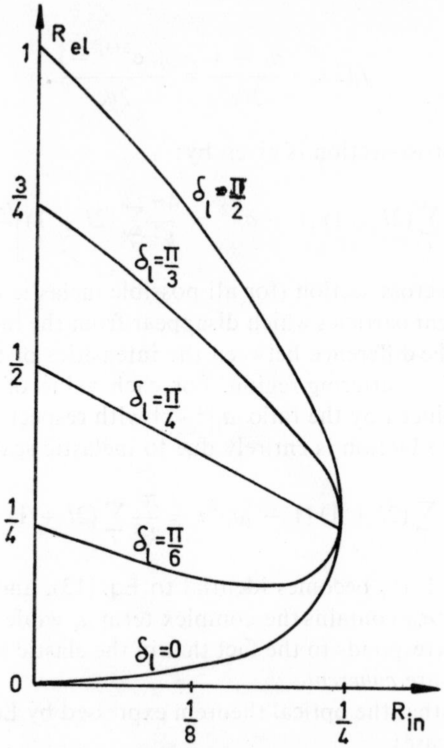

Fig. 3. Behaviour of elastic versus inelastic cross section

value of R_{in} is obtained for $\eta_l = 0$ (complete absorption): in this case $R_{\text{el}} = R_{\text{in}} = \frac{1}{4}$. One sees that elastic scattering is present also for $\delta_l = 0$, if there is absorption; it is called *diffraction scattering*.

The previous results can be generalized to the case of spin different from zero (See Section IV.1 and Ref. 3).

III.2. Effective Range Approximation

A useful parametrization for the scattering at low energy is provided by the effective range expansion which, for the l partial wave, is usually written as:

$$k^{2l+1} \cot \alpha_l = \frac{1}{A} + \frac{1}{2} r k^2 + \cdots \tag{58}$$

where A is called *scattering length* and r *effective range*.

The *zero range approximation* corresponds to keeping only the first term in the expansion (58). If there is absorption, α_l and A are complex quatities.

In the case of S-wave, writing $A = a + ib$, we have:

$$f_0(k) = \frac{1}{k(\cot \alpha_0 - i)} = \frac{a + ib}{1 + bk - iak}. \tag{59}$$

If the scattering is purely elastic: $b = 0$, and the amplitude

$$kf_0(k) = \left(\frac{1}{ak} - i\right)^{-1} \tag{60}$$

is represented in Fig. 2 by a point on the circle. If there is strong absorption: $|a/b| \ll 1$, and we can write

$$kf_0(k) = i\left(\frac{1}{bk} + 1\right)^{-1}. \tag{61}$$

The representative point in Fig. 2 lies on the imaginary axis.

The elastic cross-section is given by

$$\sigma_{\text{el}} = 4\pi \frac{a^2 + b^2}{(ak)^2 + (1 + bk)^2} \tag{62}$$

and from (55), (56), one gets for the inelastic cross-section:

$$\sigma_{\text{in}} = \frac{4\pi}{k} \frac{b}{(ak)^2 + (1 + bk)^2}. \tag{63}$$

III.3. Scattering by a Black Sphere

We consider here, as an example, the scattering by a "black" sphere, i.e. a sphere which absorbs all the particles which strike on it. We suppose that the wave length of the incident particle $1/k$ is much smaller than the radius R of the sphere.

These assumptions can be expressed as follows:

$$a_l = 0 \quad \text{for} \quad l \leq kR \quad \text{(no outgoing wave)}$$

$$a_l = 1 \quad \text{for} \quad l > kR \quad \text{(no scattering)}.$$

From Eqs. (53) and (54) one gets

$$\sigma_{\text{el}} = \sigma_{\text{in}} = \frac{\pi}{k^2} \sum_{l=0}^{l_{\max} \approx kR} (2l + 1) \simeq \pi R^2. \tag{64}$$

Both the elastic and inelastic cross-sections are equal to the classical cross-section. The elastic scattering, which is called *shadow scattering*, is due to the diffraction effects which occur at the edge of the target. The differential cross-section presents a very narrow peak in the forward direction, corresponding to an angle of the order of magnitude of $(kR)^{-1}$.

We can give some estimate of the shape of the diffraction peak. The scattering amplitude $f(\vartheta)$ is pure imaginary, as one can see from Eq. (52):

$$f(\vartheta) = \frac{i}{2k} \sum_{l=0}^{l_{max}} (2l + 1)\, P_l(\cos \vartheta). \tag{65}$$

For very small angles one can write

$$P_l(\cos \vartheta) \simeq J_0[(l + \tfrac{1}{2})\, \vartheta]$$

and the scattering amplitude, by replacing the sum over l by an integral, becomes:

$$\operatorname{Im} f(\vartheta) \simeq \frac{1}{2k} \int_0^{kR} 2\lambda J_0(\lambda\vartheta)\, \mathrm{d}\lambda = \frac{R}{\vartheta} J_1(kR\vartheta). \tag{66}$$

The value at $\vartheta = 0$ is $\operatorname{Im} f(0) = \frac{1}{2}kR^2$, in agreement with the optical theorem (55) applied to (64). The behaviour of $\operatorname{Im} f(\vartheta)/\operatorname{Im} f(0)$ versus $kR\vartheta$ is represented if Fig. 4.

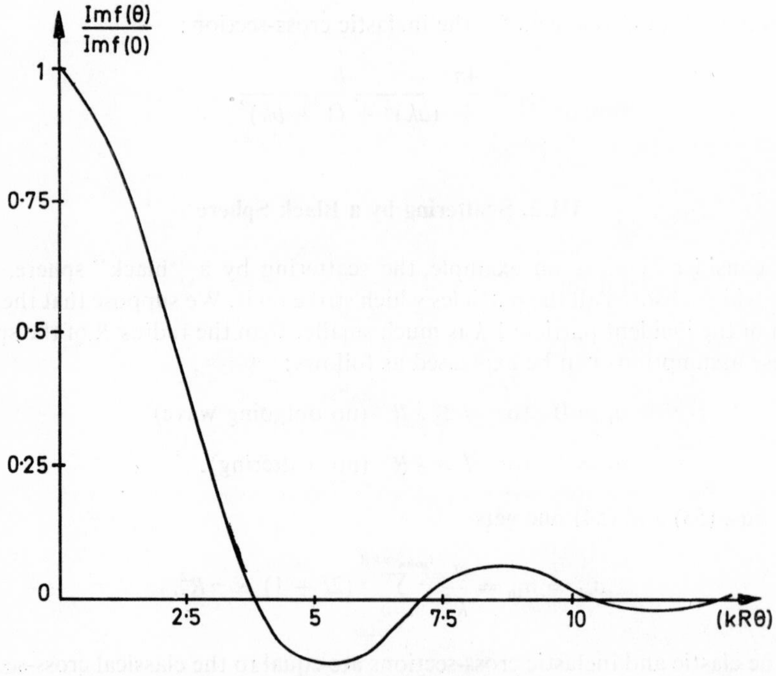

Fig. 4. Black sphere scattering amplitude.

IV. MULTI-CHANNEL FORMALISM

IV.1. The Scattering Matrix

We have considered in the previous sections the case of multi-channel processes, and we have examined in particular the elastic channel. We present here a more general approach, which allows to obtain the cross-sections for the transitions from a given initial channel to a different final channel.

We consider, for the sake of simplicity, only *two spin-zero particles* in each channel.

The asymptotic wave function describing the relative motion of the two particles in a given channel i, with orbital angular momentum l_i, is represented by

$$\Psi_{l_i}^{(i\to i)}(r) = \frac{-1}{2ik_i r}\left[e^{-i(k_i r - \frac{1}{2}l_i\pi)} - S_{ii}\, e^{i(k_i r - \frac{1}{2}l_i\pi)}\right]. \tag{67}$$

This expression represents the ingoing and outgoing spherical waves in the same channel i. It corresponds to the l-th term of Eq. (51) with a_l replaced by S_{ii}.

However, with an ingoing wave in the channel i, there will be outgoing waves also in all the other different channels which are *open* (a channel is said to be open when the available energy is greater than its threshold). The outgoing wave in the f channel is written as

$$\Psi_{l_f}^{(i\to f)}(r) = \frac{1}{2i\sqrt{k_f k_i}\, r}\, S_{fi}\, e^{i(k_f r - \frac{1}{2}l_f\pi)}. \tag{68}$$

The ratio or the flux of the outgoing wave in the channel f to the incident plane wave flux gives the cross-section

$$\sigma_{l_i}^{(i\to f)} = (2l_i + 1)\frac{\pi}{k_i^2}\,|S_{fi}|^2\,. \tag{69}$$

This formula is valid for $i \neq f$; in order to obtain the scattered wave in the elastic channel, we have to subtract from the outgoing wave in Eq. (67) the l-th term of the outgoing part of the plane wave Eq. (7):

$$\sigma_{l_i}^{(i\to i)} = (2l_i + 1)\frac{\pi}{k_i^2}\,|1 - S_{ii}|^2\,. \tag{70}$$

The expressions Eqs. (69) and (70) can be written in a single formula:

$$\sigma_{l_i}^{(i\to f)} = (2l_i + 1)\frac{\pi}{k_i^2}\,|\delta_{fi} - S_{fi}|^2\,. \tag{71}$$

The complex quantities S_{fi} ($i, f = 1, 2, \cdots n$; n = number of channels) can be ordered in an $n \times n$ matrix S, which is called the *scattering matrix*. Here and in the following, we shall consider the S-matrix in the angular momentum representation. The matrix elements S_{fi} can be obtained from a scattering operator S, by means of

$$S_{fi} = \langle f|S|i\rangle \tag{72}$$

where $|i\rangle$, $|f\rangle$ are the eigenstates in the i, f channels, specified by the magnitude of the momenta k_i, k_f, respectively, and the angular momentum l. We quote here two important properties of the S-matrix (for the proof see e.g. Ref. 3):

1) S is a *unitary matrix*: $SS^+ = 1$ (S^+ is the hermitian conjugate of S: $S^*_{ij} = S^*_{ji}$).

2) S is a *symmetrical matrix*: $\tilde{S} = S$ ($\tilde{S}$ is the transposed matrix of S: $\tilde{S}_{ij} = S_{ji}$).

The first property is connected with the *conservation of flux*, the second with *time reversal invariance.*

In the case of one channel, the S-matrix, which reduces to one element, can be written, using the first property:

$$S_l = e^{2i\delta_l} \tag{73}$$

where δ_l is the usual phase shift. In fact, the cross-section Eq. (70) with Eq. (73) becomes:

$$\sigma_l = \frac{4\pi}{k^2}(2l+1)\sin^2\delta_l$$

which coincides with the formula Eq. (13).

In the case of two channels, using both unitarity and symmetry, the S-matrix can be written as follows (see Ref. 5):

$$S_l = \begin{pmatrix} \eta_l\, e^{2i\delta_l^{(1)}} & i\sqrt{1-\eta_l^2}\, e^{i(\delta_l^{(1)}+\delta_l^{(2)})} \\ i\sqrt{1-\eta_l^2}\, e^{i(\delta_l^{(1)}+\delta_l^{(2)})} & \eta_l\, e^{2i\delta_l^{(2)}} \end{pmatrix} \tag{74}$$

where the quantities $\delta_l^{(1)}$, $\delta_l^{(2)}$, η_l are real. In this case Eq. (71) gives:

$$\sigma_l^{(i\to i)} = (2l+1)\frac{\pi}{k_i^2}|1-\eta_l\, e^{2i\delta_l^{(i)}}|^2$$

$$\sigma_l^{(i\to f)} = (2. + 1)\frac{\pi}{k_i^2}(1-\eta_l^2),$$

which agree with the results obtained in (53), (54).

For more than two channels, the situation is much more complicated. Since the S-matrix is unitary and symmetric, the number of independent real parameters in the case of n channels is $\frac{1}{2}n(n+1)$.

Let us consider the general case in which also spin complications are present. We denote by S, m_s the total spin and its z-component in the initial channel ($S = s_1 + s_2$, s_1 and s_2 spin of the incident and target particles), by S', m_s' the total spin and z-component in the final channel ($\boldsymbol{S}' = \boldsymbol{s}_1' + \boldsymbol{s}_2' + \ldots, s_1', s_2', \ldots$ spins of the final particles), by l, m and l', m' the orbital angular momenta and their z-components: by J, M the total angular momentum and total z-component. Each value of S (and S') is referred to a different channel, since a superposition of states with different S is incoherent. If the incident beam is unpolarized, it is, in fact, an incoherent mixture of incident waves in all the spin channels; their number is given by:

$$\sum_{S=|s_1-s_2|}^{s_1+s_2} (2S+1) = (2s_1+1)(2s_2+1) \tag{75}$$

Then we can fix our attention to given values of S, S'.

The differential cross-section for the process ($i \to f$) is obtained by generalizing the results of section II.1 (see also Refs. 3 and 6):

$$\frac{\mathrm{d}\sigma(S,S')}{\mathrm{d}\Omega} = \frac{1}{4k_i^2}\left|\sum_J \sum_{l=|J-S|}^{J+S} \sum_{l'=|J-S'|}^{J+S'} \sqrt{4\pi(2l+1)}\, C_{lS}(J,M;0,m_s) \right.$$
$$\left. \times [\delta_{fi} - S_{fi}(J,S,S',l',l)]\, y^M_{Jl'S'}(\vartheta,\varphi)\right|^2 \tag{76}$$

where the Y^M_{JlS} are the eigenfunctions of total angular momentum defined in (35). The matrix element S_{fi} does not depent on spin orientation, for invariance under rotation of both the co-ordinate system and spins. In general, the sets of values of l and l' may not coincide. A given l can lead to values of l' differing by two units if the intrinsic parities are the same in the initial and final states, and by one unit if there is a parity change.

By means of Eq. (76), one can evaluate the angular distribution for any reaction, in terms of the parameters S_{fi}. In Eq. (76) we have kept fixed also m_s (since $m = 0$ for the incident wave, $M = m_s$); an average over the possible orientations of m_s, and integration over all the angles, taking into account the orthogonality relations of the Clebsh-Gordon coefficients, gives for the total cross-section:

$$\sigma^{(i\to f)}(S,S') = \frac{\pi}{k_i^2}\frac{2J+1}{2S+1}\sum_{J,l,l'} |\delta_{fi} - S_{fi}|^2 \tag{77}$$

The total elastic cross-section is obtained in the particular case $i = f$ (by definition $S = S'$):

$$\sigma^{(i)}_{\text{el}}(S) = \frac{\pi}{k_i^2}\frac{2J+1}{2S+1}\sum_{J,l,l'} |1 - S_{ii}|^2 \tag{78}$$

The total inelastic cross-section is obtained by subtracting the outgoing flux in the i-channel, from the incident one:

$$\sigma^{(i)}_{\text{in}}(S) = \frac{\pi}{k_i^2}\frac{2J+1}{2S+1}\sum_{J,l,l'} (1 - |S_{ii}|^2) \tag{79}$$

IV.2. The Scattering Amplitude and the Reaction Matrix

It is useful to introduce two other matrices, besides the S-matrix. We define a matrix T, which is a generalization of the scattering amplitude for a multi-channel system, by:

$$S_{fi} = \delta_{fi} + 2ik_i^{1/2}k_f^{1/2}T_{fi} \tag{80}$$

In matrix notation:

$$S = 1 + 2ik^{1/2}Tk^{1/2} \tag{81}$$

or

$$T = k^{-1/2}\,\frac{S-1}{2i}\,k^{-1/2} \tag{82}$$

where k is a diagonal matrix.

In terms of the elements T_{fi}, the cross-section Eq. (71) becomes

$$\sigma_{l_i}^{(i\to f)} = 4\pi(2l_i + 1)\frac{k_f}{k_i}\,|T_{fi}|^2 . \tag{83}$$

One sees immediately that, in the case of one channel, T coincides with the scattering amplitude

$$T_l = \frac{e^{2i\delta_l} - 1}{2ik}. \tag{84}$$

The expressions Eqs. (67) and (68), by use of Eq. (80), can be replaced by

$$\Psi_{l_f}^{(i\to f)}(r) = \delta_{fi}\,\frac{\sin(k_f r - \frac{1}{2}l_f\pi)}{k_f r} + T_{fi}\,\frac{e^{i(k_f r - 1/2 l_f\pi)}}{r} \tag{85}$$

which is a generalization of the l-th term of Eq. (2). The expression Eq. (85) represents then an incident wave of unit amplitude in the i channel, together with an outgoing wave of amplitude T_{fi} in the f channel.

The situation in which the outgoing waves are replaced by standing waves (for all channels) is described by

$$\Phi_{l_f}^{(i\to f)}(r) = \delta_{fi}\,\frac{\sin(k_f r - \frac{1}{2}l_f\pi)}{k_f r} + K_{fi}\,\frac{\cos(k_f r - \frac{1}{2}l_f\pi)}{r}. \tag{86}$$

The quantities K_{fi} are the elements of a matrix K, called the *reaction matrix.*

It is possible to show that the following relation holds between the matrices T and K:

$$T = K(1 - ikK)^{-1} = (1 - ikK)^{-1}\,K \tag{87}$$

or, equivalently:

$$T^{-1} = K^{-1} - ik. \tag{88}$$

We will show that the definition Eq. (86) leads to the relation Eq. (87) in the particular case in which only the S waves are present in all channels (Ref. 5).

For S-waves, Eqs. (85), (86) become:

$$\Psi^{(i\to f)}(r) = \delta_{fi}\frac{\sin k_f r}{k_f r} + T_{fi}\frac{e^{ik_f r}}{r} \tag{89}$$

$$\Phi^{(i\to f)}(r) = \delta_{fi}\frac{\sin k_f r}{k_f r} + K_{fi}\frac{\cos k_f r}{r}. \tag{90}$$

The wave function $\Phi(r)$ satisfies the following condition at $r = 0$:

$$(r\Phi^{(i\to f)})_{r=0} = K_{fi} = \sum_j K_{fj}\delta_{ji} = \sum_j K_{fj}\left[\frac{d}{dr}r\Phi^{(i\to j)}\right]_{r=0}. \tag{91}$$

This is a *linear* condition which is valid for all channels i, and therefore it is valid for any linear combination of $\Phi^{(i\to f)}$. Since the Φ's form a a complete set, we can write in general the relation Eq. (91) for any wave function, in particular for the $\Psi^{(i\to f)}$ given in Eq. (89). In this way, one gets:

$$T_{fi} = \sum_j K_{fj}(\delta_{ji} + ik_j T_{ji}) \tag{92}$$

or in matrix notation

$$T = K(1 + ikT)$$

which is equivalent to Eq. (87).

By means of Eqs. (81) and (87) we can also express the K matrix in terms of the S matrix:

$$K = ik^{-1/2}(1 - S)(1 + S)^{-1} k^{-1/2}. \tag{93}$$

It is easy to show that, since the S-matrix is unitary and symmetric, the K-matrix is hermitian ($K = K^+$) and symmetric, i.e. it is a *real* matrix. Of course, the number of parameters in both matrices is the same, and given by $\frac{1}{2}n(n + 1)$ for an n channel system.

In the one channel case, using Eq. (73) we get:

$$K_l = \frac{1}{k\cot\delta_l}. \tag{94}$$

We consider now a two channel system, limiting ourselves to S waves. Following Ref. 5, we write:

$$K = \begin{pmatrix}\alpha & \beta\\ \beta & \gamma\end{pmatrix} \tag{95}$$

where α, β, γ are real quantities.

For an incident S wave in channel **1** we have

$$\begin{aligned}\Psi^{(1\to 1)}(r) &= \frac{\sin k_1 r}{k_1 r} + T_{11}\frac{e^{ik_1 r}}{r}\\ \Psi^{(1\to 2)}(r) &= T_{21}\frac{e^{ik_2 r}}{r}.\end{aligned} \tag{96}$$

The application of the condition Eq. (92) to (95) and (96) gives:

$$T_{11} = \alpha(1 + ik_1T_{11}) + i\beta k_2 T_{21}$$
$$T_{21} = \beta(1 + ik_1T_{11}) + i\gamma k_2 T_{21} \tag{97}$$

from which one gets

$$T_{11} = \frac{A}{1 - ik_1A} \tag{98}$$

with

$$A = \alpha + \frac{ik_2\beta^2}{1 - ik_2\gamma} \tag{99}$$

and

$$T_{21} = \frac{\beta}{(1 - ik_2\gamma)(1 - ik_1A)}. \tag{100}$$

From Eqs. (74) and (82), using a complex phase shift $e^{2i\alpha_1} = \eta^{2i\delta_1}$ (the subscript refers here to the channel index), on can write:

$$T_{11} = \frac{e^{i\alpha_1}\sin\alpha_1}{k_1}$$

from which it follows

$$k_1 \cot\alpha_1 = \frac{1}{A}. \tag{101}$$

The complex quantity A is the *scattering length* for channel **1**. At low energy A can be considered independent of the energy. This approximation applied e.g. to the study of the K^-p interactions at low energy (Ref. 7), corresponds to a *zero effective range*. In general, for multi-channel processes, an expansion similar to (58) can be performed for the matrix K^{-1} (Ref. 8).

For an incident S wave in channel **2**, we have, in analogy with Eq. (96):

$$\Psi^{(2\to1)}(r) = T_{12}\frac{e^{ik_1r}}{r}$$
$$\Psi^{(2\to2)}(r) = \frac{\sin k_2r}{k_2r} + T_{22}\frac{e^{ik_2r}}{r}. \tag{102}$$

In a similar way, one gets:

$$T_{22} = \frac{B}{1 - ik_2B}; \quad k_2\cot\alpha_2 = \frac{1}{B} \tag{103}$$

with

$$B = \gamma + \frac{ik_1\beta^2}{1 - ik_1\alpha} \tag{104}$$

and

$$T_{12} = \frac{\beta}{(1 - ik_1\alpha)(1 - ik_2B)}. \tag{105}$$

One can prove, by comparison, that the relation $T_{12} = T_{21}$ is satisfied.

The corresponding cross-sections are evaluated by means of Eq. (83).

IV.3. The Reduced Reaction Matrix

We have considered in the previous section only open channels. It is instructive to include in our consideration the case of a closed channel.

Going back to the two channel example, suppose that the energy at which we consider the process is below the threshold for channel **1**. We can still use the expressions Eqs. (103) and (105) for the amplitudes in channel **2**, provided we now take k_1 purely imaginary: we take $k_1 = i|k_1|$, so that the wave function $\psi^{(2\to1)}(r)$ behaves like $e^{-|k_1|r}$ and is always finite. The amplitude T_{22} is again given by:

$$T_{22}^{-1} = B^{-1} - ik_2 \tag{103}$$

with

$$B = \gamma - \frac{|k_1|\beta^2}{1 + |k_1|\alpha}. \tag{106}$$

These considerations can be extended to the case of n channels, by writing

$$K = \begin{pmatrix} \alpha & \beta \\ \tilde{\beta} & \gamma \end{pmatrix} \tag{107}$$

with

$$\alpha = K_{11}$$

$$\beta = (K_{12}\ K_{13}\ \cdots\ K_{1n})\quad \tilde{\beta} = \begin{pmatrix} K_{12} \\ K_{13} \\ \vdots \\ K_{1n} \end{pmatrix}\quad \gamma = \begin{pmatrix} K_{22} & K_{23} & \cdots & K_{2n} \\ \cdots & \cdots & \cdots & \cdots \\ \cdots & \cdots & \cdots & \cdots \\ K_{n2} & K_{n3} & & K_{nn} \end{pmatrix}$$

Suppose again that the channel **1** is closed (one can extend these considerations to the case of more closed channels replacing α by an $m \times m$ matrix, and β by an $m \times (n - m)$ matrix. Then, for the T matrix which contains only the open channels one gets the same formal relation Eq. (103′)

$$T_r^{-1} = K_r^{-1} - ik \tag{108}$$

with

$$K_r = \gamma - \tilde{\beta}|k| \frac{1}{1 + |k|\,\alpha}\beta. \tag{109}$$

The matrix K_r, which is called *reduced reaction matrix*, plays the role of a K matrix for the open channels, since the expression (108) has exactly the same form as Eq. (88). The expression (109) relates the elements of K_r to all the elements of K, connecting in this way the open with the closed channels.

IV.4. Resonances in a Multi-channel System

We extend now the formula Eq. (27) obtained for the resonant one-channel scattering amplitude to the case of many channels.

For the sake of simplicity, we consider a system of n channels all open, and replace the K and T matrices by:

$$\begin{aligned} T' &= k^{1/2}Kk^{1/2} \\ T' &= k^{1/2}Tk^{1/2}. \end{aligned} \tag{110}$$

The following considerations hold also if there are some closed channels: one has simply to replace the K and T matrices, by the reduced K_r and T_r matrices.

The K' matrix can be diagonalized by the eigenvalue equation

$$K'|\alpha\rangle = (\cot\delta_\alpha)^{-1}|\alpha\rangle. \tag{111}$$

The eigenvalues $(\cot\delta_\alpha)^{-1}$ are all real, since K' is real and symmetric. The same set of eigenstates $|\alpha >$ diagonalizes also the T matrix, as one can see from Eq. (88):

$$T'|\alpha\rangle = (\cot\delta_\alpha - i)^{-1}|\alpha\rangle = e^{i\delta\alpha}\sin\delta_\alpha|\alpha\rangle. \tag{112}$$

The matrix elements T_{fi} given in Eqs. (80) and (85) correspond, however, to the representation $\langle f|\,T\,|i\rangle$ for the T matrix, where $|i\rangle$, $|f\rangle$ are the l wave parts of the momentum eigenstates in the i, f channels. Since the eigenstates $|\alpha\rangle$ form a complete orthonormal set, one can write for each channel

$$|i\rangle = \sum_\alpha C_{i\alpha}|\alpha\rangle \tag{113}$$

where the coefficients $C_{i\alpha}$ are also real and satisfy the condition

$$\sum_\alpha C_{i\alpha}C_{j\alpha} = \delta_{ij}. \tag{114}$$

By means of Eqs. (112) and (113), one gets

$$\begin{aligned} T'_{fi} &= \langle f|T'|i\rangle = \sum_{\alpha,\beta} C_{f\beta}C_{i\alpha}\langle\beta|T'|\alpha\rangle \\ &= \sum_\alpha C_{f\alpha}C_{i\alpha}\,e^{i\delta\alpha}\sin\delta_\alpha = \sum_\alpha \frac{C_{f\alpha}C_{i\alpha}}{\cot\delta_\alpha - i}. \end{aligned} \tag{115}$$

Suppose now that one of the eigenvalues of K' becomes infinite at the energy $E = E_R$, i.e. that δ_R passes through $\pi/2$ at E_R. In analogy with the situation examined in the one channel case, we say that the amplitude T'_{fi} has a resonance at the energy E_R. If this resonance is isolated, or in other words if the other phase shifts $\delta_\alpha(\alpha \neq R)$ are small around E_R, one can write approximately in this region

$$T'_{fi} \simeq \frac{C_{fR}C_{iR}}{\cot\delta_R - i}. \tag{116}$$

In the same region we can make a linear approximation for $\cot \delta_R$ and write, in analogy with Eq. (24):

$$\operatorname{tg} \delta_R = \frac{\Gamma/2}{E_R - E} \tag{117}$$

Then, we get

$$T'_{fi} = \frac{C_{fR} C_{iR} \Gamma/2}{E_R - E - i\Gamma/2}. \tag{118}$$

If we define:

$$\Gamma_i = C_{iR}^2 \Gamma \tag{119}$$

since by Eq. (114):

$$\sum_i \Gamma_i = \Gamma, \tag{120}$$

the resonant amplitude can also be written as:

$$T'_{fi} = \frac{\frac{1}{2}\Gamma_f^{1/2}\Gamma_i^{1/2}}{E_R + E - i\Gamma/2}. \tag{121}$$

The cross-section is obtained by means of Eqs. (83)

$$\sigma_{l_i}^{(i \to f)} = \frac{\pi}{k_i^2}(2l_i + 1)\frac{\Gamma_i \Gamma_f}{(E - E_R)^2 + \Gamma^2/4}. \tag{122}$$

This is the *Breit-Wigner* formula, valid for isolated resonances. The quantities Γ_i, Γ_f are the *partial widths* for the i, f channels: they are in general functions of the energy.

We want to point out that resonances in a multi-channel system can be originated in two different ways:

1) The complete reaction matrix K can have a pole at the real value E_R of the energy, in the sense that each element of K has a pole at E_R. In this case the resonance is present in all the channels and it appears in all the reactions.

An example is given by the $P_{3/2}$ resonance of the πN^- system, which appears also in the photoproduction process $\gamma + p \to \pi^+ + n(\pi^0 + p)$ and in the Compton scattering $\gamma + p \to \gamma + p$. These processes can, in fact, be easily related by the multi-channel formalism (see e.g. ref. 9).

2) A pole can be generated at E'_R in the reduces matrix K_r by its connection with a closed channel. This pole does not appear, in general, in the complete K matrix. One example is provided by Eq. (103), with B given by (106). B goes to infinity for

$$1 + \alpha |k_1| = 0, \tag{123}$$

$k_2 \cot \alpha_2$ passes through zero and a resonance appear in channel **2**. Suppose now that the (closed) channel **1** is weakly coupled with channel **2** ($\beta \simeq 0$). The condition (91) gives in this case

$$(r\Psi^{(1\to 1)})_{r=0} = \alpha \left(\frac{\mathrm{d}}{\mathrm{d}r}(r\Psi^{(1\to 1)})\right)_{r=0} \tag{124}$$

which coincides with (123) in the case of a bound state.

One can interpret such a resonance in channel **2**, as due to the effect of a strong interaction below threshold in channel **1**. If the coupling between the two channels were rigorously zero, there would be a bound state in channel **1**; in fact, it is a *virtual bound state*, since it can decay into the open channel **2** (Ref. 5).

IV.5. Graphical Representation

The graphical representation described in section I.4. for a single-channel amplitude can be extended to the multi-channel case. Defining

$$\varkappa_{fi} = C_{fR}C_{iR} = \frac{\sqrt{\Gamma_f \Gamma_i}}{\Gamma}; \quad \varepsilon = \cot \delta_R \tag{125}$$

the amplitude (116) can be re-written as

$$T'_{fi} = \frac{\varkappa_{fi}}{\varepsilon - i} \tag{126}$$

The real and imaginary parts of T'_{fi} are given by:

$$\begin{aligned} x &= \operatorname{Re} T'_{fi} = \varkappa_{fi}\frac{\varepsilon}{\varepsilon^2+1} \\ y &= \operatorname{Im} T'_{fi} = \varkappa_{fi}\frac{1}{\varepsilon^2+1} \end{aligned} \tag{127}$$

rom which we get

$$x^2 = (\varkappa_{fi}^2 - y)\, y \tag{128}$$

For $\varkappa_{fi} = 1$, we get the limiting case of Fig. 2, i.e. a circle of radius $R = \frac{1}{2}$. If $\varkappa_{fi} < 1$, T'_{fi} lies inside the circle; however, if $\varkappa_{fi}$ is *independent of the energy*, the end point of T'_{fi} describes still a circle, centered at $x = 0$, $y = \frac{1}{2}\varkappa_{fi}$ and of radius $R = \frac{1}{2}\chi_{fi}$. The situation is described graphically in Fig. 5, where few different constant values of $\varkappa_{fi}$ are considered.

We shall consider in more detail the elastic channel, where $\chi_{fi} = \Gamma_i/\Gamma$. The quantity $\varkappa = \varkappa_{fi}$ is called *inelasticity* and it satisfies the condition $0 \leqq \varkappa \leqq 1$. It is interesting to compare the two cases $\varkappa > \frac{1}{2}$ and $\varkappa < \frac{1}{2}$. The situation is represented in Fig. 6a, 6b. It is easy to see, in analogy with Fig. 2, that the angle $\widehat{AC'B}$ is equal to $2\delta_R$, where δ_R is the phase shift given in (117).
One sees that in the case $\varkappa > \frac{1}{2}$ (Fig. 6a), δ_R increases with energy and it reaches the value $\pi/2$ at the resonance, while in the case $\varkappa < \frac{1}{2}$ (Fig. 6b), δ_R decreases through the resonance ($\delta_R = 0$ at $E = E_R$). However, in this case, it turns out

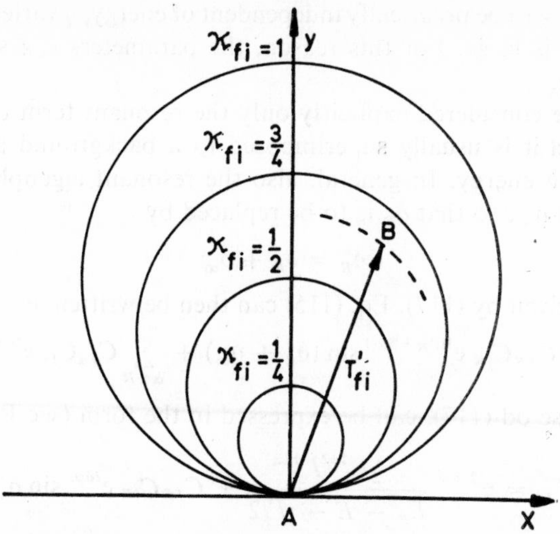

Fig. 5. Graphical representation of reaction amplitudes, neglecting non-resonant phases

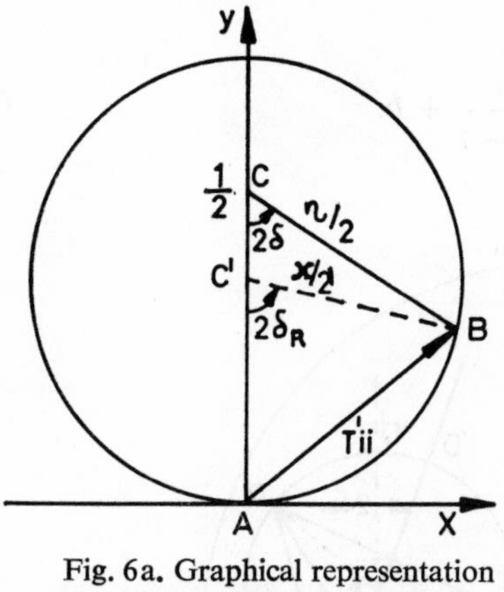

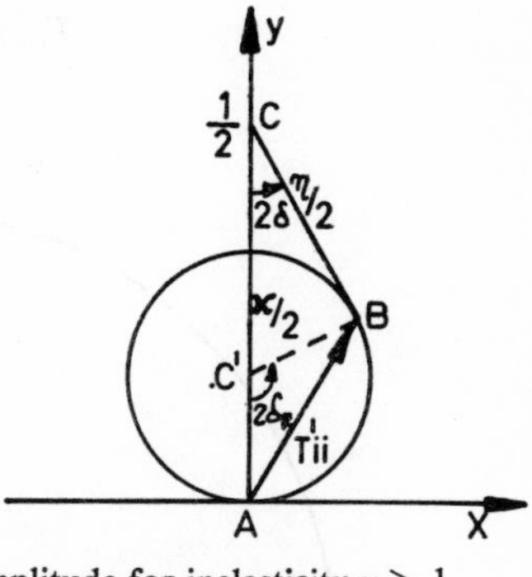

Fig. 6a. Graphical representation of elastic amplitude for inelasticity $\varkappa > \frac{1}{2}$
Fig. 6b. Graphical representation of elastic amplitude for inelasticity $\varkappa < \frac{1}{2}$

that the rate of decrease is small and the Wigner causality condition is not violated.

If one uses, instead of (126), the parametrization

$$T'_{ii} = \frac{\eta\, e^{i\delta} - 1}{2i} \tag{129}$$

analogue to (52), the real quantities η, δ have the following geometrical meanings in Figs. 6a, 6b: $CB = \eta/2$, $\widehat{ACB} = 2\delta$. This follows easily from

$$\begin{aligned} x &= \tfrac{1}{2}\eta \sin 2\delta \\ y &= \tfrac{1}{2}(1 - \eta \cos 2\delta) \end{aligned} \tag{130}$$

If one can assume $\varkappa$ to be practically independent of energy, η varies rather strongly, when inelasticity is large. For this reason, the parameters ε, $\varkappa$ seem to be more suitable than δ, η.

So far we have considered explicitly only the resonant term of a partial wave amplitude. In fact it is usually superimposed to a background amplitude which varies slowly with energy. In general, also the resonant eigenphase has a smoothly varying term δ_∞, so that δ_R is to be replaced by

$$\delta'_R = \delta_R + \delta_\infty \tag{131}$$

where δ_R is still given by (117). Eq. (115) can then be written as

$$T'_{fi} = C_{fR}C_{iR}\,\mathrm{e}^{i(\delta_R+\delta_\infty)}\sin(\delta_R+\delta_\infty) + \sum_{\alpha\neq R} C_{f\alpha}C_{i\alpha}\,\mathrm{e}^{i\delta_\alpha}\sin\delta_\alpha \tag{132}$$

which, making use od (117), can be expressed in the form (see Ref. 10):

$$\begin{aligned} T'_{fi} = \mathrm{e}^{2i\delta_\infty}\,\frac{\frac{1}{2}\Gamma_i^{1/2}\Gamma_f^{1/2}}{E_R - E - i\Gamma/2} &+ C_{fR}C_{iR}\,\mathrm{e}^{i\delta_\infty}\sin\delta_\infty \\ &+ \sum_{\alpha\neq R} C_{f\alpha}C_{i\alpha}\,\mathrm{e}^{i\delta_\alpha}\sin\delta_\alpha \end{aligned} \tag{133}$$

For the elastic channel, we can write

$$T'_{ii} = \mathrm{e}^{2i\delta_\infty}\,\frac{\varkappa}{\varepsilon - i} + b, \tag{134}$$

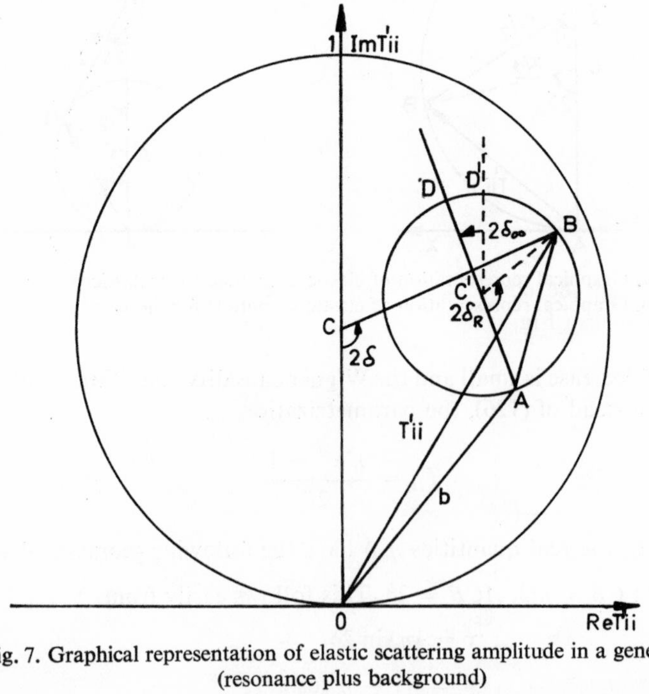

Fig. 7. Graphical representation of elastic scattering amplitude in a general case (resonance plus background)

where the "background term"

$$b = C_{iR}^2 \, e^{i\delta\infty} \sin \delta_\infty + \sum_{\alpha \neq R} C_{i\alpha}^2 \, e^{i\delta\alpha} \sin \delta_\alpha \tag{135}$$

contains all the elastic contributions from the non-resonant eigenstates with the same quantum numbers of the channel i.

The graphical representation of the amplitude (134) is clearly obtained from Fig. 6, by displacing the circle by the vector b, and rotating the diameter AB around A by an angle $2\delta_\infty$, as shown in Fig. 7.
The amplitude T'_{ii} is represented by the vector OB, with B on the small circle of radius $\varkappa/2$, while the first term on the r.h.s. of (134) is represented by AB. The angle $\widehat{AC'B}$ is still equal to $2\delta_R$, so that at the resonant energy E_R the phase of the resonant term will be different from $\pi/2$. This is related to the fact that the pole of the reaction matrix K' is no longer at E_R, but at a value E'_R corresponding to the point D' where δ'_R passes through $\pi/2$. (See Ref. 10) If one uses the representation (129) for the complete amplitude (134), one gets now: $CB = \eta/2$, $\widehat{OCB} = 2\delta$.

V. REGGE POLES

V.1. Regge poles in Potential Scattering

We consider again the scattering by a central potential and go back to Eq. (10), which we re-write here in terms of the energy E and of $z = \cos\vartheta$:

$$f(z, E) = \sum_{l=0}^{\infty} (2l + 1) f_l(E) \, P_l(z). \tag{136}$$

It is possible to transform the sum over l into a contour integral, replacing l by a continuous complex variable λ (Sommerfeld-Watson transform):

$$f(z, E) = \frac{i}{2} \int_C \frac{(2\lambda + 1)}{\sin \pi\lambda} f(\lambda, E) \, P_\lambda(-z) \, d\lambda \tag{137}$$

The contour C in the complex λ-plane is taken along the real axis (closed at infinity), as shown in Fig. 8.

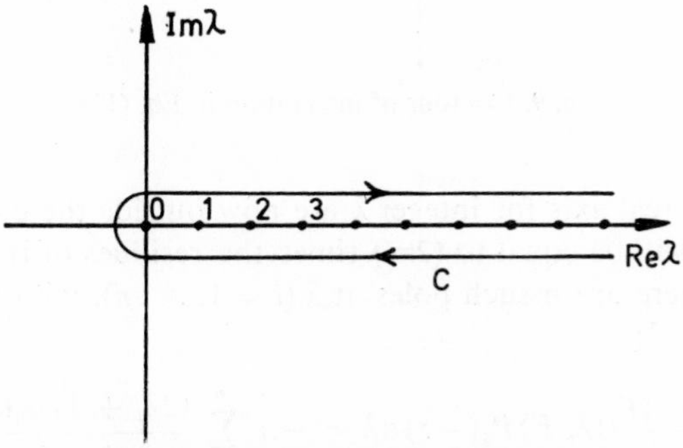

Fig. 8. Contour of integration in Eq. (137)

The equivalence of the two expressions (136), (137) can be proved by means of the Chauchy theorem, which states that the integral of a meromorphic function along a closed path (in anticlockwise sense) is equal to $(2\pi i)$ times the sum of the residue of the poles which are inside the contour. One sees that the expression (137) has a pole at each integral value of $\lambda = l = 0, 1, 2, \ldots$ Around each of these poles, the intagrand can be written as

$$\frac{i(2\lambda + 1) f(\lambda, E) P_{\lambda}(-z)}{(-1)^l 2\pi(\lambda - l)}$$

and the residue is

$$\frac{i}{2\pi}(2l + 1) f_l(E) P_l(z),$$

which gives back Eq. (136).

In using Eq. (137), possible poles of $f(\lambda, E)$ on the real axis are to be excluded by the contour.

It was shown that, for a broad class of potentials, the amplitude $f(\lambda, E)$ is a meromorphic function of λ in the half plane Re $\lambda > -\frac{1}{2}$, $E > 0$ (see e.g. Refs. 11, 12).

We can then perform the integration in Eq. (137) along the different contour C', shown in Fig. 9, where the semi-circle is to be taken at infinity.

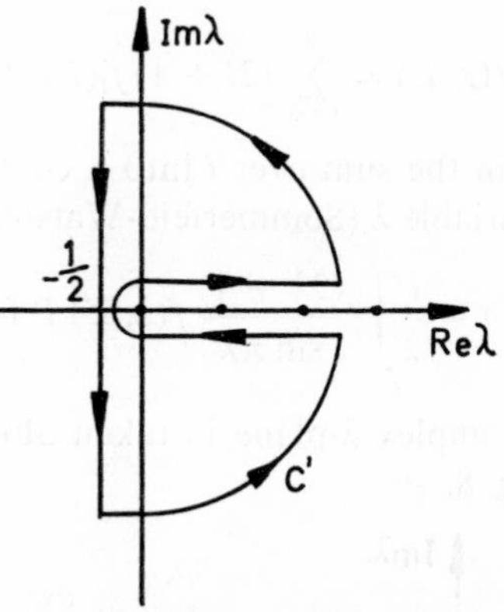

Fig. 9. Contour of integration in Eq. (138)

The poles on the real axis for integer λ are now outside the contour, so that the integral along c' will be equal to $(2\pi i)$ times the residues of the poles of $f(\lambda, E)$. Assuming that there are n such poles at $\lambda_i (i = 1, \ldots n)$, with residues $\varphi_i(E)$, we can write in general:

$$\frac{i}{2}\int_{C'} \frac{(2\lambda + 1)}{\sin \pi\lambda} f(\lambda, E) P_{\lambda}(-z)\, d\lambda = -\pi \sum_{i=1}^{n} \frac{(2\lambda_i + 1)\, \varphi_i(E)}{\sin \pi\lambda_i} P_{\lambda_i}(-z) \quad (138)$$

It was proved (Ref. 11) that, for a superposition of Yukawa potentials, the integral over the semi-circle at infinity vanishes, so that Eq. (138) can be re-written as:

$$\frac{i}{2}\int_C \frac{(2\lambda+1)}{\sin \pi\lambda} f(\lambda, E)\, P_\lambda(-z)\, \mathrm{d}\lambda - \frac{i}{2}\int_{-1/2-i\infty}^{-1/2+i\infty} \frac{(2\lambda+1)}{\sin \pi\lambda} f(\lambda, E)\, P_\lambda(-z)\, \mathrm{d}\lambda$$

$$= -\pi \sum_i \frac{(2\lambda_i+1)\,\varphi_i(E)}{\sin \pi\lambda_i} P_{\lambda_i}(-z) \tag{139}$$

and by use of Eq. (137):

$$f(z, E) = \frac{i}{2}\int_{-1/2-i\infty}^{-1/2+i\infty} \frac{(2\lambda+1)}{\sin \pi\lambda} f(\lambda, E)\, P_\lambda(-z)\, \mathrm{d}\lambda - \pi \sum_i \frac{(2\lambda_i+1)\,\varphi_i(E)}{\sin \pi\lambda_i} P_{\lambda_i}(-z). \tag{140}$$

The poles appearing in the r.h.s. of Eq. (140) are called *Regge poles*. Their position is a function of the energy: $\lambda_i(E)$.

In order to clarify their meaning, we consider the contribution of a single Regge pole on the scattering amplitude, by writing simply:

$$f(z, E) \simeq -\pi(2\lambda+1)\frac{\varphi(E)}{\sin \pi\lambda(E)} P_{\lambda(E)}(-z). \tag{141}$$

If one projects out from $f(z, E)$ the partial wave amplitude $f_l(E)$, one obtains

$$f_l(E) = \frac{1}{2}\int_{-1}^{1} f(z, E)\, P_l(z)\, \mathrm{d}z = -\frac{(2\lambda(E)+1)\,\varphi(E)}{(\lambda(E)+l+1)(\lambda(E)-l)} \tag{142}$$

Suppose now that at $E = E_R$: $\mathrm{Re}\,\lambda(\mathrm{E}_R) = l$ and $\mathrm{Im}\,\lambda(E_R)$ closed to zero; we can then expant $\mathrm{Re}\,\lambda(E)$ around R_R as follows:

$$\mathrm{Re}\,\lambda(E) \simeq l + \left(\frac{\mathrm{d}\,\mathrm{Re}\,\lambda}{\mathrm{d}E}\right)_{E=E_R}(E - E_R) \tag{143}$$

and Eq. (142) becomes

$$f_l(E) \simeq \frac{\varphi(E_R)}{\left(\frac{\mathrm{d}\,\mathrm{Re}\,\lambda}{\mathrm{d}E}\right)_{E=E_R}(E_R - E) - i\,\mathrm{Im}\,\lambda(E_R)}. \tag{144}$$

By comparison of this relation with the formula Eq. (27) for a resonant amplitude, we see that it corresponds to a resonance in the l-th partial wave at $E = E_R$, and width given by:

$$\Gamma = 2\,\mathrm{Im}\,\lambda(E_R)\Big/\left(\frac{\mathrm{d}\,\mathrm{Re}\,\lambda}{\mathrm{d}E}\right)_{E=E_R}. \tag{145}$$

It is interesting to remark that in Eq. (27), where l is a real integral number, the resonance appears as a pole in the scattering amplitude at the complex energy

$$E = E_R - i\Gamma/2 \tag{146}$$

On the other hand, in Eq. (144), the resonance appears, for a real value of the energy, as a pole at the complex value of λ:

$$\lambda(E_R) = l + i \operatorname{Im} \lambda(E_R) \tag{147}$$

In general, the quantity $\lambda(E)$ moves with the energy on the complex λ plane, describing a trajectory (*Regge trajectory*). We can say that a Regge pole represents a resonance whenever $\lambda(E)$ goes closed to a real integral value l. One sees that a Regge pole can then connect different resonances occurring at different values of l. Below threshold ($E < 0$), the Regge pole lies on the real axis (Im $\lambda(E) = 0$), and the integral values of $\lambda(E)$ correspond to bound states.

V.2. High Energy Behaviour of Scattering Cross-sections

The concepts related to Regge poles, derived in potential theory, have been extended to the strong interactions of elementary particles (Ref. 13). We shall briefly consider here the implications of these conjectures on the scattering cross-sections.

We shall use invariant notation for the scattering amplitude and the related variables (see e.g. Ref. 14). It is clear that two independent kinematical variables are sufficient for the scattering process (I)

$$A + B \to A' + B', \tag{I}$$

which is represented graphically in Fig. 10, where k_1, k_2 are the four momenta of the ingoing particles, and k_1', k_2' of the outgoing particles. The following set of variables are used in general:

$$\begin{aligned} s &= (k_1 + k_2)^2 = (k_1' + k_2')^2 \\ t &= (k_1 - k_1')^2 = (k_2 - k_2')^2 \\ u &= (k_1 - k_2')^2 = (k_2 - k_1')^2 \end{aligned} \tag{148}$$

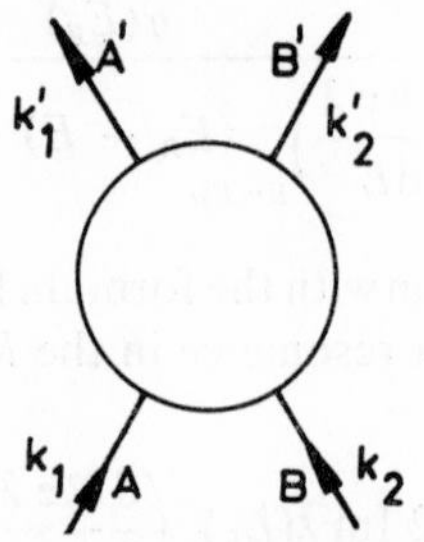

Fig. 10. Graphical representation of the scattering $A + B \to A' + B'$

We consider here, for the sake of simplicity, spin zero particles, with the same mass μ. In this case, Eqs. (148) can be written as (we use the metric $k = (k_0, i\boldsymbol{k})$):

$$\begin{aligned} s &= 4(\boldsymbol{k}^2 + \mu^2) \\ t &= -2\boldsymbol{k}^2(1 - \cos\vartheta) \\ u &= -2\boldsymbol{k}^2(1 + \cos\vartheta) \end{aligned} \tag{149}$$

where $\boldsymbol{k}$ and ϑ are the momentum and scattering angle in the c.m. system. The variables given in Eqs. (149) are related by:

$$s + t + u = 4\mu^2 \tag{150}$$

For the reaction (I), s represents the squared energy in the c.m. system ($s > 0$), and t the squared momentum transfer ($t \leqq 0$). The invariant scattering amplitude is defined by a function $A(s, t)$, which is related to the usual scattering amplitude $f(k, \vartheta)$ by

$$A(s, t) = \frac{\sqrt{s}}{2} f(k, \vartheta). \tag{151}$$

The process

$$A + \bar{A}' \rightarrow \bar{B} + B', \tag{II}$$

where $\bar{A}'$, $\bar{B}$ stand for the antiparticles of A', B, is represented by the same graph of Fig. 10, if one considers $k_1, \bar{k}_1' = -k_1$ as ingoing, and $k_2', \bar{k}_2 = -k_2$ as outgoing four-momenta. In this case one has:

$$\begin{aligned} t &= (p_1 + \bar{p}_1')^2 = 4(q^2 + \mu^2) \\ s &= (p_1 - \bar{p}_2)^2 = -2q^2(1 - \cos\bar{\vartheta}). \end{aligned} \tag{152}$$

The variable t has now the role of the squared energy ($t > 0$), and s of the squared momentum transfer ($s \leqq 0$) in the c.m. system for the reaction (II); q and $\bar{\vartheta}$ are the corresponding momentum and scattering angle.

The invariant scattering amplitude for the process (II) is again given by the function $A(s, t)$ in which the roles of the variables s, t have been interchanged with respect to the reaction (I). We can say that the same amplitude $A(s, t)$ represents the two reactions (I) and (II) when the variables s, t are defined in the two different physical regions Eqs. (149) and (152).

We assume now that the scattering amplitude has a Regge pole behaviour in the physical region for the reaction (II). We write, in analogy with Eq. (141):

$$A(s, t) = \frac{\beta(t)}{\sin \pi\lambda(t)} P_{\lambda(t)}(-\cos\bar{\vartheta}) \tag{153}$$

with

$$\cos\bar{\vartheta} = 1 - \frac{2s}{4\mu^2 - t} \tag{154}$$

and including in $\beta(t)$ terms which it is not necessary to specify here (for more details see e.g. Refs. 15, 16).

The same amplitude describes the reaction (I) for $s > 0$, $t \leqq 0$. For large values of s (high-energy for the reaction (I)), we can use the asymptotic expansion for the Legendre polynomials ($P_l(z) \sim z^l$ for large z) and write:

$$P_{\lambda(t)}(-\cos\vartheta) \simeq P_{\lambda(t)}\left(\frac{2s}{4\mu^2 - t}\right) \simeq g(t)\, s^{\lambda(t)}. \tag{155}$$

The scattering amplitude becomes

$$A(s, t) \simeq \frac{\beta(t)\, g(t)}{\sin \pi\lambda(t)}\, s^{\lambda(t)} \simeq a(t)\, s^{\lambda(t)} \tag{156}$$

and the differential cross-section for the reaction (I) can be written as:

$$\frac{d\sigma}{d\Omega} \simeq 4\,|a(t)|^2\, s^{2\lambda(t)-1}. \tag{157}$$

By use of

$$\cos\vartheta = 1 - \frac{2t}{4\mu^2 - s} \simeq 1 + \frac{2t}{s} \tag{158}$$

one can also write

$$\frac{d\sigma}{dt} \simeq 16\pi\,|a(t)|^2\, s^{2(\lambda(t)-1)}. \tag{159}$$

The optical theorem allows us to evaluate the total cross-section ($t = 0$ in the forward direction):

$$\sigma_{\text{tot}} \simeq \frac{16\pi}{s}\,\text{Im}\, A(s, 0) \simeq 16\pi\,\text{Im}\, a(0)\, s^{\lambda(0)-1}. \tag{160}$$

The experimental indication that the total cross-sections become constant at very high-energy implies:

$$\lambda(0) = 1. \tag{161}$$

This is equivalent to assuming the existence of a Regge pole which dominates the scattering amplitude at very high energies; the corresponding trajectory is called *Pomeranchuk trajectory*. We can expand $\lambda(t)$ near $t = 0$:

$$\lambda(t) \simeq 1 + \lambda'(0)\, t. \tag{162}$$

The differential cross-section Eq. (159) for small t can be written:

$$\frac{d\sigma}{dt} \simeq 16\pi\,|a(t)|^2\, e^{2\lambda'(0) t \log s}. \tag{163}$$

Theoretical conjectures lead to $\lambda'(0) > 0$. Then, since t is negative, one sees that the differential cross-section presents a forward peak which decreases exponentially with t and *shrinks* with increasing energy.

It is interesting to compare this behaviour with the diffraction peak obtained in the case of scattering by a black sphere. Form Eq. (66) we get:

$$\frac{d\sigma}{d\Omega} \simeq \left|\frac{RJ_1(kR\vartheta)}{\vartheta}\right|^2. \tag{164}$$

For small angles one gets from Eq. (158):

$$k\vartheta \simeq \sqrt{-t}$$

and Eq. (164) can be re-written for large s, in the form

$$\frac{d\sigma}{dt} \simeq \pi\left|\frac{J_1(R\sqrt{-t})}{\sqrt{-t}}\right|^2. \tag{165}$$

For reasonable values of $R (R \simeq 1$ fermi) and small values of t, this formula can be approximated by

$$\frac{d\sigma}{dt} \simeq \frac{\pi R^2}{4} \exp\left[\left(\frac{R}{2}\right)^2 t\right]. \tag{166}$$

We see that, in this case, the forward peak decreases exponentially with the momentum transfer, but it is independent of energy.

The behaviour given by Eq. (163) is a particular feature of the Regge pole hypothesis. However, in order to test this prediction with the experimental results, a more complete analysis is needed, which include, in general, more Regge trajectories. This is related to the conjecture (Refs. 13, 16) that all—stable and unstable—baryons and mesons are associated with Regge poles (poles of an S-matrix which describes the strong interactions). These poles move with energy on the complex λ-plane, where λ replaces the spin S of the particle. A particle is then described as an object with "spin" Re λ, which is different from the physical value S, except on the mass-shell: Re $\lambda(m^2) = S$. Particles with different spin can lie on the same trajectory, which is characterized by a set of quantum numbers (isotopic spin, hypercharge, etc.), and by the "evenness" or "oddness" of the values of S for mesons and $S - \frac{1}{2}$ for baryons. (Ref. 17).

More details and a discussion on the present situation of Regge poles in high energy scattering can be found in Ref. 18.

References

1. L. J. Schiff, Quantum Mechanincs, McGraw-Hill (1955).
2. E. Wigner, *Phys. Rev.* **98**, 145 (1955).
3. J. M. Blatt, and V. F. Weisskopf, Theoretical Nuclear Physics, J. Wiley and Sons (1952).
4. H. A. Bethe, and F. de Hoffmann, Mesons and Fields, Vol. II, Row, Peterson and Co.
5. R. H. Dalitz, Strange particles and strong interactions, Oxford University Press (1962).
6. E. P. Wigner, and L. Eisenbud, *Rev. of Mod. Phys.* **72**, 29 (1947).
7. R. H. Dalitz, *Rev. of Mod. Phys.* **33**, 471 (1961).

8. M. H. Ross, and G. L. Shaw, *Ann. of Phys.* **13**, 147 (1961).
9. M. Gell-Mann, and K. M. Watson, *Ann. Rev. of Nucl. Sci.* **4**, 218 (1954).
10. R. H. Dalitz, *Ann. Rev. of Nucl. Sci.* **13**, 339 (1963).
11. T. Regge, in: Lectures on High Energy Physics (1961), edited by Jaksić, Gordon and Breach Publ.
12. S. C. Frautschi, Regge poles and S-matrix theory, Benjamin Inc. (1963).
13. G. F. Chew, and S. C. Frautschi, *Phys. Rev. Letters* **7**, 394 (1961); *Phys. Rev. Letters* **8**, 41 (1961).
14. G. F. Chew, in: Dispersion Relations, edited by Screaton, Oliver and Boyd Publ. (1961).
15. S. C. Frautschi, M. Gell-Mann, and F. Zachariasen, *Phys. Rev.* **126**, 2204 (1962).
16. M. Gell-Mann, Proc. of the 1962 International Conference on High Energy Physics at CERN, edited by Prentki (pag. 533).
17. A. H. Rosenfeld, Proc. of the 1962 Int. Conf. on High Energy Physics at CERN, edited by Prentki (pag. 325).
18. R. J. N. Phillips, lecture notes, International School of Physics E. Majorana (1966).

Phase Shift Analysis

P. Waloschek †

Instituto Nazionale di Fisica Nucleare

Sezione di Bologna, Italy

CONTENTS

1. Introduction 39

2. Scattering Formulae (without Spin) 39
   - 2.1. Some Elementary Considerations 39
   - 2.2. The Beam as a Plane Wave 42
   - 2.3. The Disturbed Plane Wave 43
   - 2.4. Notation 43
   - 2.5. Cross Sections 44
   - 2.6. Angular Distributions 47
   - 2.7. Shadow Scattering 47
   - 2.8. Pure Elastic Scattering 48
   - 2.9. Resonance Scattering 49

3. Experimental Data 55
   - 3.1. Techniques 55
   - 3.2. Errors 55
   - 3.3. Fitting of Curves 56
   - 3.4. Errors on Best Fitting Parameters 58
   - 3.5. Note on Coulomb Scattering 61

4. Note on Pion-Pion Scattering 62
   - 4.1. Experimental Data 62
   - 4.2. Isotopic Spin and Symmetry 64
   - 4.3. The ϱ-Meson 65

5. Pion-Proton Scattering 67
   - 5.1. Spin and parity 67
   - 5.2. Isotopic Spin 68
   - 5.3. Summary of Formulae 69
   - 5.4. Experimental Data 71
   - 5.5. Analysis 72

6. Appendix 78
   - 6.1. System of Units 78
   - 6.2. Kinematics of Two-Body Reactions 79
   - 6.3. Spherical Harmonics 81

7. Some Useful References 82

8. The $\pi + \mathcal{N}$ Phase Shifts up to 2 Gev. (Note added in proof) 83

† Present address: CERN, Geneva, Switzerland; from June 1968: DESY, Hamburg.

1. INTRODUCTION

We are going to discuss a "scattering problem" which involves the study of two bodies or particles moving in space, in general isolated from the rest of the universe. At some relative distance there may be forces acting between the two bodies, changing their velocity vectors or their internal states. The development in time of such a system may be calculated using some *general principles, conservation laws* and a sufficiently accurate knowledge of the *forces* involved and the *initial conditions.* If such calculation happens to be possible we consider it as a highly satisfactory fact from a theoretical point of view. Otherwise one may observe experimentally what happens and try subsequently to fill the gaps in our theoretical knowledge.

Many beautiful examp lesof problems already understood are found in astronomy and electromagnetism. Not the same can be said about more recent elementary particles physics. The lack of experimental information makes it hopeless in many cases to expect a theoretical understanding. Therefore any mathematical instrument, such as the phase shift analysis here discussed, is welcome, though it may be not the only, or sometimes not the best, way of presenting the results or a theory or of an experiment.

A fundamental distinction must be made between *elastic scattering* processes, where there are no changes in the internal states of both bodies, and all others, which we will generically call *reactions*. Elastic scattering processes have particular interest and much can be learned from their analysis even without a detailed study of the reactions which may be in competition in the same collisions.

The analysis of the elastic scattering made through phase shifts (or their equivalent partial wave amplitudes) clarifies some aspects of the problem, introducing general principles and conservation laws. It provides a compact means for the presentation of results or for the comparison of theory and experiment. It is particularly useful when the number of angular momentum states involved is small.

It is not our aim to give a complete development of the arguments treated. Rather, we intend to present through a very elementary discussion a set of formulae we consider of practical interest particularly for experimentalists.

2. SCATTERING FORMULAE (WITHOUT SPIN)

2.1. Some Elementary Considerations

Let us consider a beam of particles as one finds it in accelerators: all particles have nearly the same momentum vector; they are sent through a target which is fixed in the laboratory. The energy of the incident particles should be high compared with the thermal motion energy of the target molecules. The interactions we may deal with have such short range that we can treat each target particle as being independent of the remaining ones.

All systems formed by one beam-particle and one target-particle have practically the same energy. Such systems differ from each other mainly in their *impact parameter d* defined in Fig. 1. We may as well say that each system has its particular *orbital angular momentum l* conveniently defined in the center of mass system (CMS) of the two particles:

$$l = P \cdot d \tag{1}$$

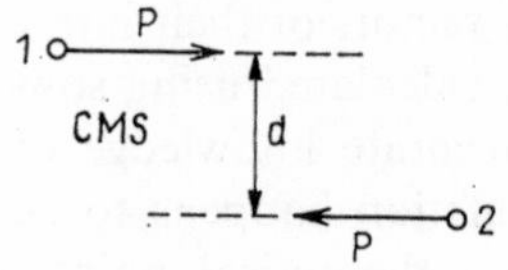

Fig. 1

If the impact parameter is greater than the *range of the forces* r_f one does not expect any interaction. This provides an upper limit for the orbital angular momentum involved:

$$l \leqq P \cdot r_f \tag{2}$$

In the range of dimensions of 10^{-13} cm there is no possibility of localizing an incident particle with such precision as to determine the impact parameter. We may as well think that the incident particles are uniformly distributed (statistically) if we consider their impact points on a plane normal to the beam. The number of incident particles with impact parameter between d_1 and d_2 will therefore be

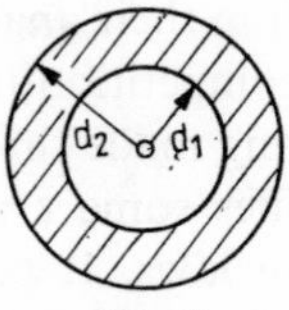

Fig. 2

proportional to the area shown in Fig. 2. If we choose d_1 and d_2 corresponding to two values of l differing by one unit we obtain the following formula for the area of the corona:

$$a_l = \pi \cdot (2l + 1)/P^2 \tag{3}$$

Let us now consider N_b beam-particles going through a target of thickness t_T, the total *track-length* inside the target is

$$L = N_b \cdot t_T \tag{4}$$

If there are ϱ particles per cm³ in the target, the number of systems of angular momentum between l and $l + 1$ will be:

$$N_l = a_l \cdot L \cdot \varrho \tag{5}$$

We may now consider a very particular type of interaction in which, every time a collision takes place with angular momentum between l and $l+1$, there is a "reaction" which changes the internal characteristic of one or both of the particles. We are not interested in following further such development, and call it "absorption into other reaction channels". The maximum number of such events we may possibly expect is N_l. The area a_l is called the *cross-section* for this absorption process. An example of this type of interaction can be imagined as a black ring, of the shape shown in Fig. 2. In a more general case the ring could have some transparency η_l^2, defined between 0 and 1, and the *absorption cross-section* would become:

$$\sigma_{r,l} = a_l \cdot (1 - \eta_l^2) \tag{6}$$

The corresponding number of absorption events (all with angular momentum between l and $l+1$) is:

$$n_l = \sigma_{r,l} \cdot L \cdot \varrho \tag{7}$$

The formula for $\sigma_{r,l}$ cannot be applied to the case of elastic scattering because of interference effects; this will be discussed in the next section.

To obtain the *total absorption cross-section* we must sum the contributions of all angular momenta:

$$\sigma_r = \sum_l \sigma_{r,l} \tag{8}$$

In the case of a *black sphere* of radius r we obtain a total absorption cross-section which equals the area presented by the sphere:

$$\sigma_b = \pi \cdot r^2 \tag{9}$$

All events in which $l \leqq r \cdot P$ are of the "absorption type". This cross-section is also called the *geometrical cross-section*, and, in the case of nuclei bombarded by small particles it can be calculated approximately with the formula

$$\sigma_b \cong \pi \cdot (1.3 A^{1/3} \cdot 10^{-13})^2 \tag{10}$$

where A is the atomic number. In the case of particles of radii of the same order of magnitude one should rather consider the radius as it is defined in Fig. 3.

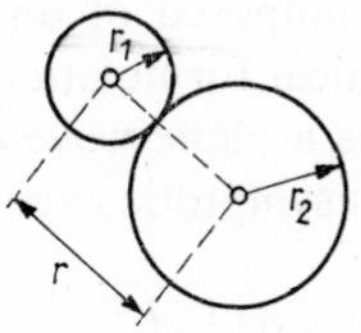

Fig. 3

If we use the formulae involving the impact parameter for quantum mechanical problems, we should remember that they have not the exact meaning as in macroscopic physics. This becomes clear through the uncertainty relations:

$$\Delta P_\perp \cdot \Delta d \gtrsim \hbar \tag{11}$$

where $P_\perp$ is the transverse momentum which, in the case of a beam of particles, is fairly well known.

The units system which is conveniently used for these calculations is given in the Appendix ($\hbar = c = 1$). We also summarize there the relativistic transformations between the laboratory (LAB) and center of mass system (CMS) for the particular case of two-body reactions, which naturally includes the elastic scattering one. In the following Sections we will call θ the scattering angle in the CMS and P the momentum in the CMS. These two parameters characterize a scattering event. The CMS-momentum P depends on the total energy available in the collision, which is equal to the *invariant mass* of the system (W). The scattering angle θ is a function of P and of another invariant: the *momentum transfer* to the target particle (t). t is the modulus of the difference between the energy-momentum vector of one of the particles, after and before the collision. The momentum transfer to the target particle, in an elastic collision is the following:

$$t = -2P^2(1 - \cos\theta) = -2MT^{\mathrm{LAB}} \tag{12}$$

where T^{LAB} is the kinetic energy of the target particle (of mass M) after the collision. (The target was at rest before the collision.) For small t:

$$t \approx -P^2\theta^2 \tag{13}$$

The total energy in the CMS (squared) is frequently called s. It is the modulus of the total energy-momentum vector of the system. A third invariant can be obtained: it is the modulus of the difference between the momentum-energy vectors of one of the particles after the collision and the other one before the collision. It is called u. The tree invariants are related as follows:

$$s + t + u = 2m^2 + 2M^2 \tag{14}$$

where m and M are the masses of the colliding particles. Total cross sections are also invariant.

2.2. The Beam as a Plane Wave

Let us now treat the system composed of one beam-particle and one target-particle using a quantum mechanical formulation. As long as there are no interactions the system is described as a plane wave e^{iPz}. At large distances from the origin ($r \gg l/P$) one can use the asymptotic expansion:

$$e^{iPz} = \sum_l \sqrt{a_l} \cdot i^{l+1} \cdot \left(\frac{e^{-i\varphi}}{r} - \frac{e^{i\varphi}}{r}\right) \cdot Y_{l,0} \tag{15}$$

where:

$$a_l = \pi\lambda^2(2l+1), \quad \varphi = rP - \frac{l\cdot\pi}{2}, \quad \lambda = \frac{\hbar}{P}$$

and $Y_{l,0}$ are the spherical harmonics defined in the Appendix.

This wave function describes a single "event" or system of incident and target particle. The probability of finding this system in a state of angular momentum l is given by a_l. This corresponds to the area of the "impact corona" already discussed in the last section. The two exponentials represent the incoming and outgoing spherical waves required to build up a plane wave.

2.3. The Disturbed Plane Wave

Anything happening between our two particles can only affect the outgoing waves $e^{i\varphi}/r$, *shifting* or *reducing* them (or both). This is conveniently represented by a complex coefficient α_l of modulus smaller or equal to one. The complete wave function of our system of two particles is:

$$\psi = \sum_l \sqrt{a_l} \cdot i^{l+1} \cdot \left(\frac{e^{-i\varphi}}{r} - \alpha_l \frac{e^{i\varphi}}{r}\right) \cdot Y_{l,0} \tag{16}$$

It decribes both the incoming particles *and* those which after the interaction cannot be distinguished from the incident ones, except for a rotation of the co-ordinate system. The latter are called "elastically scattered". The wave function describing only these events is given by the difference between the complete one and the undisturbed plane wave:

$$\psi_{sc} = \psi - e^{iPz} \tag{17}$$

The wave function ψ_{sc} contains only outgoing spherical waves, as one can verify by substituting in (17) the expansions made in (15) and (16). We may write ψ_{sc} in the form:

$$\psi_{sc} = \left[i \sum_l \sqrt{a_l}(1 - \alpha_l) Y_{l,0}\right] \cdot \frac{e^{irP}}{r} \tag{18}$$

If the interaction causes a reduction of the outgoing amplitudes ($|\alpha_l| < 1$) there will be a certain "loss" of events (absorption). These "missing" events are *not* described by ψ and ψ_{sc} because the outgoing particles are not identical to the incident ones. They are described by separate wave functions containing only outgoing spherical waves, which we are not going to discuss in detail here. In what follows we will only analyse the meaning of the fundamental equations (16) and (18).

2.4. Notation

The expression between brackets of Eq. (18) is usually called the *scattering amplitude* $f(\theta)$

$$\psi_{sc} = f(\theta) \cdot \frac{e^{irP}}{r} \tag{19}$$

One defines as *partial wave amplitude:*

$$A_l = \frac{i}{2}(1 - \alpha_l) \tag{20}$$

and therefore:

$$f(\theta) = 2 \sum_l \sqrt{a_l}\, A_l Y_{l,0} \tag{21}$$

A geometrical representation of the complex coefficient α_l is given in Fig. 4.

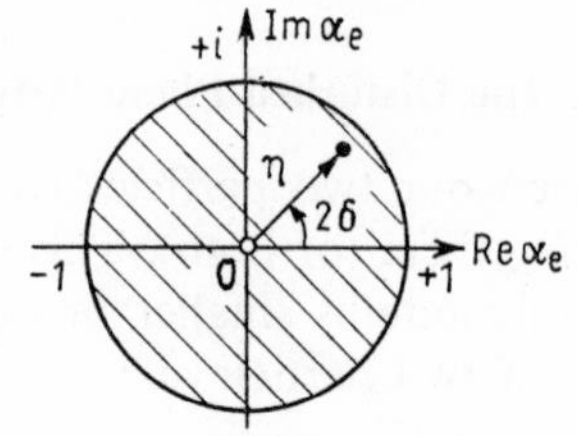

Fig. 4

α_l may be written as follows:

$$\alpha_l = \eta_l\, e^{2i\delta_l} \tag{22}$$

where we define the *phase shift* δ_l and the *absorption parameter* η_l. Both are real numbers and

$$0 \leqq \eta_l \leqq 1. \tag{23}$$

Figure 5 shows a representation of A_e. Notice that it is the same as for α_l, turned 90° and reduced to one half. This is called Argand-diagramme.

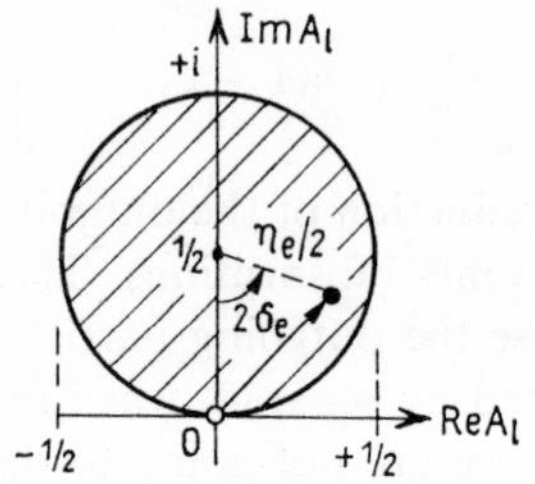

Fig. 5

Note: The complex coefficient α_l is identical to the diagonal element of the S-matrix used for the analysis of the absorption reactions.

2.5. Cross-Sections

The probability for an event to be of the absorption type is calculated from the net flux of the complete wave function ψ through a large sphere. The result gives the *absorption cross-section:*

$$\sigma_r = \sum_l a_l(1 - \eta_l^2) \tag{24}$$

The meaning of this formula was already discussed in Section 2.1. where we called η_l^2 the "transparency" of the ring of angular momentum l.

If we consider the wave function of the elastically scattered particles ψ_{sc} we obtain from its flux through a large sphere, the *scattering cross-section:*

$$\sigma_{sc} = \sum_l a_l \, |1 - \alpha_l|^2 \tag{25}$$

This formula could not be understood using the arguments of Section 2.1.; it derives from the wave character of the analysed processes. In particular for the *partial cross-sections:*

$$\sigma_{r,l} = a_l(1 - \eta_l^2) \tag{26}$$

and

$$\sigma_{sc,l} = a_l \, |1 - \alpha_l|^2 = 4a_l \, |A_l|^2 \tag{27}$$

one obtains limits which are completely *strange* to a "particles" picture. These limits are visualized in Fig. 6. The fact that σ_r and σ_{sc} can be expressed as sums of partial cross sections derives from the orthonormality of the spherical harmonics (integrals extended over the whole sphere).

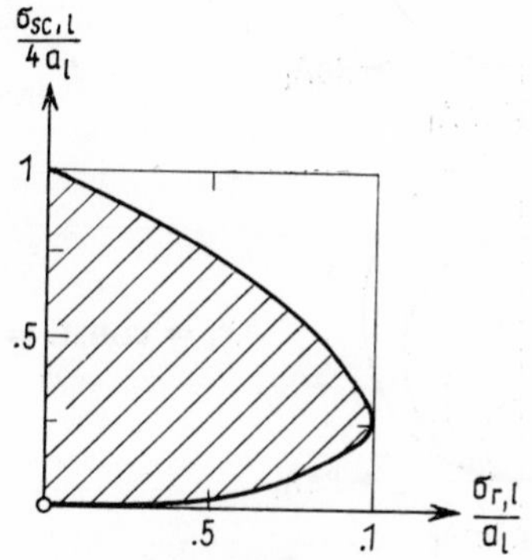

Fig. 6

The *total cross-section* is obtained from the following expression:

$$\sigma_T = \sigma_r + \sigma_{sc} \tag{28}$$

which can be used for each partial wave:

$$\sigma_{T,l} = \sigma_{r,l} + \sigma_{sc,l} = 4a_l \, \text{Im} \, A_l \tag{29}$$

Figure 7 shows some curves in the complex A_l-plane obtained keeping constant particular cross-sections. The "elasticity" x is defined as

$$x = \frac{\sigma_{sc,l}}{\sigma_{T,l}} = \frac{|A_l|^2}{\text{Im} \, A_l} \tag{30}$$

and gives rise to circles of equation:

$$\left| A_l - i\frac{x}{2} \right| = \frac{x}{2} \tag{31}$$

to which we will refer later on (Fig. 7c).

(a) $\sigma_{T,l} = \text{const.} = 4a_l \, \text{Im} \, A_l$

(b) $\sigma_{r,l} = \text{const.} = a_l(1 - \eta_l^2)$

(c) $x_l = \text{const.} = \dfrac{\sigma_{sc,l}}{\sigma_{T,l}}$

(d) $\sigma_{sc,l} = \text{const.} = 4a_l|A_l|^2$

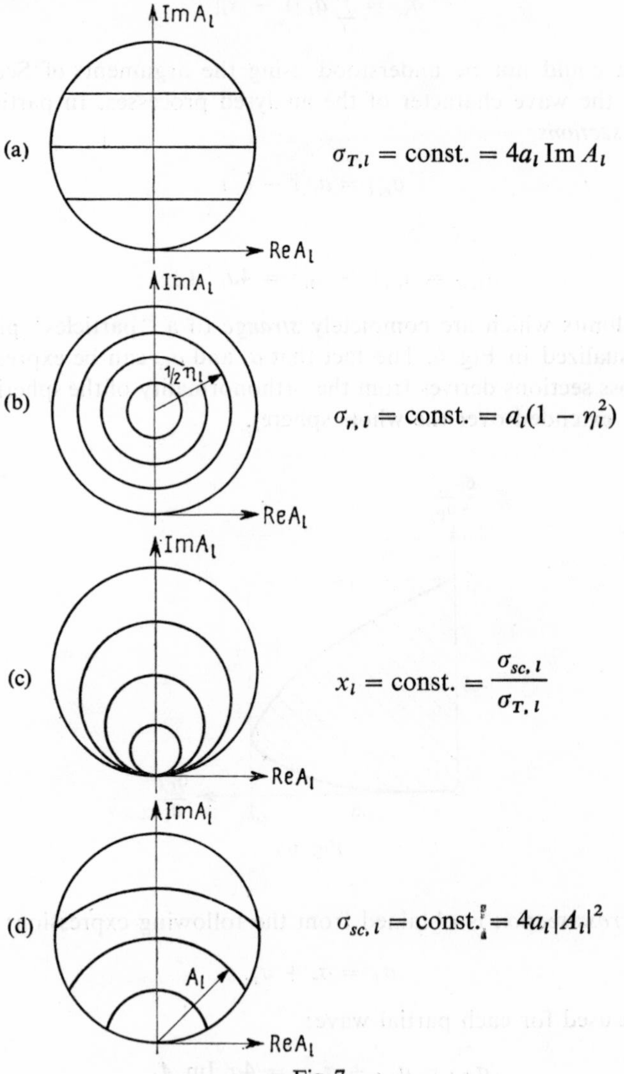

Fig. 7

If we substitute in Eq. (28) the expressions given in (24) and (25) and compare the result with Eq. (21) we obtain the relation:

$$\sigma_T = 4\pi\lambda \, \text{Im} \, f(0°) \tag{32}$$

which is called the *optical theorem*.

2.6. Angular Distributions

From the calculation of the flux of ψ_{sc} through a solid angle element $d\Omega$ one obtains the *differential cross-section for elastic scattering:*

$$d\sigma_{sc}/d\Omega = |f(\theta)|^2 \tag{33}$$

which may be written in the form:

$$d\sigma_{sc}/d\Omega = \frac{\lambda^2}{4}\left|\sum_l (2l+1)(1-\alpha_l)\,P_l\right|^2 \tag{34}$$

Introducing the expressions for the Legendre Polynomials P_l given in the Appendix, one obtains angular distributions of the form:

$$d\sigma_{sc}/d\Omega = \sum_i c_i \cdot \cos^i\theta \tag{35}$$

where the coefficients c_i are functions of the complex parameters α_l. If the angular momentum is limited to some $l^{\max}$ (by the range of the forces or some other reason), also the polynomial in $\cos\theta$ will have its degree limited to

$$i^{\max} = 2l^{\max} \tag{36}$$

This fact allows one to estimate *a priori* the complexity of the angular distributions expected in some interactions.

2.7. Shadow Scattering

Equations (24) and (25) establish relations between absorption and scattering cross-sections. Pure absorption does not exist. In other words, any absorption destroys the plane wave character of the incident beam. What remains must therefore contain some scattered part. This is called shadow scattering. It will be predominant over any other type of elastic scattering (i.e. caused by "forces") when the absorption is very strong. In particular, for the case of a completely absorbing (black) sphere we obtain a pure shadow scattering amplitude. For a radius r of the sphere, we will have

$$\eta_l = 0 \quad \text{for} \quad l \leqq r \cdot P \tag{37}$$

The phase shifts δ_l are not defined in this case. From Eq. (20) we obtain the same absorption cross-section as in Section 2.1. But Eq. (25) provides also a scattering cross-section. We will have:

$$\sigma_r^{bl} = \sigma_{sc}^{bl} = \pi r^2 \tag{38}$$

and therefore:

$$\sigma_T^{bl} = 2\pi r^2 \tag{39}$$

The elastic scattering from a black sphere has a completely determined angular distribution:

$$d\sigma_{sc}^{bl}/d\Omega = \frac{\lambda^2}{4}\left[\sum_l (2l+1)\,P_l\right]^2 \tag{40}$$

The scattering amplitude $f(\theta)$ has no real part in the present case; applying the optical theorem we obtain:

$$d\sigma_{sc}^{bl}/d\Omega(0^\circ) = \frac{r^4}{4\lambda^2} \tag{41}$$

For high values of r/λ the scattering angular distribution becomes very much peaked forwards. This is called the *diffraction peak*. An example is shown in Fig. 8 for $l^{\max} = r/\lambda = 18$. The point at 0° is determined by Eq. (41) and is

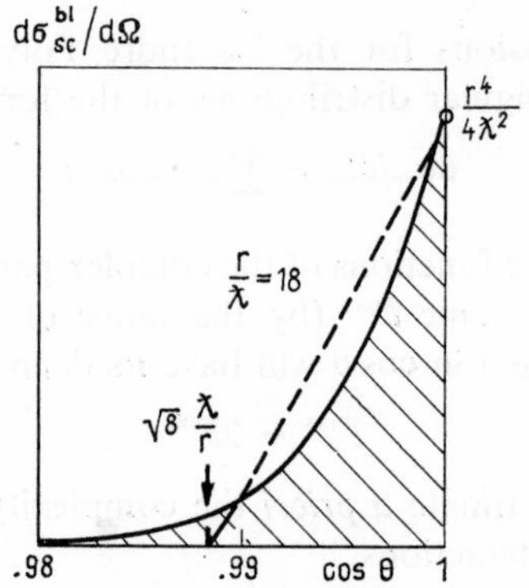

Fig. 8

called the *optical point*. The example shown could correspond roughly to $\pi + C$ scattering at an energy of ~1 GeV. Since the diffraction peak contains nearly all the elastic scattering events, one can estimate that it is confined to scattering angles smaller than $\sim\sqrt{8}\cdot\lambda/r$.

If we draw the curve of Fig. 8 on semilogarithmic paper we obtain an approximate straight line which can be expressed as an exponential in $(1 - \cos\theta)$. Keeping in mind that the momentum transfer t is given by $2P^2(1 - \cos\theta)$ and that the diffraction peak is confined to angles smaller than $\sqrt{8\lambda/r}$ we obtain the expression:

$$d\sigma/d\Omega \approx (d\sigma/d\Omega)_{0^\circ}\cdot e^{-\frac{r^2}{3}\cdot t} \tag{42}$$

This is a reasonable approximation for the diffraction peak even in the case of a sphere which is not completely "black".

2.8. Pure Elastic Scattering

Let us now consider the case in which there is no absorption at all and therefore for all values of l involved in the collision

$$\eta_l = 1$$

The elastic scattering angular distribution and cross-section, which are all we can measure in an experiment, are completely determined by a set of real phase shifts δ_l. In our graphical representations of the parameters α_l and A_l only the points on the circumference are allowed.

The partial wave amplitude will have the expression:

$$A_l = i\,e^{i\delta_l} \cdot \sin \delta_l \tag{43}$$

The formula for the cross-section becomes:

$$\sigma_T = \sigma_{sc} = 4 \sum_l a_l \sin^2 \delta_l \tag{44}$$

and the differential cross-section:

$$d\sigma/d\Omega = \lambda\!\!\!^{-2} \left| \sum_l (2l + 1) \cdot e^{i\delta_l} \sin \delta_l P_l \right|^2 \tag{45}$$

which can be written in the form:

$$d\sigma/d\Omega = \lambda\!\!\!^{-2} \left[\sum_l (2l + 1) \cdot \cos \delta_l \cdot \sin \delta_l P_l \right]^2 + \lambda\!\!\!^{-2} \left[\sum_l (2l + 1) \sin^2 \delta_l P_l \right]^2 \tag{46}$$

It may happen that all phase shifts are very small, particularly at low energies. If all $\delta_l \lesssim 5°$ and therefore $\cos \delta_l \approx 1$ and $\sin \delta_l \approx \delta_l$ one may use an approximate formula, valid to a few percent:

$$d\sigma/d\Omega \approx \lambda\!\!\!^{-2} \left[\sum_l (2l + 1) \cdot \delta_l \cdot P_l \right]^2 \tag{47}$$

and for the cross-section:

$$\sigma_T = \sigma_{sc} \approx 4 \sum_l a_l \delta_l^2 \tag{48}$$

2.9. Resonance Scattering

2.9.1. Elastic Resonance without Background. There is one interesting situation in which the energy dependence of a phase shift can tell us something without any theory. That is the case in which its value, at a certain energy, causes the cross-section to go to its maximum possible value, namely:

$$\sigma_{sc,l} = 4a_l \tag{49}$$

This happens for:

$$\delta_l = 90° \quad \alpha_l = -1 \quad A_l = i \tag{50}$$

The cross-section takes half its maximum value for $\delta_l = 45°$ and for $\delta_l = 135°$. If there is a more or less linear energy dependence, one obtains a cross-section of the form shown in Fig. 9. One calls this in general a *resonance* at the energy E_0 and full width Γ. Such resonances are frequently found in elementary particle physics.

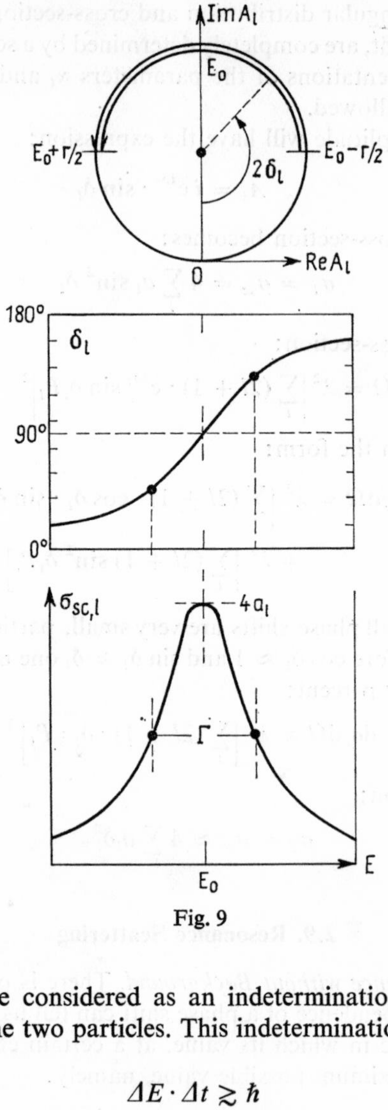

Fig. 9

The width Γ can be considered as an indetermination in the energy of the system composed of the two particles. This indetermination is related to the time the state can live:

$$\Delta E \cdot \Delta t \gtrsim \hbar \tag{51}$$

and consequently its *mean life* τ is approximately:

$$\tau \simeq \hbar/\Gamma \tag{52}$$

The resonances here discussed have therefore well-defined *mean life*, *angular momentum* (spin) and *mean energy* (mass). There is no reason for not calling them "particles" or "states" of very short life. They can be described as "compound systems" having a complex energy

$$E = E_0 - i\,\Gamma/2 \tag{53}$$

In first approximation one can show that the scattering phase shift at energies near to such a resonance (E_0) is given by

$$\tan \delta = \tfrac{1}{2}\Gamma/(E_0 - E) \tag{54}$$

and the corresponding cross-section

$$\sigma_l = a_l \frac{\Gamma^2}{(E_0 - E)^2 + \Gamma^2/4} \tag{55}$$

which is the function plotted in Fig. 9 (Breit–Wigner formula).

2.9.2. Background of Different Angular Momentum. Up to here we have discussed the effect on the cross-section of a single phase shift going through 90°. Other partial waves present at the same energy will add their contributions to the total cross-section.

The angular distribution at the resonance energy is in general characteristic of the angular momentum l, but interference effects of waves of different angular momentum may complicate the situation. Let us analyse the case in which all other phase shifts are small and do not change with the energy. Then, the non-resonant waves are confined to a small region along the real axis near to the origin. However, the resonant A_l is near to $+i$. Therefore resonant and non-resonant amplitudes are nearly orthogonal at the resonance energy.

The interesting conclusion is that when one calculates $|f(\theta)|^2$ all interference terms between the resonant amplitude and the non-resonant ones will vanish *and* change sign at energies near to the resonance. The interference terms appear in the angular distributions in the coefficients of odd powers of the $\cos\theta$-polynomials. Therefore, a change of sign will in general cause an inversion of an eventual forwards-backwards asymmetry of the angular distribution.

2.9.3. Background of the Same Angular Momentum. Some additional interactions may affect the outgoing waves [see Eq. (16)] and can be written in the following form:

$$\alpha_l = \alpha_{0,l} \cdot \alpha_l^{\text{res}} \tag{56}$$

where $\alpha_{0,l}$ represents some background and α_l^{res} the resonant part.

Figure 10 shows the case of a superimposed absorption process which is independent of the energy of the system:

$$\alpha_{0,l} = \eta_{0,l} = \text{const} \tag{57}$$

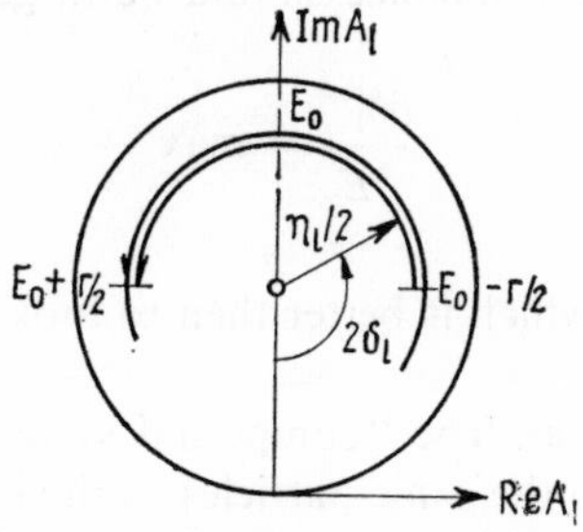

$$\alpha_l = \eta_{0,l} \cdot e^{2i\delta_l^{\text{res}}}$$

Fig. 10

We see that the general features are similar to those without background, but the cross section ($= 4a_l \operatorname{Im} A_l$) fails to reach the maximum expected for that particular l. In fact:

$$\sigma_{T,l}^{\max} = 4a_l \cdot \frac{1 + \eta_{0,l}^2}{2} \tag{58}$$

The resonance "circle" is *reduced* by a factor $\eta_{0,l}/2$.

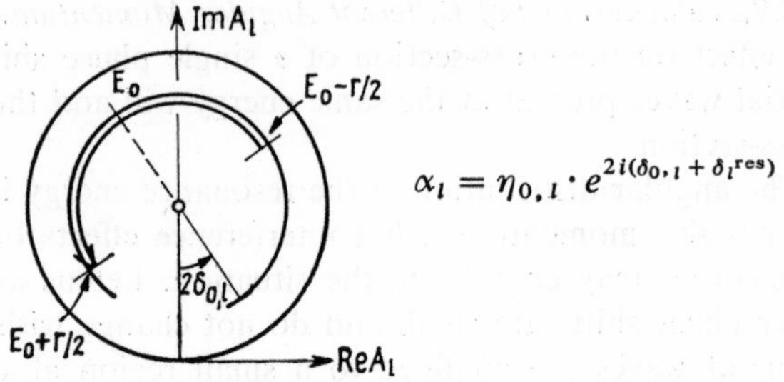

Fig. 11

Figure 11 shows the case of an additional phase shift of the same l caused by forces which do not depend on the energy (in the interval here considered). We have:

$$\alpha_{0,l} = \eta_{0,l} \cdot e^{2i\delta_{0,l}} \tag{59}$$

and therefore:

$$\alpha_l = \eta_{0,l} \cdot e^{2i(\delta_{0,l} + \delta_e^{\text{res}})} \tag{60}$$

The resonance circle is now also *turned* by an angle $2\delta_{0,l}$. The resonance energy E_0 does not coincide with the energy at which the elastic and total cross-sections arrive to their maximae. The phase shift at the resonance point is not 90°.

If the background is energy-dependent the situation may become still more complicated. The localization of the resonance energy E_0 may be quite difficult. A characteristic fact at the resonance should be in general that

$$\frac{\partial \delta_l^{\text{res}}}{\partial E} = \max \tag{61}$$

This provides a criterium which is better then to look for the point where δ_l goes through 90°.

2.9.4. Inelastic Resonances. The "compound system" considered in 2.9.1 was assumed to decay only into the same particles as the incident ones (elastic scattering). In a more general case this "compound" may also have other decay modes which we would consider as reactions. The branching ratio for the different decay modes should be an intrinsec property of the "compound". It should not depend on the energy (mass) of the system except for kinematic factors (energy available for the secondary particles; we neglect such effects in the present discussion). If there are no background contributions we may say that a constant decay ratio is equivalent to a constant "elasticity" $x = \sigma_{el,l}/\sigma_{T,l}$ which was already defined in 2.5. Curves of constant x in the A_l diagramme were shown in Fig. 7c. They are circles tangent to the real axis at the origin and of diameter x. We reproduce them in Fig. 12 together with the approximate energy dependence of the phase shifts for the case of "resonances". Cross-sections can be expressed by Breit–Wigner formulae except for a scale factor which reduces the maximum σ_T to

$$\sigma_{T,l}^{\max} = 4a_l \cdot x \tag{62}$$

The phase shifts go through 90° only if $x > 5$. For $x < 5$ they go through 0° at the resonance energy. The absorption coefficients η_l have a minimum at E_0.

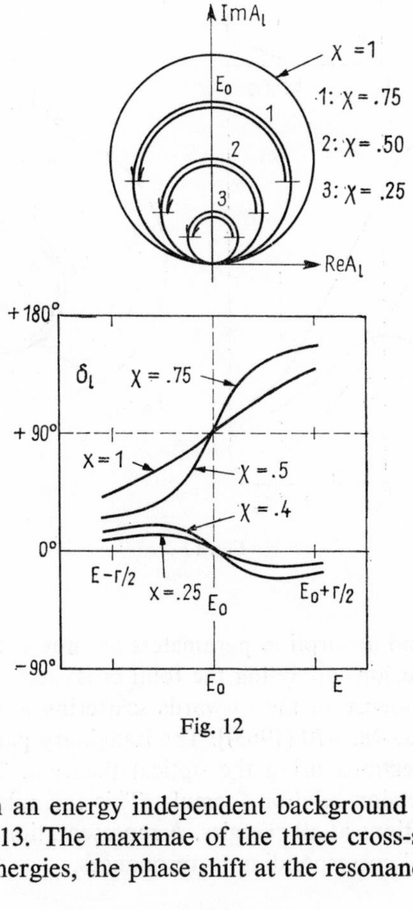

Fig. 12

If we assume again an energy independent background we obtain figures like those shown in Fig. 13. The maximae of the three cross-sections $\sigma_{sc,l}$, $\sigma_{r,l}$ and $\sigma_{T,l}$ are at different energies, the phase shift at the resonance energy is not at 90°.

The situation is best understood with the help of the complex diagramme A_l as it was remarked by Adair [*Phys. Rev.* **113**, 338 (1959)]. We may still add that these kind of resonances appear in nature (see an example in Fig. 31) and that they are even more complicated: the background depends on the energy, the elasticity is not constant and several resonances may partially overlap. For a complete understanding the inelastic channels must be investigated.

$$\eta_{0,l} = .4$$
$$\delta_{0,l} = 30°$$
$$\chi \cong .5$$

$$\alpha_l = \eta_{0,l} \cdot \eta_l^{res} \cdot e^{2i(\delta_{0,l} + \delta_l^{res})}$$

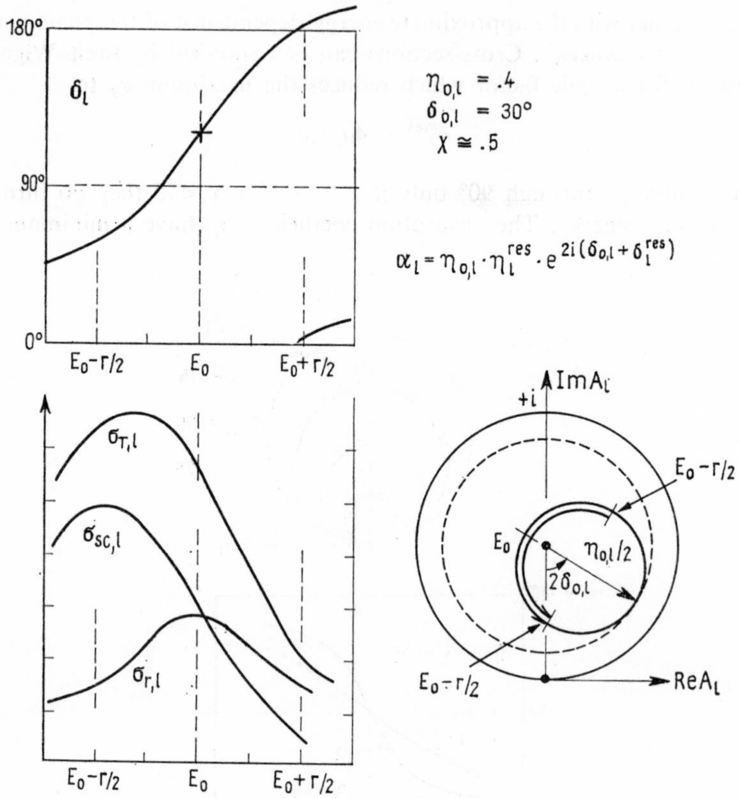

Fig. 13

If the phase shifts and absorption parameters are not known one can arrive to some interesting conclusions analysing the total cross-sections. This is best done using the energy dependence of the forwards scattering amplitude $f(0°)$ [Höhler and Ebel, *Nuclear Phys.* **48**, 470 (1963)]. The imaginary part of $f(0°)$ is obtained from the total cross-sections using the optical theorem. The real part can be obtained using a dispersion relation formula. This formula includes an integral over the total cross-sections at all energies. A representation of $f(0°)$ in a complex plane presents "loops" corresponding to resonances.

3. EXPERIMENTAL DATA

3.1. Techniques

Experimental information is obtained in the form of cross-sections and angular distributions. Measurements are usually made exposing a target of well-known composition and dimensions to a beam of particles. One also expects in the near future to perform experiments with colliding beams. The particles emerging from the region of the collision are detected with a variety of techniques which at present are classified in two big groups: *visual* techniques and *electronic* techniques. For some recently developed devices this classification is not clear.

By *visual techniques*, one understands those in which one can "see" each event, possibly on a photograph. Mostly used at present are bubble chambers, but very important results have also been obtained using nuclear emulsions, cloud and diffusion chambers. Spark chambers are also widely used for the "visual" observation of particle trajectories. In all these techniques, single events are selected on the film (scanning), carefully measured and, after a more or less elaborate computation, classified. Finally the events are collected in histograms which represent the distribution curve of the parameter plotted in abscissa; this may be the $\cos\theta$ in the CMS for a scattering problem.

In the so called *electronic techniques* the results are obtained in general as "counts" of a more or less complicated coincidence system. Among many possible components, the scintillation counter is certainly the most used. The set-up is in general built according to the specific parameter one likes to investigate. Essential for these techniques is the fact that one selects the events to be counted; the time necessary to decide if an event should be counted or not is of the order of 10^{-5} to 10^{-8} seconds. Therefore very rare events can be picked-out in reasonable time.

An intermediate position between visual and electronic techniques is occupied by the spark chamber: it can be triggered by a counter system, therefore selecting a-priori the events, and an examination and accurate measurement can be performed afterwards. Counter hodoscopes and digitized spark chambers, which directly previde the co-ordinates of the particle trajectories, are already used in computer controlled "on-line" installations.

3.2. Errors

3.2.1. Energy Resolution. This is determined by the beam set-up. An accuracy of a few percent is normal in high energy experiments. Sometimes the energy-loss inside the target must be taken into account; this is particularly important in big bubble chambers and at low energies.

3.2.2. Angular Resolution. This depends on the technique used for the measurement of the trajectories. In the case of histograms based on visual data, the width of the single interval of an angular distribution gives an indetermination of the angle. This width is chosen by the experimentalist according to the measurement errors on the angles (this must include the effects of multiple Coulomb scattering) and to the number of events he may plot on a single histogram. If there is no particular indication one assumes that the angular resolution is at least of the same order as the width of the intervals.

In electronic experiments the solid angle covered by a counter determines the angular interval. Also here the size of the interval is chosen in such a way that the statistical accuracy is sufficient. The limit is in general imposed by the available accelerator time. Since the results are not presented in the form of histograms, an indication of the angular resolution is always necessary.

3.2.3. Accuracy of the Normalization. When several measurements of differential cross-sections are made simultaneously (this is obviously the case in bubble chambers) there is a constant factor for all of them which determines the scale in millibarns. This is called the normalization factor. It is obtained from the following data: the beam monitor (which in the case of bubble chambers is a scanner counting the beam tracks), the composition of the beam (which must be carefully measured), the composition of the target and its thickness (in the case of bubble chambers, the track-length). It is not easy to obtain all these data with an accuracy better than a few percent and it is in general convenient to indicate this "normalization error" separately from the "relative errors" we are going to discuss in the next paragraph.

3.2.4. Relative Errors. The number of events to be included in each angular interval (differential cross-section) will be affected by several sources of error: first of all there is the *statistical accuracy*, which as we said before is in general limited by time and money reasons; secondly there are several *biases* which may consist of the inclusion of background events or of the elimination (loss) of some good events, both of which vary with angle. Events are lost in the visual scanning of photographs, in the computer due to wrong input data, because of inefficient counter coincidences, etc. Others are wrongly included (background) due to misclassifications or because they were produced in a different target substance. The latter case may happen in the walls of the target or if the target itself is a composed substance (propane bubble chamber, polyethylene target). One will try to subtract this background in the best possible way (empty target measurements, etc.) but some uncertainty will always remain.

Except for the statistical errors, all others are very difficult to estimate correctly. Frequently they are *not* included in the errors published and the reader is forced to make his own more or less reasonable assessments; the evasive sentence is in general: "errors are only statistical ones" and must be taken as a serious warning. These kind of difficulties must be taken into account, particularly when data of different experiments is combined in a single analysis.

3.3. Fitting of Curves

The general form of the scattering angular distributions was discussed in Section 2.6. The number of free parameters η_l and δ_l will depend on the maximum angular momentum involved. In a more general case there will be a splitting of these parameters due to spin and isotopic spin conditions. But the final curve can always be expressed, as a polynomial in $\cos\theta$. To define such a polynomial one needs at least as many experimental points as its degree plus one. If the number of points is higher one should apply the least squares method to obtain a best fitting curve.

The expression for the angular distribution as a polynomial in $\cos\theta$ is quite instructive, and, if nothing is known about an interaction, it is the best way of starting an investigation. It should be kept in mind that the coefficients of this polynomial are *not* the free parameters of the problem; in fact, a best fit in $\sum c_i \cos^i\theta$ can easily provide negative cross-sections which have no meaning. This would never come out of the correct form (34) which contains the really free parameters η_l and δ_l.

The least squares method is applied, varying the free parameters up to a minimization of the χ^2-function defined in Fig. 14. In order to compare different best-fits, one normalizes the χ^2's by dividing by the degree of freedom defined as the difference between the number of (experimental) points and the number of free parameters of the fitting curve.

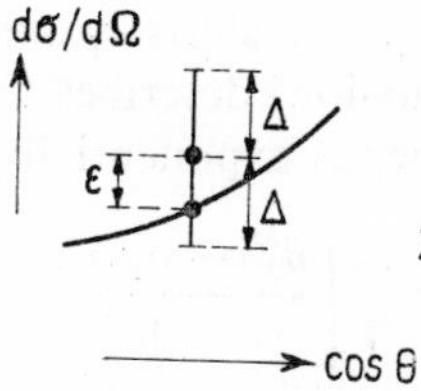

$$\chi^2 \propto \sum (\varepsilon/\Delta)^2$$

Fig. 14

It is assumed for this method that the errors on $d\sigma/d\Omega$ are much bigger than the uncertainties on $\cos\theta$ (angular resolution). This is in general not true, but a correct formula for the χ^2 using both experimental errors as shown in Fig. 15, would make the calculations extremely unwieldy. One should therefore not be surprised if sometimes, using standard best fit programmes, very high values of

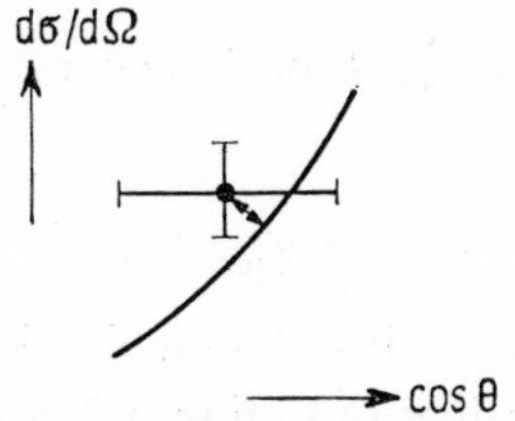

Fig. 15

χ^2 come out. Some prevention of this difficulty can be made by always keeping the angular resolution high (small intervals on $\cos \theta$), even if the statistical error on $d\sigma/d\Omega$ becomes very high.

An accurate investigation of the χ^2 may provide several solutions for the free parameters. These are called *ambiguities*, and are of different types: some are purely mathematical, like an inversion of the signs of all phase shifts; others are due to the particular experimental information which provides several minima for the χ^2-function. In general, to decide between different "ambiguous" solutions new experimental material must be provided.

In Section 5.5. we are going to discuss a computer programme for the analysis of pion-proton scattering giving some details of the input data required and of its output. The use of such a programme presupposes a certain knowledge of the fundamental formulae of the concrete scattering case. The formulae actually used in the programme may be more complicated and accurate, but the general arguments about the possibility of obtaining a set of best-fitting parameters must be understood previously by the user.

3.4. Errors on Best-Fitting Parameters

The probability that a set of phase shifts δ_l and absorption parameters η_l (we may call them all δ_i in this discussion) describes the result of some measurements of cross-sections $\sigma_j^M \pm \Delta\sigma_j^M$ depends exponentially on

$$\chi^2 = \sum_i \left[\frac{\sigma_i^M - \sigma_i(\delta_1 \dots \delta_n)}{\Delta\sigma_i^M} \right]^2 \tag{63}$$

We assumed here that the errors of measurement are uncorrelated and gaussian. Otherwise the formula for the χ^2 would become somewhat more complicated but the following considerations would remain unchanged.

We may consider χ^2 as a function of the parameters δ_i $(i = 1 \dots n)$. In the n-dimensional space in which these parameters are the co-ordinate axis we may imagine the $\chi^2(\delta_1 \dots \delta_n)$ as a "density"-function. Let us assume that a computer programme succeeded in finding a point of minimum density in this space: $\bar{\delta}_1 \dots \bar{\delta}_n$. We also assume that the value $\chi^2_{\min}$ is compatible with the one expected from statistical considerations (degrees of freedom).

We will now analyse the situation around the point of minimum χ^2. In normal cases a surface which encloses the point of minimum χ^2 will have the equation

$$\chi^2 = \chi^2_{\min} + \text{positive constant} \tag{64}$$

In particular the surface:

$$\chi^2 = \chi^2_{\min} + 1 \tag{65}$$

will enclose a volume which contains all combinations of the δ_i's which are less probable than the optimum values $(\bar{\delta}_i)$ up to a factor $1/e$. Therefore this volume has the meaning of a standard error in n dimensions.

A two-dimensional example is shown in Fig. 16. The projections of the "error-area" on the two axis give the standard errors of the two parametres δ_1 and δ_2.

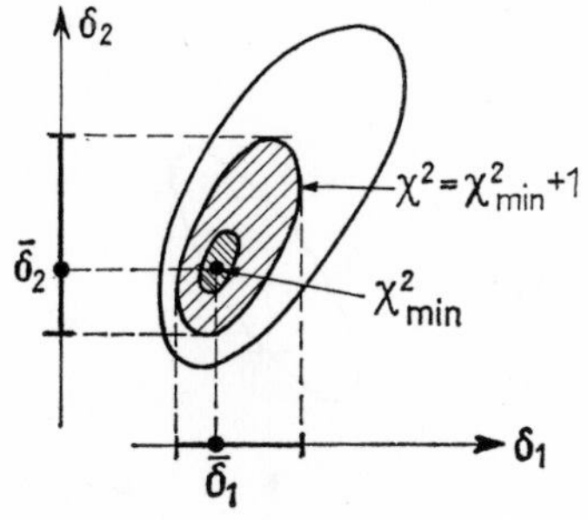

Fig. 16

If the "error-volume" is sufficiently small it becomes possible to develope the χ^2-function around its minimum using the second derivatives which can be calculated numerically (remember that the first derivatives are zero). The expression for χ^2 will then be of the form:

$$\chi^2 = \chi^2_{\min} + \sum_{ij} a_{ij}(\delta_i - \bar{\delta}_i)(\delta_j - \bar{\delta}_j) \tag{66}$$

The surfaces of constant χ^2 are now n-dimensional ellipsoids, the error-volume becomes an "error-ellipsoid".

Let us consider the case in which all coefficients a_{ij} are zero, except for $i = j$ (diagonal matrix). The χ^2-function becomes:

$$\chi^2 = \chi^2_{\min} + \sum_i [(\delta_i - \bar{\delta}_i)/a_{ii}^{-1/2}]^2 \tag{67}$$

The coefficients $a_{ii}^{-1/2}$ have exactly the meaning of standard errors. This is the case of uncorrelated parameters δ_i; the "error ellipsoid" has its axis (eigen-vectors) parallel to the δ-axis, as is shown in Fig. 17.

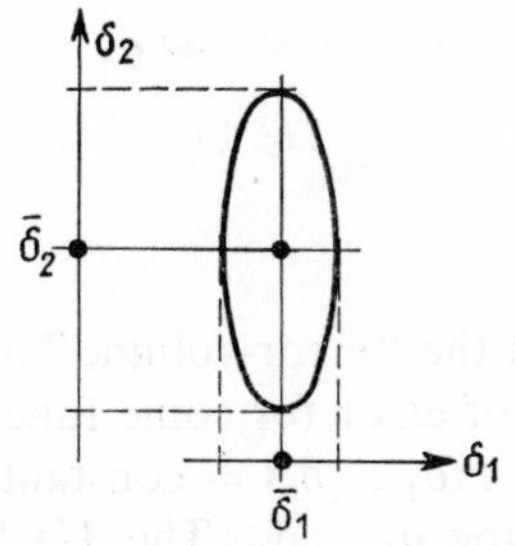

Fig. 17

The general case of a non-diagonal a_{ij}-matrix is shown in two dimensions in Fig. 18. The diagonal elements of the a_{ij}-matrix determine the points A, B, C and D. The absolute $1/e$ probability limits for δ_1 and δ_2 are given by the projec-

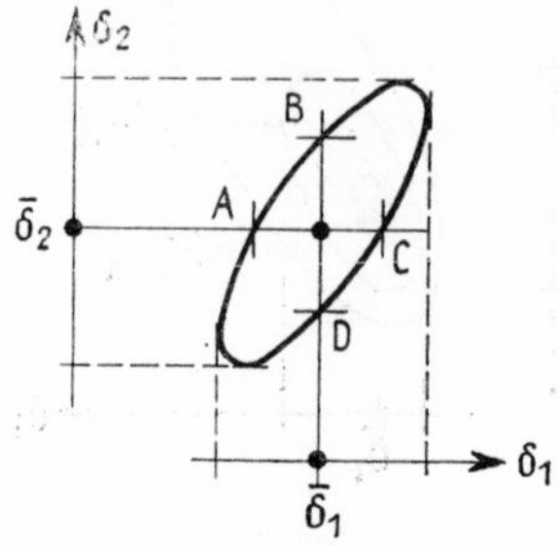

Fig. 18

tions of the ellipse on the two co-ordinate axis. The correlation of δ_1 and δ_2 is numerically expressed by the non-diagonal elements of the a_{ij}-matrix.

In n dimensions the calculation of the $1/e$ limits of a single δ_i may become quite difficult, particularly if the ellipsoid approximation is not sufficiently accurate. An information which can help to estimate errors is the knowledge of the "eigen-vectors" of the error-ellipsoid. They can be easily calculated from the a_{ij}-matrix. Particularly if one axis of the ellipsoid is much bigger than any other one (see Fig. 19) it is possible to estimate errors from this "leading" eigen-vector combined with the diagonal elements of the error matrix.

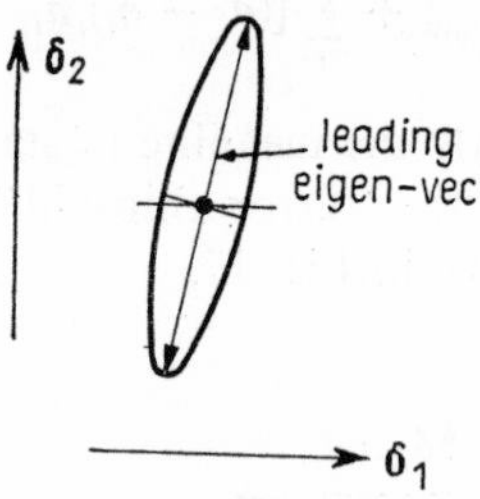

Fig. 19

These considerations about the "error-volume" are of great importance if one wants to calculate the limits of error for some function of the δ's which we may call $F(\delta_1 \ldots \delta_n)$. The equation $F(\delta_1 \ldots \delta_n) =$ constant is represented by surfaces in the n-dimensional space of the $\delta_1 \ldots \delta_n$. The $1/e$ limits for $F(\delta_1 \ldots \delta_n)$ will be given by the two particular F-surfaces which are tangent to the error-volume.

Let us take a simple exemple: how one obtains the $1/e$ limits of the function:

$$F(\delta_1 \dots \delta_n) = \delta_1 - \delta_2 \tag{68}$$

First we must project the n-dimensional ellipsoid on the δ_1–δ_2-plane. (If we would use only the elements a_{ij} corresponding to δ_1 and δ_2 we would be making a section of the ellipsoid, not a projection.) The projected ellipsoid may look like Fig. 20. The lines at 45° are of F = constant. The tangents to the ellipse give the

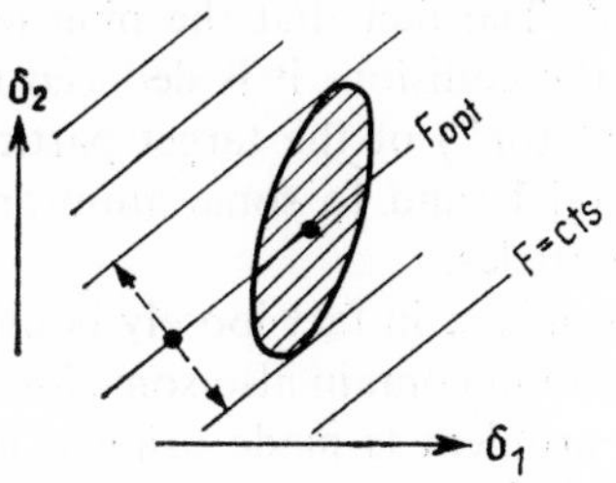

Fig. 20

$1/e$ limits. The same method can be generalized for the case of non elliptical error volume. Calculations should then be made numerically, step by step or directly during the best-fit calculations.

3.5. Note on Coulomb Scattering

Frequently the scattering particles have electric charge. We believe we know enough about the scattering due to Coulomb forces and therefore include it in the formulae for the total and differential cross-sections as a well-known term. Actually, Coulomb scattering is not easily treated using the phase shift formalism. This is already clear when one regards the long range of the electric forces.

The scattering due to Coulomb forces depends strongly on the relative velocity of the two particles. It is important at low energies and small angles, as one can see from the (non relativistic) expression:

$$(\mathrm{d}\sigma/\mathrm{d}\Omega)_{\mathrm{coul}} = \lambda\!\!\!^{-2} \left[\frac{z_1 z_2 e^2}{\hbar v(1 - \cos\theta)}\right]^2 \tag{69}$$

where z_1 and z_2 are the number of electric charges e of each particle and v is their relative velocity ($e^2/\hbar c = 1/137$). One may use this formula to establish if in an experiment Coulomb scattering must be taken into account. In particular cases it may also be sufficiently accurate for the actual correction, as we will discuss in low energy pion-proton scattering.

In modern best fit programmes for phase shift analysis the Coulomb interaction is included in the calculation of the angular distributions which are compared with the experimental data. The calculations are quite complicated and we are not describing them here.

4. NOTE ON PION-PION SCATTERING

4.1. Experimental Data

It is not possible at present to construct pion "targets". It may be possible in the future to obtain pion-pion collisions in crossing beams of pions. The nearest information we can get today arises from the bombardment of pions "loosely" bound to nucleons. The situation is quite similar to the case of neutrons when deuterium targets are used. The fact that the pion (or neutron) was "loosely" bound is found out after the collision: it is deduced from the small momentum transfer to the rest ("spectator") of the target particle. It may also be noticed that electrons are in general bound to some atom and, for many purposes are treated as "free" target particles.

In deuterium, real neutrons are in fact loosely bound to protons. In a nucleon the virtual "pion cloud" should contain also some loosely bound pions. A mathematical treatment of this problem is made using a model, the one particle exchange (OPE) model which has been very popular during recent years. One

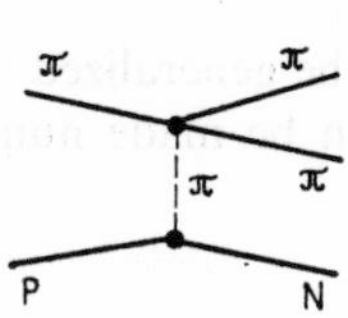

Fig. 21

imagines that a virtual pion is emitted by the nucleon and is knocked by the incident pion according to the graph shown in Fig. 21. The model gives a formula for the calculation of the total and differential cross-sections for elastic pion-pion scattering, based on data from the reaction

$$\pi + p \rightarrow \pi + \pi + N \tag{70}$$

in which only events with small LAB momentum of the nucleon were selected. One may notice that with a single incident pion energy a certain range of $(\pi + \pi)$-CMS masses are simultaneously investigated. Therefore in a single experiment the energy dependence of the cross-sections is found.

Several experimental groups have used the method described above. In Figs. 22a to 22d the total pion-pion cross-sections for $\pi^- + \pi^0$, $\pi^- + \pi^+$, $\pi^+ + \pi^0$, $\pi^+ + \pi^+$ are presented as they were obtained by the Saclay–Orsay–Bari–Bologna collaboration using the bubble chamber technique. Such a big collaboration became indispensable for the analysis of the ~20,000 events required to obtain only a few hundred events with small momentum transfer.

The results given in Figs. 14a and b were obtained from the analysis of the reactions

$$\pi^- + p \rightarrow \pi^- + \pi^0 + p \tag{71}$$

and

$$\pi^- + p \to \pi^- + \pi^+ + n \tag{72}$$

The incident pions had a momentum of 1.6 GeV/c. For Figs. 14c and 14d data from the reactions

$$\pi^+ + p \to \pi^+ + \pi^0 + p \tag{73}$$

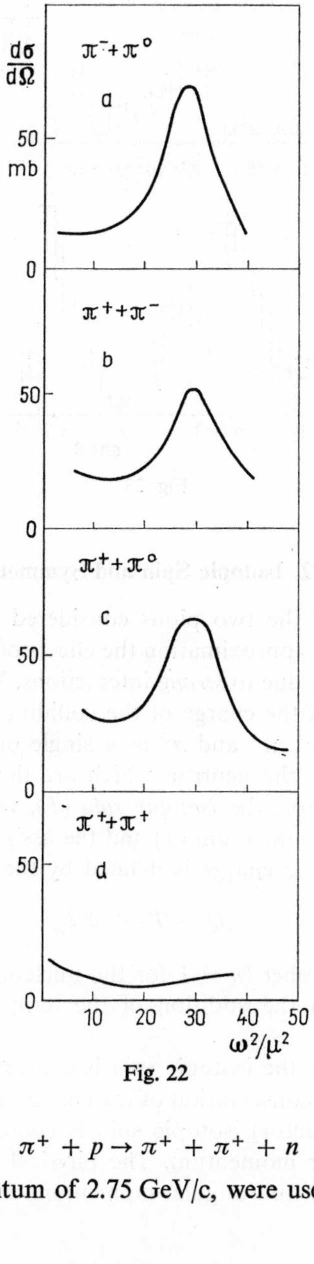

Fig. 22

and

$$\pi^+ + p \to \pi^+ + \pi^+ + n \tag{74}$$

with incident pion momentum of 2.75 GeV/c, were used.

In the same experiment, data about the pion-pion angular distribution was obtained. The most interesting result is the one for $\pi^- + \pi^0$ scattering shown in Fig. 23, for different intervals of the squared pion-pion mass (the energy of the wo pions in their CMS is called ω, the pion mass μ).

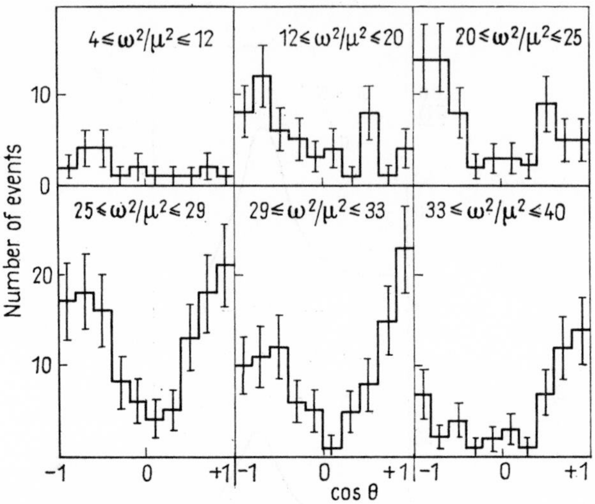

Fig. 23

4.2. Isotopic Spin and Symmetry

The relative velocity of the two pions considered in the last section is high enough to neglect in a first approximation the effects of Coulomb forces. The high cross-sections observed are due to *strong* interactions. We assume that these interactions are independent of the charge of the colliding particles and therefore we treat the three particles: π^+, π^- and π^0 as a single one. The same thing can be done with the proton and the neutron which are then called "nucleons". One introduces a vector operator, the *isotopic spin* (T), which has the mathematical properties of the angular momentum (J) and the assignment 1 for the pion and $\frac{1}{2}$ for the nucleon. The electric charge is defined by the third component of T:

$$Q = T_3 + n/2 \tag{75}$$

where n is the baryon number ($n = 1$ for the nucleon). (For other particles this formula is corrected with the addition of the term $S/2$ where S is called the strangeness.)

The third component of the isotopic spin is conserved in all interactions; this is equivalent to the law of conservation of the charge. In *strong* interactions it also happens that the total (vector) isotopic spin is conserved, in complete analogy with the ordinary angular momentum. The physical properties depend only on the *total* isotopic spin and *total* angular momentum. For particular charge states, (as for particular third components M of the angular momentum), one obtains physical properties by geometrical considerations (that is if we restrict ourselves to strong interactions).

The system formed by two pions can be in the isotopic spin states 0, 1, 2, according to the sum rules for two $T = 1$ vectors. The different charge states of this system are related as follows:

$$\begin{aligned}
T = 2,\quad T_3 = +2 &= |\pi^+\pi^+\rangle \\
+1 &= \sqrt{1/2}\,|\pi^0\pi^+\rangle + \sqrt{1/2}\,|\pi^+\pi^0\rangle \\
0 &= \sqrt{1/6}\,|\pi^-\pi^+\rangle + \sqrt{2/3}\,|\pi^0\pi^0\rangle + \sqrt{1/6}\,|\pi^+\pi^-\rangle \\
-1 &= \sqrt{1/2}\,|\pi^-\pi^0\rangle + \sqrt{1/2}\,|\pi^0\pi^-\rangle \\
-2 &= |\pi^-\pi^-\rangle \qquad (76) \\
T = 1,\quad T_3 = +1 &= -\sqrt{1/2}\,|\pi^0\pi^+\rangle + \sqrt{1/2}\,|\pi^+\pi^0\rangle \\
0 &= -\sqrt{1/2}\,|\pi^-\pi^+\rangle + \sqrt{1/2}\,|\pi^+\pi^-\rangle \\
-1 &= -\sqrt{1/2}\,|\pi^-\pi^0\rangle + \sqrt{1/2}\,|\pi^0\pi^-\rangle \\
T = 0,\quad T_3 = \quad 0 &= \sqrt{1/3}\,|\pi^-\pi^+\rangle - \sqrt{1/3}\,|\pi^0\pi^0\rangle + \sqrt{1/3}\,|\pi^+\pi^-\rangle
\end{aligned}$$

where the Clebsch–Gordan coefficients have been used.

We see that the $T = 1$ wave function is anti-symmetric. Therefore Bose-statistics requires that the angular momentum of the system is odd. For $T = 0$ and $T = 2$ we will have even values for the angular momentum. The total number of waves which may contribute to the elastic scattering amplitude is so reduced by a factor 2. At low energy we may have only S, P and D waves and therefore we only need to deal with the following phase shifts:

l	T	phase shift
0	0	δ_{00}
0	2	δ_{02}
1	1	δ_{11}
2	0	δ_{20}
2	2	δ_{22}

(77)

4.3. The ϱ-Meson

Except for the $\pi^+ + \pi^+$ cross-section, all others present some peak in the region of $30\mu^2$ which corresponds to a CMS energy of ~750 MeV of the two pions. (Fig. 22). The $\pi^+ + \pi^+$ system is a pure state of $T = 2$; therefore we exclude this state as responsible for the 750 MeV peaks on the other cross-sections. The angular distribution at 750 MeV contains a $\cos^2\theta$ term which would correspond to a P-wave. If we limit the analysis to S and P waves we would have already identified the $T = J = 1$ resonance called the ϱ-meson. The isotopic spin assignment is confirmed by the ratio of the cross-sections of the different charge channels:

$$\frac{(\pi^- + p \to \varrho^\circ + n)}{(\pi^- + p \to \varrho^- + p)} \cong 2 \tag{78}$$

in agresement with the OPE-model. The spin $J = 1$ of the resonance would correspond to $(\pi\text{–}\pi)$ cross-sections about 30% higher than those observed (experiment + OPE-model).

If one calculates the forwards-backwards asymmetry of the angular distributions shown in Fig. 23 one obtains the result shown in Fig. 24. The asymmetry

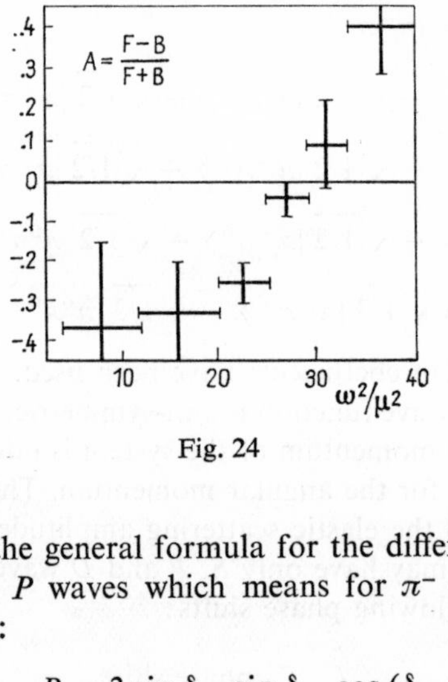

Fig. 24

can be calculated from the general formula for the differential cross-section (38) introducing only S and P waves which means for $\pi^- + \pi^0$, only δ_{02} and δ_{11} (since $T_3 = -1$, $T \neq 0$):

$$A = \frac{F - B}{F + B} = \frac{3 \sin \delta_{02} \sin \delta_{11} \cos (\delta_{11} - \delta_{02})}{\sin^2 \delta_{02} + 3 \sin^2 \delta_{11}} \tag{79}$$

If we assume that the S-wave forms a small and constant background we can understand the change of sign of A as an inversion of the interference term between S and P wave which happens near to the point where δ_{11} goes through 90° as it was already discussed in Section 2.9. This provides additional evidence for the resonant character of δ_{11}.*

The existence of the ϱ-meson was later confirmed in many other experiments and it is well established that it is a short living particle of spin 1, $T = 1$, mass = 765 MeV and width ~100 MeV.

* Note: The asymmetry factor A is independent of the "normalization" of the angular distributions (Section 3.2.3.). This is particularly important in the present case, where the normalization depends on the model used.

5. PION-PROTON SCATTERING

5.1. Spin and Parity

The system composed of a pion and a proton has intrinsic spin $S = \frac{1}{2}$. This spin is added (vector addition) to the orbital angular momentum l to obtain the total angular momentum J which is conserved in any interaction, together with its third component M. Systems with spin need not, in general, conserve their orbital angular momentum l and its third component m_l. Any variations must be compensated for by opposite changes in the spin S and its third component m_s.

In the particular case of intrinsic spin $\frac{1}{2}$, the orbital angular momentum could change by one unit, conserving J and M. For instance, a pion coming in with $l = 0$, $J = \frac{1}{2}$, could go out with $l = 1$, $J = \frac{1}{2}$. This kind of transition changes the parity of the system. It is believed that in *strong* interactions (like the elastic scattering here discussed) this is not possible: parity is conserved.

A different case is that of the decay of the Λ^0-hyperon into $\pi^- + P$. The initial system has well defined total angular momentum ($S = J = \frac{1}{2}$) and parity. One finds both values of l (0 and 1) in the outgoing ($\pi^- + p$)-system. This is due to the fact that parity is not conserved in *weak* interactions like the Λ^0-decay.

If the spin of a strongly interacting system happens to be equal to, or greater than, 1, changes in l of two (or more) units are possible. Even values of Δl are therefore possible in parity conserving, strong interactions. In reactions in which new particles are created, with different parities, the situation becomes different and one can establish a-priori the possible changes of l.

In the system of spin $\frac{1}{2}$, changes in the third component of l are still possible (conserving parity, J, M, S and l). They must be compensated for by an inversion of m_s which is called *spin-flip*. We can find a co-ordinate system in which the "spin-flipped" scattering products cannot be distinguished from an initial system of two incident particles. Therefore we may include these events in the complete wave function ψ which describes the incident and elastically scattered particles. In a general way we may write the complete wave function as follows:

$$\psi = \begin{pmatrix}\alpha\\ \beta\end{pmatrix} e^{iPz} + \begin{pmatrix}\alpha\\ \beta\end{pmatrix} f \frac{e^{iPr}}{r} + \begin{pmatrix}\beta\\ \alpha\end{pmatrix} g \frac{e^{iPr}}{r} \tag{80}$$

where f and g represent the scattering amplitudes for non-spin-flip and spin-flip respectively, and

$$\alpha = \chi_{1/2}^{+1/2}, \quad \beta = \chi_{1/2}^{-1/2} \tag{81}$$

are the spin functions. The expansion in spherical harmonics is here a bit more complicated than in the case without spin (Section 2.3.). It provides the expressions for f and g:

$$f(\theta) = \lambda^2 \sum_l \left[A_{l+}(l+1) + A_{l-} l\right] P_l(\cos\theta) \tag{82}$$

$$g(\theta) = \lambda^2 \sum_l \left[A_{l+} - A_{l-}\right] P_l^1(\cos\theta) \tag{83}$$

where the partial wave amplitudes $A_{l\pm}$ correspond to the states of $J = l \pm \frac{1}{2}$.

There is one partial wave amplitude for each value of J and P (the parity). This means that the physical properties of our system do not depend on $M = J_3$ (M depend on the co-ordinate system chosen) nor on l (which is conserved due to parity considerations only).

5.2. Isotopic Spin

The isotopic spin of a system formed by a pion ($T = 1$) and a proton ($T = \frac{1}{2}$) can be either $\frac{1}{2}$ or $\frac{3}{2}$. Any such system can be expressed as a linear combination of these two fundamental isotopic spin states. The systems which can be easily made in the laboratory are $\pi^+ + p$ and $\pi^- + p$ bombarding hydrogen targets with beams of charged pions. Their compositions are the following:

$$|\pi^+ + P\rangle = \left|T = \frac{3}{2}, T_3 = +\frac{3}{2}\right\rangle \tag{84}$$

$$|\pi^- + p\rangle = \sqrt{\frac{1}{3}}\left|T = \frac{3}{2}, T_3 = -\frac{1}{2}\right\rangle - \sqrt{\frac{2}{3}}\left|T = \frac{1}{2}, T_3 = -\frac{1}{2}\right\rangle \tag{85}$$

In an interaction, the $T = \frac{1}{2}$ component of (85) will be in general differently absorbed or shifted from the $T = \frac{3}{2}$ part:

$$|\psi_{sc}\rangle = A^{3/2}\sqrt{\frac{1}{3}}\left|T = \frac{3}{2}, T_3 = -\frac{1}{2}\right\rangle - A^{1/2}\sqrt{\frac{2}{3}}\left|T = \frac{1}{2}, T_3 = -\frac{1}{2}\right\rangle \tag{86}$$

The ratio of $T = \frac{1}{2}$ to $T = \frac{3}{2}$ is now changed and the final state is no longer a pure ($\pi^- + p$)-system. Its new composition is obtained by substituting in (86) the general expressions:

$$\left|T = \frac{3}{2}, T_3 = -\frac{1}{2}\right\rangle = \sqrt{\frac{1}{3}}|p\pi^-\rangle + \sqrt{\frac{2}{3}}|n\pi^0\rangle \tag{87}$$

$$\left|T = \frac{1}{2}, T_3 = -\frac{1}{2}\right\rangle = -\sqrt{\frac{2}{3}}|p\pi^-\rangle + \sqrt{\frac{1}{3}}|n\pi^0\rangle \tag{88}$$

One obtains:

$$|\psi_{sc}\rangle = \frac{1}{3}(A^{3/2} + 2A^{1/2})|p\pi^-\rangle + \frac{\sqrt{3}}{2}(A^{3/2} - A^{1/2})|n\pi^0\rangle \tag{89}$$

This is valid for each partial wave amplitude and for f and g (59). We will therefore have two reactions included in our complete wave function:

$$\pi^- + p \to \pi^- + p \tag{90}$$

$$\pi^- + p \to \pi^0 + n \tag{91}$$

which are called "elastic scattering" and "charge-exchange scattering" respectively. The second can hardly be regarded as "elastic" but in the frame of the isotopic spin formalism it must be included here. The experimental verification of the deduced relations is the strongest support of the formalism. Some corrections must be applied because of the different mass of the final particles.

For positive pions only one channel is possible:

$$\pi^+ + p \rightarrow \pi^+ + p \tag{92}$$

and the scattering amplitudes are defined by the pure $T = \frac{3}{2}$ state. We may write the expressions for the partial wave amplitudes for the three reactions (90) to (92) as follows:

$$A_{l\pm}^{-} = \frac{1}{3}(A_{l\pm}^{3} + 2A_{l\pm}^{1}) \tag{93}$$

$$A_{l\pm}^{cx} = \frac{\sqrt{3}}{2}(A_{l\pm}^{3} - A_{l\pm}^{1}) \tag{94}$$

$$A_{l\pm}^{+} = A_{l\pm}^{3} \tag{95}$$

The notation used is: $A_{l\pm}^{2T}$; it can be extended to $\eta_{l\pm}^{2T}$ and $\delta_{l\pm}^{2T}$. It is customary to denote the *S*-wave phase shifts by δ_{2T} and the *P*-wave phase shifts by $\delta_{2T,2J}$ as originally introduced by Fermi.

5.3. Summary of Formulae

For an *unpolarized hydrogen* target the differential cross-section is given by:

$$d\sigma/d\Omega = |f(\theta)|^2 + |g(\theta)|^2 \tag{96}$$

If the initial protons are *polarized* (P_i), there will be a "left-right" asymmetry depending on the angle between the normal to the scattering plane ($\hat{n}$) and the direction of the initial polarization (P_i):

$$d\sigma/d\Omega = |f(\theta)|^2 + |g(\theta)|^2 + 2\,\mathrm{Im}\,[f^*(\theta)\cdot g(\theta)]\cdot(\hat{n}\cdot P_i) \tag{97}$$

The recoil proton is in general polarized, even if the initial polarization was zero. If one calculates the expectation value for the proton spin after the collision one obtains, in the case of an unpolarized target:

$$P(\theta) = (-2\,\mathrm{Im}\,[f^*(\theta)\cdot g(\theta)]\,\hat{n})/(d\sigma/d\Omega) \tag{98}$$

and in the case of an initially polarized target:

$$\begin{aligned} P(\theta) = \{&-2\,\mathrm{Im}\,[f^*(\theta)\cdot g(\theta)]\cdot\hat{n} - 2\,\mathrm{Re}\,[f^*(\theta)\,g(\theta)]\,(\hat{n}\times P_i) \\ &+ (|f(\theta)|^2 + |g(\theta)|^2)\,(\hat{n}\cdot P_i)\,\hat{n} \\ &+ (|f(\theta)|^2 - |g(\theta)|^2)\,[\hat{n}\times(\hat{n}\times P_i)]\}/(d\sigma/d\Omega) \end{aligned} \tag{99}$$

Comparing (97) and (98) one sees that they are both functions of the term $\text{Im}\,(f^*g)$. An experiment in which the recoil proton polarization is measured is therefore equivalent to one in which the left-right asymmetry of $d\sigma/d\Omega$ is measured using a polarized target. Targets containing highly polarized hydrogen are at present available, but no data on pion-proton scattering has yet been published, to our knowledge.

The formulae (96) to (99) can be applied to the three reactions (90) to (92), using the expressions for the scattering amplitudes (82) and (83), in which the partial wave amplitudes (93) to (95) are introduced. One may also calculate the cross-sections for pure isotopic spin states, using the same method.

If we restrict ourselves to S and P waves we can write the complete expressions for the differential cross-sections:

$$d\sigma^+/d\Omega = \lambda^2[|A_3 + (2A_{33} + A_{31})\cos\theta|^2 + |A_{33} - A_{31}|^2 \sin^2\theta] \tag{100}$$

$$d\sigma^-/d\Omega = \frac{\lambda^2}{9}[|A_3 + 2A_1 + (2A_{33} + A_{31} + 4A_{13} + 2A_{11})\cos\theta|^2 + |A_{33} - A_{31} + 2A_{13} - 2A_{11}|^2 \sin^2\theta] \tag{101}$$

$$d\sigma^{cx}/d\Omega = \frac{2\lambda^2}{9}[|A_3 - A_1 + (2A_{33} + A_{31} - 2A_{13} - A_{11})\cos\theta|^2 + |A_{33} - A_{31} - A_{13} + A_{11}|^2 \sin^2\theta] \tag{102}$$

$$A = \frac{i}{2}(1 - e^{2i\delta}) \tag{103}$$

Coulomb scattering can be approximately included in the non-spin-flip amplitude by adding a term:

$$(e^2/\hbar v)/(1 - \cos\theta) \tag{104}$$

which is negative for π^+ and positive for π^-. This corresponds to the Rutherford formula when all phase shifts are zero [see Section 3.4. Eq. (48)].

At pion energies of less than 50 MeV all phase shifts happen to be smaller than 7°. In this case one may apply the approximation:

$$A \approx \delta \tag{105}$$

which was already used in Section 2.8.; formulae (100) to (102) then become very convenient for "hand" calculations.

For the total cross-sections one obtains the following interesting relations:

$$\sigma^+ = \sigma^{3/2} \tag{106}$$

$$\sigma^- = \tfrac{1}{3}(\sigma^{3/2} + 2\sigma^{1/2}) \tag{107}$$

and in terms of phase shifts:

$$\sigma^T = 4\pi\lambda^2 \sum_l [(l + 1)\sin^2 \delta_{l+}^{2T} + l \sin^2 \delta_{l-}^{2T}]. \tag{108}$$

5.4. Experimental Data

Results on pion-proton scattering and charge exchange were obtained using electronic techniques, nuclear emulsions and bubble chambers. Figure 25 shows an angular distribution obtained at 120 MeV using a bubble chamber. A typical picture containing three scattering events is shown in Fig. 26.

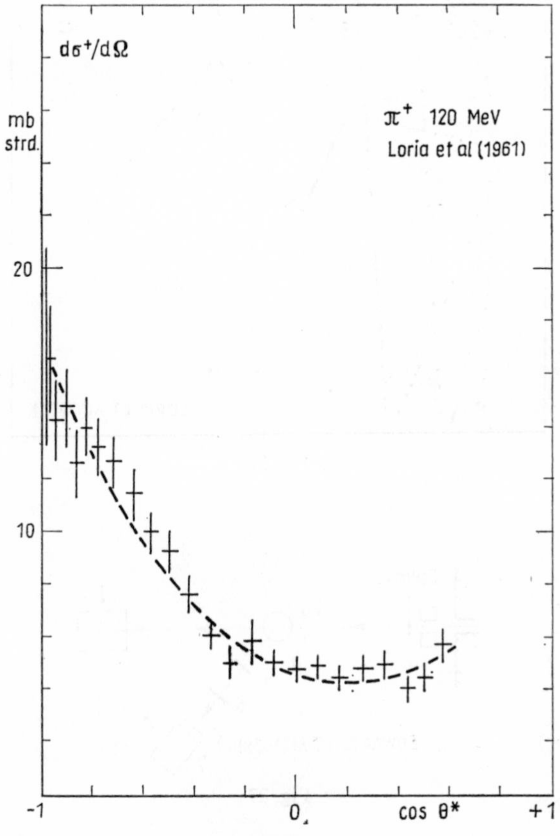

Fig. 25

Figure 27 shows a typical set-up for an electronic measurement of a differential cross-section. The pion is scattered in liquid hydrogen (T) and detected by the counter telescope 4, 5, 6 and 7 (Čerenkov). The beam is monitored by means of an ionization chamber (I). The solid angle is defined by counter 6. The results obtained are given in Fig. 28.

Altogether, under 1 GeV there are over 1000 values of the differential cross-sections already published. Only 9 experiments were done for the measurement

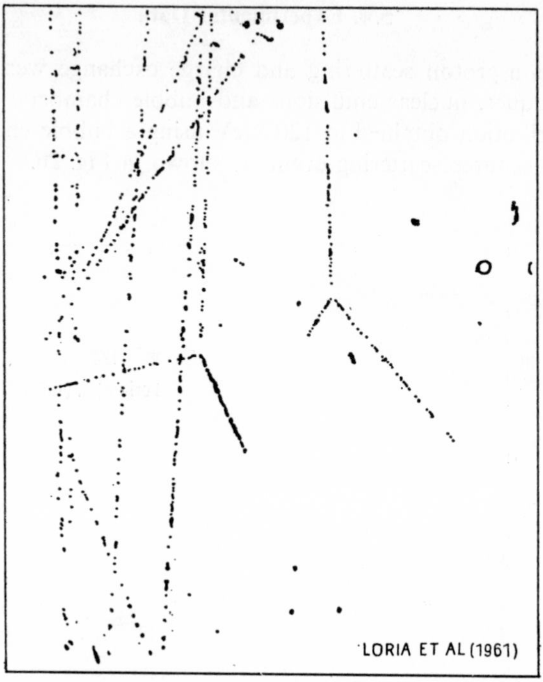

Fig. 26

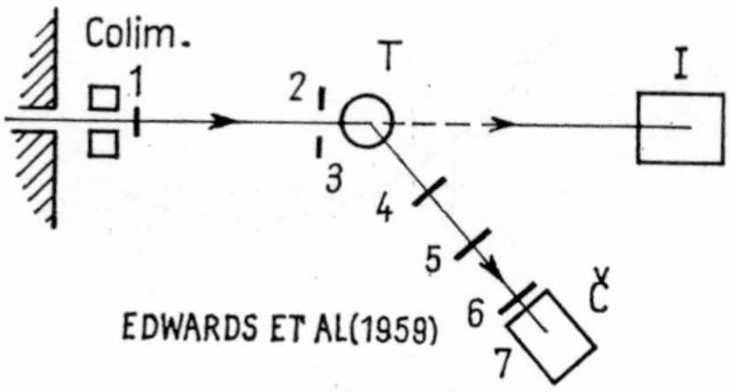

Fig. 27

of the recoil nucleon polarization and none using polarized targets.

5.5. Analysis

At low energy only S and P waves are important; some interesting conclusions can be obtained from a very rough analysis. The most important is the evidence for the resonance in the $T = J = \frac{3}{2}$ state which is called today the "first" or $(\frac{3}{2}, \frac{3}{2})$ Isobar. The $\pi^+ + p$ total cross-section shown in Fig. 21 presents the typical peak, which is centred at about 180 MeV. In the $\pi^- + p$ cross-section there is a similar peak, but three times smaller, which is in agreement with $T\,a = \frac{3}{2}$ assignment. The angular distribution and cross-section at the peak establish that the angular momentum is $\frac{3}{2}$.

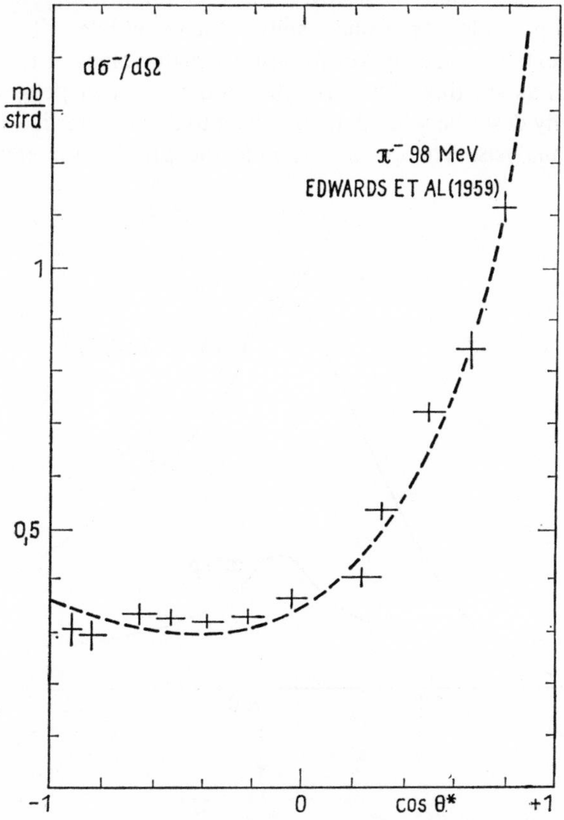

Fig. 28

Other resonances were found during the last years at higher energies. They are not so clear as the $\frac{3}{2}$, $\frac{3}{2}$-one, because of absorption phenomena which complicate the analysis. Under 200 MeV, elastic scattering (S and P waves) is dominant, allowing a reasonable analysis (at least of the resonance) using little data and "by hand" methods of analysis. We may mention the very instructive graphical method of Ashkin for the determination of the S and P phase shifts.

A method frequently followed (and still in use) was to fit first the angular distribution with a polynomial in $\cos\theta$ and then to solve the system of equations relating phase shifts with the coefficients of the polinomial. More or less adequate methods were used to subtract the Coulomb scattering contribution.

Frequently it happened that the phase shifts were a function of the experimental data *and* of the method of analysis. Therefore all experimental data available are being reanalysed at present using complicated computer programmes, which are still being improved. Their accuracy is already such that new experimental data is required at several energies (particularly at low energies) to clarify the situation.

However, the older analysis resolved the very important problem of deciding between several possible sets of phase shifts which could describe the experimental data (ambiguities). The already known approximate values of the phase shifts are now very useful as starting values for the modern best fit programmes.

We now briefly describe what data are given to a computer in order to performe a phase shift analysis. We use as example the programme Phase III which is

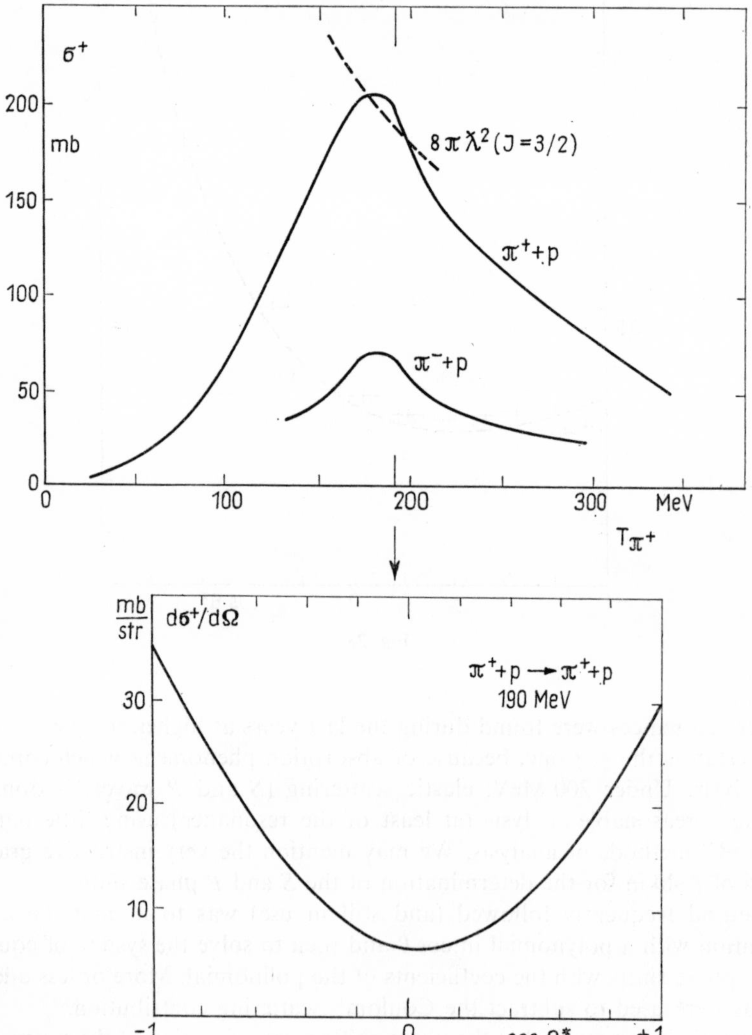

Fig. 29

available at CERN and was written by C. Lovelace. The complete programme does not enter in a standard IBM 7094 computer of 32,000 memory positions. This gives an idea of its size.

The input is formed by *experimental data*, *theoretical data* and *initial values*. Some working instructions are also included. The experimental data must correspond to a single energy of incident pion or to a small energy interval (several MeV). It may include total and differential cross-sections for $\pi^+ + p$, $\pi^- + p$ and charge exchange scattering and values of the polarization of the recoil nucleon. As "theoretical data" one gives the machine those phase shifts or absorption parameters which cannot be determined using the experimental data, or would be poorly determined. This data is imposed on the programme. For very small phase shifts (high l) one may use the values deduced using dispersion relations. Furthermore, one must indicate to the programme how many waves should be taken into account, in agreement with some a-priori considerations based on formulae like those given in Section 5.3.

The programme contains very elaborate formulae which calculate the expected experimental results for a set of phase shifts δ and absorption parameters η, including all Coulomb scattering contributions. The results of these calculations are compared with the effective experimental data given to the programme; a χ^2 value is so obtained. Then the programme modifies the values of the δ and η (free) parameters in order to find smaller values of χ^2, which mean better fits. This process stops when a minimum of the χ^2-function is found. Some research will still be done to see if there are other minima of χ^2 in a certain region around the first one found.

For the phase shifts and absorption parameters which gave the best χ^2, all experimental "predictions" are printed out. These include all cross-sections, angular distributions and polarizations. The δ's and η's are given together with their *error matrix*. This is a very important point for further use of the phase shifts; one may notice that the error on any function of the phase shifts (to be calculated later) can only be obtained if the original error matrix is known.

There exist more sophisticated computer programmes than the single energy analysis programme above described. These are programmes in which the energy dependence of the scattering parameters is also investigated. They accept experimental data of a certain energy interval; each phase shift is described by a function of the energy which contains the "free parameters" of the best fit. The fact that some phase shifts have a resonance type behavior makes this analysis very difficult. The success of this method depends on the more or less well made guess of the form of the functions which describe δ and η. The fact that the phase shifts are already known with reasonable precision helps in the choice of these functions. The final utility of these calculations is to provide a set of parameters which give the values of δ and η and therefore all the scattering data at any energy. They are called *energy dependent phase shift analysis*.

Results of this type of analysis are already published. We refer to the work of Roper *et al.* (1965). The values of the minimum χ^2 obtained in the best fits are at least a factor two greater then those expected from statistical considerations:

"The large ratios of χ^2 to the 'expected' χ^2 are undoubtedly due to two main causes: (1) the inconsistencies among the data, and (2) the fact that the energy-dependent forms can at best only approximate the actual shape." Nevertheless we show in Fig. 30 the results obtained for the *S*, *P* and *D* wave phase shifts and absorption parameters in the energy region of 0 to 700 MeV. In order to give an

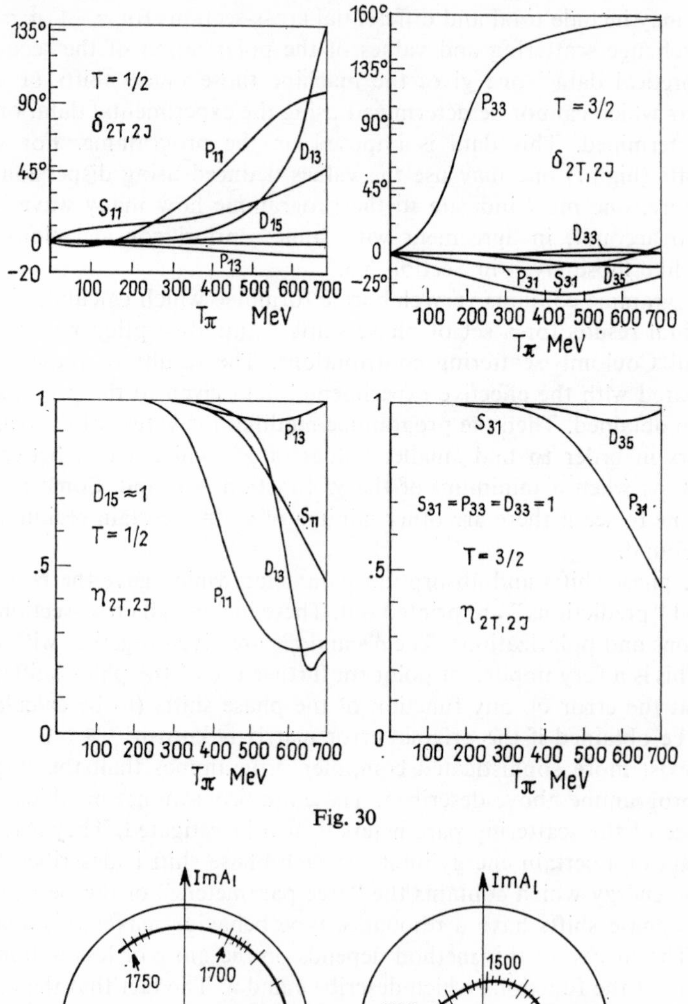

Fig. 30

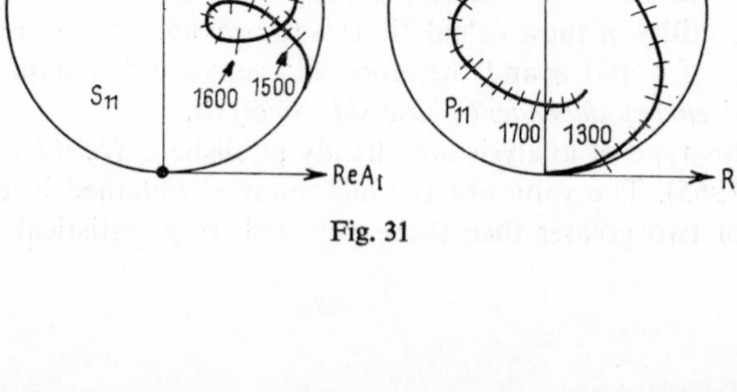

Fig. 31

idea of the discrepancies between this and the older analysis made, the authors also include a more detailed figure for the 0 to 120 MeV region. It appears evident that at low energies new experimental data are required. We may also remark that the Roper *et al.* programme is being improved and should in the future provide the error matrix of the parameters used. The only estimation of the errors possible at present is based on the differences between the different best fits made: it is of the order of 1° for the low energy phase shifts. Figure 31 shows the Argand diagrames for the S_{11} and P_{11} waves as one can "guess" them with the available information. The numbers indicate CMS energies.*

---

* See note added in proof (§ 8), p. 83.

6. APPENDIX

6.1. System of Units

$$\hbar = c = 1$$

mass, *energy* and *momentum* are measured in MeV,
velocity and *angular momentum* have no units, they are numbers,
length and *time* are obtained in MeV^{-1}.
Equivalences of units are deduced from the numerical values:

$c = 2.9979 \times 10^{10}\ \text{cm/s} = 1$
$\hbar c = 1.9732 \times 10^{-11}\ \text{MeV} \cdot \text{cm} = 1$

In this units system some relations become particularly simple:

the De Broglie wavelength	$\lambda\!\!\!^{-} = 1/p$
the Compton wavelength	$\lambda\!\!\!^{-}_c = 1/m$
the Heisenberg relations	$\Delta x \cdot \Delta p_x \gtrsim 1$
	$\Delta \Phi \cdot \Delta J_x \gtrsim 1$
	$\Delta t \cdot \Delta E \gtrsim 1$

the invariant mass m of a system of total energy E, total momentum P and velocity $\beta = v/c$

$\gamma = 1/\sqrt{1 - \beta^2}, \quad \eta = \beta \cdot \gamma$

$E = \gamma \cdot m, \quad P = \beta \cdot \gamma \cdot m$

$E^2 = m^2 + p^2$
$\beta = P/E$
$\gamma = E/m$
$\eta = P/m$

6.2. Kinematics of Two-Body Reactions

Incident particle:

mass .... m_1
momentum .... P_1
kinetic energy .... T_1
total energy .... E_1

$$E_1^2 = P_1^2 + m_1^2$$

$$E_1 = m_1 + T_1$$

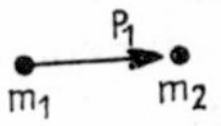

Fig. 32

Target particle:

mass .... m_2

LAB-System:

momentum .... P_L
total energy .... E_L

$$P_L = P_1$$

$$E_L = E_1 + m_2$$

CMS-System:

total energy .... W
particle masses .... M_1, M_2
particle energies .... E_1^*, E_2^*
momentum ...... $P_1^* = P_2^* = P^*$
scattering angle .... θ^*
longitudinal momentum .. $P_{\parallel}^*$
transverse momentum .... $P_{\perp}^*$

$$W^2 = E_L^2 - P_L^2$$

$$E_{1,2}^* = (W^2 + M_{1,2}^2 - M_{2,1}^2)/2W$$

$$P^{*2} = E_{1,2}^{*2} - M_{1,2}^2$$

$$P_{\parallel}^* = P^* \cos\theta^*$$

$$P_{\perp}^* = P^* \sin\theta^*$$

CMS to LAB transformation:

relative velocity .... β
$1/\sqrt{1-\beta^2} =$ .... γ
$\beta \cdot \gamma =$ .... η

$$\gamma = E_L/W$$

$$\eta = P_L/W$$

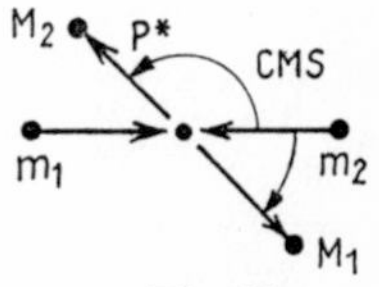

Fig. 33

for each particle:

LAB long. momentum ... $P_{||}$
LAB tran. momentum .... $P_{\perp}$
LAB total energy .... E
LAB scattering angle ..... θ

$$P_{||} = \gamma \cdot P_{||}^* + \eta \cdot E^*$$

$$P_{\perp} = P_{\perp}^*$$

$$E = \gamma \cdot E^* + \eta \cdot P_{||}^*$$

$$\operatorname{tg}\theta = P_{\perp}/P_{||}$$

Notes: for elastic scattering: $m_1 = M_1$, $m_2 = M_2$, for two-body decays: $m_2 = 0$.

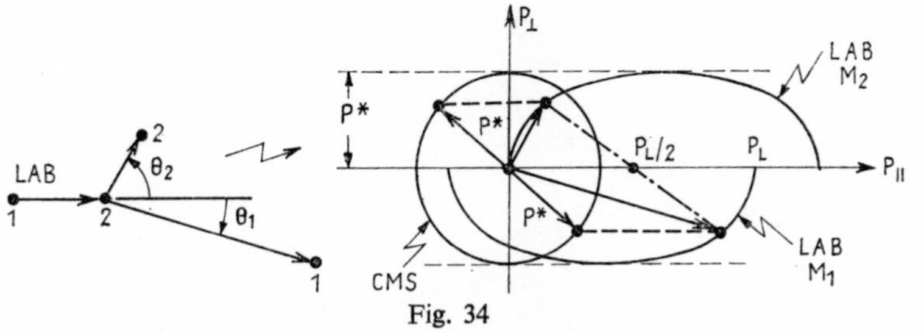

Fig. 34

The formulae of last page are in general used in computer programmes. Fast by-hand calculations can be done using tables or graphs which are available for frequently found initial systems ($\varepsilon + p$, $\pi + p$, $K + p$, $p + p$, etc.). They are given as functions of the incident LAB momentum or kinetic energy and usually provide:

$$W \quad P^* \quad \beta \quad \gamma \quad \eta$$

With this data plus the Energy-Momentum curves of the secondary particles one can easily obtain any required kinematic data. The momentum diagramme shown in Fig. 34 is quite useful. Observe the "correlation point" at $P_L/2$.

6.3. Spherical Harmonics

$$Y_{lm}(\theta, \varphi) = \sqrt{\frac{2l+1}{4\pi} \cdot \frac{(l-|m|)!}{(l+|m|)!}} \cdot P_l^m(\cos\theta) \cdot e^{im\varphi}$$

These functions are solutions of the angular part of the wave equation:

$$\left[-\frac{\hbar^2}{2m}\nabla^2 + V(r)\right] u(r) = Eu(r) \qquad u(r) = R(r) \cdot Y(\theta, \varphi)$$

They form a *complete* set of functions, which means that any quadratically integrable function (over 4π) can be written as a linear combination of spherical harmonics. Furthermore they are *orthonormal*, which means:

$$\int_{4\pi} Y^*_{lm} \cdot Y_{l'm'} \cdot d\Omega = \delta_{mm'}\,\delta_{ll'}$$

The following properties may be useful:

$$Y^*_{lm} = (-1)^m \cdot Y_{l,-m} \qquad P_l = \sqrt{4\pi/(2l+1)} \cdot Y_{l,0}$$

Legendre Polynomials:	*Associated Legendre Functions:*
$P_0 = 1$	$P_1^1 = \sqrt{1-x^2}$
$P_1 = x$	$P_2^1 = \sqrt{1-x^2} \cdot 3x$
$P_2 = (3x^2 - 1)/2$	$P_3^1 = \sqrt{1-x^2} \cdot \frac{3}{2} \cdot (5x^2 - 1)$
$P_3 = (5x^3 - 3x)/2$	$P_4^1 = \sqrt{1-x^2} \cdot \frac{10}{8} \cdot (14x^3 - 6x)$
$P_4 = (35x^4 - 30x^2 + 3)/8$	$P_n^m = P_n^{-m} = \left(\sqrt{1-x^2}\right)^{\lvert m\rvert} \frac{d^{\lvert m\rvert}}{dx^{\lvert m\rvert}} P_n$
$P_5 = (63x^5 - 70x^3 + 15x)/8$	

$$P_{n+1} = [(2n+1) \cdot x \cdot P_n - n \cdot P_{n-1}]/(n+1)$$

These polynomials are *not* normalised in area:

$$P_n(1) = 1 \qquad P_n^m(\pm 1) = 0$$

Used in the expressions of the spherical harmonics:

$x \equiv \cos\theta$ and therefore $\sqrt{1-x^2} = \sin\theta$

7. SOME USEFUL REFERENCES

Scattering of particles and phase shift analysis are treated in most textbooks of quantum mechanics. See e.g.:

L. Schiff, Quantum Mechanics, McGraw-Hill 1955 Ch. V, p. 92;

L. D. Landau and E. M. Lifschitz, Quantum Mechanics, Pergamon Press 1959, Ch. XIV.

A general introduction to the study of scattering and reaction processes is given by

J. Blatt and V. Weisskopf, Theoretical Nuclear Physics, J. Wileys & S., 1952, Ch. VIII, which is generalized for any two-body reaction involving particles with arbitrary spin in the first part of the article by

J. Blatt and L. Biedenharn, *Rev. Mod. Phys.* **24**, 258 (1952).

Many questions of interest in scattering processes are treated by

J. Sakurai, Invariance Principles and Conservation Lows, Princeton Univ. Press 1964.

The classical introduction to pion-nucleon scattering and isotopic spin is the series of lectures of

E. Fermi, *Nuovo Cimento Suppl.* **11**, 17 (1955). More details are found in

H. Bethe and F. De Hoffmann, Mesons and Fields, Row, Peterson & Co. 1956 Vol. II.

The latest review on resonant states, including pion-pion and pion-nucleon systems, normal "particles" and excellent bibliography is

A. Rosenfeld et al. UCRL – 8030 Jan. 1968, reproduced by CERN and submitted to Rev. of Mod. Phys.

Accurate information on pion-nucleon scattering including latest analysis of data and complete bibliography, are found in

C. Lovelace, report to the 1966 Berkeley Conference, CERN preprint TH 705, 10 October 1966 and

L. Roper, R. Wright and B. T. Feld, *Phys. Rev.* **138**, B 190 (1965) where all experimental papers up to 700 MeV are listed, including those used in the present notes as exemples.

Note: This very partial bibliography is only intended as a guide for an introduction to the arguments treated.

8. The $\pi + \mathcal{N}$ Phase Shifts up to 2 Gev (NOTE ADDED IN PROOF)

During the last year very impressive progress has been made in the phase shift analysis of $\pi + \mathcal{N}$ scattering. The present state is best described by the figures given by C. Lovelace at the Heidelberg Conference 1967 (CERN-TH-837, October 1967). There one can find examples of all types of resonances. We reproduce here the data corresponding to 15 partial waves up to 2 GeV (incid. π). The author's permission for the reproduction of these figures is gratefully aknowledged.

The procedure used to select particular values of δ and η among the many ambiguous solutions present at the higher energies is based on continuity arguments. Three groups: Berkeley, Cern and Saclay have done this using quite different methods. The Cern results were obtained making use of dispersion relations which give additional constraints for the fits. For more details the reader is referred to Lovelace's report.

Lovelace's list of pion-nucleon resonances of October 1967

	Wave	Mass	Γ_{tot}l	x
Well established:	P_{33}	1235.8	125.1	1.000
	P_{11}	1466	211	0.658
	D_{13}	1526	114	0.570
	S_{31}	1635	177	0.284
	D_{15}	1678	173	0.391
	F_{15}	1692	132	0.683
	S_{11}	1709	300	0.786
	F_{37}	1946	221	0.386
	G_{17}	2265	298	0.349
	$H_{3,11}$	~2400	~340	~0.18
Probable:	S_{11}	1548	116	0.326
	P_{33}	1688	281	0.098
	F_{35}	1913	350	0.163
	P_{31}	1934	339	0.299
	D_{13}	2057	293	0.260
Interpretation in doubt:	D_{33}	1691	269	0.137
	P_{13}	~1863	~296	~0.207
	D_{35}	~1954	~311	~0.154
Unconfirmed:	P_{11}	~1751	327	0.320
	F_{17}	1983	225	0.128
	H_{19}	~2450	~350	~0.4

Masses and Γ in MeV (CMS).
$x = \sigma_{el}/\sigma_{tot}$, elasticity.

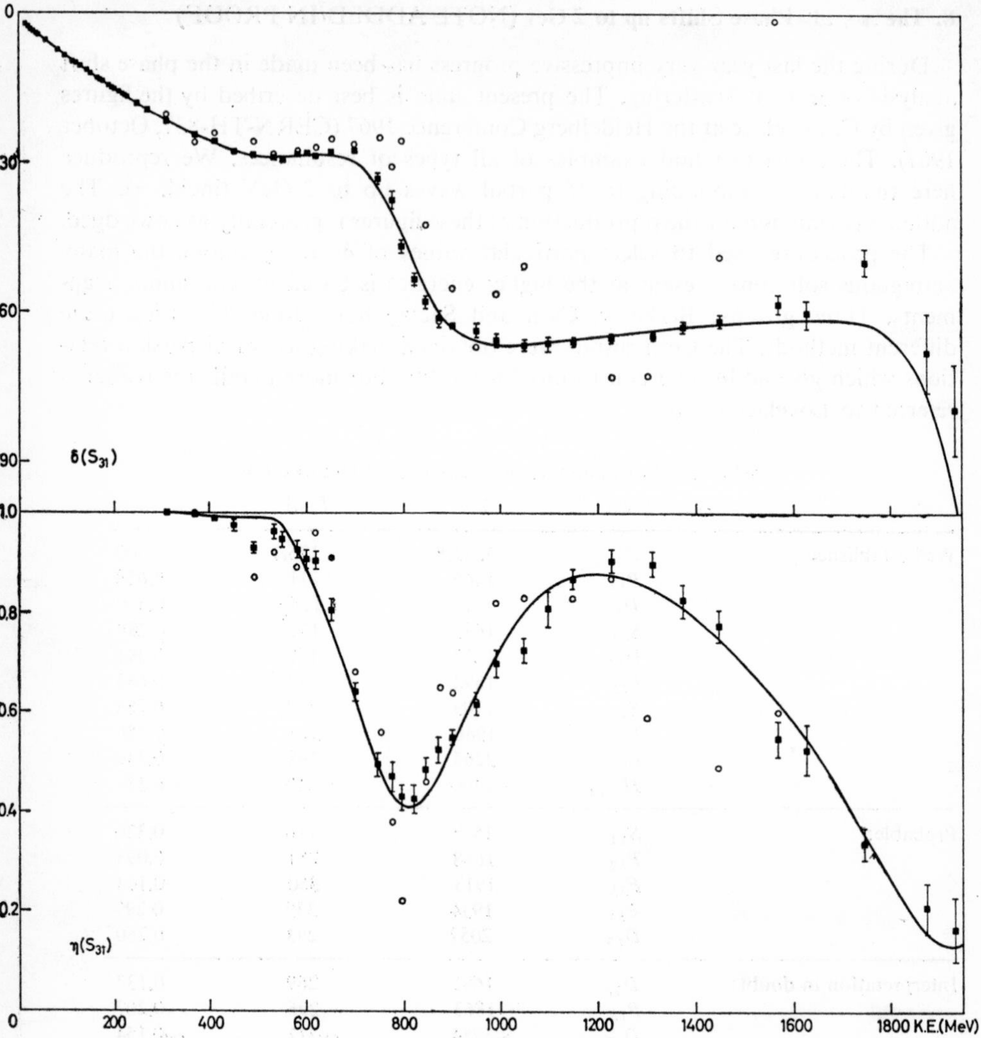

Fig. 35. S_{31} showing old resonance. The solid squares are the CERN phases, the solid line the dispersion relation fit to them, the open circles are the new Saclay phases.

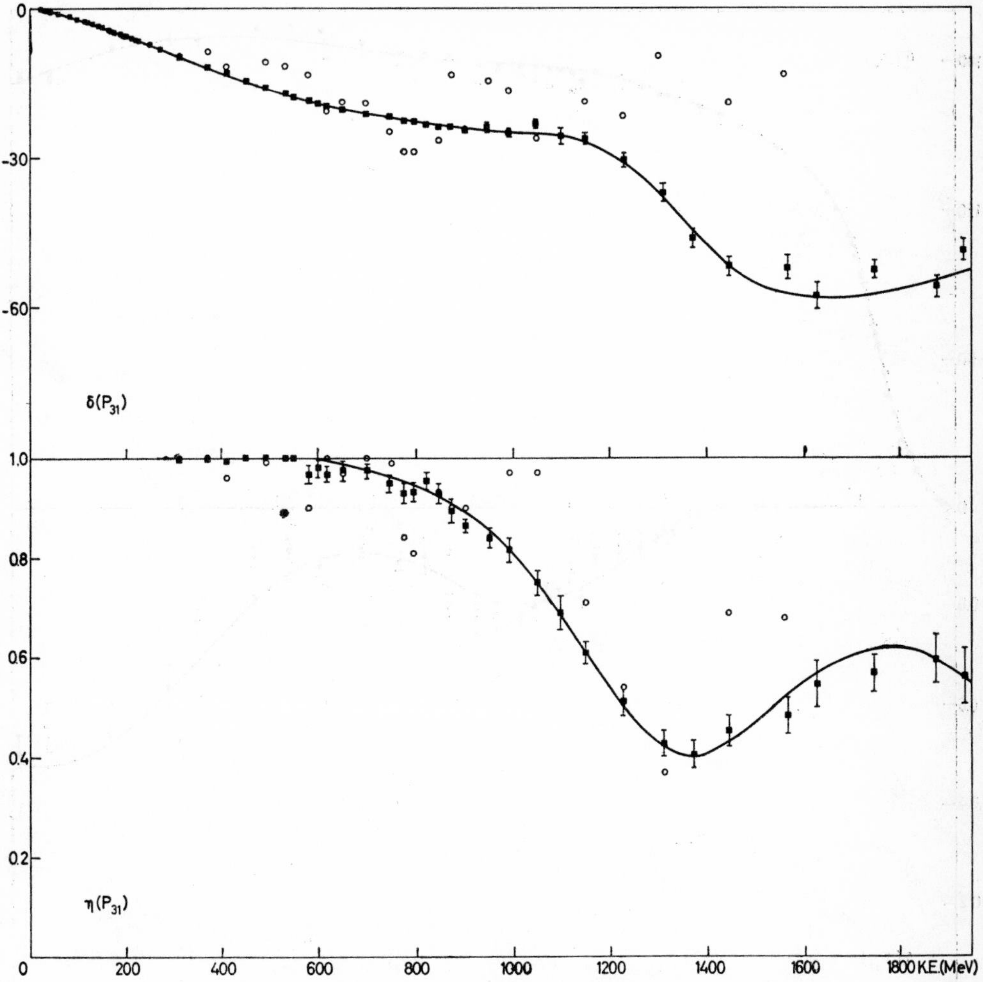

Fig. 36. P_{31} showing new CERN resonance. Notation as for Fig. 35.

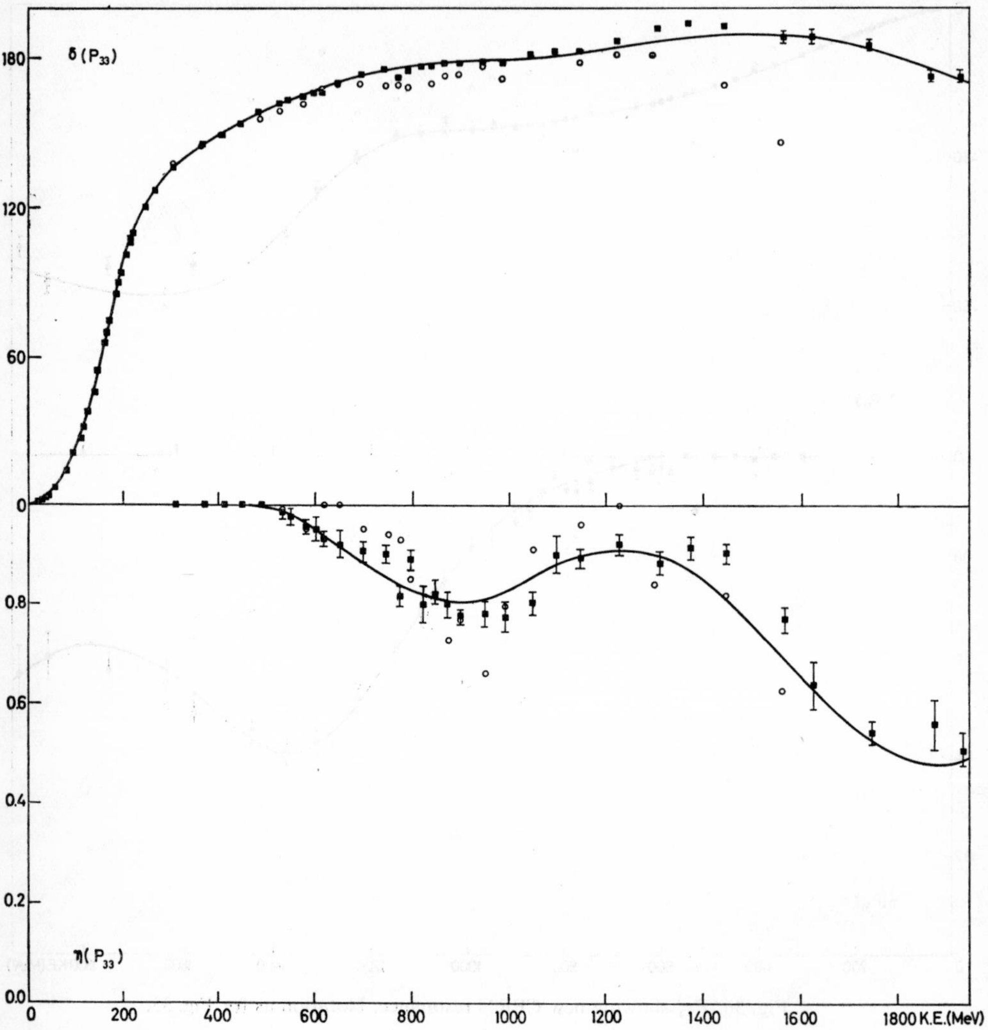

Fig. 37. P_{33} showing old and new resonances. Notation as for Fig. 35.

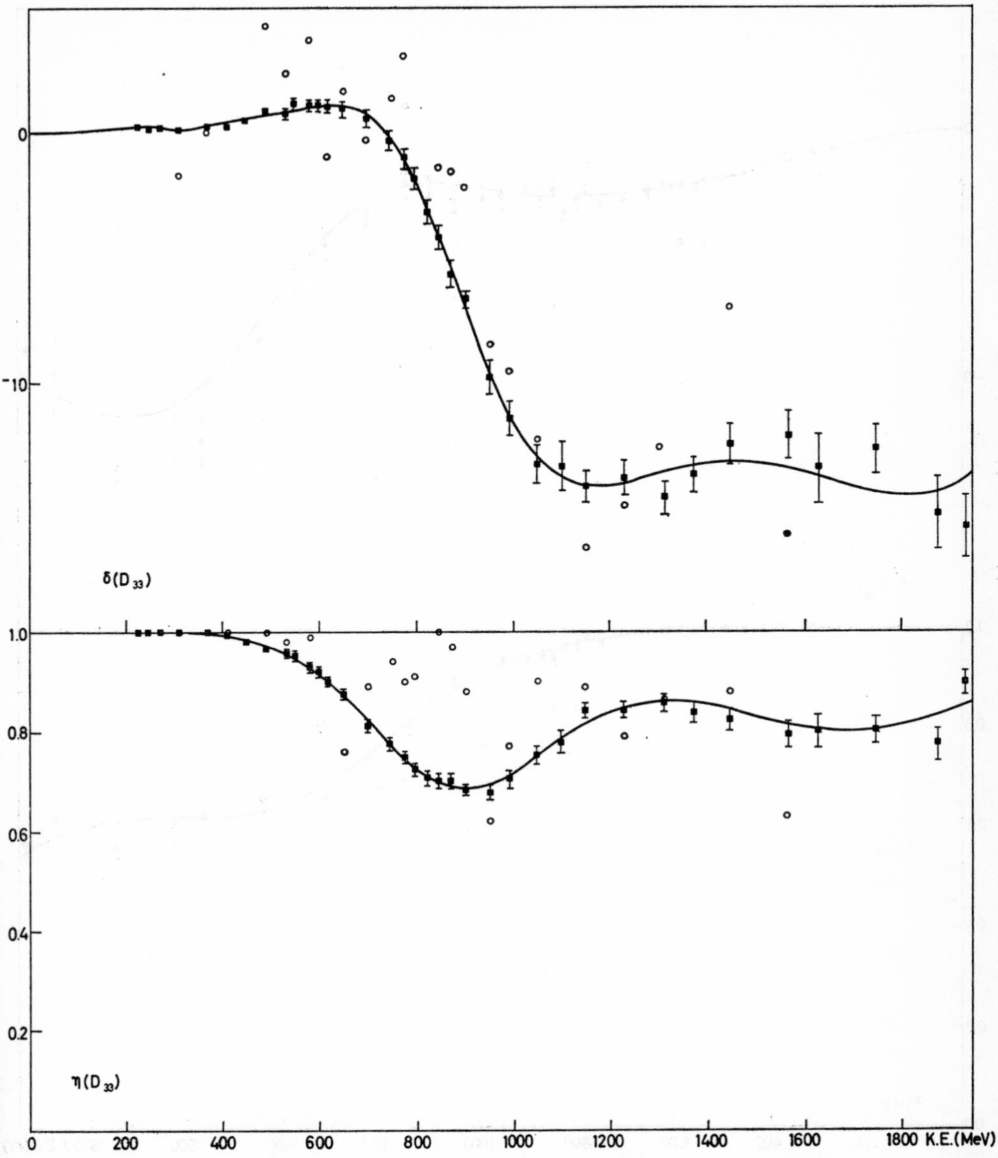

Fig. 38. D_{33} showing new CERN resonance. Notation as for Fig. 35.

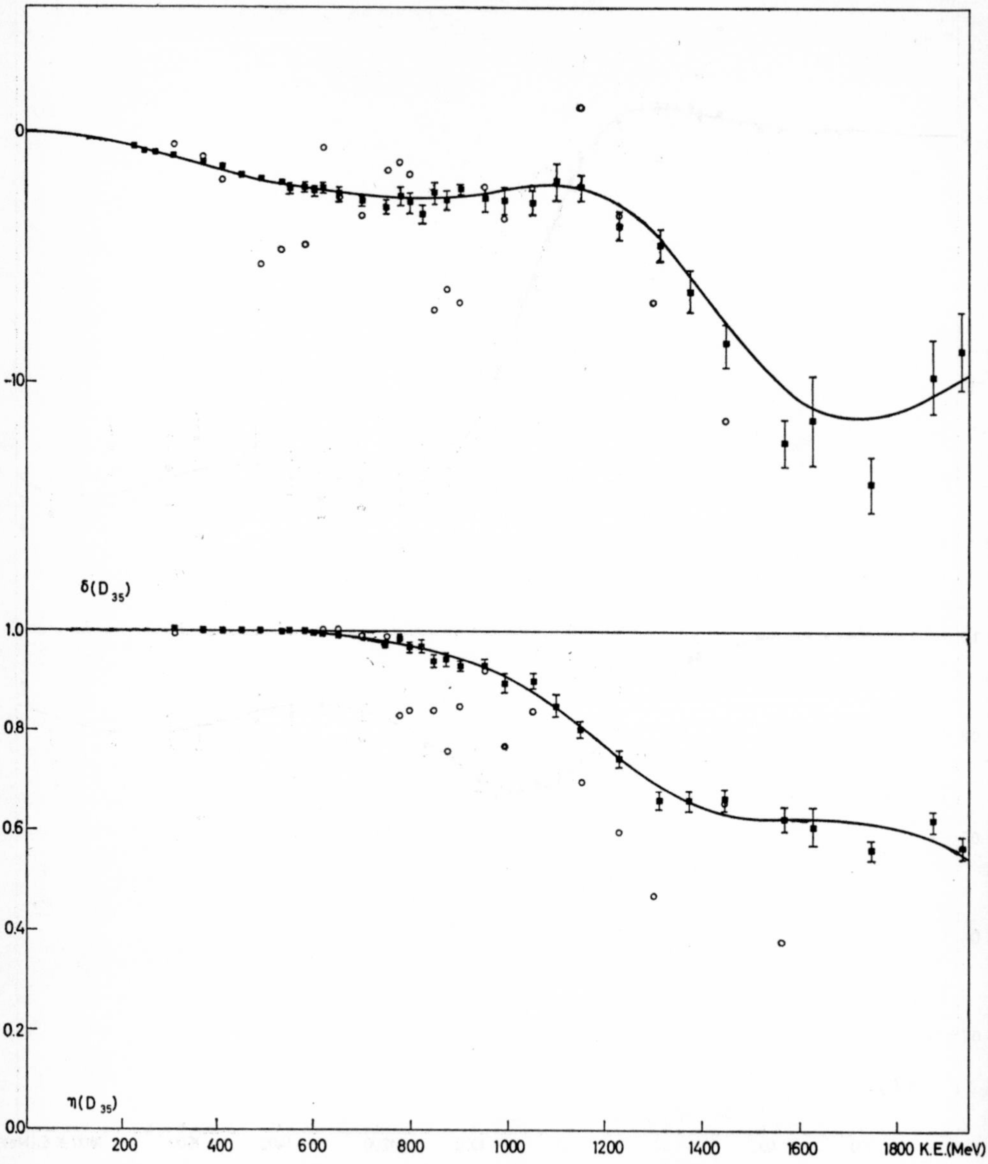

Fig. 39. D_{35} showing new resonance or threshold effect. Notation as for Fig. 35.

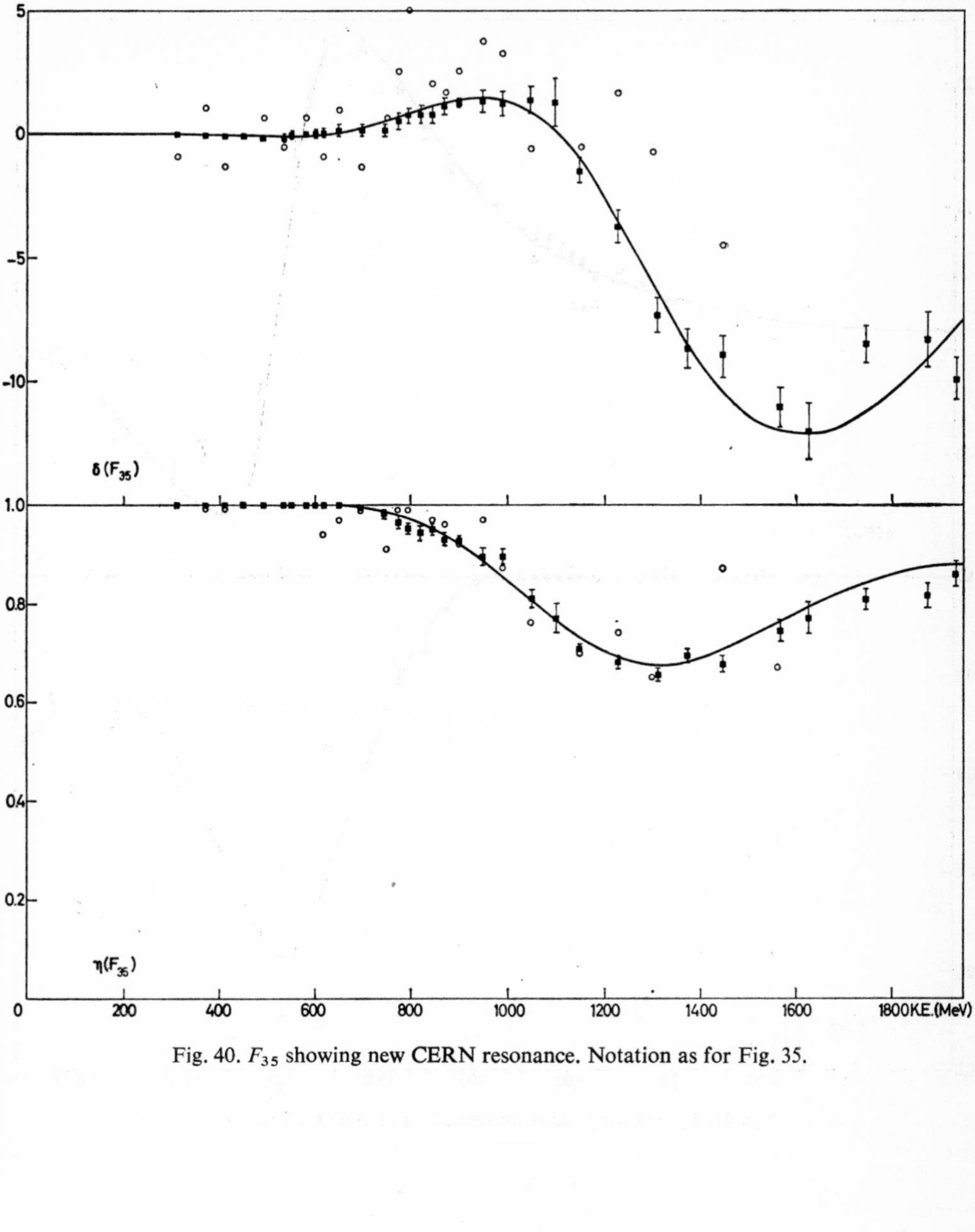

Fig. 40. F_{35} showing new CERN resonance. Notation as for Fig. 35.

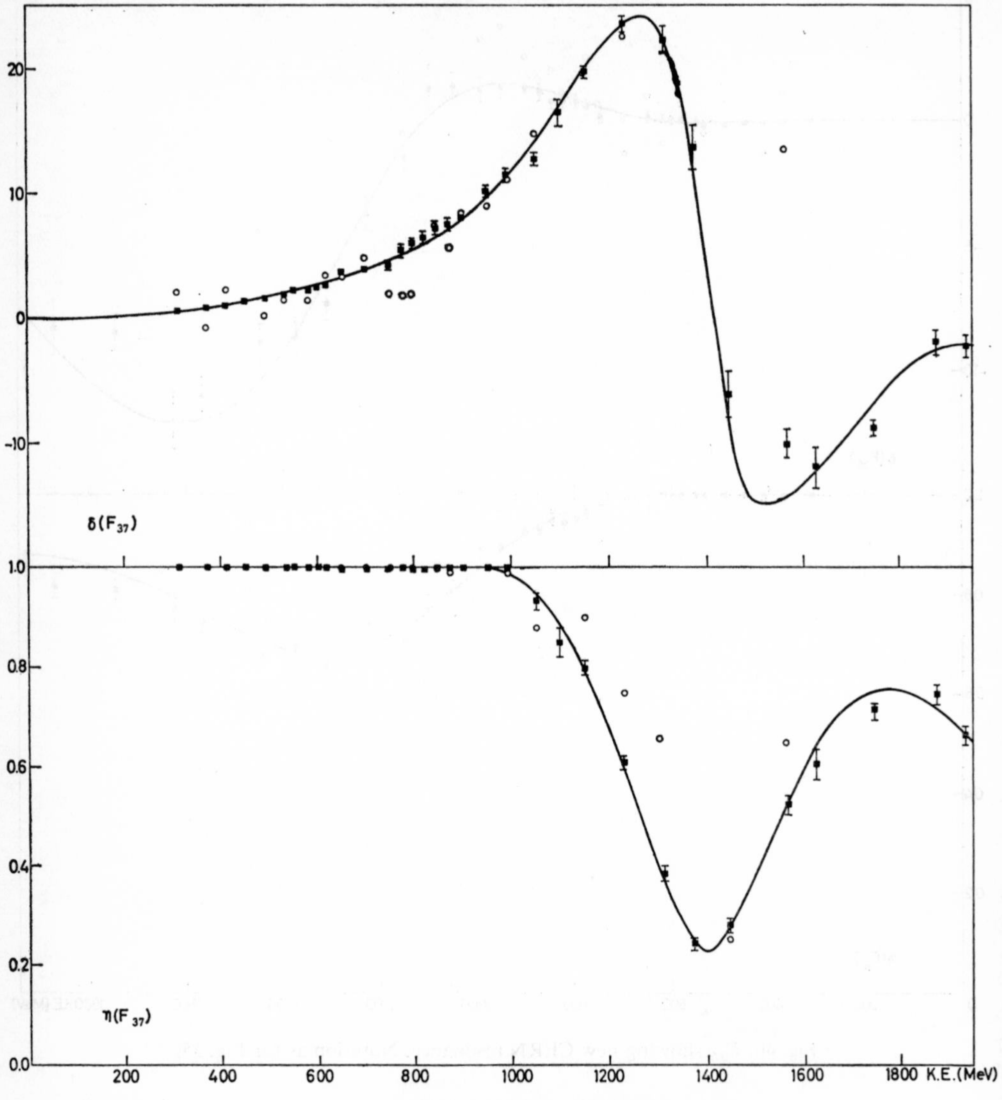

Fig. 41. F_{37} showing old resonance. Notation as for Fig. 35.

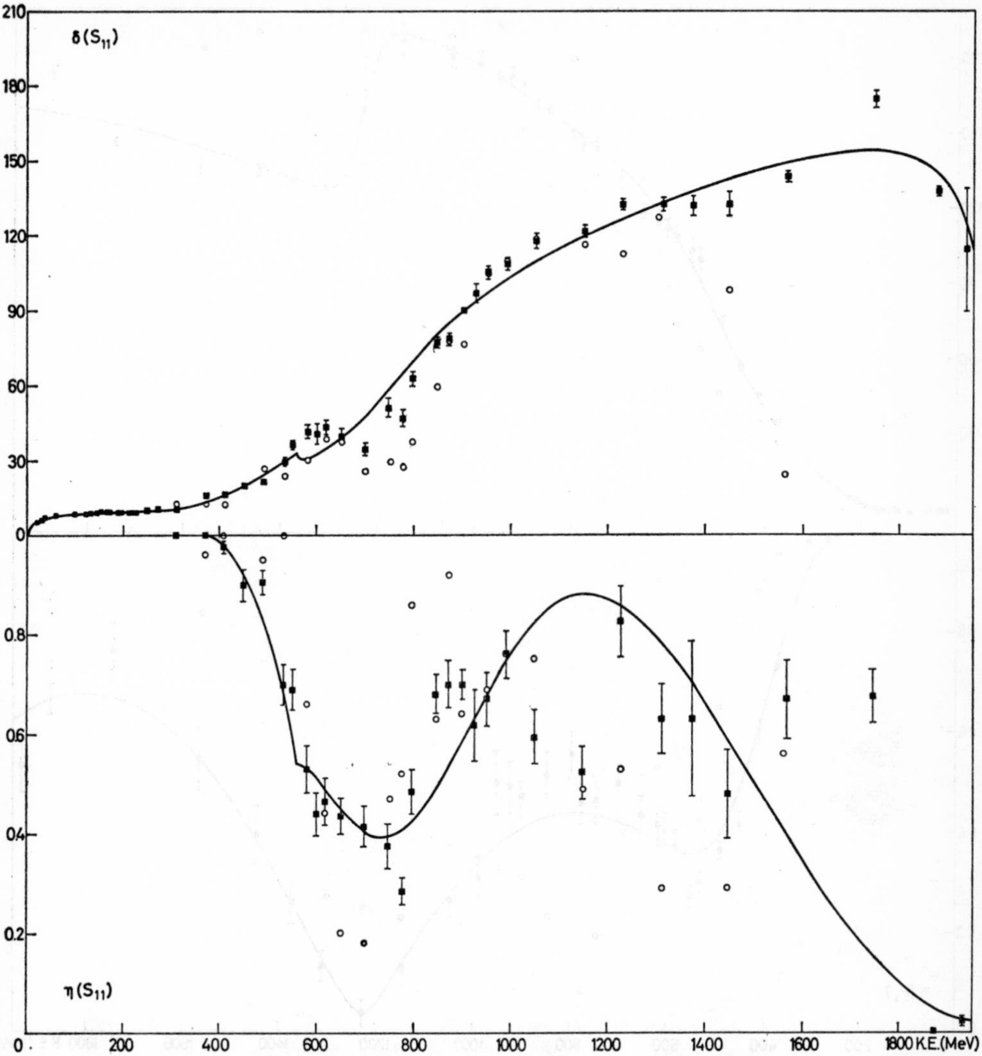

Fig. 42. S_{11} showing old resonance. Notation as for Fig. 35. Here the CERN dispersion relation fiit is unsatisfactory, possibly due to the narrowness of the lower resonance found in other analyses.

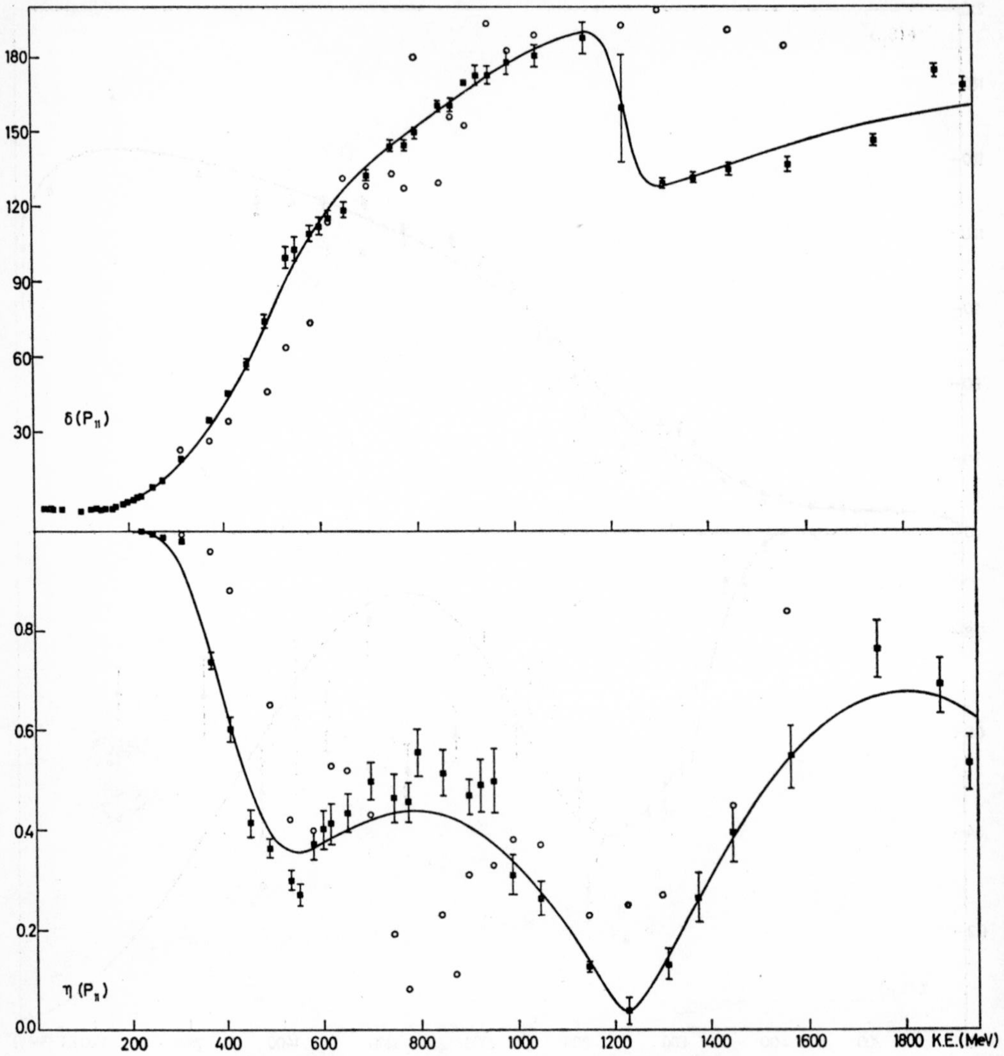

Fig. 43. P_{11} showing old and new resonances. Notation as for Fig. 35.

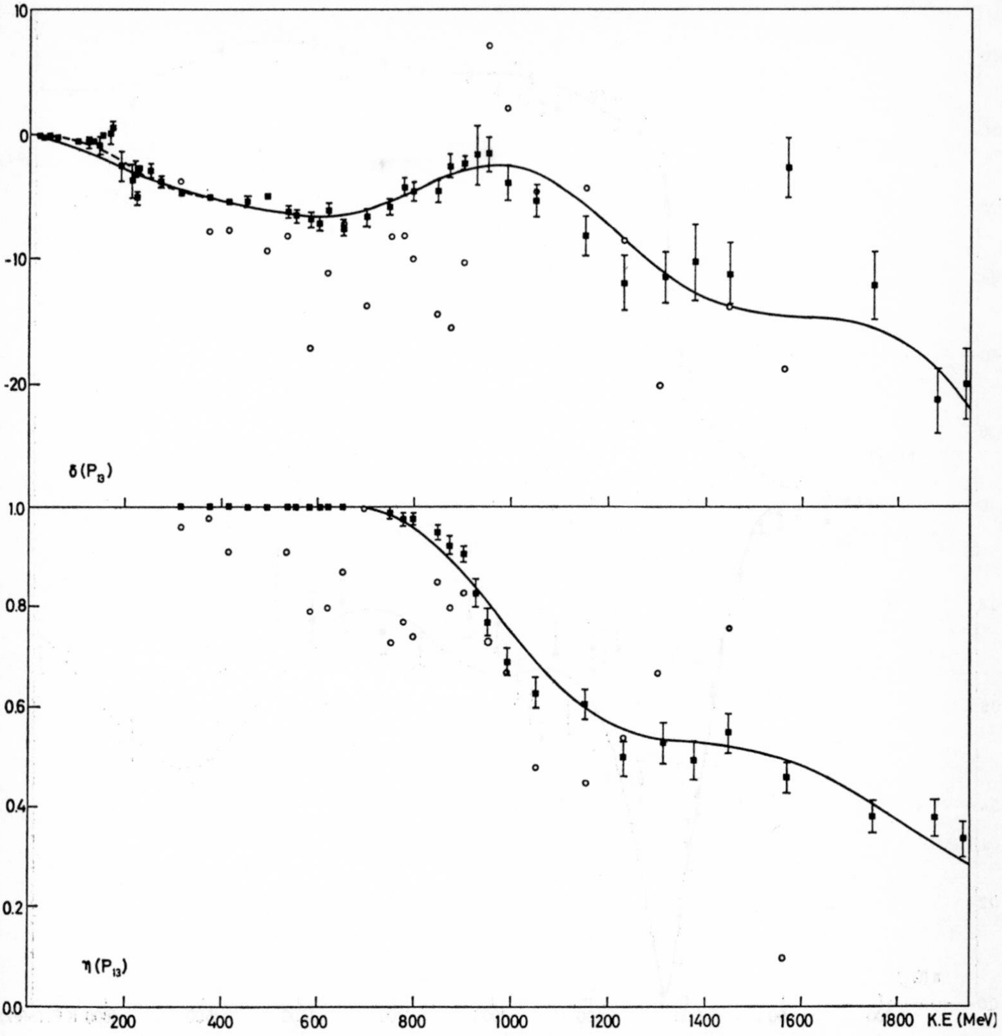

Fig. 44. P_{13} showing new resonance or threshold effect. Notation as for Fig. 35.

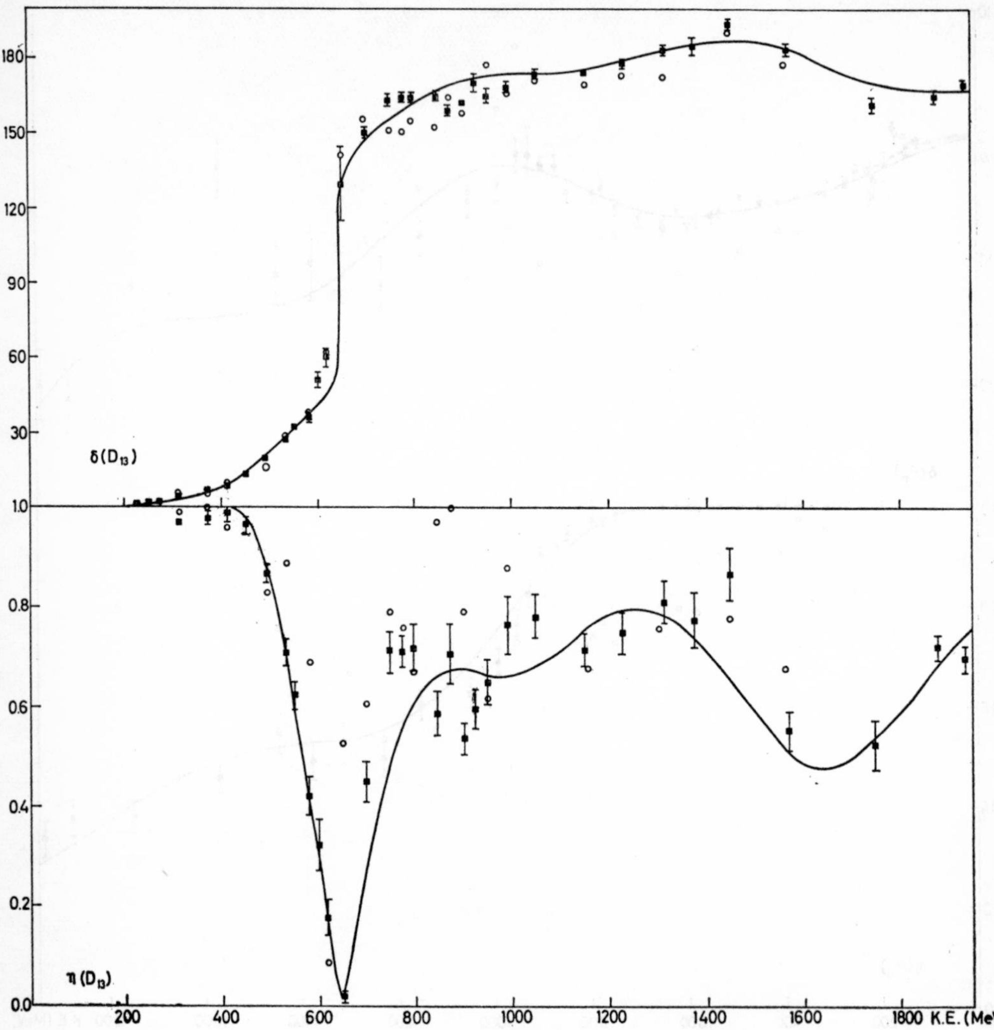

Fig. 45. D_{13} showing old and new resonances. Notation as for Fig. 35.

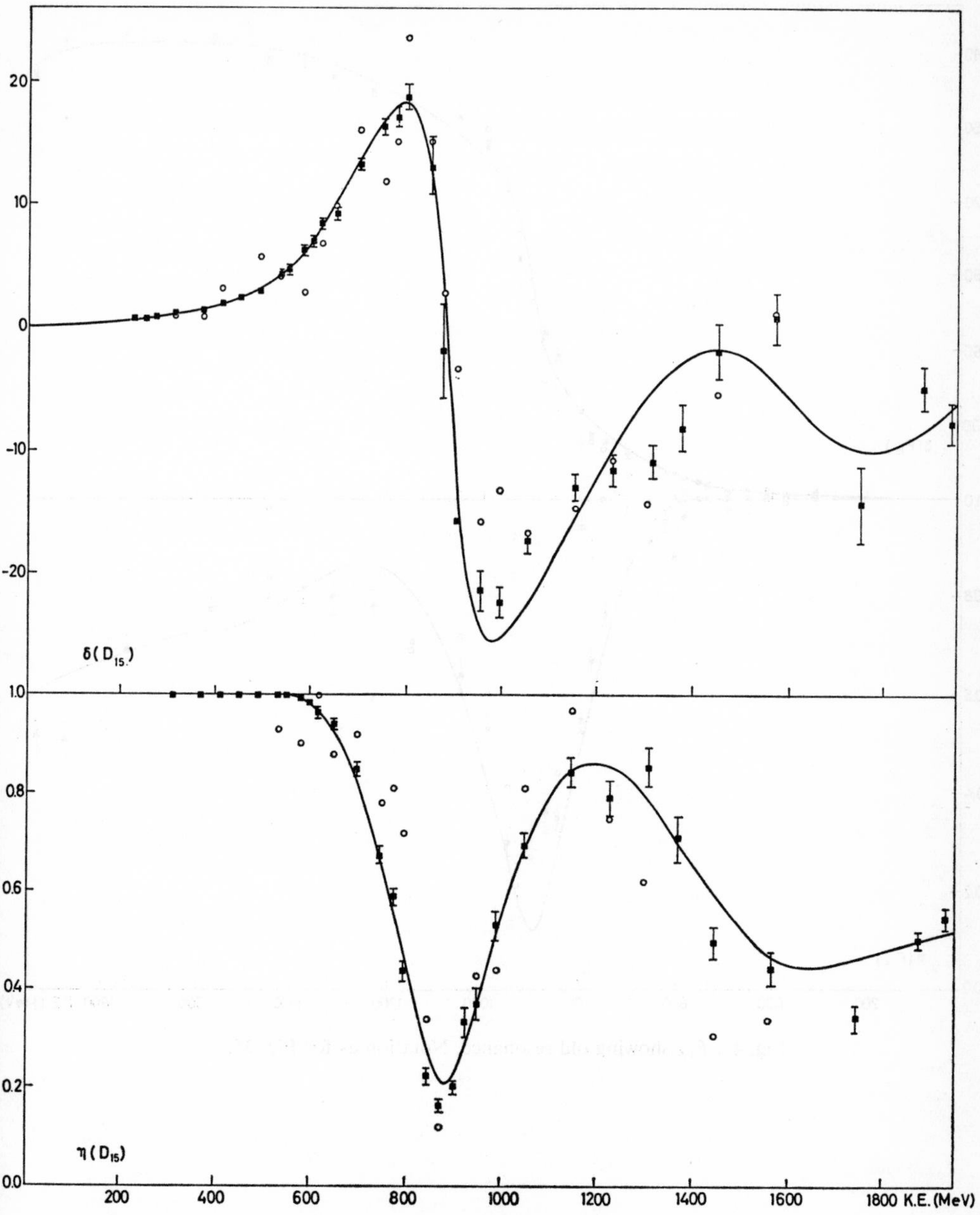

Fig. 46. D_{15} showing old resonance. Notation as for Fig. 35.

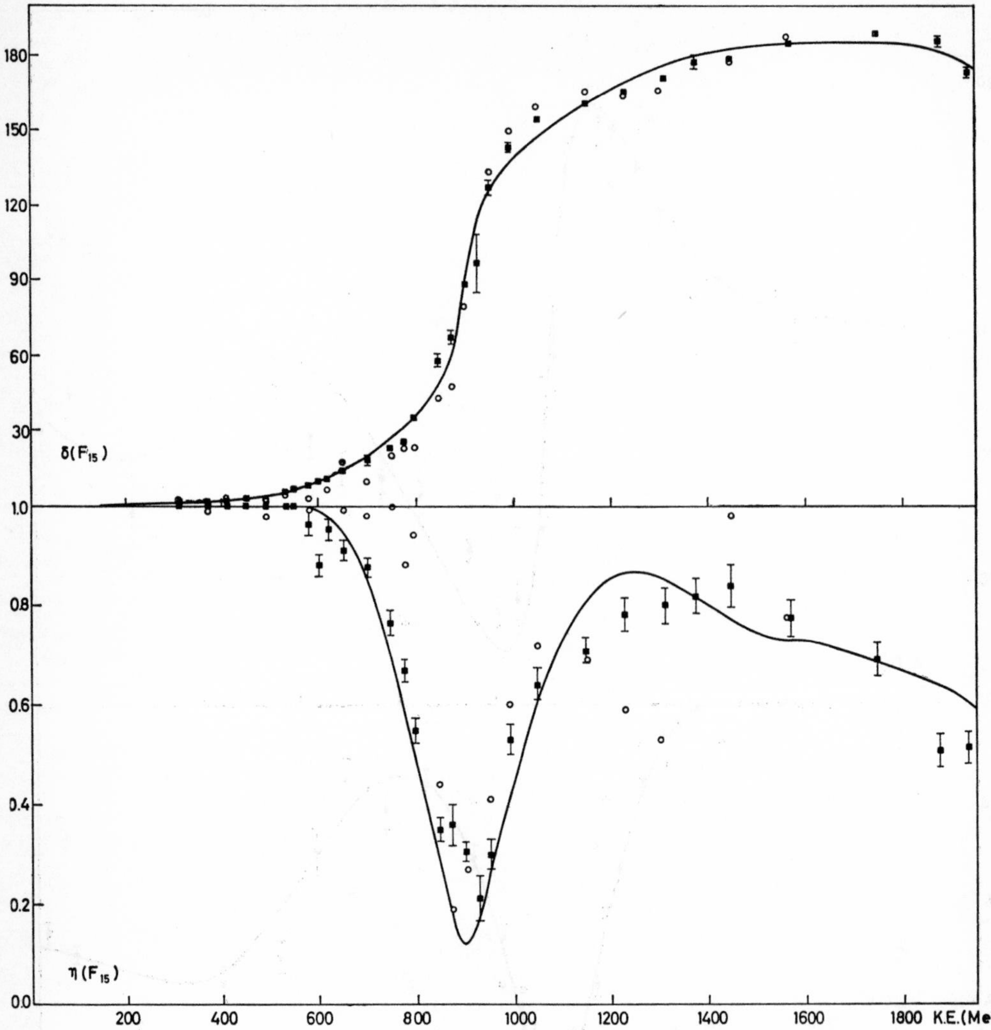

Fig. 47. F_{15} showing old resonance. Notation as for Fig. 35.

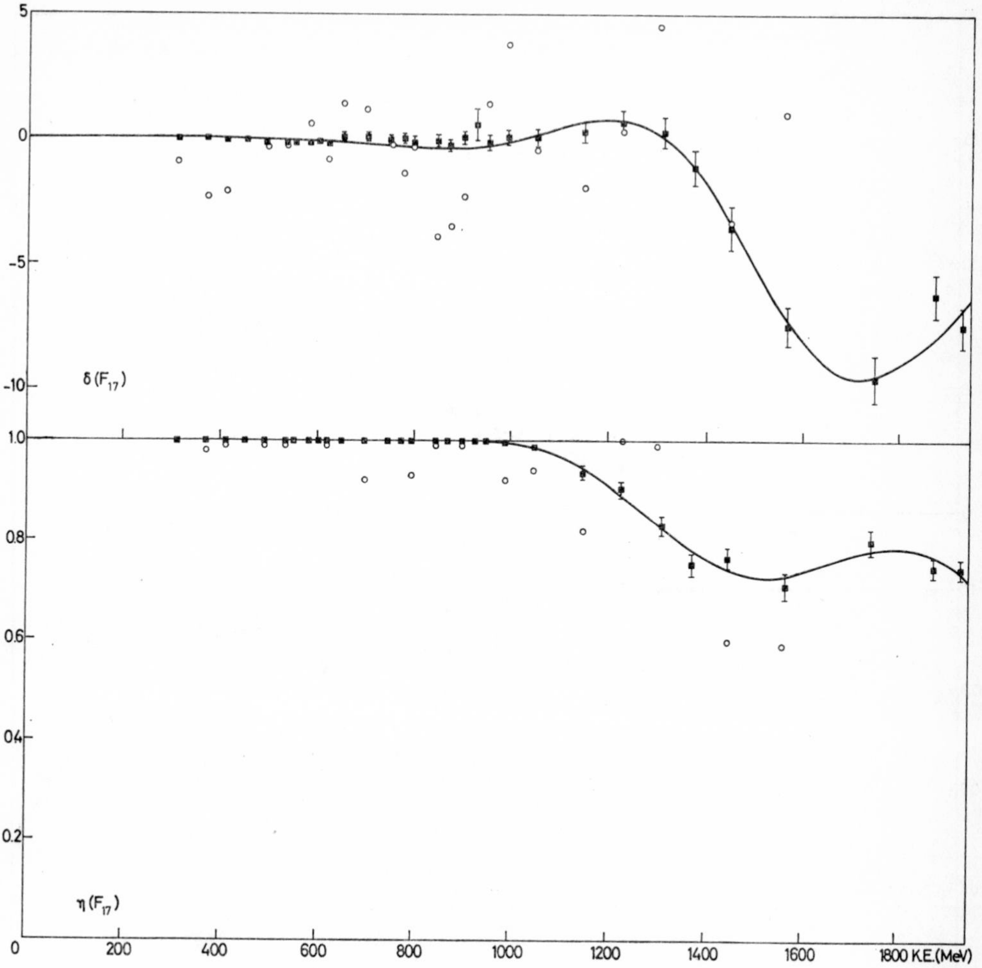

Fig. 48. F_{17} showing new CERN resonance. Notation as for Fig. 35.

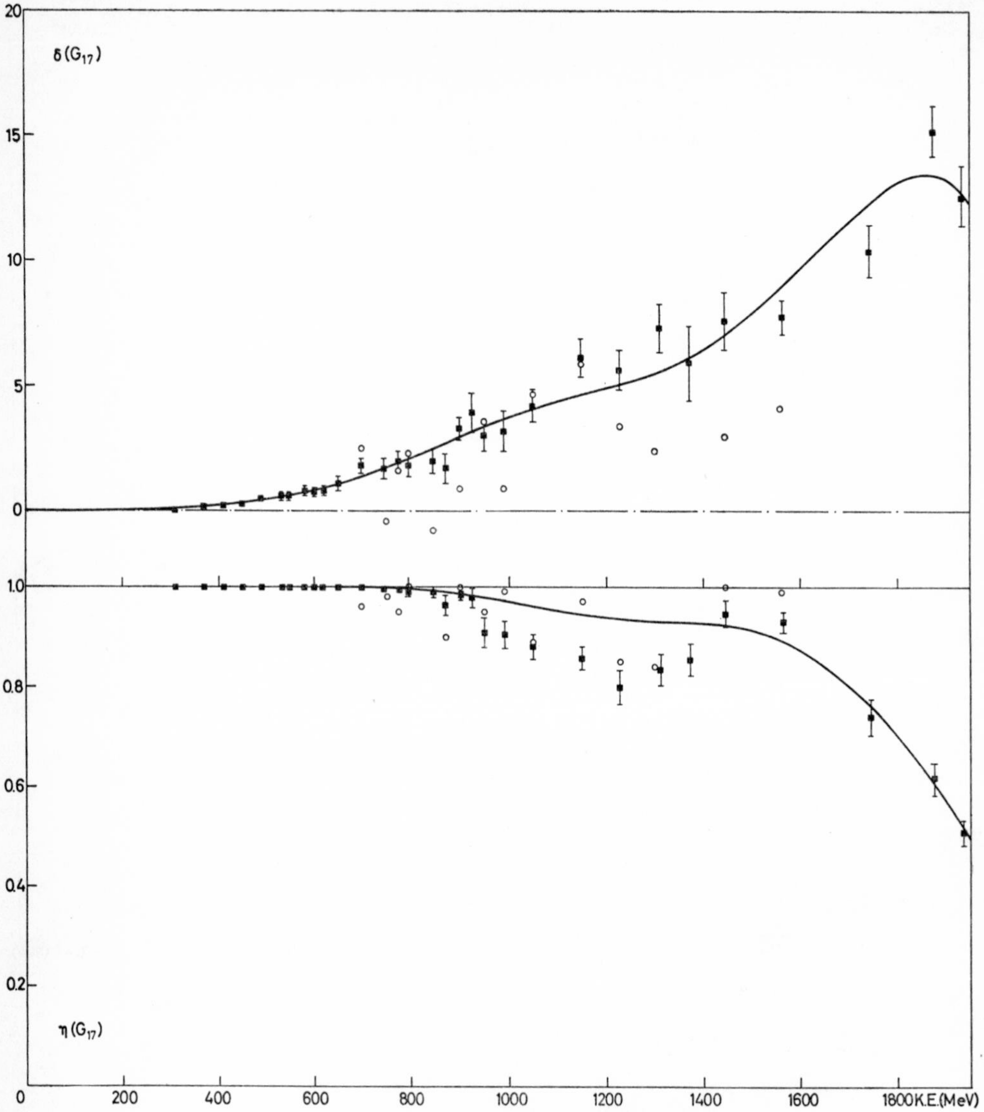

Fig. 49. G_{17} showing lower half of old resonance. Notation as for Fig. 35.

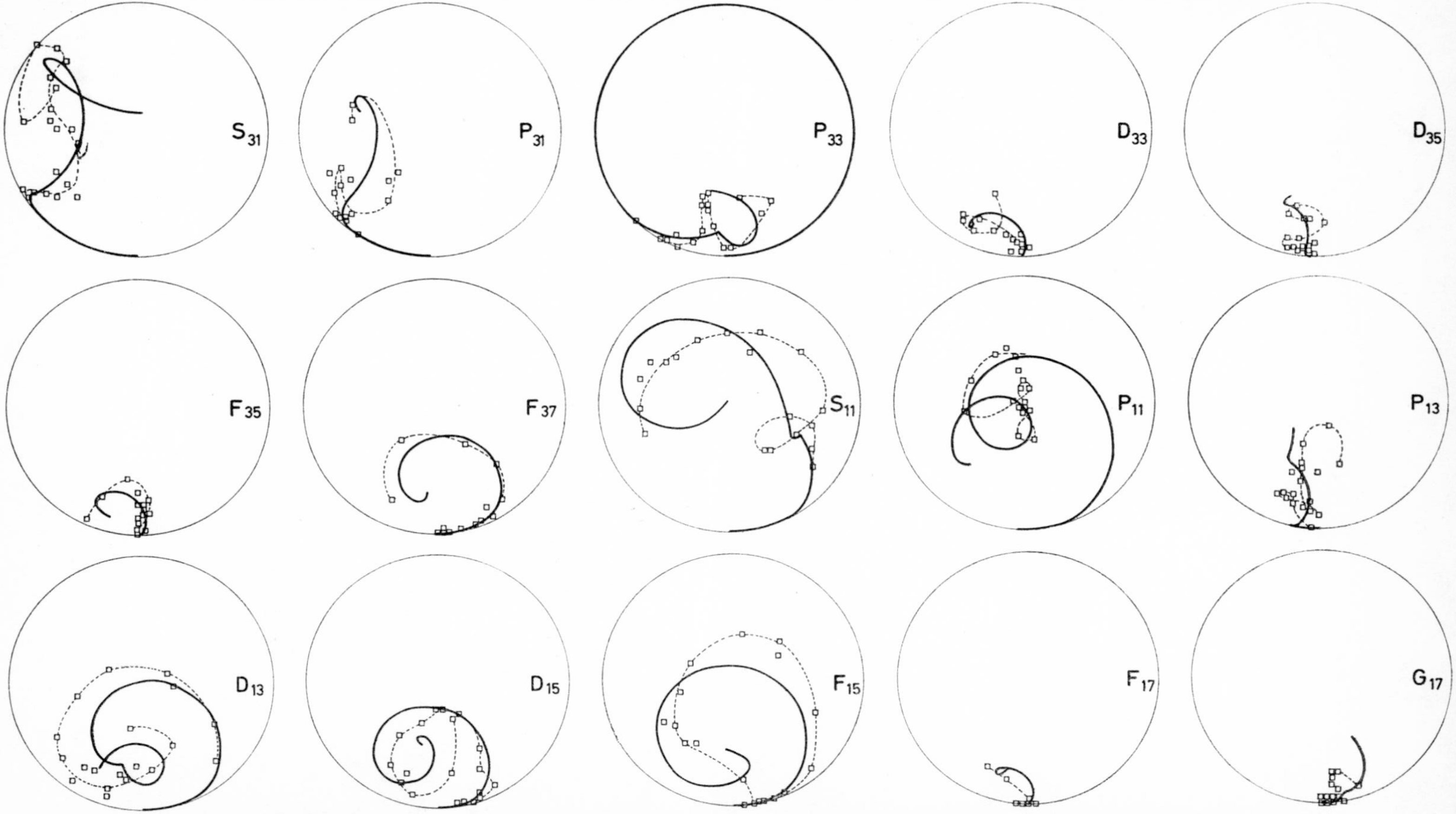

Fig. 50. Plots in the complex plane of the Berkeley phases (open squares) and CERN phases (solid line). Note the resonances in P_{31} and F_{35}, the second resonances in P_{33} and D_{13}, and the threshold effects in D_{35} and P_{13}. The dotted lines are to show the sequence of the Berkeley points.

7*

Angular Analysis of Elementary Particle Reactions

P. MOUSSA* and R. STORA

Service de Physique Théorique
Centre d'Etudes Nucléaires de Saclay
BP n^0 2—91, Gif-sur-Yvette France

CONTENTS

Introduction 103

0. Symmetry Laws and Collision Theory 104
   a) Wigner's formulation of symmetry laws in quantum mechanics 105
   b) Collision theory: the S-matrix 107

I. One Particle States 109
   a) The inhomogeneous Lorentz group 109
   b) The Lie algebra and the physical representations 110
   c) Theoretical constructions 117
   d) Examples 119
   e) Discrete operations 125
   f) Assemblies of identical particles: Fock space 129
   g) Applications to S-matrix theory—density matrices, projectors, transition probabilities 133

II. Analysis of Two Particle States 134
   a) l-s coupling 136
   b) Multipole coupling 128
   c) Helicity coupling 141
   d) Relationship between various coupling schemes 142
   e) Angular analysis of reactions $A_1 + A_2 \to A_3 + A_4$ 143
   f) Convergence of angular expansions 145
   g) Threshold behaviours of reduced amplitudes 148

III. Analysis of Three Particle States 150
   a) Couplings in cascade 150
   b) The symmetric coupling 152
   c) Recoupling coefficients 153

Appendix I. Basic Facts About the Lorentz Group 155
   a) The four sheets of the Lorentz group 155
   b) Subgroups 156
   c) Representations of $SL(2, C)$ 157

* Attaché au CNRS

d) Products of representations, Clebsch-Gordan coefficients 158
e) $SU(2)$ versus $SL(2,R)$ 159
f) Fourier analysis 159
g) Elements of Minkowski geometry 160

Appendix II. Angular Expansions for Two Body Reactions Involving Low Spin Particles 162

Appendix III. Reduction formulae 168

Conclusion 174

Acknowledgements 175

General References 175

Bibliography 175

INTRODUCTION

Most current experiments in High Energy Physics aim at measuring some matrix element of the S-matrix. Symmetry laws are of great help in analysing such quantities in simpler terms. Among them, one which has so far withstood all fluctuations of theoretical understanding and experimental checking is provided by the invariance of physical phenomena under the group of inhomogeneous, proper, orthochronous Lorentz transformations. Invariance under space and time reflections, on the other hand, seems to hold only approximately, for some classes of phenomena. We shall primarily discuss here consequences of relativistic invariance, following a line of reasoning due to E. P. Wigner, which is, without any doubt, the most penetrating, and leads in a completely rational fashion to all known results concerning the phenomenological angular analysis of particle collisions. It has the further advantage that it is applicable to any symmetry group, as we shall see from some particular examples.

We shall assume here that the reader is reasonably familiar with non relativistic angular momentum theory, as it is expounded in many text books, as well as with basic facts concerning the inhomogeneous Lorentz group. Relevant results and pertinent references will however, either be quoted in the body of the text or collected in appendices for the reader's convenience.

In 0, we shall set up the general framework in which we are working, namely, a) the formulation of symmetry laws in quantum mechanics and the basic theorem of Wigner, and b) the implications of these for collision amplitudes.

In I, we shall describe "particles" of arbitrary "masses" and "spins", following Wigner's analysis. Assemblies of identical particles subject to Fermi or Bose statistics will then be described in terms of the corresponding fields. Close contact will be made with the perhaps familiar descriptions of spin 0 (Klein Gordon), spin $\frac{1}{2}$ (Dirac), and spin 1 (Maxwell, Proca), particles.

In II, we shall analyse "two particle" states, in terms of the so-called $l - s$, multipole, and helicity couplings, and write down the corresponding analysis of a reaction involving two incoming and two outgoing particles. Contact will be made with reactions involving particles of low spins and a collection of, maybe familiar looking, formulae will be found in an appendix.

Unitarity of the S-matrix will be seen to allow the definition of phase shifts under special conditions whereas analyticity assumptions will be shown to yield threshold behaviours of familiar looking types. Such assumptions are of course either subject to controversy, or consequences of somewhat sophisticated models, and go far beyond the exactness of a symmetry law.

In Chapter III, we examine three particle states for which relativistic effects are slightly more subtle than for two particle states. $l - s$ or helicity couplings in cascade are compared to a symmetric coupling which one might pictorially call Casimir–Dalitz coupling.

Among technical appendices, one is devoted to "reduction formulae" pertaining to a field theory of the LSZ type, in order to make a bridge with a still current description of reactions between particles with spins.

The content of these notes is a re-exposition of material which has so far been presented to assemblies of theorists or mathematicians. It is hoped that it will not sound too abstract to experimentalists. The line of argument is of a highly theoretical nature, and is due to Wigner and coworkers or followers. The outcome, though, is impressively close to phenomenology i.e. the description of collision experiments in terms of momenta spins, etc.* and their analyses according to conservation laws. Thus, the reader will judge whether it is worth paying the price of an abstract approach.

0. SYMMETRY LAWS AND COLLISION THEORY

This section will presumably be the hardest of all, since it is supposed to recall some "well known" facts and will therefore eventually anticipate on some results displayed in the following chapters.

We first have to describe briefly how we do quantum mechanics.

The simplest situation is this: we work with a Hilbert space $\mathscr{H}$, an irreducible set $\mathcal{O}$ of observables represented by bounded self adjoint operators in $\mathscr{H}$—by irreducible we mean that every bounded operator commuting with all observables is a multiple of unity—; states are represented by all density matrices ϱ, i.e. self adjoint operators with a trace which we take equal to 1 as a normalization condition. The number Tr $A\varrho$ represents the expectation value of observable A in state ϱ. ϱ also represents the observable whose expectation value in a given state ϱ' will give the probability for state ϱ to occur in ϱ' (otherwise called the transition probability from state ϱ to state ϱ'). Among all possible states are "pure" states with density matrix $|\Phi\rangle\langle\Phi|$ for any $|\Phi\rangle$ in $\mathscr{H}$. In particular, the transition probability from pure state $|\Phi\rangle\langle\Phi|$ to pure state $|\Psi\rangle\langle\Psi|$ is given by $|\langle\Phi\mid\Psi\rangle|^2$.

In this description a pure state is equivalently described by a ray in $\mathscr{H}$, i.e. the set $|\underline{\Phi}\rangle$ of vectors of the form $\omega|\Phi\rangle$, ω being any complex number of modulus 1 (phase factor), and $|\Phi\rangle$, some vector in $\mathscr{H}$.

A more general and realistic set up is obtained by setting $\mathscr{H} = \bigoplus_i \mathscr{H}_i$, a direct sum of Hilbert spaces, each observable A having a representative A_i in $\mathscr{H}_i$, i.e. $A = \sum_1 E_i A_i E_i$ (E_i being the projector on $\mathscr{H}_i$), pure states lying within some $\mathscr{H}_i$. This structure implies that the E_i's generate a commutative algebra of

* The connection of such a description with that of space time localized events which are actually observed can be established by suitable introduction of space time together with more detailed assumptions about the structure of S-matrix than those made here [27].

operators commuting with all A's. This algebra is called the superselection algebra and the $\mathscr{H}_i$'s are called superselection sectors. This situation describes well the fact that some commuting observables do commute with all others (e.g. the so called charges, electric, baryonic, etc.). Index i thus labels the spectrum of superselection operators.

We will stick to this scheme which is neither the most general nor the most sophisticated (II, V).

a) Wigner's formulation of symmetry laws in quantum mechanics

We shall say that a symmetry law $\mathscr{S}$ holds, if to each observable A there corresponds a transformed observable ${}^{\mathscr{S}}A$, and to each state ϱ a transformed state ${}^{\mathscr{S}}\varrho$ such that each observable (resp. state) is the image by $\mathscr{S}$ of some other observable (resp. state), and that:

$$\mathrm{Tr}\, A\varrho = \mathrm{Tr}\,{}^{\mathscr{S}}A\,{}^{\mathscr{S}}\varrho\,.$$

From what we said before, there exists thus, in each superselection sector $\mathscr{H}_i$, a mapping of rays $|\underline{\Phi}_i\rangle \to |{}^{\mathscr{S}}\underline{\Phi}_i\rangle$ which preserves transition probabilities:

$$|\langle\underline{\Psi}_i|\underline{\Phi}_i\rangle|^2 = |\langle{}^{\mathscr{S}}\underline{\Psi}_i|{}^{\mathscr{S}}\underline{\Phi}_i\rangle|^2.$$

(In order to make sure that a pure state goes over into a pure state, one can use the fact that $\mathrm{Tr}\,\varrho^2 = 1$ is characteristic of purity and that ϱ is an observable.)

Then, forgetting from now on superselection indices, one has, in each superselection sector, the fundamental:

Wigner's Theorem[1]

To every symmetry law $\mathscr{S}: |\underline{\Psi}\rangle \to |{}^{\mathscr{S}}\underline{\Psi}\rangle$, $(|\langle\underline{\Phi}\mid\underline{\Psi}\rangle|^2 = |\langle{}^{\mathscr{S}}\underline{\Phi}\mid{}^{\mathscr{S}}\underline{\Psi}\rangle|^2)$, there corresponds an additive operator $U(\mathscr{S})$, namely, such that $U(\mathscr{S})\,(|\Phi\rangle + |\Psi\rangle) = U(\mathscr{S})\,|\Phi\rangle + U(\mathscr{S})\,|\Psi\rangle$ for all $|\Phi\rangle$ and $|\Psi\rangle$ in $\mathscr{H}$, which is either unitary or antiunitary, namely, $UU^+ = U^+U = \mathbf{1}$, where U^+ is defined by $\langle\Phi|U^+|\Psi\rangle = \langle U\Phi\mid\Psi\rangle$ in the unitary case and $\langle\Phi|U^+|\Psi\rangle = \langle U\Phi\mid\Psi\rangle^*$ in the antiunitary case, and such that $U(\mathscr{S})|\Phi\rangle$ belongs to the ray $|{}^{\mathscr{S}}\underline{\Phi}\rangle$ whenever $|\Phi\rangle$ belongs to the ray $|\underline{\Phi}\rangle$.

The operator $U(\mathscr{S})$ is uniquely defined up to a multiplicative phase factor.

Let now G be a symmetry group, that is a set containing a unit element e, and endowed with a (not necessarily commutative) product:

$$g_1, g_2 \in G \to g_1 \cdot g_2 \in G,$$

such that

1) $e \cdot g = g \cdot e = g$

2) $g_1 \cdot (g_2 \cdot g_3) = (g_1 \cdot g_2) \cdot g_3$

3) for all $g \in G$ there is an inverse g^{-1} such that $g \cdot g^{-1} = g^{-1} \cdot g = e$,

each element of which defines a symmetry operation $|\underline{\Psi}\rangle \to |{}^{g}\underline{\Psi}\rangle$ which is transition probability preserving and "onto".

First of all $U(e) = \omega\mathbf{1}$, where ω is a phase factor, because of the uniqueness of $U(e)$ up to a phase and the fact that $\mathbf{1}$ is a solution. We shall choose $\omega = 1$.

Next, from Wigner's theorem—first part—both $U(g_1)\, U(g_2)$ and $U(g_1 g_2)$ realise the ray correspondence $|\underline{\Psi}\rangle \to |{}^{g_1 g_2}\underline{\Psi}\rangle$, and, from the last part, they differ at most by a phase factor $\omega(g_1, g_2)$:

$$U(g_1)\, U(g_2) = \omega(g_1, g_2)\, U(g_1 g_2). \tag{0,a,1}$$

The operators $U(g)$ fulfilling Eq. (0,a,1) are said to form a representation of G up to a phase. Two representations $U(g)$, $U'(g)$, where both $U(g)$ and $U'(g)$ are either unitary or antiunitary, with factor systems $\omega(g_1, g_2)$, $\omega'(g_1, g_2)$, such that:

$$\omega(g_1, g_2) = \omega'(g_1, g_2)\, \theta(g_1 \cdot g_2)\, [\theta(g_2)]^{-\varepsilon(g_1)} [\theta(g_1)]^{-1},$$

where $\theta(g)$ is a phase factor, are said to belong to the same *type*; here, $\varepsilon(g) = +1$ if $U(g)$ is unitary, $\varepsilon(g) = -1$ if $U(g)$ is antiunitary. For instance, $\mathscr{U}(g)$ and $\theta^{-1}(g)\, \mathscr{U}(g)$ belong to the same type.

The classification of physical systems under a symmetry group G thus depends on;

— $\varepsilon(g)$
– a type of factor system $\omega(g_1, g_2)$
– given $\varepsilon(g)$, $\omega(g_1, g_2)$, a class of representation up to unitary equivalence.

Remarks

I – if G is a connected Lie group $\varepsilon(g) = +1$ for all g because the product of two unitary operators is unitary, whereas the product of a unitary and an antiunitary operator is antiunitary.

II — if G contains an element ϱ whose square is the identity e, and $U(\varrho)$ is antiunitary

$$U(\varrho)\, U(\varrho) = \omega(\varrho, \varrho)\, U(e) = \omega(\varrho, \varrho)\, \mathbf{1}$$

for a possible choice of $U(e)$,

$$\begin{aligned} U(\varrho)\, U(\varrho)\, U(\varrho) &= U(\varrho)\, \omega(\varrho, \varrho)\, \mathbf{1} = \omega^*(\varrho, \varrho)\, U(\varrho) \\ &= \omega(\varrho, \varrho)\, U(e)\, U(\varrho) = \omega(\varrho, \varrho)\, U(\varrho), \end{aligned}$$

thus

$$\omega^2(\varrho, \varrho) = 1 \quad \text{or} \quad \omega(\varrho, \varrho) = \pm 1.$$

b) Collision theory: the *S*-matrix

We now have a description of a physical system in a Hilbert space $\mathscr{H}$ in which there is given a representation up to a factor of the symmetry group G.

A collision theory is set up if $\mathscr{H}$ can be spanned by a collection of states $|\alpha \text{ in}\rangle$ representing possible incoming beams and targets, as well as states $|\beta \text{ out}\rangle$ representing states possibly produced in a collision experiment*. The reasonable assumption that every incoming state can be produced as the result of a collision experiment implies that in and out states labelled by the same quantum numbers—both of which have then to exist—give rise to the same observed attributes:

$$|\langle\beta, i, \text{in}|\alpha, i, \text{in}\rangle| = |\langle\beta, i, \text{out}|\alpha, i, \text{out}\rangle|.$$

We have now supplied the index i labelling superselection sector $\mathscr{H}_i$, which is spanned by both sets of vectors $|\alpha, i, \text{in}\rangle$ and $|\alpha, i, \text{out}\rangle$. Wigner's theorem then ensures the existence of a unitary or antiunitary operator S_i acting on $\mathscr{H}_i$, defined up to a phase, from which one can construct the S operator; $S = \sum_i E_i S_i E_i$, which is either unitary or antiunitary; (we shall show actually in a moment that Lorentz invariance and positivity of the energy force it to be unitary).

The collision amplitude $\langle\beta \text{ out} \mid \alpha \text{ in}\rangle$ can thus be expressed as:

$$\langle\beta_{\text{out}}|\alpha_{\text{in}}\rangle = \langle\beta_{\text{in}}|S|\alpha_{\text{in}}\rangle = \langle\beta_{\text{out}}|S|\alpha_{\text{out}}\rangle,$$

(with a possible complex conjugation on the second form, were S antiunitary!), in and out states and observables being connected by:

$$\langle\alpha \text{ out}| = \langle\alpha \text{ in}|S,$$

$$A_{\text{out}} = S^+ A_{\text{in}} S.$$

Assuming now that collision probabilities are invariant under a group G:

$$|\langle\beta|S|\alpha\rangle|^2 = |\langle{}^g\beta|S|{}^g\alpha\rangle|^2,$$

one obtains

$$\langle\beta|S|\alpha\rangle = \omega(g, \alpha, \beta)\,\langle{}^g\beta|S|{}^g\alpha\rangle$$

or

$$\omega(g, \alpha, \beta)\,\langle{}^g\beta|S|{}^g\alpha\rangle^*,$$

where ω is a phase factor. (This argument starts as the proof of Wigner's theorem, cf. Ref. (0), Chap. XV, 1, 2, Th. II and III.)

* α and β represent collections of quantum numbers characterizing the possible prepared or produced states, e.g. momentum, spin, etc. consistent with eventual symmetry laws.

Using the linearity (or antilinearity) of S, one easily finds that:

1) $\omega(g, \alpha, \beta)$ is independent of α and β within any coherent subspace $\mathscr{H}_i$ of $\mathscr{H}$.
2) the first alternative holds when $U(g)$ is unitary, the second one when $U(g)$ is antiunitary.

Next, one proves that $\omega(g)$ is a representation of G in the sense that:

$$\omega(g_1 g_2) = [\omega(g_1)]^{\varepsilon(g_2)} \omega(g_2).$$

If G is connected, then $\omega(g)$ is a true one dimensional representation of G.

At any rate, within a coherent subspace, one has*:

$$U^{-1}(g)\, SU(g) = \omega(g)\, S.$$

That $\omega(g)$ is the trivial representation of G can be enforced by the socalled cluster decomposition property of the S-matrix†, derivable for instance from axiomatic field theories, which states that if two experiments are carried out far apart, the overall S-matrix element factorizes into the product of the two individual S-matrix elements.

On the other hand, if the one dimensional representations of G consist of the identity representation exclusively, (which is the case for relativistic invariance[II]), then commutation of $U(g)$ with S is automatically ensured. It is the same kind of an argument which indeed forces the S-matrix to be unitary: let $\{a, A\}$ be any inhomogeneous Lorentz transformation—a denoting the translation part, A denoting the homogeneous part as described in Chapter I—. Invariance reads, according to the above described arguments:

$$U_{\text{out}}^{-1}(a, A)\, SU_{\text{out}}(a, A) = \omega(a, A)\, S,$$

and here[II], $\omega(a, A) = 1$. Hence:

$$SU_{\text{out}}(a, A)\, S^{+} = U_{\text{out}}(a, A) = U_{\text{in}}(a, A).$$

Let $A = 1$, $U(a) \sim \mathbf{1} + iP \cdot a$, for small a, where P is the momentum operator.
Then

$$SiPS^{+} = iP$$

i.e.

$$SPS^{+} = P \quad \text{if} \quad S \text{ is unitary}$$

$$-SPS^{+} = P \quad \text{if} \quad S \text{ is antiunitary.}$$

So, if we assume as will become physically reasonable fairly soon that the spectrum of P is contained in the future light cone, the last possibility is ruled out (cf. a similar argument in Ch. I, section e).

* This does not apply to time reversal and such symmetry laws for which the expression of symmetry reads $|\langle\beta_{\text{out}}|\alpha_{\text{in}}\rangle|^2 = |\langle{}^T\alpha_{\text{out}}|{}^T\beta_{\text{in}}\rangle|^2$. For these, one finds $U^{-1}(T)SU(T) = \omega(T)S^{+}$.

† This argument was first given to us by M. Froissart. For a closely related discussion, see Ref. 28.

I. ONE PARTICLE STATES[2]

a) The inhomogeneous proper orthochronous Lorentz group $\mathscr{P}_+^\uparrow$ and its covering group $\overline{\mathscr{P}}_+^\uparrow$

Unless otherwise specified, G will be $\mathscr{P}_+^\uparrow$, the inhomogeneous proper orthochronous Lorentz group, i.e. the group of transformations $\{a, \Lambda\}$ where a is a four vector $a = (a^0, \boldsymbol{a} = \{a^1, a^2, a^3\})$ and Λ a four by four matrix, with determinant $+1$, which is pseudo-orthogonal for the metric $G = \{g^{\mu\nu} = 0, \mu \neq \nu; g^{00} = -g^{11} = -g^{22} = -g^{33} = 1\}$, i.e. such that $\Lambda^T G \Lambda = G$, and has the properties $\det \Lambda = +\mathbf{1}$, $\Lambda_0{}^0 > 0$. This is the group of changes of Lorentz frames, preserving the direction of time flow and the orientation in three dimensional space like planes. Let x^μ be the coordinates of a four-vector in frame $\mathscr{F}$, x'^μ its coordinates in frame $\mathscr{F}'$, then:

$$x'^\mu = a^\mu + \Lambda^\mu{}_\nu x^\nu$$

$$(x' - y')^2 = (x - y)^2 = (x - y)\, G(x - y) = (x^0 - y^0)^2 - (\boldsymbol{x} - \boldsymbol{y})^2.$$

The group law is $\{a, \Lambda\}\{a', \Lambda'\} = \{a + \Lambda a', \Lambda\Lambda'\}$.

In this case, Wigner's analysis shows[11] that unitary representations of $\mathscr{P}_+^\uparrow$ up to a phase are true representations of a group $\overline{\mathscr{P}}_+^\uparrow$, (the universal covering group of $\mathscr{P}_+^\uparrow$), constructed as follows:

Let

$$\sigma_\mu = \left\{\sigma_0 = \begin{pmatrix}1 & 0\\ 0 & 1\end{pmatrix} \quad \sigma_1 = \begin{pmatrix}0 & 1\\ 1 & 0\end{pmatrix} \quad \sigma_2 = \begin{pmatrix}0 & -i\\ i & 0\end{pmatrix} \quad \sigma_3 = \begin{pmatrix}1 & 0\\ 0 & -1\end{pmatrix}\right\}$$

be the set of Pauli matrices.

With each four vector a, associate the hermitian 2×2 matrix

$\underset{\sim}{a} = a^\mu \sigma_\mu$, $[a^\mu = \frac{1}{2} \operatorname{tr} \underset{\sim}{a}\sigma_\mu]$.

Let SL(2, C) be the group of 2×2 complex matrices of determinant 1.

With each vector a and matrix $A \in$ SL(2, C), associate the vector $A \cdot a$ defined by

$$\underbrace{A \cdot a} = A\underset{\sim}{a}A^+;$$

one finds

$$\det \underbrace{A \cdot a} = \det \underset{\sim}{a} = a^2 = a \cdot a$$

$$\frac{\partial (A \cdot a)^0}{\partial a^0} = \operatorname{tr} \frac{1}{2} AA^+ > 0$$

$$A \cdot (a + b) = A \cdot a + A \cdot b;$$

$A \cdot a$ is thus obtained from a by an orthochronous Lorentz transformation which can furthermore be proved to be proper (det $= +1$). Two elements $+A$ and $-A$ correspond to the same Lorentz transformation.

$\overline{\mathscr{P}}_+^\uparrow$ is thus the set of elements $\{a, A\}$ with the group law

$$\{a, A\}\,\{a', A'\} = \{a + A \cdot a', AA'\}.$$

We shall see shortly that it is precisely this distinction between $\mathscr{P}_+^\uparrow$ and $\overline{\mathscr{P}}_+^\uparrow$ which allows for the existence of half integer spins.

We now proceed to look for inequivalent unitary representations of $\overline{\mathscr{P}}_+^\uparrow$. It can be shown[11] that any "continuous" unitary representation can be decomposed into a sum, or rather an integral, of irreducible ones. (i.e. schematically any Hilbert space of representation can be ordered so that

$$U(g) = \begin{pmatrix} U_1(g) & 0 & \dots & 0 \\ 0 & U_2(g) & \dots & 0 \\ \dots & \dots & \dots & \dots \\ 0 & 0 & \dots & U_n(g) \end{pmatrix},$$

each constituant not being decomposable in this fashion.)

We shall now construct in a heuristic way those irreducible representations which we shall need for physical applications.

b) The Lie Algebra of $\mathscr{P}_+^\uparrow$ and the physical representations

Let

$$U(a, A) = e^{iP.a}\, e^{\frac{i}{2}\omega_{\mu\nu}J^{\mu\nu}}$$

be the exponential form of the representation.* P is the hermitian generator of translations, interpreted as the energy momentum operator, $-J^{\nu\mu} = J^{\mu\nu}$ is the hermitian generator of the Lorentz transformation in the (μ, ν) two-plane, of which there are six, $\omega_{\mu\nu}$ being the angle (either circular if $\mu, \nu \neq 0$, or hyperbolic if μ or $\nu = 0$).

The group law implies

$$\begin{aligned} &e^{-iPa'}\, e^{iPa}\, e^{iPa'} = e^{iPa} \\ &e^{-\frac{i}{2}\omega'_{\mu\nu}J^{\mu\nu}}\, e^{iPa}\, e^{\frac{i}{2}\omega'_{\mu\nu}J^{\mu\nu}} = e^{iP.\Lambda^{-1}(\omega')a} \qquad \text{(I,b,1)} \\ &e^{-\frac{i}{2}\omega'_{\mu\nu}J_{\mu\nu}}\, e^{\frac{i}{2}\omega_{\mu\nu}J^{\mu\nu}}\, e^{\frac{i}{2}\omega'_{\mu\nu}J^{\mu\nu}} = e^{\frac{i}{2}J^{\mu\nu}\Lambda_\mu{}^{\mu'}(-\omega')\Lambda_\nu{}^{\nu'}(-\omega')\omega_{\mu'\nu'}} \end{aligned}$$

* Actually, not every Lorentz transformation can be written in purely exponential form, but can always be written as a product of exponentials.

whose infinitesimal versions are (a' and ω' small)

$$[P_\mu, P_\nu] = 0$$

$$[P_\mu, J_{\nu\lambda}] = i[g_{\lambda\mu}P_\nu - g_{\nu\mu}P_\lambda] \tag{I,b,2}$$

$$[J_{\mu\nu}, J_{\varrho\sigma}] = i[g_{\mu\varrho}J_{\nu\varrho} + g_{\nu\sigma}J_{\mu\varrho} - g_{\mu\sigma}J_{\nu\varrho} - g_{\nu\varrho}J_{\mu\sigma}].$$

The last two commutation relations just say that P_μ and $J_{\mu\nu}$ behave respectively as vector and tensor operators under Lorentz transformations.

As usual we shall look for a maximal set of commuting observables.

The four P's commute and we let p be an "eigenvalue".* Let us now look for Lorentz transformations Λ which leave p invariant, and write $\Lambda = e^{\frac{i}{2}\omega_{\mu\nu}I^{\mu\nu}}$ where $I^{\mu\nu}$ are the four by four matrices which generate the $\mu\nu$ transformations in p space:

$$(I^{\mu\nu})^{\varkappa\lambda} = -i(g^{\mu\varkappa}g^{\nu\lambda} - g^{\mu\lambda}g^{\nu\varkappa}).$$

The invariance of p implies $\omega_{\mu\nu}p^\nu = 0$ which is solved according to $\omega_{\mu\nu} = \varepsilon_{\mu\nu\varrho\sigma}\, s^\varrho p^\sigma$ where $\varepsilon_{\mu\nu\varrho\sigma}$ is the totally antisymmetric tensor $\varepsilon_{0123} = +1$, $\varepsilon_{\mu\nu\varrho\sigma} = \pm 1$ according as $\mu\nu\varrho\sigma$ is an even/odd permutation of (0123), and s a four vector whose component along p is irrelevant. Thus the $U(\Lambda(p))$'s representing Lorentz transformations which leave p invariant are:

$$U(\Lambda(p)) = e^{\frac{i}{2}\varepsilon_{\mu\nu\varrho\sigma}J^{\mu\nu}s^\varrho p^\sigma}.$$

Let then $|p\rangle$ be a vector of representation space such that $P|p\rangle = |p\rangle$

$$U(\Lambda(p))|p\rangle = e^{\frac{i}{2}\varepsilon_{\mu\nu\varrho\sigma}J^{\mu\nu}s^\varrho p^\sigma}|p\rangle$$

$$= e^{-iW\,s}|p\rangle,$$

where $W_\mu = -\frac{1}{2}\,\varepsilon_{\mu\nu\varrho\sigma}J^{\nu\varrho}P^\sigma$.

One easily finds from (I,b,2):

$$[W_\mu, P_\nu] = 0,$$

$$[W_\mu, W_\nu] = -i\varepsilon_{\mu\nu\varrho\sigma}W^\varrho P^\sigma, \tag{I,b,3}$$

and

$$[J_{\mu\nu}, W_\lambda] = i(g_{\mu\lambda}W_\lambda - g_{\nu\lambda}W_\mu)$$

(the latter indicating that W behaves as a four vector under Lorentz transformations).

One furthermore notes the identity

$$W \cdot P = 0 \tag{I,b,3'}$$

which stems from the antisymmetry of $\varepsilon_{\mu\nu\varrho\sigma}$. (This was indeed contained in the construction of $W(p)$ as generating Lorentz transformations leaving p unchanged). From these commutation rules one observes that $P \cdot P = P^2$, and $W \cdot W = W^2$

* Wherever "eigenvalue" is written, it is implied that continuous spectrum may lead to the consideration of improper eigenvectors.

commute with all P^{μ}'s and $J^{\mu\nu}$'s. Their "eigenvalues" label the representation (one can indeed show that no other function of P, J commutes with all P's, J's).

Then, P being taken diagonal with eigenvalue p such that $p^2 = m^2$, m^2 fixed, since W commutes with P, $W|p\rangle$ is still an eigenvector of P with eigenvalue p; we shall call $W(p)$ the "restriction" of the operator W to the eigenspace of P corresponding to the eigenvalue p. We have of course $W(p) \cdot p = 0$ so that $W(p)$ can be expanded along a basis of independent vectors orthogonal to p. At this point, we have to make distinctions according as p is time-like ($p^2 > 0$), light-like ($p^2 = 0$), space-like ($p^2 < 0$), or identically zero.

1) $p^2 > 0$ $p^0 > 0$ or $p^0 < 0$*

One can attach to each p three space-like vectors $n_i(p)$:

$$n_i(p) \cdot n_j(p) = -\delta_{ij} \quad i, j = 1, 2, 3$$

$$p \cdot n_i(p) = 0 \quad \det(p, n_1(p)\, n_2(p)\, n_3(p)) = \pm 1 \tag{I,b,4}$$

according as

$$p^0 \gtrless 0$$

and expand:

$$W(p) = \sum_{i=1}^{3} W_i(p)\, n_i(p) \tag{I,b,5}$$

where $W_i(p) = -W(p) \cdot n_i(p)$.

From (I,b,3), one finds for the commutation rules between

$$S_i(p) = \frac{W_i(p)}{m} \tag{I,b,6}$$

$$[S_i(p), S_j(p)] = i\varepsilon_{ijk} S_k(p) \tag{I,b,7}$$

where $\varepsilon_{ijk} = \pm 1$ according as ijk is an $\begin{pmatrix}\text{even}\\ \text{odd}\end{pmatrix}$ permutation of 1, 2, 3. The $S_i(p)$ are generators of the SU(2) subgroup of $\overline{\mathscr{P}}_+^{\uparrow}$ which leaves p invariant. Thus,

$$\sum_i^3 S_i^2(p) = -\frac{W^2}{m^2}$$

has possible eigenvalues $s(s+1)$, s integer or half integer.

Together with each p one can diagonalize $S_3(p)$ whose eigenvalues s_3 range by integer steps from $-s$ to $+s$. In other words, we have now defined basis vectors

$$|[p], s_3\rangle$$

fulfilling

$$P|[p], s_3\rangle = p|[p], s_3\rangle$$

$$S_3(p)\,|[p], s_3\rangle = s_3|[p], s_3\rangle \tag{I,b,8}$$

* In physics, one always has to deal with representations with $p^0 > 0$, some formal manipulations however use those with $p^0 < 0$.

and

$$(S_1 \pm iS_2)(p)\,|[p]\,s_3\rangle = \sqrt{s(s+1) - s_3(s_3 \pm 1)}\,|[p]\,s_3 \pm 1\rangle; \qquad \text{(I,b,8)}$$

$[p]$ reminding us that the corresponding state is defined relative to a set p, $n_i(p)$ subject to (I,b,4). $[p]$ will be understood as an element of SL(2, C) corresponding to the Lorentz transformation which transforms

$$\overset{0}{p} = (\pm m, 0, 0, 0), \quad n_1(\overset{0}{p}) = (0, 1, 0, 0), \quad n_2(\overset{0}{p}) = (0, 0, 1, 0), \quad n_3(\overset{0}{p}) = (0, 0, 0, 1)$$

into p, $n_1(p)$, $n_2(p)$, $n_3(p)$ respectively.

The choice of $[p]$, which is arbitrary, first makes precise on which four vector $n_3(p)$ orthogonal to p the spin operator W/m is measured, and how the phase of the corresponding state is chosen (choice of $n_1(p)$, $n_2(p)$ and sign of $[p]$ in SL(2, C)).

The commutation rules (I,b,1) and (I,b,2) show that:

$$|[p], s_3\rangle = U([p])\,|[\overset{0}{p}], s_3\rangle. \qquad \text{(I,b,9)}$$

One sees easily that the $S_i(\overset{0}{p}) = -\frac{1}{2}\,\varepsilon_{ijk} J_{jk}$ are just the generators of the SU(2) subgroup of SL(2, C), which corresponds to space rotations.

For any operation u of SU(2), one has the usual spin s representation:

$$U(u)\,|[\overset{0}{p}], s_3\rangle = |[\overset{0}{p}], s_3'\rangle\,\mathscr{D}^s_{s'_3 s_3}(u).$$

Hence, according to (I,b,8):
firstly*

$$|[p]', s_3\rangle = |[p], s_3'\rangle\,\mathscr{D}^s_{s'_3 s_3}([p]^{-1}\,[p]'), \qquad \text{(I,b,10)}$$

which shows how a spin state changes when the frame $\{n_i(p)\}$ is changed (note that $[p]^{-1}\,[p]'$ take $\overset{0}{p}$ to p, p back to $\overset{0}{p}$ and is thus an SU(2) operation);
and secondly:

$$\begin{aligned} U(a, A)\,|[p], s_3\rangle &= U(a)\,U(A)\,|[p], s_3\rangle \\ &= U(a)\,U([A\cdot p])\,U([Ap]^{-1}\,A[p])\,|[p]\,s_3\rangle \\ &= U(a)\,U([A\cdot p])\,|[\overset{0}{p}], s_3'\rangle\,\mathscr{D}^s_{s'_3 s_3}([Ap]^{-1}\,A[p]) \qquad \text{(I,b,11)} \\ &= U(a)\,|[A\cdot p], s_3'\rangle\,\mathscr{D}^s_{s'_3 s_3}([Ap]^{-1}\,A[p]) \\ &= e^{i(A\cdot p)\cdot a}|[A\cdot p]\,s_3'\rangle\,\mathscr{D}^s_{s'_3 s_3}([Ap]^{-1}A[p]), \end{aligned}$$

which yields the transformation of a state under an inhomogeneous Lorentz transformation. This transformation law is intuitive if one is willing to represent a state by a four vector p (its momentum) and a four vector $n_3(p)$ together with

* $|[p]', s_3\rangle = U([p]')\,|[\overset{0}{p}], s_3\rangle = U([p])\,U([p]^{-1})\,U([p]')\,|[\overset{0}{p}], s_3\rangle$
$= U([p])\,|[\overset{0}{p}], s_3\rangle\,\mathscr{D}^s{}_{s'_3 s_3}([p]^{-1}[p]').$

a number s_3; its spin s_3 along $n_3(p)$. This state seen in a different frame obtained from the latter by a "Lorentz transformation". A, will have momentum $A \cdot p$ and spin s_3 along $A \cdot n_3(p)$ which is a priori different from $n_3(A \cdot p)$ since for each value p the attached frame was arbitrarily chosen.

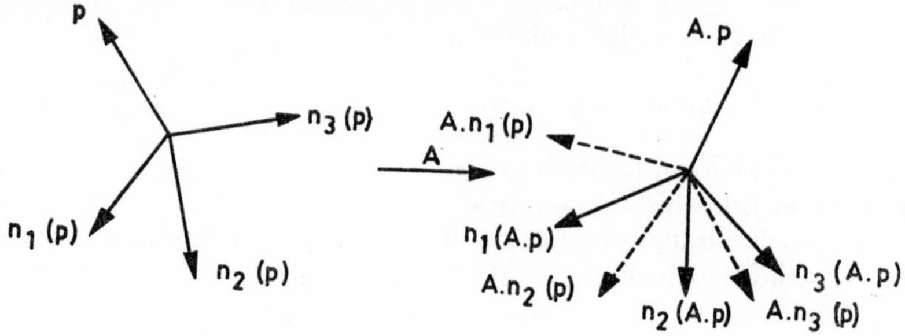

Fig. 1

The Wigner rotation is just the one which expresses

$$|A[p], s_3\rangle = |[A \cdot p], s'_3\rangle \, \mathscr{D}^s_{s'_3 s_3}([A \cdot p]^{-1} A[p])$$

according to (I,b,10).

It now remains to ensure the unitarity of $U(a, A)$ for a scalar product expressing the orthogonality of states with different momenta. We write this scalar product in a Lorentz invariant way*;

$$\langle [p'], s'_3 | [p], s_3 \rangle = 2\omega_p \delta(\mathbf{p} - \mathbf{p}') \, \delta_{s_3 s'_3} \tag{I,b,12}$$

$$\omega_p = \sqrt{\mathbf{p}^2 + m^2}.$$

Any state $|\Psi\rangle$ of representation space can be expanded in the basis $|[p], s_3\rangle$ according to

$$|\Phi\rangle = \int \frac{d^3p}{2\omega_p} \sum_{s_3} \varphi_{s_3}([p]) \, |[p], s_3\rangle \tag{I,b,13}$$

$$\varphi_{s_3}([p]) = \langle [p], s_3 | \Phi \rangle, \tag{I,b,14}$$

the scalar product being

$$\langle \Psi | \Phi \rangle = \int \frac{d^3p}{2\omega_p} \sum_{s_3} \psi^*_{s_3}([p]) \, \varphi_{s_3}([p]). \tag{I,b,15}$$

Writing

$${}^{(a,A)}\varphi_{s_3}([p]) = \langle [p], s_3 \, | U(a, A) | \, \Phi \rangle \tag{I,b,16}$$

* The Lorentz invariance can be checked by

$$\int f(p) \theta_+(\overset{0}{p}) \, \delta(p^2 - m^2) \, d^4p = \int \frac{d^3p}{2\omega_p} f(\omega_p, \mathbf{p})$$

for the wave function of a transformed state, one finds;

$$^{(a,A)}\varphi_{s_3}([p]) = e^{ip\cdot a}\mathscr{D}^s_{s_3s'_3}([p]^{-1}A[A^{-1}p])\,\varphi_{s'_3}([A^{-1}p]). \qquad \text{(I,b,17)}$$

Note that for $|\Phi\rangle$ in the Hilbert space, normalized to 1,

$$\langle\Phi|\Phi\rangle = 1 = \int \frac{d^3p}{2\omega_p}\sum_{s_3}|\varphi_{s_3}([p])|^2.$$

States $|[q],\sigma\rangle$ with wave functions

$$\langle[p], s_3|[q],\sigma\rangle = 2\omega_q\delta(\boldsymbol{q}-\boldsymbol{p})\,\delta_{s_3\sigma}$$

are thus not in the Hilbert space, as is usual for plane wave states.

2) $p^2 = 0 \quad p^0 > 0, \quad p^0 < 0.$

Here we have two cases: either the spin quantum number W^2 is different from zero but in which case, however, the representation does not correspond to an object seen in physics, or, $W^2 = 0$.

Now, if $p^2 = 0$, $W(p)^2 = 0, p\cdot W(p) = 0$ one has necessarily $W(p) = \lambda(p)p$ (this is simply geometry).

Let us again attach space like vectors to p, this time using only two: $n_i(p)$, $i = 1, 2$ $p\cdot n_i(p) = 0$, $n_1(p)\cdot n_2(p) = 0$, $\det(t, n_1(p)\,n_2(p), p) \gtrless 0$ (according as $p^0 \gtrless 0$).

Let $\overset{0}{p} = (\pm 1, 0, 0, 1)$, $n_1(\overset{0}{p}) = (0, 1, 0, 0)$, $n_2(\overset{0}{p}) = (0, 0, 1, 0)$ and let $[p]$ be the Lorentz transformation which takes $\overset{0}{p}$, $n_1(\overset{0}{p})$, $n_2(\overset{0}{p})$ into p, $n_1(p)$, $n_2(p)$.

The Lorentz transformations which leave $\overset{0}{p}$ invariant have the form

$$\begin{pmatrix} e^{\frac{i\Phi}{2}} & Z e^{-i\frac{\Phi}{2}} \\ 0 & e^{\frac{-i\Phi}{2}} \end{pmatrix}^{*}$$

where Φ is the rotation parameter, x, y $(Z = x + iy)$ the translation parameter of a two dimensional euclidian group (a degenerate form of the previous rotation group).

Indeed $W(p)\cdot p = 0$ implies

$$W(p) = \lambda(p)\,p + \sum_i^2 W_i(p)\,n_i(p) \qquad \text{(I,b,18)}$$

* $A\begin{pmatrix}2&0\\0&0\end{pmatrix}A^+ = \begin{pmatrix}2&0\\0&0\end{pmatrix} = \underset{\sim}{\overset{0}{p}} \rightarrow \begin{pmatrix}a&b\\c&d\end{pmatrix}\begin{pmatrix}1&0\\0&0\end{pmatrix}\begin{pmatrix}a^*&c^*\\b^*&d^*\end{pmatrix} = \begin{pmatrix}1&0\\0&0\end{pmatrix}$

$\rightarrow |a|^2 = 1,\ ca^* = ac^* = cc^* = 0,\quad ad - bc = 1$

yields the result.

(Similarly in the $\underset{\sim}{\overset{0}{p}} = (1,000)$ case, $A\begin{pmatrix}1&0\\0&1\end{pmatrix}A^+ = \begin{pmatrix}1&0\\0&1\end{pmatrix} = \underset{\sim}{\overset{0}{p}} \rightarrow AA^+ = 1\ A \in \mathrm{SU}(2)$.

with the commutation rules

$$[W_1(p), W_2(p)] = 0$$

$$[\lambda(p), W_1(p)] = iW_2(p) \tag{I,1,19}$$

$$[\lambda(p), W_2(p)] = -iW_1(p)$$

$$-W^2(p) = W_1^2(p) + W_2^2(p) = 0 \rightarrow W_1(p) = W_2(p) = 0,$$

i.e. one represents the translation of this euclidean group by $\mathbb{1}$ (gauge invariance). The rotation Φ is thus represented by $e^{i\lambda\Phi}$, λ integer of half integer (again because of the two fold covering coming from SL(2, C) versus Lorentz).

We thus have basis vectors $|[p], \lambda\rangle$ defined by

$$\lambda(p)\,|[p], \lambda\rangle = \lambda|[p], \lambda\rangle,$$

$$W_i(p)\,|[p], \lambda\rangle = 0. \tag{I,b,20}$$

λ, integer or half integer, is the helicity of the massless particle. The second equation expresses gauge invariance; if $[p]$ and $[p]'$ are two frames corresponding to the same momentum, one has

$$n_1'(p) = n_1(p)\cos\varphi - n_2(p)\sin\varphi + \alpha_1 p$$

$$n_2'(p) = n_1(p)\sin\varphi + n_2(p)\cos\varphi + \alpha_2 p$$

and

$$|[p]', \lambda\rangle = |[p], \lambda\rangle\, e^{i\lambda\varphi}$$

$$= |[p], \lambda\rangle\, \mathscr{D}^{|\lambda|}_{\lambda\lambda}([p]^{-1}\,[p]'), \tag{I,b,21}$$

which shows that $|[p], \lambda\rangle$ is independent of α_1, α_2 and, as before

$$U(a, A)\,|[p], \lambda\rangle = e^{i(A.p).a}\,|[A\cdot p], \lambda\rangle\, \mathscr{D}^{|\lambda|}_{\lambda\lambda}([A\cdot p]^{-1}\,A[p])^* \tag{I,b,22}$$

with the scalar product

$$\langle[p]', \lambda|[p], \lambda\rangle = 2\omega_p\delta(\mathbf{p} - \mathbf{p}') \tag{I,b,23}$$

and the expansion

$$|\Phi\rangle = \int \frac{d^3p}{2\omega_p}\,\varphi([p], \lambda)\,|[p], \lambda\rangle. \tag{I,b,24}$$

Remarks

i) We shall not describe here the representations corresponding to $p^2 < 0$, which are as unphysical as those corresponding to $p^2 = 0$ $W^2 \neq 0$, although

* At this point we need know that $\mathscr{D}(A)$ is defined for A arbitrary and $\mathscr{D}^{|\lambda|}_{\lambda\lambda}(A) = (a)^{2|\lambda|}$ or $(d)^{2|\lambda|}$ according as $\lambda \gtrless 0$ (see footnote, previous page, and Appendix one.)

they may be of formal use, as well as those for which $p = 0$, except for the trivial one $U(a, \Lambda)\,|0\rangle = |0\rangle$, which is called the vacuum representation.

ii) As far as massless particles are concerned, the presence of a single helicity state is familiar in the neutrino case for which parity is not an operation of the symmetry group; in the photon case however, the presence of both helicities is due to the fact that parity is included in the symmetry group, as we shall see later.

We shall now open a parenthesis which takes us back to every day's theoretical life or text-book treatments, but we insist that from the physical point of view this parenthesis is completely redundant and may be harmlessly skipped.

c) Theoretical Constructions

They are mainly based on the observation that the quantities $\mathscr{D}^s_{\sigma\sigma'}(u)$, usually defined for $u \in \mathrm{SU}(2)$ $(uu^\dagger = 1)$ and fulfilling

$$\sum_{\sigma'} \mathscr{D}^s_{\sigma\sigma'}(u)\, \mathscr{D}^s_{\sigma'\tau}(u') = \mathscr{D}^s_{\sigma\tau}(uu') \quad \text{(group law)}$$

$$\mathscr{D}^s_{\sigma\sigma'}(u) = \mathscr{D}^s_{\sigma'\sigma}(u^T) = \mathscr{D}^{s\,*}_{\sigma'\sigma}(u^\dagger),$$

are still defined for any two by two complex matrix and fulfill the same identities.

We shall occasionally need properties of the matrix $C = i\sigma_2$

$$CAC^{-1}A^T = (\det A)\,\mathbf{1}$$

$C = -C^T = C^*$, $C^2 = -1$; $\mathscr{D}^s(C)$ will still be called C when no confusion may arise.

Spinor Amplitudes

i) $p^2 = m^2 > 0$.

From

$$\varphi_{s_3}([p]') = \mathscr{D}^s_{s_3 s'_3}([p]'^{-1}[p])\, \varphi_{s'_3}([p]),$$

one observes that

$$\varphi_A(p) = \mathscr{D}^s_{As_3}([p]')\, \varphi_{s_3}([p]') = \mathscr{D}^s_{As'_3}([p])\, \varphi_{s'_3}([p]) \qquad \text{(I,c,1)}$$

is independent of $[p]$, i.e. only depends on the four vector p. Similarly, using the unitarity of $[p]'^{-1}[p] = ([p]'^{-1}[p])^{\dagger -1} = [p]'^{\dagger}[p]^{\dagger -1}$

$$\hat{\varphi}_A(p) = \mathscr{D}^s_{As_3}([p]'^{\dagger -1})\, \varphi_{s_3}([p]') = \mathscr{D}^s_{As'_3}([p]^{\dagger -1})\, \varphi_{s'_3}([p]) \qquad \text{(I,c,2)}$$

enjoys the same property (note that $[p]^{\dagger -1} \neq [p]$ since $[p]$ is not unitary).

These are called the spinor amplitudes associated with state $|\Phi\rangle$.

They transform simply according to

$$^{(a,A)}\varphi(p) = \mathscr{D}^s(A)\,\varphi(A^{-1}\cdot p)\,e^{ip\cdot a} \tag{I,c,3}$$

$$^{(a,A)}\hat{\varphi}(p) = \mathscr{D}^s(A^{\dagger -1})\,\hat{\varphi}(A^{-1}\cdot p)\,e^{ip\cdot a} \tag{I,c,4}$$

$$\langle \Psi, \Phi\rangle = \int \frac{d^3p}{2\omega_p} \sum_A \hat{\psi}^*_A(p)\,\varphi_A(p) = \int \frac{d^3p}{2\omega_p} \sum_A \psi^*_A(p)\,\hat{\varphi}_A(p) \tag{I,c,5}$$

$$\langle \Psi, \Phi\rangle = \int \frac{d^3p}{2\omega_p} \sum_{A,A'} \psi^*_A(p)\,\mathscr{D}^s_{AA'}\left(\frac{\tilde{p}}{m}\right)\varphi_{A'}(p)$$

$$= \int \frac{d^3p}{2\omega_p} \sum_{A,A'} \hat{\psi}^*_A(p)\,\mathscr{D}^s_{AA'}\left(\frac{\underset{\sim}{p}}{m}\right)\hat{\varphi}_A(p) \tag{I,c,5}$$

where we have used

$$[p]\,[p]^\dagger = [p]\,\mathbf{1}[p]^\dagger = [p]\frac{\overset{0}{\underset{\sim}{p}}}{m}[p]^\dagger = \frac{\underset{\sim}{p}}{m} = \frac{p^0 + \boldsymbol{p}\boldsymbol{\sigma}}{m}$$

$$[p]^{\dagger -1}\,[p]^{-1} = [p]^{\dagger -1}\,\mathbf{1}[p]^{-1} = [[p]^{\dagger -1}]\frac{\overset{\tilde{0}}{p}}{m}[p]^{-1} = \frac{\tilde{p}}{m} = \frac{p^0 - \boldsymbol{p}\cdot\boldsymbol{\sigma}}{m} \tag{I,c,6}$$

and the "Dirac equations":

$$\varphi(p) = \mathscr{D}^s\left(\frac{\underset{\sim}{p}}{m}\right)\hat{\varphi}(p) \quad \hat{\varphi}(p) = \mathscr{D}^s\left(\frac{\tilde{p}}{m}\right)\varphi(p) \tag{I,c,7}$$

ii) $p^2 = 0$.

From

$$\varphi([p]', \lambda) = \mathscr{D}^{|\lambda|}_{\lambda\lambda}([p]'^{-1}\,[p])\,\varphi([p], \lambda),$$

we have*

$$\hat{\varphi}^-_A(p) = \mathscr{D}^{|\lambda|}_{A\lambda}([p]'^{\dagger -1})\,\varphi([p]', \lambda) = \mathscr{D}^{|\lambda|}_{A\lambda}([p]^{\dagger -1})\,\varphi([p], \lambda),$$

for $\lambda < 0$, where we used

$$\mathscr{D}^{|\lambda|}_{A\lambda}([p]'^{\dagger -1})\,\mathscr{D}^{|\lambda|}_{\lambda\lambda}([p]'^{-1}\,[p]) = \mathscr{D}^{|\lambda|}_{A\lambda}\left([p]'^{\dagger -1}\,\frac{1-\sigma_3}{2}\,[p]'^{-1}\,[p]\right)$$

$$= \mathscr{D}^{|\lambda|}_{A\lambda}\left(\frac{\tilde{p}}{2}[p]\right) = \mathscr{D}^{|\lambda|}_{A\lambda}([p]^{\dagger -1}),$$

and

$$\varphi^+_A(p) = \mathscr{D}^{|\lambda|}_{A\lambda}([p]')\,\varphi([p]', \lambda) = \mathscr{D}^{|\lambda|}_{A\lambda}([p])\,\varphi([p], \lambda)$$

* We need the following results: $\mathscr{D}^j_{mm'}\left(\frac{1+\sigma_3}{2}\right) = \delta_{j,m}\,\delta_{j,m'}$ and

$$\mathscr{D}^j_{mm'}\left(\frac{1-\sigma_3}{2}\right) = \delta_{j,-m}\,\delta_{j,-m'}$$

for $\lambda > 0$, where we used similarly

$$[p]' \frac{1+\sigma_3}{2} [p]'^{\dagger} = [p] \frac{1+\sigma_3}{2} [p]^{\dagger} = \frac{\underset{\approx}{p}}{2}.$$

Remarks

In this case, spinor amplitudes have but one independent component, i.e. they are subject to constraint equations (see Ref. 4).

The uncapped and capped ones still transform according to $\mathscr{D}(A)$, and $\mathscr{D}(A^{\dagger-1})$ respectively.

Also, note that $\varphi^-(p)$ and $\hat{\varphi}^+(p)$ do not exist (Ref. 3 is in error in this respect).

d) Examples

1) $m^2 > 0, \quad s = 0, \quad p^0 > 0.$

One has wave functions $\varphi(p)$ defined on the positive hyperboloid, with the scalar product

$$\langle \Phi, \Psi \rangle = \int \frac{d^3 p}{2\omega_p} \varphi^*(p)\, \psi(p).$$

Given $\varphi(p)$ sufficiently regular, one can construct the distribution $\varphi(p)\, \theta(p^0)\, \delta(p^2 - m^2) = \tilde{\Phi}(p)$ whose Fourier transform $\Phi(x) = \int e^{ipx} \tilde{\Phi}(p)\, d^4 p$ is a positive frequency solution of the Klein–Gordon equation.

The scalar product then reads

$$\langle \Phi, \Psi \rangle = \frac{1}{i(2\pi)^3} \int_{x^0 = t} \Phi^*(x)\, \overleftrightarrow{\partial^0} \Psi(x)\, d^3 x,$$

and the transformation law is

$$^{(a,A)}\varphi(x) = \varphi(\Lambda x + a).$$

One could argue similarly for the negative energy solutions; both of them span representation spaces with characteristics $m^2 > 0$, $s = 0$, $p^0 \gtrless 0$.

One can set a one to one correspondence between negative energy solutions and positive energy ones by

$$\Psi^-(x)^* = \Phi^+(x).$$

Then from the point of view of relativity, solutions of the Klein–Gordon equation can be interpreted as describing two kinds of particles with the same mass and zero spin.

2) $m^2 > 0, \quad s = \frac{1}{2}, \quad p^0 > 0$

We write the Dirac equations

$$\varphi(p) = \frac{p}{m}\hat{\varphi}(p), \quad \hat{\varphi}(p) = \frac{\tilde{p}}{m}\varphi(p),$$

and let

$$\Phi(p) = \frac{1}{\sqrt{2}}\begin{pmatrix}\varphi(p)\\ \hat{\varphi}(p)\end{pmatrix}.$$

Then one has $(\not{p} - m)\,\Phi(p) = 0$

$$\not{p} = \gamma^0 p^0 - \boldsymbol{\gamma}\cdot\boldsymbol{p},$$

$$\gamma^0 = \begin{pmatrix}0 & \mathbf{1}\\ \mathbf{1} & 0\end{pmatrix} \quad \gamma^i = \begin{pmatrix}0 & -\sigma_i\\ \sigma_i & 0\end{pmatrix},$$

with the transformation law

$${}^{\{a,A\}}\Phi(p) = e^{ip\cdot a} S(A)\,\Phi(A^{-1}\cdot p)$$

where

$$S(A) = \begin{pmatrix}\mathscr{D}^{\frac{1}{2}}(A) & 0\\ 0 & \mathscr{D}^{\frac{1}{2}}(A^{-1\dagger})\end{pmatrix}$$

if

$$A = e^{i\frac{\sigma}{2}n + \frac{\sigma}{2}v} \quad S(\Lambda) = e^{\frac{i}{2}\varepsilon_{ijk}\frac{\sigma^{ij}}{2}n^k + \frac{\sigma_{0i}}{2}v^i}$$

$$= e^{\frac{i}{2}\omega_{\mu\nu}\frac{\sigma^{\mu\nu}}{2}}$$

where

$$\omega_{ij} = \varepsilon_{ijk}n^k \quad \omega_{0i} = v_i$$

$$\sigma^{\mu\nu} = \frac{1}{2i}\{\gamma^\mu, \gamma^\nu\}.$$

The scalar product is given by

$$\langle\Phi, \Psi\rangle = \int \Phi^*(p)\,\gamma^0\Psi(p)\,\frac{d^3p}{2\omega_p} = \int \bar{\Phi}(p)\,\Psi(p)\,\frac{d^3p}{2\omega_p},$$

where $\bar{\Phi}(p) = \Phi^*(p)\,\gamma^0$. This scalar product stays positive as long as $p^0 > 0$.
We also write

$$\langle\Phi, \Psi\rangle = \int \bar{\Phi}(p)\,\frac{m\gamma^0}{\omega_p}\,\Psi(p)\,\frac{d^3p}{2\omega_p},$$

which is sometimes used and is positive for both $p^0 \gtrless 0$.

Further Dirac matrices are defined as

$$\beta = \gamma^0, \quad \alpha^i = \gamma^0\gamma^i = \begin{pmatrix} -\sigma_i & 0 \\ 0 & \sigma_i \end{pmatrix} = -\alpha_i$$

$$\gamma^5 = \gamma^0\gamma^1\gamma^2\gamma^3 = i\begin{pmatrix} \mathbf{1} & \\ & -\mathbf{1} \end{pmatrix}.$$

The spin operator is

$$W_\mu = -\frac{1}{2}\varepsilon_{\mu\nu\varrho\sigma}\frac{\sigma^{\nu\varrho}}{2}\frac{p^\sigma}{m};$$

it allows one to define a basis for solutions of the Dirac equation through

$$W(p)\cdot n_3(p)\, U([p], s_3) = s_3 U([p], s_3)$$

$$W(p)\cdot(n_1 \pm in_2)(p)\, U([p], s_3) = \sqrt{\frac{1}{2}\left(\frac{1}{2}+1\right) - s_3(s_3 \pm 1)}\; u([p], s_3 \pm 1)$$

$$W\cdot n_i(p) = -\gamma^5 \not{n}_i(p),$$

which yields

$$U\cdot([p], s_3) = \frac{1}{\sqrt{2}}\begin{pmatrix} \mathscr{D}^{\frac{1}{2}}_{\cdot s_3}([p]) \\ \mathscr{D}^{\frac{1}{2}}_{\cdot s_3}([p]^{\dagger -1}) \end{pmatrix}$$

with the normalization $\bar{u}([p], s_3')\, u([p], s_3) = \delta_{s_3 s_3'}$.

The solutions of the Dirac equations for $p^0 > 0$ can thus be expanded according to

$$\Phi(p) = \sum_{s_3} f([p], s_3)\, u([p], s_3),$$

and one finds the f's transform according to (I,b,17) and their scalar product is again given by (I,b,15).

For $p^0 < 0$ similar results hold and lead to the complex conjugate representation.

3) $m^2 > 0,\ s = 1,\ p^0 > 0.$

$\varphi_A(p)$ and $\hat{\varphi}_A(p)$ can be considered as complex vectors defined on the upper sheet $p^0 > 0$ of the hyperboloid $p^2 = m^2$. We may express them in cartesian form $\boldsymbol{\gamma}(p)$, using

$$\frac{1}{\sqrt{2}}(\boldsymbol{\sigma}\cdot\boldsymbol{\varphi})_{mm'} = \begin{pmatrix} \frac{1}{2} & \frac{1}{2} & 1 \\ m & -m' & A \end{pmatrix}(-1)^{1/2-m'}\varphi_A$$

then, (I,c,3) and (I,c,4) can be written as*:

$$(\boldsymbol{\sigma}\cdot {}^{\{a,A\}}\boldsymbol{\varphi}) = A(\boldsymbol{\sigma}\cdot\boldsymbol{\varphi})\,A^{-1},$$

the Dirac equation:

$$\begin{cases} \varphi(p) = \mathscr{D}^1\left(\dfrac{\underset{\sim}{p}}{m}\right)\hat{\varphi}(p) \\[2ex] \hat{\varphi}(p) = \mathscr{D}^1\left(\dfrac{\tilde{p}}{m}\right)\varphi(p), \end{cases}$$

* This transformations law can be compared with the transformation under rotation group of $\boldsymbol{\sigma u}$, $\boldsymbol{u}$ real three-vector, $\boldsymbol{\sigma} R\boldsymbol{u} = \mathscr{U}(R)\boldsymbol{\sigma u}\mathscr{U}^+(R)$, and allows us to consider A as a complex rotation (element of the complex orthogonal group).

then reads:

$$\begin{cases} \dfrac{p^0 - p\sigma}{m}(\sigma \cdot \varphi) = (\sigma \cdot \hat{\varphi})\dfrac{p^0 - p\sigma}{m} \\[2ex] (\sigma \cdot \varphi)\dfrac{p^0 + p\sigma}{m} = \dfrac{p^0 + p\sigma}{m}(\sigma \cdot \hat{\varphi}) = \left(\sigma\hat{\varphi}^* \dfrac{p^0 + p\sigma}{m}\right)^\dagger. \end{cases}$$

If we introduce antisymmetric tensors $F_{\mu\nu}$ and $\mathscr{F}_{\mu\nu}$ by: $F^{0i} = E^i$, $F^{ij} = \varepsilon^{ijk}H^k$, where $\boldsymbol{E}$ and $\boldsymbol{H}$ are real vectors defined by $\varphi = \boldsymbol{E} + i\boldsymbol{H}$ (similarly $\hat{\varphi} = \mathscr{H} - i\mathscr{E}$ defines $\mathscr{F}$). The Dirac equation then reads:

$$p_\mu\left(F^{\mu\nu} + \frac{i}{2}\varepsilon^{\mu\nu\varrho\sigma}F_{\varrho\sigma}\right) = p_\mu\left(\mathscr{F}^{\mu\nu} - \frac{i}{2}\varepsilon^{\mu\nu\varrho\sigma}\mathscr{F}_{\varrho\sigma}\right)$$

i.e.

$$p_\mu G^{\mu\nu} = 0, \quad \text{with} \quad G^{\mu\nu} = F^{\mu\nu} - \mathscr{F}^{\mu\nu} + \frac{i}{2}\varepsilon^{\mu\nu\varrho\sigma}(F_{\varrho\sigma} + \mathscr{F}_{\varrho\sigma})$$

an arbitrary complex antisymmetric tensor.

One can thus find A_μ such that

$$G^{\mu\nu} = \tfrac{1}{2}\varepsilon^{\mu\nu\varrho\sigma}p_\varrho A_\sigma,$$

and the scalar product can be rewritten

$$\langle \mathscr{G}, G\rangle = \int \mathrm{d}\Omega\,(p)\,\overline{\mathscr{G}}^{\mu\nu}(p)\,G_{\mu\nu}(p)\,\frac{1}{m^2}$$

$$= -\int \mathrm{d}\Omega(p)\,\overline{\mathscr{A}}^{\mu}(p)\left(g_{\mu\nu} - \frac{p_\mu p_\nu}{m^2}\right)A^\nu(p),$$

so that one can choose $p_\mu A^\mu = 0$ with the scalar product

$$\langle \mathscr{A}, A\rangle = -\int \mathrm{d}\Omega(p)\,\overline{\mathscr{A}}_\mu(p)\,A^\mu(p).$$

This is the usual representation of spin 1 particles by vector fields transverse to the momentum. One can recover the Wigner amplitude by writing

$$A(p) = \sum_1^3 f_i([p])\,n_i([p])$$

$$p \cdot n_i([p]) = 0 \quad n_i([p]) \cdot n_j([p]) = -\delta_{ij},$$

and from the transformation law

$${}^{\{a,\Lambda\}}A_\mu(p) = \mathrm{e}^{ip\cdot a}\Lambda_\mu{}^\nu A_\nu(\Lambda^{-1}p),$$

recover the Wigner transformation for $f_i([p])$.

4) $m^2 > 0$, $s = 3/2$

One may transform the spinor amplitudes $\varphi_A(p)\,(\hat{\varphi}_A(p))$, $-3/2, \leqq A \leqq +3/2$, into totally symmetric spinor amplitudes $\varphi_{\alpha_1\alpha_2\alpha_3}$ $(\alpha_1, \alpha_2, \alpha_3 = \pm\frac{1}{2})$, the relevant $\mathscr{D}_{AA'}$, matrices being replaced by $\mathscr{D}_{\alpha_1\alpha_1'}\mathscr{D}_{\alpha_2\alpha_2'}\mathscr{D}_{\alpha_3\alpha_3'}$.

From the symmetry condition,

$$\begin{pmatrix} \frac{1}{2} & \frac{1}{2} & 0 \\ \alpha_1 & \alpha_2 & 0 \end{pmatrix} \varphi_{\alpha_1\alpha_2\alpha_3} = 0.$$

Let

$$\begin{pmatrix} \frac{1}{2} & \frac{1}{2} & 1 \\ \alpha_1 & \alpha_2 & M \end{pmatrix} \varphi_{\alpha_1\alpha_2\alpha_3} = \varphi_{M\alpha_3},$$

whereby the $\mathscr{D}$'s turn into $\mathscr{D}_{MM'}\mathscr{D}_{\alpha_3\alpha_3'}$. Indices M and α_3 can be capped separately by application of the relevant $\mathscr{D}\left(\frac{p^0 + p\sigma}{m}\right)$. If $\boldsymbol{S}$ are the spin 1 operators, the spin 3/2 condition

$$\begin{pmatrix} \frac{1}{2} & 1 & \frac{1}{2} \\ \alpha_1 & M & \beta \end{pmatrix} \varphi_{M\alpha_1} = 0,$$

reads

$$\frac{1 - \boldsymbol{S}\cdot\boldsymbol{\sigma}}{3}\,\varphi = 0 \quad \text{i.e.} \quad \boldsymbol{\varphi} = i\boldsymbol{\sigma} \times \boldsymbol{\varphi}$$

where M is turned into a vector index, α being considered as a spin $\frac{1}{2}$ index.

The simultaneous consideration of $\varphi_{\hat{M}\alpha}\varphi_{M\hat{\alpha}}\varphi_{\hat{M}\hat{\alpha}}$ and the corresponding Dirac equations allows us to define $\Psi_{\mu\alpha}$ where μ is a four vector index, and α a Dirac spinor index, the constraints being:

$$p \cdot \Psi = 0, \quad (\not{p} - m)\,\Psi = 0,$$

and

$$\begin{aligned} \Psi_\mu &= [\tfrac{1}{2}(S_{\lambda\varkappa}\sigma^{\lambda\varkappa})\,\Psi]_\mu \\ &= i\sigma_\mu{}^\nu\Psi_\nu, \end{aligned}$$

hence

$$\gamma^\mu\Psi_\mu = 0.$$

Note that if Ψ_μ fulfills both the Dirac equation and the transversality condition, $\Phi = \gamma^5\gamma^\mu\Psi_\mu$ is just its spin $\frac{1}{2}$ component.

5) $m^2 > 0$, $s = 2$.

One can similarly switch from the Wigner description to one in terms of a symmetric transverse, traceless tensor: $G_{\mu\nu}(p)$:

$$\begin{aligned} G_{\mu\nu}(p) &= G_{\nu\mu}(p) \\ p^\mu G_{\mu\nu}(p) &= 0 \\ G^\mu_\mu(p) &= 0, \end{aligned}$$

with the scalar product $(F, G) = \int \mathrm{d}\Omega\,(p)\,\bar{F}_{\mu\nu}(p)\,G^{\mu\nu}(p)$.

One can expand $G_{\mu\nu}(p) = \sum_A f_A([p])\, Y^A_{\mu\nu}([p])$ where the $Y^A_{\mu\nu}([p])$'s are constructed from $n_i(p)$ as $Y^A(x)$ is constructed in terms of x_i, $i = 1, 2, 3$ ($Y^A(x)$; solid harmonics of order 2] e.g.

$$Y^0_{\mu\nu}([p]) = n^3_\mu n^3_\nu - \frac{1}{3}\left(g_{\mu\nu} - \frac{p_\mu p_\nu}{m^2}\right).$$

The transformation law

$$^{\{a\cdot A\}}G_{\mu\nu}(p) = e^{iA\cdot p\cdot a} A_\mu{}^{\mu'} A_\nu{}^{\nu'} G_{\mu'\nu'}(A^{-1}\cdot p),$$

induces on the f_A's the Wigner rotation.

6) $m = 0$.

The previous constructions have quite decent limits which one may construct starting from the Wigner form; the selection of one helicity value requires however the use of an extra projector:

i) $\lambda = \pm\frac{1}{2}$.

$$p\Psi = 0$$

$$W_\mu \Psi = \pm\frac{1}{2} p_\mu \Psi = \frac{1}{2}\varepsilon_{\mu\nu\varrho\sigma}\frac{\sigma^{\nu\varrho}}{2} p^\sigma \Psi$$

$$= \frac{1}{2}\gamma_5 \sigma_{\mu\nu} p^\nu \Psi$$

$$= \frac{1}{2}\gamma_5 \frac{\gamma_\mu\gamma_\nu - g_{\mu\nu}}{i} p^\nu \Psi,$$

by use of the Dirac equation, we get

$$W_\mu \Psi = \frac{i\gamma_5}{2} p_\mu \Psi = \pm\frac{1}{2} p_\mu \Psi,$$

hence the projector condition $(1 \pm i\gamma_5)\Psi = 0$.

ii) $\lambda = \pm 1$

Let $F_{\mu\nu}$ be the antisymmetric tensor which describes a spin 1 particle, with $\partial^\mu F^*_{\mu\nu} = 0$ where $F^*_{\mu\nu} = \frac{1}{2}\varepsilon_{\mu\nu\varrho\sigma}F^{\varrho\sigma}$; the projector condition corresponding to helicity ± 1 is then found to be "self or antiself duality":

$$F_{\mu\nu} \pm iF^*_{\mu\nu} = 0.$$

In terms of the vector description, besides the transversality condition, one finds that $A_\mu(p)$ is defined modulo p, i.e. $A_\mu(p)$, $A_\mu(p) + \lambda(p)\, p_\mu$ represent the same state (as indeed the scalar product is insensitive to a gauge transformation). If $n_1(p)$, $n_2(p)$ are such that

$$\det(n_1(p), n_2(p), p, n) > 0$$

where n is some positive time axis, then helicity states $\lambda = \pm 1$ are described by $\frac{n_1 \pm i n_2}{\sqrt{2}}(p)$ (which isotropic vectors are indeed independent of the choice of n_1, n_2).

e) Discrete Operations[2,5]

If the symmetry group is enlarged so that includes space and time inversions:

$$x \to \underline{x} = \Pi x \qquad \Pi = \begin{pmatrix} 1 & & & 0 \\ & -1 & & \\ & & -1 & \\ 0 & & & -1 \end{pmatrix} = G \tag{I,e,1}$$

where G is the matrix of the metric tensor:

$$GLG^{-1} = L^{-1T}$$

$$x \to -\underline{x} = Tx \qquad T = \begin{pmatrix} -1 & & & 0 \\ & 1 & & \\ & & 1 & \\ 0 & & & 1 \end{pmatrix} \tag{I,e,2}$$

$$x \to -x = \Pi T x \qquad \Pi T = \begin{pmatrix} -1 & & & 0 \\ & -1 & & \\ & & -1 & \\ 0 & & & -1 \end{pmatrix}, \tag{I,e,3}$$

one has, in order to construct representations up to a phase of the enlarged group, to specify the actions of these discrete operations on $\overline{\mathscr{P}}_+^\uparrow$.

One has:

$$\begin{aligned} \Pi(a, A)\, \Pi^{-1} &= (\underline{a}, A^{\dagger -1}) \\ T(a, A)\, T^{-1} &= (-\underline{a}, A^{\dagger -1}) \\ \Pi T(a, A)\, (\Pi T)^{-1} &= (-a, A). \end{aligned} \tag{I,e,4}$$

These relationships do not specify the extended "covering group" completely, but hold, whatever the solution, and are sufficient for the construction of representations.

Proof.

Every Lorentz transformation Λ can be written $\Lambda = LR$ where L is a pure Lorentz transformation and R is a rotation. Correspondingly $A(\Lambda) = H\mathscr{U}$ where H is hermitian and $\mathscr{U}$ is unitary.

$$\Lambda^{-1T} = L^{-1T} R^{-1T} = L^{-1} R$$

$$A(\Lambda^{-1T}) = H^{-1} U = A^{\dagger -1}.$$

(There cannot be any arbitrary sign factor in front, because such a sign $\varepsilon_\pi(A)$ must fulfill the group law $\varepsilon_\pi(A)\,\varepsilon_\pi(A') = \varepsilon_\pi(AA')$ and has thus to be unity).

We now look for representations up to a phase of the "extended covering group". Upon restriction to the restricted group, they will yield representations of the latter. There will thus be in representation space, bases of the type $|[p], s_3, \eta\rangle$, $|[p], \lambda, \eta\rangle$ where η are degeneracy labels. We shall furthermore restrict ourselves to representations where $U(\Pi)$ is unitary and $U(\Pi T)$, $U(T)$, antiunitary, in order to deal with representations for which the spectrum of the momentum operator contains only time like or light like values.

Indeed, from the group law;

$$U(\Pi)\,e^{iP\cdot a}U^{-1}(\Pi) = e^{iP\cdot \underline{a}}.$$

Hence

$$U(\Pi)\,e^{iP\cdot a}U^{-1}(\Pi)\,|p\rangle = e^{ip\cdot \underline{a}}|p\rangle$$

$$e^{iP\cdot a}U^{-1}(\Pi)\,|p\rangle = e^{\varepsilon ip\cdot \underline{a}}U^{-1}(\Pi)\,|p\rangle$$

$\varepsilon = +1$ if $U(\Pi)$ is unitary,

$\varepsilon = -1$ if $U(\Pi)$ is antiunitary.

Thus $U^{-1}(\Pi)\,|p\rangle$ has momentum $\varepsilon \underline{p}$ $(p \cdot \underline{a} = \underline{p} \cdot a)$

$$\varepsilon \underline{p} \in \overline{V}^+ \quad \text{if} \quad p \in \overline{V}^+ \rightarrow \varepsilon = +1.$$

A similar argument implies that $U(T)$, $U(\Pi T)$ are antiunitary.

Since $\Pi^2 = T^2 = (\Pi T)^2 =$ identity, there exist phases ω such that:

$$U(\Pi)^2 = \omega_\Pi$$

$$U(\Pi T)^2 = \omega_{\Pi T}$$

$$U(T)^2 = \omega_T.$$

From a previous argument (Ch. 0, § a) Remark II) $\omega_{\Pi T} = \pm 1$, $\omega_T = \pm 1$.

i) Representation of space inversions.

We shall only deal with massive particles leaving the case of massless ones as an exercise.

$$\begin{aligned} U(\Pi)\,U(a, A)\,U^{-1}(\Pi)\,|[p], s_3, \eta\rangle &= U(\underline{a}, A^{\dagger -1})\,|[p], s_3, \eta\rangle \\ &= e^{i\underline{a}\Lambda^{-1T}p}\,|[\Lambda^{-1T}p], s'_3, \eta\rangle\, \mathscr{D}^s_{s'_3 s_3}([\Lambda^{-1T}p]^{-1}\, A^{\dagger -1}\,[p]) \\ &= e^{ia\Lambda\underline{p}}|[\Lambda^{-1T}p], s'_3, \eta\rangle\, \mathscr{D}^s_{s'_3 t'_3}([\Lambda^{-1T}p]^{\dagger}\,[\Lambda\underline{p}]) \\ &\quad \times \mathscr{D}^s_{t'_3 t_3}([\Lambda\underline{p}]^{-1}\,A[\underline{p}])\, \mathscr{D}^s_{t_3 s_3}([\underline{p}]^{-1}\,[p]^{\dagger -1}), \end{aligned}$$

where we have used for the Wigner rotation $\mathscr{D}(R) = \mathscr{D}(R^{\dagger -1})$.

Hence

$$U(a, A)\, U^{-1}(\Pi)\, |[p], s_3, \eta\rangle\, \mathscr{D}_{s_3 t_3}([p]^\dagger [\underline{p}])$$

$$= U^{-1}(\Pi)\, e^{ia\underline{\Lambda p}}\, |[\underline{\Lambda p}], s_3', \eta\rangle\, \mathscr{D}^s_{s'_3 t'_3}([\underline{\Lambda p}]^\dagger [\Lambda p])\, \mathscr{D}^s_{t'_3 t_3}([\underline{\Lambda p}]^{-1} \underline{A}[p]),$$

which means that

$$U^{-1}(\Pi)\, |[p], s_3, \eta\rangle\, \mathscr{D}^s_{s_3 t_3}([p]^\dagger [p])$$

transforms as a vector

$$|\underline{p}, s_3\rangle$$

(note that $[p]^\dagger\, [\underline{p}]$ is a Wigner rotation:

$$[p]^\dagger\, [\underline{p}]\, [\underline{p}]^\dagger\, [p] = [p]^\dagger\, \frac{p^0 - \boldsymbol{p\sigma}}{m}\, [p] = [p]^\dagger\, [p]^{\dagger -1}\, [p]^{-1}\, [p] = 1\Big).$$

Thus, one may write

$$U^{-1}(\Pi)\, |[p], s_3, \eta\rangle = |[\underline{p}], s_3', \eta'\rangle\, \mathscr{D}^s_{s'_3 s_3}([\underline{p}]^{-1}\, [p]^{\dagger -1})\, \tilde{\Pi}_{\eta'\eta},$$

where $\tilde{\Pi}_{\eta'\eta}$ is a numerical matrix in the degeneracy parameters:

$$\tilde{\Pi}\tilde{\Pi}^\dagger = 1 \qquad \tilde{\Pi}^2 = \omega_{\Pi}^{-1}.$$

If one wants an irreducible representation, $\tilde{\Pi}$ fulfilling the above requirements has to be one dimensional: $\tilde{\Pi}_{\eta'\eta} = \eta_{\Pi}^{-1}$.

The final result is:

$$U(\Pi)\, |[p], s_3\rangle = \eta_\Pi\, |[\underline{p}], s_3'\rangle\, \mathscr{D}^s_{s'_3 s_3}([\underline{p}]^{-1}\, [p]^{\dagger -1})$$

$$= \eta_\Pi\, |[\underline{p}], s_3'\rangle\, \mathscr{D}^s_{s'_3 s_3}([\underline{p}]^\dagger\, [p]) \qquad \text{(I,e,5)}$$

Exercise.

Repeat the argument for massless particles. Show, as expected, that couples of opposite helicities occur.

Remarks.

If $[p]$ is taken to be the pure Lorentz transformation transforming the time axis (1, 0, 0, 0) to p:

$$[p] = \frac{m + p^0 + \boldsymbol{p\sigma}}{\sqrt{2m(m + p^0)}}$$

$[\underline{p}^\dagger] = [\underline{p}] = [p]^{-1}$, hence no Wigner rotation appears in the above formula.

ii) Representation of Space-time inversion.

$$U(\Pi T)\,U(a, A)\,U^{-1}(\Pi T)\,|[p], s_3, \eta\rangle$$
$$= U(-a, A)\,|[p], s_3, \eta\rangle$$
$$= \mathrm{e}^{-ia\cdot\Lambda p}\,|[\Lambda p], s_3', \eta\rangle\, \mathscr{D}^s_{s'_3 s_3}([\Lambda p]^{-1} A[p]).$$

Hence [watch the effect of antiunitarity of $U(\Pi T)$]

$$U(a, A)\,U^{-1}(\Pi T)\,|[p], s_3, \eta\rangle = \mathrm{e}^{ia.\Lambda p}\,U(\Pi T)^{-1}\,|[\Lambda p], s_3', \eta\rangle\, \mathscr{D}^{s*}_{s'_3 s_3}([\Lambda p]^{-1} A[p])$$
$$= \mathrm{e}^{ia\cdot\Lambda p}\,U(\Pi T)^{-1}\,|[\Lambda p], s_3', \eta\rangle\, \mathscr{D}^s_{s'_3 t'_3}(C)\, \mathscr{D}^s_{t'_3 t_3}([\Lambda p]^{-1} A[p])\, \mathscr{D}^s_{t_3 s_3}(C^{-1})$$

(where we used $CAC^{-1} = A^{-1T}$, $C = i\sigma_2$, and unitarity of the Wigner rotation).

One deduces

$$U(\Pi T)^{-1}\,|[p], s_3, \eta\rangle = |[p], s_3', \eta'\rangle\, \mathscr{D}^s_{s'_3 s_3}(C)\, \widetilde{\Pi T}_{\eta'\eta}.$$

Now we have

$$U(\Pi T)^2 = \omega_{\Pi T} = \pm 1.$$

Hence

$$\omega_{\Pi T} = (-)^{2s}\, \widetilde{\Pi T}\widetilde{\Pi T}^*,$$

(where we used $CC^* = -1$).

If $\omega_{\Pi T}(-)^{2s} = +1$ $\widetilde{\Pi T}$, which is unitary and symmetric, can thus be diagonalized by a real orthogonal matrix, the irreducible version of which is one dimensional. In this case, one has:

$$\omega_{\Pi T} = (-)^{2s} = U(\Pi T)^2 \tag{I,e,6}$$
$$U(\Pi T)\,|[p], s_3\rangle = \eta_{\Pi T}\,|[p], s_3'\rangle\, \mathscr{D}^s_{s'_3 s_3}(C),$$

that is, space-time inversion reverses spin.

We shall not deal here with the so-called abnormal type which arises when $\omega_{\Pi T}(-)^{2s} = -1$; each particle in this case has to have an internal degree of freedom which takes up two values in the case of an irreducible representation.

Exercise.

Same problem in the case of massless particles. One helicity is enough.

iii) Representation of Time inversions.

A similar calculation yields for the "normal type":

$$\omega_T = (-)^{2s} = U(T)^2 \tag{I,e,7}$$
$$U(T)\,|[p], s_3\rangle = \eta_T\,|[\underline{p}], s_3'\rangle\, \mathscr{D}^s_{s'_3 s_3}([\underline{p}]^\dagger\,[p]\,C).$$

(If $[p]$ is the Wigner boost $[p] = \dfrac{m + p^0 + \boldsymbol{p\sigma}}{\sqrt{2m(m + p^0)}}$, time inversion reverses both momentum and spin!).

Remark.

Note the phase relationship

$$U(\Pi)\,U(\Pi T) = \eta_\Pi \eta_{\Pi T} \eta_T^* U(T).$$

iv) Phase normalization.

In the course of the preceding discussion, we were left with three phase factors: η_Π, $\eta_{\Pi T}$, η_T, for each particle. Furthermore, in each superselection sector we can alter the phase of $U(\Pi)$ so that $U^2(\Pi) = 1$, thus for each elementary system in this sector one must have $\eta_\Pi^2 = 1$ i.e. $\eta_\Pi = \pm 1$. $U(\Pi)$ can be eventually normalized so that for a given elementary system η_Π is $+1$; the η_Π's of other systems then have some fixed values ± 1 which are their intrinsic parities with respect to the elementary system chosen for reference. Next recall $U(\Pi) \cdot U(\Pi T) = \eta_\Pi \eta_{\Pi T} \eta_T^* U(T)$. It is clear from Wigner's theorem that, within a superselection sector $\eta_\Pi \eta_{\Pi T} \eta_T^* = \omega$ a given phase. By redefining e.g. $U'(\Pi T) = 1/\omega\; U(\Pi T)$ one has $U(\Pi) U(T) = U(\Pi T)$ and by redifining states $|[p], s_3\rangle' = \sqrt{\eta_T}\,|[p], s_3\rangle$, (I,e,5) is preserved whereas (I,e,7) looses its η_T and (I,e,6) becomes $U(\Pi T)\,|\,[p], s_3\rangle = \eta_\Pi |[p], s_3'\rangle\, \mathscr{D}_{s_3' s_3}(C)$. In other words, without any further assumption, one can choose $\eta_T = 1$, $\eta_{\Pi T} = \eta_\Pi$ in formulae (I,e,5), (I,e,6), (I,e,7).

f) Representation of assemblies of identical particles: Fock space

i) Once the description of one particle states is accurately known, the construction of many identical particle states fulfilling either Bose or Fermi statistics proceeds in a well known way* by applying to a vacuum state $|0\rangle$ products of creation operators labelled according to one particle states: here $a^\dagger([p], s_3)$, which fulfill commutation or anticommutation relations with their adjoints $a([p'], s_3)$ according to the normalization condition:

$$[a([p], s_3), a^\dagger([p'], s_3')]_\pm = 2\omega_p \delta(\boldsymbol{p} - \boldsymbol{p}')\, \delta_{s_3 s'_3}. \tag{I,f,1}$$

The vacuum state is further characterized by the property that it is annihilated by all annihilation operators:

$$a([p], s_3)\,|0\rangle = 0. \tag{I,f,2}$$

In this formulation, one has:

$$|[p], s_3\rangle = a^\dagger([p], s_3)\,|0\rangle. \tag{I,f,3}$$

The covariance property

$$|[p], s_3\rangle = |[p]', s_3'\rangle\, \mathscr{D}^s_{s'_3 s_3}([p]'^{-1}\,[p]),$$

implies that $a^\dagger[(p], s_3)$ is defined for all $[p]$'s with the transformation law

$$a^\dagger([p], s_3) = a^\dagger([p]', s_3')\, \mathscr{D}^s_{s'_3 s_3}([p]'^{-1}\,[p]). \tag{I,f,4}$$

* That this procedure is necessary in demonstrated in ref. 28.

If one wants to describe various kinds of non identical particles, one can show[6] that they can be constructed from a unique vacuum by application of creation and annihilation operators $a_i^{(\dagger)}([p])$ which can at will be chosen to commute or anticommute for different i's, without any physical implication.

ii) Additive operators.

We recall a useful construction: let $|i\rangle$ be a basis of a Hilbert space of one particle states, and $a_i^\dagger$ the corresponding creation operators in Fock space. To every operator $\mathcal{Q}$ in this Hilbert space, with matrix elements $\langle j|\mathcal{Q}|i\rangle$, one can associate a field operator:

$$Q = \sum_{i,j} a_j^\dagger \langle j|\mathcal{Q}|\, i\rangle\, a_i . \tag{I,f,5}$$

Then, as a consequence of commutation relations or anticommutation

$$[a_i, a_j^\dagger]_\pm = \langle i|j\rangle . \tag{I,f,6}$$

Commutation relations

$$[\mathcal{P}, \mathcal{Q}]_- = \mathcal{R} \quad \text{yield} \quad [P, Q]_- = R . \tag{I,f,7}$$

Exercise.

Given the momentum P, and angular momentum operators $J_{\mu\nu}$ for one particle states, construct the corresponding field operators.

Remark.

The momentum of a state with many particles of definite momenta is the sum of the individual momenta.

This is not true for the "spin" w_μ, as we shall see soon: the spin of a system of particles with definite spins includes an orbital part.

iii) Fields.

This paragraph is a digression from pure phenomenology. Assumptions particular to local field theories yield however sufficiently strong and useful results to be worth mentioning.

α) One type of particles.

Let $|0\rangle$ be the vacuum state and $a^\dagger([p], s_3)$ be the creation operators.

One may construct free fields:

$$\begin{aligned}\varphi_A(x) = \frac{1}{(2\pi)^{3/2}} \int \frac{d^3p}{2\omega_p} [\mathcal{D}^s_{As_3}([p])\, a([p], s_3)\, e^{-ip\cdot x} \\ + \mathcal{D}^s_{As_3}([p]\, C^{-1})\, a^\dagger([p], s_3)\, e^{ip\cdot x}]\end{aligned} \tag{I,f,8}$$

$$\begin{aligned}\tilde{\varphi}_A(x) &= \mathcal{D}^s_{AA'}(C)\, \varphi^\dagger_{A'}(x) \\ &= \frac{1}{(2\pi)^{3/2}} \int \frac{d^3p}{2\omega_p} [\mathcal{D}^s_{As_3}([p]^{\dagger -1})\, a([p], s_3)\, e^{-ip\cdot x} \\ &\quad + \mathcal{D}^s_{As_3}([p]^{\dagger -1}\, C)\, a^\dagger([p], s_3)\, e^{ip\cdot x}],\end{aligned} \tag{I,f,9}$$

which transform respectively under Poincaré transformation according to

$$U(a, A)\, \varphi_A(x)\, U^{-1}(a, A) = \mathscr{D}^s_{AA'}(A^{-1})\, \varphi_{A'}(A \cdot x + a), \qquad \text{(I,f,10)}$$

$$U(a, A)\, \tilde{\varphi}_A(x)\, U^{-1}(a, A) = \mathscr{D}^s_{AA'}(A^{\dagger})\, \tilde{\varphi}_{A'}(A \cdot x + a), \qquad \text{(I,f,11)}$$

where $U(a, A)$ is the representation in Fock space deduced from the one particle representation:

$$U(a, A)\, a^{\dagger}([p], s_3)\, U^{-1}(a, A) = a^{\dagger}([A \cdot p], s_3')\, \mathscr{D}^s_{s'_3 s_3}([A \cdot p]^{-1} A[p])\, \mathrm{e}^{iAp.a},$$

$$U(a, A)\, |0\rangle = |0\rangle .$$

The connection between spin and statistics:

If one assumes local commutativity in the form

$$[\overset{(\sim)}{\varphi}(x), \overset{(\sim)}{\varphi}(x')]_{\pm} = 0 \quad \text{for} \quad (x - x')^2 < 0$$

then one deduces that the + or − signs (Fermi or Bose statistics) have to be used according as s is half-integer or integer.

The same conclusion holds for the more complicated fields to be introduced presently. These fields are free fields [they fulfill in particular the Klein–Gordon equation $(\Box_x + m^2)\, \varphi_A(x) = 0$], and the Dirac equation

$$\varphi_A(x) = \mathscr{D}^s_{AA'}\left(\frac{\partial_0 + \partial\sigma}{-im}\right) \tilde{\varphi}_{A'}(x),$$

$$\tilde{\varphi}_A(x) = \mathscr{D}^s_{AA'}\left(\frac{\partial_0 - \partial\sigma}{-im}\right) \varphi_{A'}(x),$$

and can serve as asymptotic fields in a theory of the LSZ type.

β) Neutral multiplets.

Assume that besides Lorentz invariance, one has an internal compact symmetry group G, so that particles are labelled as basis vectors of a finite dimensional representation $\mathscr{U}$ of G:

we have creation operators $a^{\dagger}([p], s_3, \mu)$ behaving according to

$$U(g)\, a^{\dagger}([p], s_3, \mu)\, U^{-1}(g) = a^{\dagger}([p], s_3, \mu')\, \mathscr{U}_{\mu'\mu}(g) \qquad \text{(I,f,12)}$$

for $g \in G$, where $U(g)$ is the Fock space version of $\mathscr{U}$.

If the complex conjugate representation $\mathscr{U}^*$ is equivalent to $\mathscr{U}$, that is, there exists S such that

$$\mathscr{U}(g) = S\mathscr{U}^*(g)\, S^{-1}; \qquad \text{(I,f,13)}$$

one can construct fields behaving locally under G:

$$U(g)\, \varphi_{A,\mu}(x)\, U^{-1}(g) = \varphi_{A,\mu'}(x)\, \mathscr{U}_{\mu'\mu}(g),$$

$$\varphi_{A,\mu}(x) = \frac{1}{(2\pi)^{3/2}} \int \frac{\mathrm{d}^3 p}{2\omega_p} [\mathscr{D}_{As_3}([p])\, a([p], s_3, \mu)\, \mathrm{e}^{-ip\cdot x} + \mathscr{D}_{As_3}([p]C^{-1})\, a^{\dagger}([p], s_3, \mu')\, S_{\mu'\mu}\, \mathrm{e}^{\dagger ip\cdot x}] \qquad \text{(I,f,14)}$$

[this is in particular so for $G = \mathrm{SU(2)}$ and for some representations of SU(3)].

Exercise.

Construct $\tilde{\varphi}_{A,\mu}(x)$

γ) Charged multiplets.

If $\mathscr{U}$ and $\mathscr{U}^*$ are not equivalent, it is impossible to construct local fields in terms of creation operators transforming under G according to $\mathscr{U}(G)$. If however one introduces particles transforming according to $\mathscr{U}^*(G)$:

$$U(g)\, b^\dagger([p], s_3, \mu)\, U^{-1}(g) = b^\dagger([p], s_3, \mu')\, \mathscr{U}^*_{\mu'\mu}(g) \qquad \text{(I,f,15)}$$

and identically with the $a^\dagger$'s under (a, A), one can construct:

$$\varphi_{A,\mu}(x) = \frac{1}{(2\pi)^{3/2}} \int \frac{d^3p}{2\omega_p} [\mathscr{D}_{As_3}([p])\, a([p], s_3, \mu)\, e^{-ip\cdot x} + \mathscr{D}_{As_3}([p]\, C^{-1})\, b^\dagger([p], s_3, \mu)\, e^{ip\cdot x}] \qquad \text{(I,f,16)}$$

which transform locally according to

$$U(g)\, \varphi_{A,\mu}(x)\, U^{-1}(g) = \varphi_{A,\mu'}(x)\, \mathscr{U}^*_{\mu'\mu}(g). \qquad \text{(I.f.17)}$$

In order that local commutativity might hold, it is necessary to assume that the a's and b's commute or anticommute according as the spin is integer or half integer—which, from a previous remark has no physical consequence.

$a^\dagger(p, s_3, \mu)$ and $b^\dagger(p, s_3, \mu)$ are said to create charge conjugate particles.

The operation which interchanges them is charge conjugation:

$$\mathscr{C} a^\dagger([p], s_3, \mu)\, \mathscr{C}^{-1} = b^\dagger([p], s_3, \mu),$$

$$\mathscr{C} a([p], s_3, \mu)\, \mathscr{C}^{-1} = b([p], s_3, \mu).$$

$$\mathscr{C}\mathscr{C}^+ = \mathscr{C}^+\mathscr{C} = 1.$$

The charge conjugate field $\varphi^c_{A,\mu}(x)$ is obtained from $\varphi_{A,\mu}$ by this interchange.

Example.

$G = U(1)$:

$$U(\alpha)\, a^\dagger([p], s_3)\, U^{-1}(\alpha) = e^{i\alpha m}\, a^\dagger([p], s_3),$$

where $e^{im\alpha}$ is a one dimensional representation labelled by the integer m (usually $m = 1$!).

Exercise.

Construct $\tilde{\varphi}$, $\tilde{\varphi}^c$

φ and $\tilde{\varphi}^c$ transform according to $\mathscr{U}^*(G)$
$\tilde{\varphi}$ and φ^c transform according to $\mathscr{U}(G)$
φ and φ^c transform according to $\mathscr{D}(A^{-1})$
$\tilde{\varphi}$ and $\tilde{\varphi}^c$ transform according to $\mathscr{D}(A^\dagger)$.

The action of space and time inversions is easily deduced from the study of one particle states:

$$U(\Pi)\,\varphi_A(x)\,U^{-1}(\Pi) = \eta_\Pi^* \tilde{\varphi}_A(\underline{x}),$$
$$U(\Pi)\,\tilde{\varphi}_A(x)\,U^{-1}(\Pi) = \eta_\Pi^* \varphi_A(\underline{x}),$$
$$U(T)\,\varphi_A(x)\,U^{-1}(T) = \eta_T^* \varphi_{A'}(-x^0, \mathbf{x})\,\mathscr{D}_{A'A}(C), \tag{I,f,18}$$
$$U(T)\,\tilde{\varphi}_A(x)\,U^{-1}(T) = \eta_T^* \tilde{\varphi}_{A'}(-x^0, \mathbf{x})\,\mathscr{D}_{A'A}(C),$$
$$U(\Pi T)\,\varphi_A(x)\,U^{-1}(\Pi T) = \eta_{\Pi T}^* \tilde{\varphi}_{A'}(-x)\,\mathscr{D}_{A'A}(C),$$
$$U(\Pi T)\,\tilde{\varphi}_A(x)\,U^{-1}(\Pi T) = \eta_{\Pi T}^* \varphi_{A'}(-x)\,\mathscr{D}_{A'A}(C),$$

and identical equations for the charge conjugate fields.

Remark.

In deriving these transformation laws, do not forget that $U(T)$ and $U(\Pi T)$ are antiunitary!

Connection between intrinsic parities of particles and antiparticles.

The foregoing equations hold if and only if

$$\eta_\Pi \eta_{\overline{\Pi}} = (-)^{2s},$$
$$\eta_T^* = \eta_{\overline{T}},$$
$$\eta_{\Pi T}^* = \eta_{\overline{\Pi T}}(-)^{2s}$$

where the $\eta_{\overline{T}}$ are the phase factors pertaining to antiparticles. This is a mere consequence of locality. According to the phase conventions made in (e,iv,) only the first condition is relevant: it says that the relative intrinsic parity of a fermion and an antifermion is odd whereas the relative intrinsic parity of a boson and an antiboson is even—taking into account the connection between spin and statistics!—

g) Application to S-matrix theory—Density matrices, projectors, transition probabilities

i) Irreducible systems.

Statistical mixtures of one particle states are, as is well known, represented by density matrices which are positive definite self adjoint operators with trace 1. In the present case, they are represented by kernels of the type $\varrho_{\sigma\sigma'}([p],[p'])$ [or $\varrho_{AA'}(p,p')$ in the spinor representation], with

$$\varrho_{\sigma\sigma'}([p],[p']) = \varrho_{\sigma'\sigma}^*([p'],[p])$$

and

$$\int \frac{d^3p}{2\omega_p} \sum_\sigma \varrho_{\sigma\sigma}([p_s,[p]) = 1\,.$$

They behave under Lorentz transformations just as $|[p],\sigma\rangle\langle[p'],\sigma'|$ would do.

Projectors on sets of states are on the other hand similarly represented by self adjoint positive definite, bounded operators represented by kernels of the type $P([p], \sigma, [p'], \sigma')$ which fulfill the reproducing property $P^2 = P$:

$$\int \frac{d^3 p''}{2\omega''} \sum_{\sigma''} P([p], \sigma, [p''], \sigma'') \, P([p''], \sigma'', [p]', \sigma') = P([p], \sigma, [p'], \sigma').$$

ii) Many particle systems.
These are the same as in i), except that $[p], \sigma$ represents a collection

$$\{[p_1], \sigma_1, \cdots, [p_n], \sigma_n\}.$$

iii) Transition probabilities.
Let T be the transition operator defined in terms of the S-matrix by $S = 1 - iT$. The density matrix of the final state produced from initial state ϱ_i is

$$\varrho_f = S\varrho_i S^\dagger.$$

The average value of any observable $\mathscr{F}$ in this state is:

$$\langle \mathscr{F} \rangle = tr\varrho_f \mathscr{F}.$$

In particular, if $\mathscr{F}$ is an hermitian mixture of projectors on a set of states, which annihilates the subspace in which ϱ_i is non zero ($\mathscr{F}\varrho_i = \varrho_i \mathscr{F} = 0$), one obtains in this way the transition probability from the state ϱ_i to the states $\mathscr{F}$:

$$W_{\mathscr{F}, \varrho_i} = trS\varrho_i S^\dagger \mathscr{F} = trT\varrho_i T^\dagger \mathscr{F}.$$

The density matrix restricted to states selected by $\mathscr{F}$ is

$$\varrho_{f/\mathscr{F}} = \frac{\mathscr{F}\varrho_f \mathscr{F}}{tr\mathscr{F}\varrho_f \mathscr{F}} = \frac{\mathscr{F}S\varrho_i S^\dagger \mathscr{F}}{tr\mathscr{F}S\varrho_i S^\dagger \mathscr{F}} = \frac{\mathscr{F}T\varrho_i T^\dagger \mathscr{F}}{tr\mathscr{F}T\varrho_i T^\dagger \mathscr{F}},$$

the last equality holding when $\mathscr{F}\varrho_i = \varrho_i \mathscr{F} = 0$.

II. ANALYSIS OF TWO PARTICLE STATES

The space of two particle states, a basis of which can be labelled as $|[p_1]\sigma_1, [p_2]\sigma_2\rangle$, where σ_1, σ_2 are spin projections (or helicities, in the massless case) on an axis determined by the $[p_i]$'s is acted upon by a representation of the Poincaré group (or rather its covering) which is the tensor product of the two one particle representations of masses $m_{1,2}$ ($p_i^2 = m_i^2$) and spins $s_{1,2}$ ($-s_i \leqq \sigma_i \leqq +s_i$):

$$U(a, A) \, |[p_1]\,\sigma_1, [p_2]\,\sigma_2\rangle = e^{ia \cdot A \cdot (p_1 + p_2)} \, |[A \cdot p_1]\,\sigma_1'; [A \cdot p_2]\,\sigma_2'\rangle$$

$$\times \, \mathscr{D}^{s_1}_{\sigma'_1 \sigma_1}([Ap_1]^{-1} A[p_1]) \, \mathscr{D}^{s_2}_{\sigma'_2 \sigma_2}([Ap_2]^{-1} A[p_2]) \qquad \text{(II.1)}$$

(if one particle is massless and has helicity σ, replace $\mathscr{D}_{\sigma'\sigma}$ by $\mathscr{D}_{\sigma\sigma}$, without any summation).

Such a representation is not irreducible. It is the purpose of the present chapter to reduce it, that is to define in its Hilbert space basis "vectors" $|[P], \mu; J\ \eta\rangle$ which behave irreducibly:

$$U(a, A)\,|[P], \mu; J, \eta\rangle = e^{iAP\cdot a}\,|[A\cdot P], \mu'; J, \eta\rangle\, \mathscr{D}^{J}_{\mu'\mu}([A\cdot P]^{-1}A[P]) \qquad \text{(II.2)}$$

where:

P^2 is the mass of this state, J its total spin, η a Poincaré invariant set of degeneracy parameters (we shall find indeed that the $[P^2, J]$ component of the overall representation occurs several times), and to compute the Clebsch–Gordan coefficients:

$$\langle [p_1], \sigma_1; [p_2], \sigma_2\,|[P], \mu; J, \eta\rangle$$

which occur in the expression of the new basis vectors in terms of the former ones:

$$|[P], \mu; J, \eta\rangle = \int \frac{d^3p_1}{2\omega_1}\frac{d^3p_2}{2\omega_2}\sum_{\sigma_1,\sigma_2} |[p_1], \sigma_1; [p_2], \sigma_2\rangle \times \langle [p_1], \sigma_1; [p_2], \sigma_2\,|[P_\lrcorner, \mu; J, \eta\rangle. \qquad \text{(II.3)}$$

The new basis will be so defined that the Clebsch–Gordan coefficients are matrix elements of a unitary matrix:

$$|[p_1], \sigma_1; [p_2], \sigma_2\rangle = \int dP^2 \int \frac{d^3P}{2\omega_{P^2}(\boldsymbol{P})}\sum_{J,\eta,\mu} |[P], \mu; J, \eta\rangle \times \langle [P], \mu; J, \eta\,|[p_1], \sigma_1; [p_2], \sigma_2\rangle. \qquad \text{(II.4)}$$

The initial basis already makes the translation operator $U(a)$ diagonal, i.e. the state $|[p_1]\,\sigma_1[p_2]\sigma_2\rangle$ has total momentum $P = p_1 + p_2$.

One sees thus that the total mass P^2 may range from $(m_1 + m_2)^2$ up to ∞. P obviously lies in the future light cone.

For fixed P, we may parametrize p_1, p_2 such that $p_1 + p_2 = P$ through the "relative barycentric momentum" four vector:

$$q_{1,2} = -q_{2,1} = \frac{1}{2}\left(p_1 - p_2 - \frac{(m_1^2 - m_2^2)}{P^2}P\right) = p_1 - \frac{p_1\cdot P}{P^2}P = -\left(p_2 - \frac{p_2\cdot P}{P^2}P\right) \qquad \text{(II.5)}$$

which is so constructed that it lies in the 2-plane defined by p_1 and p_2 and is orthogonal to P:

$$q_{1,2}\cdot P = 0. \qquad \text{(II.6)}$$

Note for future reference that

$$q_{1,2}^2 = -\frac{\lambda(m_1^2, m_2^2, P^2)}{4P^2}$$

a standard function of P^2, where

$$\lambda(z_1, z_2, z_3) = z_1^2 + z_2^2 + z_3^2 - 2(z_1z_2 + z_1z_3 + z_2z_3).$$

P being fixed, $q_{1,2}$ thus depends on two polar angles, on the sphere

$$q_{1,2} \cdot P = 0, \quad q_{1,2}^2 = -\frac{\lambda(m_1^2 m_2^2 P^2)}{4P^2}.$$

The inverse formulae are:

$$p_1 = \frac{P^2 + m_1^2 - m_2^2}{2P^2} P + q_{1,2}$$

$$p_2 = \frac{P^2 - m_1^2 + m_2^2}{2P^2} P - q_{1,2}$$

It is intuitive that the spin (total intrinsic angular momentum) of the compound system is made up of the angular momentum carried by the orbital motion, associated with $q_{1,2}$ and the individual spins of the two particles.

Before one can quietly add these in the rest frame of the compound system (barycentric frame: P, time axis), one has to be able to compare the "spins" of particles 1 and 2 which are not at rest in this frame. The matter will then turn out to be reduced to a composition of angular momenta which will be exact.

a) *l–s* coupling

Let us indeed reexpress the transformation law of $|[p_1], \sigma_1, [p_2], \sigma_2\rangle$ in terms of center of mass variables:

$$[p_i]_P = [p_i, P]\,[P] \quad (m_i \neq 0) \tag{II.a.0}$$

where $[P]$ defines a frame attached to P, and $[p_i, P]$ is some Lorentz transformation taking the unit vector of P into the unit vector of p_i. (The case when p_i is the momentum of a massless particle will be dealt with later, as its interpretation in terms of addition of angular momenta is slightly more delicate.)

Let us now define the symbolic vector

$$\boldsymbol{q}_{1,2} = \{q_i = -q_{1,2} \cdot n_i(P)\} \tag{II.a.1}$$

where

$$n_i(P) = [P]\, n_i(\overset{0}{P})$$

and $\overset{0}{P} = (1, 0, 0, 0)$, some laboratory time axis. We shall denote by $\hat{\boldsymbol{q}}$ the corresponding unit vector $\hat{\boldsymbol{q}} = \dfrac{\boldsymbol{q}}{\sqrt{\boldsymbol{q}^2}}$.

If $q_{1,2} \to A \cdot q_{1,2}$ (which results from $p_1 \to A \cdot p_1$, $p_2 \to A \cdot p_2$),

$$\boldsymbol{q}_{1,2} \to \{-(A \cdot q_{1,2}) \cdot n_i(AP)\} = \{-q_{1,2}[P] \cdot [[P]^{-1} A^{-1}[AP]]\, n_i(\overset{0}{P})\}$$

$$= \{q_j R_i^{-1j}(A, P)\},$$

i.e.

$$A\boldsymbol{q} = R(A, P)\, \boldsymbol{q},$$

where $R(A, P)$ is the Wigner rotation $[AP]^{-1}\ A[P]$.

Let us thus define:

$$|[P], \boldsymbol{q}, \sigma_1\sigma_2\rangle = |[p_1]_P, \sigma_1, [p_2]_P, \sigma_2\rangle \tag{II.a.2}$$

(a simple change of variables).

$$U(a, A)\, |[P], \boldsymbol{q}, \sigma_1, \sigma_2\rangle = e^{i(A.P).a} |[AP], R(A, P)\, \boldsymbol{q}, \sigma_1'\sigma_2'\rangle$$
$$\mathscr{D}^{s_1}_{\sigma'_1\sigma_1}([AP]^{-1}\, [Ap_1, AP]^{-1}\, A[p_1, P]\, [P])\, \mathscr{D}^{s_2}_{\sigma'_2\sigma_2}$$
$$\times\ ([AP]^{-1}\, [Ap_2, AP]^{-1}\, A[p_2, P]\, [P]).$$

We see that if we choose $[p_i, P] = [p_i \leftarrow P]_\varphi$, the product of the pure Lorentz transformation in the 2-plane (p_i, P), which takes $\hat{P}$, to $\hat{p}_i$, followed (or preceded!) by a rotation of angle φ independent of p_i, P, around this two plane, the spin rotations indicated above reduce to Wigner rotations $R(A, P)$ because:

$$A[p_1 \leftarrow P]_\varphi = [Ap_1, AP]_\varphi\, A.$$

We next decompose the $\boldsymbol{q}$ dependence into spherical waves:

$$|[P]\, \boldsymbol{q}, \sigma_1, \sigma_2\rangle = \sum_{l,m} \sqrt{\frac{2l+1}{4\pi}}\, \mathscr{D}^l_{m,0}(\Omega_q)\, |[P]\, l, m, \sigma_1, \sigma_2\rangle \tag{II,a,3}$$

i.e.

$$|[P]\, l, m, \sigma_1, \sigma_2\rangle = \int \mathrm{d}\Omega_q \mathscr{D}^{l*}_{m,0}(\Omega_q) \sqrt{\frac{2l+1}{4\pi}}\, |[P], \boldsymbol{q}, \sigma_1, \sigma_2\rangle.$$

Here:

$$\Omega_q = [P]^{-1}\, \Omega(\hat{q}_{1,2} \leftarrow n_3(P))_\varphi\, [P]$$

where $\Omega(\hat{q}_{1,2} \leftarrow n_3(P))_\varphi$ is the pure "rotation" preserving P and transforming $n_3(P)$ into $\hat{q}_{1,2}$, followed by a rotation φ around the two plane P, $q_{1,2}$ to which $\mathscr{D}^l_{m,0}$ is of course insensitive.

We shall occasionally note

$$\sqrt{\frac{2l+1}{4\pi}}\, \mathscr{D}^{l*}_{m,0}(\Omega_q) = Y^l_m(\boldsymbol{q}).$$

The transformation law then becomes:

$$U(a, A)\, |[P]\, l, m, \sigma_1, \sigma_2\rangle = e^{i(A.P).a} |[AP]\, l, m', \sigma_1', \sigma_2'\rangle$$
$$\times\ \mathscr{D}^l_{m'm}([AP]^{-1}\, A[P])\, \mathscr{D}^{s_1}_{\sigma'_1\sigma_1}([AP]^{-1}\, A[P_,)$$
$$\times\ \mathscr{D}^{s_2}_{\sigma'_2\sigma_2}([AP]^{-1}\, A[P])$$

where we have used

$$\mathscr{D}^{l*}_{m,0}([P]^{-1}\Omega(\hat{q}_{1,2} \leftarrow n_3(P))\,[P])$$

$$= \mathscr{D}^{l*}_{m,0}(\{[P]^{-1}\,A^{-1}[AP]\}\cdot\{[AP]^{-1}\,\Omega(\widehat{Aq} \leftarrow n_3(AP))\,[AP]\}$$

$$\times\,\{[AP]^{-1}\,\Omega^{-1}(\widehat{Aq} \leftarrow n_3(AP))\,A\Omega(\hat{q} \leftarrow n_3(P))\,[P]\})$$

and the fact that the last expression between curly brackets is a rotation around the third axis and can thus be dropped, since we are computing $\mathscr{D}^{l}_{m,0}$.

So, by usual addition of angular momenta:

$$|[P], \mu, j;\, l, s\rangle = |[P]\, l, m\sigma_1\sigma_2\rangle \begin{pmatrix} s_1 & s_2 & s \\ \sigma_1 & \sigma_2 & \sigma \end{pmatrix}\begin{pmatrix} l & s & j \\ m & \sigma & \mu \end{pmatrix}$$

transforms irreducibly according to

$$U(a, A)\,|[P], \mu, j;\, l, s\rangle = e^{i(AP)\cdot a}|[AP]\,\mu';\, j, l, s\rangle$$

$$\times\,\mathscr{D}^{j}_{\mu'\mu}([AP]^{-1}\,A[P]). \qquad \text{(II,a,4)}$$

One can further see that if one requires these states to behave canonically under space reflections the rotation angles φ which might accompany $[p_i \leftarrow P]$ must be taken equal to zero or π. The intrinsic parity of such a state is then:

$$\eta^{(1)}_{\pi}\eta^{(2)}_{\pi}(-)^{l}.$$

We collect now the final formula, including normalizations:

$$\langle[p_1], \sigma_1;\, [p_2], \sigma_2|[P], \mu, j, l, s, P^2\rangle$$

$$= \frac{2\sqrt{P^2}\,\sqrt{2}}{\lambda^{1/4}(P^2, m_1^2, m_2^2)}\,\delta^4(P - p_1 - p_2) \sum_{\substack{\sigma'_1,\sigma'_2 \\ \sigma=\sigma'_1+\sigma'_2 \\ m=\mu-\sigma}} \mathscr{D}^{s_1}_{\sigma_1\sigma'_1}([p_1]^{-1}\,[p_1 \leftarrow P]\,[P])$$

$$\times\,\mathscr{D}^{s_2}_{\sigma_2\sigma'_2}([p_2]^{-1}\,[p_2 \rightarrow P]\,[P]) \begin{pmatrix} s_1 & s_2 & s \\ \sigma'_1 & \sigma'_2 & \sigma \end{pmatrix}\begin{pmatrix} l & s & j \\ m & \sigma & \mu \end{pmatrix} Y^{l}_{m}(\hat{q}). \qquad \text{(II,a,5)}$$

b) Multipole coupling

We have remarked that, when one, or both particles are massless, it becomes impossible to transform them to rest in the barycentric frame. Also, we know that a massless particle has only one "spin" (helicity) state. In order to reduce the situation to one where the rotation group in the barycentric frame is involved, it is convenient to choose a frame attached to p_1 such that $n_i(p_1)\cdot P = 0$, which, by analogy with the photon case, we shall call a radiation gauge:

$$[p_1]_r = \Omega(\hat{q}_{1,2} \leftarrow n_3(P))\,[\omega_1\hat{P} + |q_{1,2}|\,n_3(P) \leftarrow \hat{P} + n_3(P)]\,[P]$$
$$= [p_1 \leftarrow \hat{P} + \hat{q}_{12}]\,\Omega(\hat{q}_{12} \leftarrow n_3(P))\,[P], \tag{II,b,1}$$

where ω is the massless particle barycentric energy, and $[\omega\hat{P} + |q_{1,2}|\,n_3(P) \leftarrow \hat{P} + n_3(P)]$ (resp.: $[p_1 \rightarrow \hat{P} + \hat{q}_{12}]$) is the pure Lorentz transformation, acting in the 2-plane $(\hat{P}, n_3(P))$ (resp.: $(\hat{P}, q_{12})$], and transforming $\hat{P} + n_3(P)$ (resp.: $\hat{P} + \hat{q}_{12}$) (lightlike) into $\omega\hat{P} + |q_{1,2}|n_3(P)$ (resp.: p_1), and $\Omega[\hat{q}_{1,2} \leftarrow n_3(P)]$ is again a rotation taking $n_3(P)$ to $\hat{q}_{1,2}$, in the 2-plane $(n_3(P), q_{1,2})$.

In the case of a massive particle, the frame which plays a similar role is the helicity frame:

$$[p_1]_h = [p_1 \leftarrow P]\,\Omega(\hat{q}_{1,2} \leftarrow n_3(P))\,[P] \tag{II,b,2}$$

whose third axis:

$$n_3(p_1) = [p_1 \leftarrow P]\,\hat{q}_{1,2} = \frac{P - \dfrac{p_1 \cdot P}{m_1^2}\,p_1}{\sqrt{-P^2 + \dfrac{(p_1 \cdot P)^2}{m_1^2}}} \tag{II,b,3}$$

is the so called helicity axis in the barycentric frame (orthogonal to p_1, of course, in the two plane (P, p_1)].

In the following, $[p_1]$ will be taken as $[p_1]_r$ or $[p_1]_h$ according as $m_1^2 = 0$, $m_1^2 > 0$, and in the case of a massless particle no spin index summation will be allowed.

Let us then compute $\mathscr{D}^{s_1}_{\sigma_1'\sigma_1}([Ap_1]^{-1}\,A[p_1])$.

From the commutability of A across pure Lorentz transformations or rotations, the argument reduces, in both cases to

$$R(A, p_1) = \varphi = [AP]^{-1}\,\Omega(\widehat{Aq}_{1,2} \leftarrow n_3(AP))^{-1}\,A\Omega(\hat{q}_{1,2} \rightarrow n_3(P))\,[P]$$
$$= \Omega_{Aq}^{-1}\,R(A, P)\,\Omega_q$$

which, not only is a rotation, but leaves $n_3(\overset{0}{P})$ invariant, so that $\mathscr{D}^{s_1}_{\sigma'_1\sigma_1}(\varphi)$ is diagonal; hence the formal identity between calculations with a massless particle in the radiation gauge and a massive particle described in terms of helicity.

Assuming that $[p_2] = [p_2 \leftarrow P][P]$, we thus get:

$$U(a, A)\,|[P], \boldsymbol{q}, \lambda_1\sigma_2\rangle = e^{i(A\cdot P)a}|[AP], R(A \cdot P)\,\boldsymbol{q}, \lambda_1\sigma_2'\rangle$$
$$\mathscr{D}^{(s_1)}_{\lambda_1\lambda_1}([AP]^{-1}\,\Omega(\widehat{Aq}_{1,2} \leftarrow n_3(AP))\,A\Omega(q_{1,2} \leftarrow n_3(P))\,[P])$$
$$\times\, \mathscr{D}^{(s_2)}_{\sigma'_2\sigma_2}([AP^{-1}\,A[P]).$$

We now remark that the functions:

$$\sqrt{\frac{2k+1}{4\pi}}\,\mathscr{D}^k_{m\lambda_1}([P]^{-1}\Omega(\hat{q}_{1,2} \leftarrow n_3(P))\,[P]) = \sqrt{\frac{2k+1}{4\pi}}\,\mathscr{D}^k_{m\lambda_1}(\Omega_q)$$

form for fixed λ_1 and varying k and m, $k - \lambda_1$ being an integer, just as good a complete set of functions of $\boldsymbol{q}$ on the unit sphere, as did $\mathscr{D}^l_{mo}(\Omega_q)$. We may thus write:

$$|[P], \boldsymbol{q}, \lambda_1, \sigma_2\rangle = \sum_{km} \sqrt{\frac{2k+1}{4\pi}}\, |[P], k, m, \lambda_1, \sigma_2\rangle\, \mathscr{D}^k_{m\lambda_1}(\Omega_q),$$

i.e.:

$$|[P], k, m, \lambda_1, \sigma_2\rangle = \int \mathrm{d}\Omega_q \sqrt{\frac{2k+1}{4\pi}}\, |[P], \boldsymbol{q}, \lambda_1, \sigma_2\rangle\, \mathscr{D}^k_{\lambda_1 m}(\Omega_q^{-1}).$$

The transformation law then becomes:

$$U(a, A)\, |[P], k, m, \lambda_1, \sigma_2\rangle = \mathrm{e}^{i(AP)\cdot a} |[AP], k, m', \lambda_1, \sigma'_2\rangle$$
$$\mathscr{D}^k_{m'm}([AP]^{-1} A[P])\, \mathscr{D}^{s_2}_{\sigma'_2\sigma_2}([AP]^{-1} A[P]),$$

where we have used:

$$\mathscr{D}^{s_1}_{\lambda_1\lambda_1}(\Omega_{Aq}^{-1} R(A, P)\, \Omega_q)\, \mathscr{D}^k_{\lambda_1 m}(\Omega_q^{-1}) = \mathscr{D}^k_{\lambda_1 m}(\Omega_{Aq}^{-1} R(A, P)),$$

which is true because $\Omega_{Aq}^{-1} R(A, P)\, \Omega_q$ is a rotation about the third axis.

One achieves the reduction with the construction of

$$|[P], \mu; j, k, \lambda_1\rangle = |[P]\, k, m, \lambda_1\sigma_2\rangle \begin{pmatrix} k & s_2 & | & j \\ m & \sigma_2 & | & \mu \end{pmatrix} \qquad \text{(II,b,5)}$$

which transforms according to

$$U(a, A)\, |[P], \mu; j, k, \lambda_1\rangle = \mathrm{e}^{i(AP)\cdot a} |[AP], \mu'; j, k, \lambda_1\rangle\, \mathscr{D}^j_{\mu'\mu}([AP]^{-1} A[P]). \qquad \text{(II,b,6)}$$

Such a state will be called a multipole state, with total angular momentum of particle 1 equal to k, helicity of particle 1 equal to λ_1.

The corresponding Clebsch–Gordan coefficient is

$$\langle [p_1]\, \sigma_1 [p_2\ \ \sigma_2 | [P], \mu; j, k, \lambda_1, P^2\rangle = \frac{2\sqrt{P^2}\sqrt{2}}{\lambda^{1/4}(P^2, m_1^2, m_2^2)} \sqrt{\frac{2k+1}{4\pi}}\, \delta^4(P - p_1 - p_2)$$

$$\times \sum_{\substack{\sigma'_2 \\ m = \mu - \sigma'_2}} \mathscr{D}^{s_1}_{\sigma_1\lambda_1}([p_1]^{-1} [p_1]_{rh})\, \mathscr{D}^{s_2}_{\sigma_2\sigma'_2}([p_2]^{-1} [p_2 \leftarrow P]\, [P])$$

$$\begin{pmatrix} k & s_2 & | & j \\ m & \sigma'_2 & | & \mu \end{pmatrix} \mathscr{D}^{k*}_{m\lambda_1}([P]^{-1}\, \Omega(q_{1,2} \leftarrow n_3(P))\, [P]), \qquad \text{(II,b,7)}$$

where h means helicity ($m_1^2 \neq 0$), r means radiation ($m_1^2 = 0$), in which case $\sigma_1 = \lambda_1$.

Note the useful formula, for k integer

$$\sqrt{\frac{2k+1}{4\pi}}\, \mathscr{D}^{k*}_{m,\varepsilon|\lambda|}(\Omega_q) = \frac{[e(q)]^{\otimes|\lambda|} \cdot (lq)^{\otimes|\lambda|}}{\sqrt{(k-\lambda+1)\cdots(k+\lambda)}}\, Y^k_m(\boldsymbol{q})$$

where

$$
\begin{aligned}
e(q) &= e_1(q) + i\varepsilon e_2(q) \\
e_1(q) &= \Omega_q(1, 0, 0) \\
e_2(q) &= \Omega_q(0, 1, 0) \\
\boldsymbol{q} &= \Omega_q(0, 0, 1) \quad \text{with} \quad \Omega_q = [P]^{-1}\,\Omega(q_{1,2} \leftarrow n_3(P))\,[P] \\
\boldsymbol{l}_q &= \frac{1}{i}\,\boldsymbol{q} \times \nabla_q
\end{aligned}
$$

which takes us back to familiar formulae for the photon multipoles.

c) Helicity coupling

For both particles, 1 and 2, one chooses either the radiation gauge or the helicity frame, but following Jacob and Wick[17], we shall reverse for particle 2, the vectors $n_3(p_2)$ and $n_1(p_2)$ if $m_2^2 \neq 0$ or the vector $n_1(p_2)$ if $m_2 = 0$; this can be done by writing:

$$
\begin{cases}
[p_1]_h = [p_1 \leftarrow P]\,\Omega(\hat{q}_{1,2} \leftarrow n_3(P))\,[P] & \text{for} \quad m_1 \neq 0 \\
[p_2]_h = [p_2 \leftarrow P]\,\Omega(\hat{q}_{1,2} \leftarrow n_3(P))\,[P]\,Y & \text{for} \quad m_2 \neq 0
\end{cases}
$$

$$
\text{or} \begin{cases}
[p_1]_r = \Omega(q_{1,2} \leftarrow n_3(P))\,[\omega_1 \hat{P} + |q_{1,2}|\, n_3(P) \leftarrow \hat{P} + n_3(P)]\,[P] \\
\quad\;\; = [p_1 \leftarrow \hat{P} + \hat{q}_{12}]\,\Omega(\hat{q}_{12} \leftarrow n_3(P))\,[P] \quad \text{for} \quad m_1 = 0 \\
[p_2]_r = \Omega(q_{1,2} \leftarrow n_3(P))\,[\omega_2 \hat{P} - |q_{1,2}|\, n_3(P) \leftarrow \hat{P} - n_3(P)]\,[P]\,Y
\end{cases}
$$

$$
= [p_2 \leftarrow \hat{P} - \hat{q}_{12}]\,\Omega(q_{1,2} \leftarrow n_3(P))\,[P]\,Y \quad \text{for} \quad m_2 = 0
$$

where Y is a rotation through an angle $(+\pi)$ about the Y axis. We shall use $\mathscr{D}^s_{mm'}(Y) = \delta_{m,-m'}(-1)^{s+m}$, and:

$$
\mathscr{D}^j_{\lambda_1-\lambda_2,\mu}(\Omega_q^{-1})\,\mathscr{D}^{s_1}_{\lambda_1\lambda_1}(\Omega_{Aq}^{-1} R(A, P)\,\Omega_q)\,\mathscr{D}^{s_2}_{\lambda_2\lambda_2}(Y^{-1}\Omega_{Aq}^{-1} R(A, P)\,\Omega_q\, Y)
$$

$$
= \mathscr{D}^j_{\lambda_1-\lambda_2,\mu}(\Omega_{Aq}^{-1} R(A, P)).
$$

We now find that the state:

$$
|[P], \mu; j, \lambda_1, \lambda_2\rangle = \int \mathrm{d}\Omega_q \sqrt{\frac{2j+1}{4\pi}}\, |[P], \boldsymbol{q}, \lambda_1, \lambda_2\rangle\, (-1)^{s_2-\lambda_2}\, \mathscr{D}^j_{\lambda_1-\lambda_2,\mu}(\Omega_q^{-1}) \tag{II,c,1}
$$

transforms according to:

$$
U(a, A)\, |[P]\, \mu; j\lambda_1\lambda_2\rangle = \mathrm{e}^{i(AP)\cdot a} |[AP], \mu', j, \lambda_1\lambda_2\rangle\, \mathscr{D}^j_{\mu'\mu}([AP]^{-1} A[P]). \tag{II,c,2}
$$

Remark.

For both particles we have used the same rotation $\Omega(\hat{q}_{1,2} \leftarrow n_3(P))$.

The additional phase factor $(-1)^{s_2-\lambda_2}$ in (II,c,1) is necessary if one wants to get good parity transformation properties, as pointed out by Jacob and Wick.

The Clebsch–Gordan coefficient is:

$$\langle [p_1]\,\sigma_1 [p_2]\,\sigma_2 | [P], \mu; j, \lambda_1, \lambda_2, P^2 \rangle$$
$$= \frac{2\sqrt{P^2}\sqrt{2}}{\lambda^{1/4}(P^2, m_1^2, m_2^2)} \sqrt{\frac{2j+1}{4\pi}}\, \delta^4(P - p_1 - p_2)$$
$$(-1)^{s_2-\lambda_2}\, \mathscr{D}^{s_1}_{\sigma_1\lambda_1}([p_1]^{-1}[p_1]_{h_r})\, \mathscr{D}^{s_2}_{\sigma_2\lambda_2}([p_2]^{-1}[p_2]_{h_r})\, \mathscr{D}^{j*}_{\mu\lambda_1-\lambda_2}(\Omega_q).$$

d) Relationship between various coupling schemes

The states $|[P], \mu; j, \eta\rangle$ defined in preceding sections according to the various coupling schemes, are always normalized to:

$$\langle [P], \mu; j, \eta \,|[P'], \mu'; j', \eta'\rangle = \delta(P - P')\, \delta_{jj'} \delta_{\mu\mu'} \delta_{\eta\eta'}.$$

Thus, they form an orthonormal basis. Furthermore, they are complete. $\delta_{\eta\eta'}$ means $\delta_{ll'}\delta_{ss'}$ for *ls* coupling, $\delta_{kk'}\delta_{\lambda_1\lambda'_1}$ for multipole coupling and $\delta_{\lambda_1\lambda_1'}\delta_{\lambda_2\lambda_2'}$ for helicity coupling. It is useful to write down, the unitary transformation which relates two different coupling schemes corresponding to basis $|[P], \mu; j, \eta\rangle$ and $|[P], \mu; j, \varphi\rangle$. Using formulae for the Clebsch–Gordan coefficients, one obtains:

$$\langle [P'], \mu'; j', \eta \,|[P], \mu; j, \varphi\rangle = \delta(P - P')\, \delta_{jj'} \delta_{\mu\mu'} S^j_{\eta\varphi}.$$

The calculation of $S^j_{\eta\varphi}$ in the various cases offers no difficulty although it is rather lengthy. One gets:

$$S^j_{\langle\lambda_1\lambda_2; l, s\rangle} = \sqrt{\frac{2l+1}{2j+1}} \begin{pmatrix} s_1 & s_2 & s \\ \lambda_1 & -\lambda_2 & \lambda \end{pmatrix} \begin{pmatrix} l & s & j \\ 0 & \lambda & \lambda \end{pmatrix}$$

$$S^j_{\langle k, \lambda'_1; \lambda_1\lambda_2\rangle} = \delta_{\lambda_1\lambda'_1} \sqrt{\frac{2k+1}{2j+1}} \begin{pmatrix} k & s_2 & j \\ \lambda_1 & -\lambda_2 & \lambda \end{pmatrix}$$

and

$$S^j_{\langle k, \lambda'_1, l, s\rangle} = \sqrt{(2l+1)(2s+1)} \begin{pmatrix} l & s_1 & k \\ 0 & \lambda'_1 & \lambda'_1 \end{pmatrix} W(s_1 s_2 l, j | s, k)$$

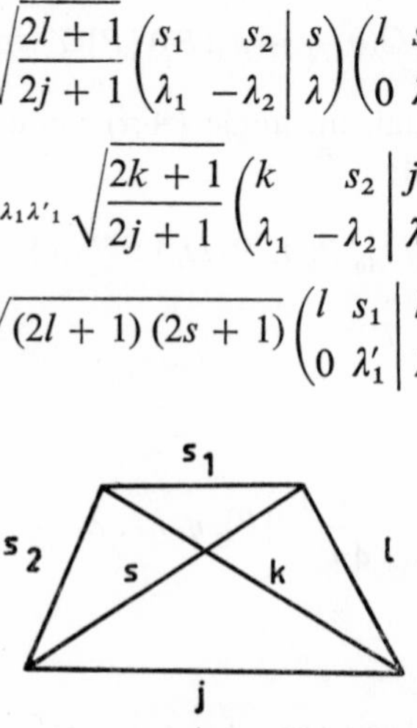

Fig. 2

where W is the Racah coefficient (see for example reference 0, Appendix c), associated with the Fig. 2 *.

Remark.

All these $S_{\eta\varphi}$ are real. This is of course due to the conventions used here (one can easily see that they are taken such that η and φ are time reversal invariant, so that the $S^j_{\eta\varphi}$'s have to be real).

e) Angular analysis of reactions involving two incoming and two outgoing particles

Consider a reaction

$$A_1 + A_2 \to A_3 + A_4$$

$$\begin{array}{llllll} \text{with masses:} & m_1 & m_2 & m_3 & m_4 & \\ \text{spins:} & s_1 & s_2 & s_3 & s_4 & \qquad \text{(II,e,1)} \\ \text{momenta:} & p_1 & p_2 & p_3 & p_4 & \\ \text{and} & & & & & \\ \text{spin projections:} & \sigma_1 & \sigma_2 & \sigma_3 & \sigma_4 . & \end{array}$$

Let $S - \mathbf{1} = iT$ be the transition operator.

We recall that relativistic invariance imposes

$$U(a, A)\, SU^{-1}(a, A) = S. \qquad \text{(II,e,2)}\dagger$$

This allows us to use fruitfully an intermediate state expansion in terms of states which reduce products of representations occuring in the initial as well as in the final state:

$$\langle [p_3]\,\sigma_3,\, [p_4]\,\sigma_4,\, |T|\, [p_1]\,\sigma_1,\, [p_2]\,\sigma_2\rangle$$

$$= \int\limits_{(m_3+m_4)^2}^{\infty} \mathrm{d}M_{34}^2 \int\limits_{(m_1+m_2)^2}^{\infty} \mathrm{d}M_{12}^2 \int \frac{\mathrm{d}^3 P_{34}}{2\omega_{34}} \int \frac{\mathrm{d}^3 P_{12}}{2\omega_{12}} \sum_{\substack{\eta_{34},\eta_{12} \\ J_{34},J_{12} \\ \mu_{34},\mu_{12}}} \cdots$$

$$\cdots \langle [p_3],\, \sigma_3,\, [p_4],\, \sigma_4 | [P_{34}]\, \mu_{34};\, J_{34},\, \eta_{34},\, M_{34}^2\rangle$$

$$\langle [P]_{34},\, \mu_{34};\, J_{34},\, \eta_{34},\, M_{34}^2\, |T|\, [P]_{12},\, \mu_{12};\, J_{12},\, \eta_{12},\, M_{12}^2\rangle \qquad \text{(II,e,3)}$$

$$\langle [P]_{12},\, \mu_{12};\, J_{12},\, \eta_{12},\, M_{12}^2 | [p_1]\,\sigma_1,\, [p_2]\,\sigma_2\rangle.$$

* Such diagrams differ from those used in part (II, f).

† Invariance under reflections reads:

$U(\Pi)SU^{-1}(\Pi) = S.\quad U(T)SU^{-1}(T) = S^+,\quad U(\Pi T)SU^{-1}(\Pi T) = S^+$

where phases have been put equal to one by virtue of the cluster decomposition property quoted in chapter 0, § b in the case of $U(\Pi)$, and by phase renormalization in the case of $U(T)$ and $U(\Pi T)$ which are antiunitary.

Poincaré invariance (Wigner[(IV)]–Eckart theorem) shows that:

$$\langle [P]_{34}, \mu_{34}; J_{34}, \eta_{34}, M_{34}^2 \,|T|\, [P]_{12}, \mu_{12}; J_{12}, \eta_{12}, M_{12}^2 \rangle$$

has the form

$$\delta^4(P_{34} - P_{12})\, \delta_{J_{12},J_{34}} \delta_{\mu_{12},\mu_{34}} T^{J_{12}}_{\eta_{34},\eta_{12}}(P_{12}^2)$$
$$= \delta(M_{34}^2 - M_{12}^2)\, 2\omega_{34} \delta^3(\boldsymbol{P}_{34} - \boldsymbol{P}_{12})\, \delta_{J_{12},J_{34}} \delta_{\mu_{12},\mu_{34}} T^{J_{12}}_{\eta_{34},\eta_{12}}(P_{12}^2) \qquad \text{(II,e,4)}$$

where $T^J_{\eta_{34},\,\eta_{12}}(P^2)$ is a reduced matrix element.

We further define partially reduced Clebsch–Gordan coefficients through*

$$\langle [p]\,\sigma, [p']\,\sigma' | [P], \mu; J, \eta, P^2 \rangle = \delta^4(P - p - p')\, \mathscr{D}^s_{\sigma\tau}([p]^{-1})$$
$$\mathscr{D}^{s'}_{\sigma'\tau'}([p']^{-1})\, \langle\langle p, \tau, p', \tau' | [P], \mu; J, \eta, P^2 \rangle\rangle \qquad \text{(II,e,5)}$$

with the result:

$$\langle [p_3\;\; \sigma_3, [p_4], \sigma_4 \,|T|\, [p_1]\,\sigma_1, [p_2], \sigma_2 \rangle$$
$$= \delta^4(p_1 + p_2 - p_3 - p_4) \sum_{\substack{J,\mu \\ \eta_{12},\eta_{34}}} \mathscr{D}^{s_3}_{\sigma_3\tau_3}([p_3]^{-1})\, \mathscr{D}^{s_4}_{\sigma_4\tau_4}([p_4]^{-1})$$
$$\times \langle\langle p_3, \tau_3, p_4, \tau_4 | [P], \mu, J, \eta_{34}, P^2 \rangle\rangle\, T^J_{\eta_{34},\eta_{12}}(P^2) \qquad \text{(II,e,6)}$$
$$\langle\langle [P], \mu; J, \eta_{12}, P^2 | p_1, \tau_1, p_2, \tau_2 \rangle\rangle\, \mathscr{D}^{s_1}_{\tau_1\sigma_1}([p_1]^{\dagger-1})\, \mathscr{D}^{s_2}_{\tau_2\sigma_2}([p_2]^{\dagger-1})$$

where $P = p_1 + p_2 = p_3 + p_4$ (in which, of course spin index summations have to be omitted when massless particles are involved).

If the $[p_i]$'s are chosen so that they are adapted to the kind of coupling in which particle i is involved [e.g. $[p_i]_l = [p_i \leftarrow P][P]$ in the case of an l, s coupling], the expansion has a form which has a completely non relativistic looking appearance.

For example:

$$\langle [p_3]_l\, \sigma_3 [p_4]_l\, \sigma_4 \,|T|\, [p_1]_l\, \sigma_1 [p_2]_l\, \sigma_2 \rangle = \frac{8P^2\, \delta^4(p_1 + p_2 - p_3 - p_4)}{\lambda^{1/4}(P^2, m_1^2, m_2^2)\, \lambda^{1/4}(P^2, m_3^2, m_4^2)}$$
$$\sum_{\substack{J,\mu \\ s_{12} l_{12} \\ s_{34} l_{34}}} \begin{pmatrix} s_3 & s_4 & s_{34} \\ \sigma_3 & \sigma_4 & \sigma_{34} \end{pmatrix} \begin{pmatrix} l_{34} & s_{34} & J \\ m_{34} & \sigma_{34} & \mu \end{pmatrix} Y^{l_{34}}_{m_{34}}(\hat{\boldsymbol{q}}_{34})\, T^J_{\substack{l_{34},l_{12} \\ s_{34},s_{12}}}(P^2)\, Y^{l_{12}}_{m_{12}}(\hat{\boldsymbol{q}}_{12})$$
$$\begin{pmatrix} J & l_{12} & s_{12} \\ \mu & m_{12} & \sigma_{12} \end{pmatrix} \begin{pmatrix} s_{12} & s_1 & s_2 \\ \sigma_{12} & \sigma_1 & \sigma_2 \end{pmatrix}. \qquad \text{(II,e,7)}$$

Such sums over μ will be evaluated in appendix II in familiar operator form in the case where the spins involved are low. Consequences of space and time reflections (connecting time reversed reactions) are easily derived.

* In other words we express the components of $|P, \mu; j, \rangle$ on a "spinor" basis.

One may wonder at this point why we indulged in such a luxury of details concerning the specification of spin bases. The reasons for such care will become apparent in the study of three particle systems, a cornerstone of which is the precise construction of two particle states.

Also, when one studies reactions occurring in cascade, it is convenient to be able to shift reference frames, convenient frames not being necessarily identical for two successive reactions.

We end up with a last important example: the expansion in terms of helicity amplitudes:

$$\langle [p_3]_h, \lambda_3, [p_4]_h, \lambda_4 |T| [p_1]_h, \lambda_1, [p_2]_h, \lambda_2 \rangle = \frac{8P^2\, \delta^4(p_1 + p_2 - p_3 - p_4)}{\lambda^{1/4}(P^2, m_1^2, m_2^2)\, \lambda^{1/4}(P^2, m_3^2, m_4^2)}$$

$$(-1)^{s_2 - \lambda_2 + s_4 - \lambda_4} \sum_J \frac{2J+1}{4\pi} \mathscr{D}^J_{\lambda_3 - \lambda_4, \lambda_1 - \lambda_2}(\theta)\, T^J_{\lambda_3, \lambda_4, \lambda_1, \lambda_2}(P^2) \qquad \text{(II,e,8)}$$

with

$$\cos\theta = -\hat{q}_{1,2} \cdot \hat{q}_{3,4}$$

where the summation over μ:

$$\sum_\mu \mathscr{D}^J_{\lambda_3 - \lambda_4, \mu}(\Omega^{-1}_{q_{3,4}})\, \mathscr{D}^J_{\mu, \lambda_1 - \lambda_2}(\Omega_{q_{1,2}})$$

is easily performed provided all helicity frames (i.e. the Ω_q's) are so defined that $n_2^\mu(p_i) = \varepsilon^{\mu\nu\varrho\sigma} p_{1\nu} p_{2\varrho} p_{3\sigma}$ which is orthogonal to all p_i's, since then $[P]\Omega^{-1}_{q_{3,4}}\Omega_{q_{1,2}}[P]^{-1}$ leaves $n_2(P) = \varepsilon_{\mu\nu\varrho\sigma} p_1^\nu p_2^\varrho p_3^\sigma$ invariant.

*Exercise.****

Express unitarity of the S-matrix, below three particle production threshold in terms of the reduced matrix $T^J_{\eta_{34}, \eta_{12}}(P^2)$, using

$$\mathbf{1} = \sum_{\substack{\text{2particle}\\ \text{states}}} \int \frac{d_3 p_1}{2\omega_1} \frac{d_3 p_2}{2\omega_2} \sum_{\sigma_1, \sigma_2} |[p_1], \sigma_1 [p_2], \sigma_2\rangle \langle [p_1]\, \sigma_1 [p_2]\, \sigma_2|$$

$$= \int dP^2 \int \frac{d^3 P}{2\omega_P} \sum_{J, \eta, \mu} |[P], \mu; J, \eta, P^2\rangle \langle [P], \mu; J, \eta, P^2|.$$

f) Convergence of angular expansions as a consequence of analyticity assumptions

It is customary (cf. appendix III) to define spinor amplitudes according to:

$$\langle [p_3], \sigma_3, [p_4], \sigma_4 |T| [p_1], \sigma_1, [p_2], \sigma_2 \rangle$$

$$= \delta^{(4)}(p_1 + p_2 - p_3 - p_4)\, \mathscr{D}^{s_3}_{\sigma_3 A_3}([p_3]^{-1})\, \mathscr{D}^{s_4}_{\sigma_4 A_4}([p_4]^{-1}) \qquad \text{(II,f,1)}$$

$$M_{A_3 A_4 \dot{A}_1 \dot{A}_2}(p_3 p_4 p_1 p_2)\, \mathscr{D}^{s_1}_{\dot{A}_1 \sigma_1}([p_1]^{\dagger -1})\, \mathscr{D}^{s_2}_{\dot{A}_2 \sigma_2}([p_2]^{\dagger -1})$$

$$= \delta^{(4)}(p_1 + p_2 - p_3 - p_4)\, \mathscr{D}^{s_3}_{\sigma_3 A_3}([p_3]^{-1})\, \mathscr{D}^{s_4}_{\sigma_4 A_4}([p_4]^{-1})$$

$$M_{A_3 A_4 A_1 A_2}(p_3 p_4 p_1 p_2)\, \mathscr{D}^{s_1}_{A_1 \sigma_1}(C^{-1}[p_1])\, \mathscr{D}^{s_2}_{A_2 \sigma_2}(C^{-1}[p_2]).$$

Exercise.

Find the relationship between $M_{A_3A_4\dot{A}_1\dot{A}_2}$ and $M_{A_3A_4A_1A_2}$.

A current assumption[7] is that $M_{A_3A_4A_1A_2}(p_1p_2p_3p_4)$ is holomorphic in a (complex) Lorentz invariant domain of the mass shell $p_1 + p_2 = p_3 + p_4$, $p_i^2 = m_i^2$, where it is furthermore covariant under the complex Lorentz group:

$$M_{A_3A_4A_1A_2}(L\cdot p_1, L\cdot p_2, L\cdot p_3, L\cdot p_4) = \mathscr{D}^{s_3}_{A_3A'_3}(A(L))\,\mathscr{D}^{s_4}_{A_4A'_4}(A(L))$$
$$\mathscr{D}^{s_1}_{A_1A'_1}(A(L))\,\mathscr{D}^{s_2}_{A_2A'_2}(A(L))\,M_{A'_3A'_4A'_1A'_2}(p_1, p_2, p_3, p_4). \qquad \text{(II,f,2)}$$

Covariance implies a decomposition:

$$M_{A_3A_4A_1A_2}(p_1p_2p_3p_4) = \begin{pmatrix} s_3 & s_4 & s_{34} \\ A_3 & A_4 & A_{34}\end{pmatrix}\begin{pmatrix} s_1 & s_2 & s_{12} \\ A_1 & A_2 & A_{12}\end{pmatrix}\begin{pmatrix} s_{34} & s_{12} & \Sigma \\ A_{34} & A_{12} & A\end{pmatrix}$$
$$\times\, M^{\Sigma}_{A}(p_1p_2p_3p_4), \qquad \text{(II,f,3)}$$

hence it follows:

$$M^{\Sigma}_{A}(L\cdot p_1, L\cdot p_2, L\cdot p_3, L\cdot p_4) = \mathscr{D}^{\Sigma}_{AA'}(A(L))\,M^{\Sigma}_{A'}(p_1, p_2, p_3, p_4). \qquad \text{(II,f,4)}$$

This decomposition is easily inverted.

Note that from covariance also, putting $A(L) = -\mathbf{1}$, one obtains the result that $s_1 + s_2 + s_3 + s_4$, and consequently Σ, must be integers.

One can show[7,8] that under some technical restrictions M^{Σ} can be decomposed according to:

$$M^{\Sigma}_{A}(p_1p_2p_3p_4) = \sum_{\varkappa\pm} A^{\Sigma}_{\varkappa\pm}\,(s_{12}s_{13}s_{14})\,Y^{\Sigma,\varkappa\pm}_{A}(p_1p_2p_3p_4) \qquad \text{(II,f,5)}$$

where the $A^{\Sigma}_{\varkappa\pm}$'s are holomorphic functions of:

$$s_{12} = (p_1 + p_2)^2,\; s_{13} = (p_1 - p_3)^2$$

and

$$s_{14} = (p_1 - p_4)^2, \left(s_{12} + s_{13} + s_{14} = \sum_1^4 m_i^2\right)$$

in the image on the space of invariants s_{1j}, $2 \leqq j \leqq 4$, of the original holomorphy domain, and

$$Y^{\Sigma,\varkappa_+}_{A}(p_1p_2p_3p_4) = \begin{pmatrix} \varkappa_+, & \Sigma - \varkappa_+, & \Sigma \\ \mu, & \nu, & A\end{pmatrix} Y^{(\varkappa^+)}_{\mu}(p_1, p_2)\,Y^{(\Sigma-\varkappa_+)}_{\nu}(p_1, p_3)$$
$$\text{(II,f,6)}$$
$$Y^{\Sigma,\varkappa_-}_{A}(p_1p_2p_3p_4) = \begin{pmatrix} \varkappa_-, & \Sigma + 1 - \varkappa_-, & \Sigma \\ \mu, & \nu, & A\end{pmatrix} Y^{(\varkappa_-)}_{\mu}(p_1, p_2)\,Y^{(\Sigma+1-\varkappa_-)}_{\nu}(p_1, p_3).$$

Here, the relativistic spherical harmonics[III,8] $Y^{L}_{M}(a, b)$ are defined as follows: consider the "complex semi-bi-vector" associated with a, b:

$$e(a, b) = a_0\mathbf{b} - b_0\mathbf{a} + i\mathbf{a} \times \mathbf{b}$$

and write:

$$Y^{L}_{M}(a, b) = Y^{L}_{M}(e(a, b))$$

the right hand side being the solid spherical harmonic (homogeneous harmonic polynomial of degree L) of argument $e(a, b)$.

Remarks.

The above construction works if p_1, $m_1^2 \neq 0$ is replaced by any p_i such that $p_i^2 = m_i^2 \neq 0$.
If, $a = (1, 0, 0, 0)$ $Y_M^L(a, b) = Y_M^L(b)$.

$$Y_M^L(\alpha a + \beta b, b) = \alpha^L Y_M^L(a, b); \; Y_M^L(b, a) = (-)^L \, Y_M^L(a, b).$$

For each Σ there are $\Sigma + 1 + \Sigma = 2\Sigma + 1$ amplitudes $A_{\varkappa_\pm}^{\Sigma}$, hence, a total of $(2s_1 + 1)(2s_2 + 1)(2s_3 + 1)(2s_4 + 1)$.

Example.

The $A_{\varkappa_\pm}^{\Sigma}$'s fulfill the Mandelstam representation.

Theorem[9].

The natural domain of convergence of multipole expansions, for fixed energy $P^2 = s_{12} = s_{34}$, in terms of the variable

$$z = \cos\theta_{12,34} = -\hat{q}_{1,2} \cdot \hat{q}_{34}$$

is the largest ellipse, with foci ± 1 in which the $A_{\varkappa_\pm}^{\Sigma}(s_{12}, \cos\theta_{12,34})$ are holomorphic. The rate of convergence is governed by the large semi axis of this ellipse.

Sketch of the proof: Assume $\mu \geqq \lambda \geqq 0$; One first proves that $T_{\lambda\mu}(s_{12}, z)$ has the form

$$(1 - z)^{\frac{\mu-\lambda}{2}} \, (1 + z)^{\frac{\lambda+\mu}{2}} \, \tau_{\lambda\mu}(s_{12}, z)$$

where $\tau_{\lambda\mu}(s_{12}, z)$ has for fixed s_{12} the same z-analyticity properties as the $A_{\varkappa_\pm}^{\Sigma}$'s. One furthermore notices that:

$$\text{i.e.} \quad d_{\lambda\mu}^j(\theta) = \left(\frac{1 - z}{2}\right)^{\frac{\mu-\lambda}{2}} \left(\frac{1 + z}{2}\right)^{\frac{\mu+\lambda}{2}} \left[\frac{(j + \mu)!\,(j - \mu)!}{(j + \lambda)!\,(j - \lambda)!}\right]^{1/2} P_{j-\mu}^{\mu-\lambda,\mu+\lambda}(z),$$

where, for fixed λ, μ, the $P_{j-\mu}^{\mu-\lambda,\mu+\lambda}(z)$ are orthogonal polynomials on the interval $(-1, +1)$, for the measure $\left(\frac{1 - z}{2}\right)^{\mu-\lambda} \left(\frac{1 + z}{2}\right)^{\mu+\lambda} dz$.

Thus:

$$\text{i.e.} \qquad T_{\lambda\mu}(s_{12}, z) = \left(\frac{1 - z}{2}\right)^{\frac{\mu-\lambda}{2}} \left(\frac{1 + z}{2}\right)^{\frac{\mu+\lambda}{2}} \sum_j T_{\lambda\mu}^j(s_{12}) \, P_{j-\mu}^{\mu-\lambda,\mu+\lambda}(z),$$

and, by a classical theorem[10], the expansion $\sum_j \ldots$ has just the domain of convergence stated in the theorem. Similar results hold for any λ, μ, with a slightly different proof.

If one assumes analyticity in a cut plane in z, as stems from the Mandelstam[11] representation, or in the Lehmann ellipse[11] which emerges from postulates of local field theories, one sees that the ellipse of convergence collapses on the interval $(-1, +1)$ at high energy; hence, as the energy increases, the convergence becomes worse and worse.

The convergence of other multipole expansions is of course a consequence of that of the helicity expansion as is seen from the way they are connected.

g) Threshold behaviour of reduced amplitudes[12]

We shall be concerned here with threshold behaviours of reduced matrix elements $T^{J}_{\substack{l_{34}l_{12}\\ s_{34}s_{12}}}(s)$ which are also consequences of analyticity in the momentum transfer variables, provided that we assume the amplitudes $A^{\Sigma}_{\varkappa\pm}$ to be bounded in the energy variable in a neighbourhood of the threshold under consideration, throughout their analyticity domain in the $\cos\theta$ variable.

Since we shall be concerned with a neighbourhood of:

$$s = \max\{(m_1 + m_2)^2, \quad (m_3 + m_4)^2\} \neq 0$$

we can use an expansion of the spinor amplitudes in terms of

$$Y^{\Sigma,\varkappa\pm}_{A}(p_1, p_2, p_3, p_4) = \begin{pmatrix} \varkappa_{\pm}, \Sigma - \varkappa_{\pm} + {0 \atop 1} & \Sigma \\ \mu \qquad \nu & A \end{pmatrix} Y^{\varkappa\pm}_{\mu}(P, q_{1,2})\, Y^{\left(\Sigma - \varkappa_{\pm} + {0 \atop 1}\right)}_{\nu}(P, q_{3,4})$$

thus introducing the possibility of poles at $s_{12} = 0$ in the coefficients $A^{\Sigma}_{\varkappa\pm}(s_{12}, s_{13}, s_{14})$.

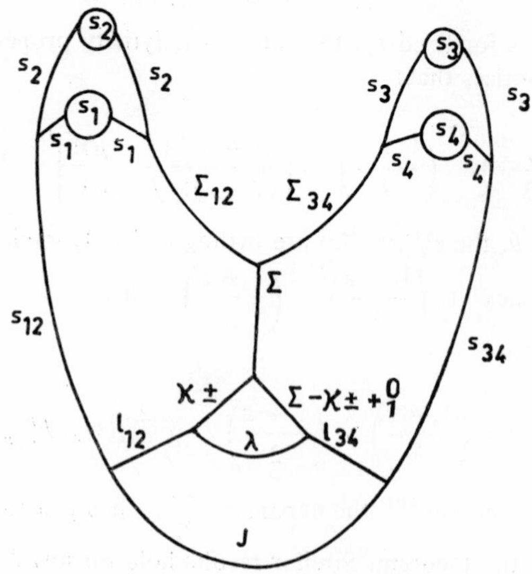

Fig. 3

We then compute the angular integral which yields $T^J_{l_{34},\, l_{12} \atop s_{34},\, s_{12}}(s)$ and represent it in terms of a graph[13]:
which has the following meaning: each vertex 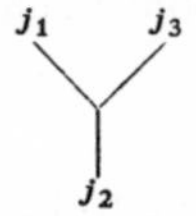

indicates a Clebsch–Gordan coeficient $\begin{pmatrix} j_1 & j_2 & j_3 \\ m_1 & m_2 & m_3 \end{pmatrix}$ and a link between two vertices indicates a summation over the corresponding magnetic index; a necessary orientation at each vertex which should indicate in what order the Clebsch–Gordan coefficient has to be written has been omitted as it is of no use for our purpose; finally each circle 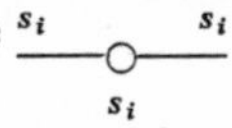

indicates a matrix element $\mathscr{D}^{s_i}_{\sigma_i \sigma_i'}(\hat{p}_i \to \hat{P})$.

The angular momentum λ comes from assuming that $A^{\Sigma}_{\varkappa\pm}(s_{12}, z)$ has a representation of the type:

$$A^{\Sigma}_{\varkappa\pm}(s_{12}, z) = \int \frac{A^{\Sigma}_{\varkappa\pm}(s_{12}, z')\, dz'}{z' - z}$$

where the path of integration lies close to the boundary of the ellipse of analyticity in z and using the expansion:

$$\frac{1}{z' - z} = \sum_{\lambda} (2\lambda + 1)\, P_\lambda(z)\, Q_\lambda(z')$$

together with the addition theorem

$$\frac{2\lambda + 1}{4\pi} P_\lambda(z) = \sum_m Y^\lambda_m(\hat{q}_{12})\, Y^\lambda_m(\hat{q}_{34}).$$

Vertices $(l_{12}, \varkappa_\pm, \lambda)$ and $(l_{34}, \Sigma - \varkappa_\pm + {0 \atop 1}, \lambda)$ come from integrations over $d\Omega_{q_{12}}$, $d\Omega_{q_{34}}$, respectively, provided the angular dependences of the $\mathscr{D}^{s_i}_{\sigma_i \sigma_i'}(p_i \leftarrow P)$ are neglected, (the regularity of these matrices around threshold makes this possible); there emerge, thus, factors

$$|q_{1,2}|^{\varkappa\pm}\, |q_{3,4}|^{\Sigma - \varkappa\pm + {0 \atop 1}},$$

from, the solid harmonics in terms of which spinor amplitudes are constructed. Such a graph is finally accompanied by a factor $Q_\lambda(z')$ weighted by the corresponding weight functions.

Now, to a singularity $s_{13} = s^0_{13}$ or $s_{14} = s^0_{14}$, there corresponds, at energy s_{12} a singularity in z of the type:

$$\zeta^0(s_{12}) / |q_{1,2}|\, |q_{3,4}|$$

where ζ^0 is slowly varying around threshold. Furthermore, at threshold the argument of Q_λ goes to infinity like $\zeta / |q_{1,2}| |q_{3,4}|$, so that:

$$Q_\lambda(\zeta' / |q_{1,2}|\, |q_{3,4}|) \sim \frac{|q_{1,2}|^{\lambda+1}\, |q_{3,4}|^{\lambda+1}}{|\zeta'|^{\lambda+1}}.$$

Thus: $\oint A^{\Sigma}_{\varkappa_\pm}(s_{12}, z')dz'\, Q_\lambda(z')$ is of the order of $|q_{1,2}|^\lambda |q_{3,4}|^\lambda$ where one power has been taken down from the estimate of Q^λ, due to the size of the contour of integration. The threshold behaviour is thus given by:

$$|q_{1,2}|^{\varkappa_\pm + \lambda}\, |q_{3,4}|^{\Sigma - \varkappa_\pm + {0 \atop 1} + \lambda}$$

where the exponents have to be minimized according to the triangular inequalities imposed by the non vanishing of Clebsch–Gordan coefficients.

a) Elastic scattering: $|q_{1,2}| = |q_{3,4}| = |q|$. The power to be minimized is $\Sigma + {0 \atop 1} + 2\lambda$. Now:

$$\varkappa_\pm + \lambda \geqq l_{12}, \quad \Sigma - \varkappa_\pm + {0 \atop 1} + \lambda \geqq l_{34},$$

hence, in general, we have the threshold behaviour

$$T^J_{\substack{l_{12}l_{34}\\ s_{12}s_{34}}} \sim |q|^{l_{12}+l_{34}}$$

(unless the coefficient vanishes accidentally).

b) Inelastic scattering if $m_1 + m_2 < m_3 + m_4$, the power to be minimized is $\Sigma - \varkappa_\pm + {0 \atop 1} + \lambda \geqq l_{24}$, hence, in general the threshold behaviour is:

$$T^J_{\substack{l_{12}l_{34}\\ s_{12}s_{34}}} \sim |q_{34}|^{l_{34}}$$

(with similar restrictions).

Remark.

This argument is a substitute for classical arguments in potential scattering theory. Singularities in momentum transfers s_{13} and s_{14} essentially play the roles of ranges of direct and exchange potentials.

III. ANALYSIS OF THREE PARTICLE STATES

a) Couplings in cascade

Assume we have a representation of the Poincaré group acting on a space with basis $|[p_1], \sigma_1; [p_2], \sigma_2; [p_3], \sigma_3\rangle$. We may first transform it into:

$$|[p_{12}], \mu_{12}; j_{12}, \eta_{12}; [p_3], \sigma_3\rangle$$

where η_{12} is a set of degeneracy parameters which labels the coupling of particles 1 and 2. Since the frame $[p_{12}]$ is arbitrary, it can be chosen appropriately to couple the system (12) with system (3), with a coupling specified by degeneracy parameters $\eta_{12,3}$:

$$|[p_{123}], \sigma_{123}; j_{12}, \eta_{12}, j_{12,3}, \eta_{12,3}\rangle.$$

It is at this point that the expression of the state $|[p_{12}], \mu_{12}; j_{12}, \eta_{12}\rangle$ for an arbitrary frame $[p_{12}]$ is really useful. Let us for instance write down the Clebsch–Gordan coefficient for $\eta_{12}, \eta_{12,3}$, sets of l–s coupling degeneracy parameters:

$$\langle [p_1], \sigma_1, [p_2], \sigma_2, [p_3], \sigma_3 | [p_{123}], \mu_{123}; p_{12}^2, s_{12}, l_{12}, j_{12}, p_{123}^2, s_{12,3} l_{12,3}, j_{12,3}\rangle$$

$$= \frac{2\sqrt{p_{12}^2}\sqrt{2}}{\lambda^{1/4}(m_1^2, m_2^2, p_{12}^2)} \frac{2\sqrt{p_{123}^2}\sqrt{2}}{\lambda^{1/4}(m_3^2, p_{12}^2, p_{123}^2)}$$

$$\times\, \delta^4(p_{123} - p_1 - p_2 - p_3)\, \delta(p_{12}^2 - (p_1 + p_2)^2) \times \cdots$$

$$\times \sum_{\substack{\sigma'_1\sigma'_2\sigma'_3 \\ \sigma_{12}=\sigma'_1+\sigma'_2 \\ \mu_{12}=\sigma_{12}+m_{12} \\ \sigma_{123}=\mu_{12}+\sigma'_3}} \mathscr{D}^{s_1}_{\sigma_1\sigma'_1}([p_1]^{-1}[p_1 \to p_{12}][p_{12} \to p_{123}][p_{123}])$$

$$\times\, \mathscr{D}^{s_2}_{\sigma_2\sigma'_2}([p_2]^{-1}[p_2 \leftarrow p_{12}][p_{12} \leftarrow p_{123}][p_{123}])\, \mathscr{D}^{s_3}_{\sigma_3\sigma'_3}([p_3]^{-1}[p_3 \leftarrow p_{123}][p_{123}]),$$

$$\begin{pmatrix} s_1 & s_2 & s_{12} \\ \sigma'_1 & \sigma'_2 & \sigma_{12} \end{pmatrix} \begin{pmatrix} l_{1,2} & s_{12} & j_{12} \\ m_{12} & \sigma_{12} & \mu_{12} \end{pmatrix} Y^{l_{1,2}}_{m_{12}}(\hat{q}'_{1,2}),$$

$$\begin{pmatrix} j_{12} & s_3 & s_{123} \\ \mu_{12} & \sigma'_3 & \sigma_{123} \end{pmatrix} \begin{pmatrix} l_{12,3} & s_{123} & j_{123} \\ m_{12,3} & \sigma_{123} & \mu_{123} \end{pmatrix} Y^{l_{12,3}}_{m_{123}}(\hat{q}_{12,3}), \qquad \text{(III,a,1)}$$

$$q_{1,2} = \frac{1}{2}\left(p_1 - p_2 - \frac{m_1^2 - m_2^2}{p_{12}^2}\, p_{12}\right),$$

$$p_{12} = p_1 + p_2,$$

$$q'_{12} = [\hat{p}_{123} \leftarrow p_{12}]\, q_{12} \qquad (\text{note: } q'_{12} p_{123} = 0),$$

$$q_{12,3} = \frac{1}{2}\left(p_{12} - p_3 - \frac{p_{12}^2 - m_3^2}{p_{123}^2}\, p_{123}\right),$$

$$\boldsymbol{q} = \{-q \cdot n_i(p_{123})\}.$$

The occurence of $\boldsymbol{q}'_{12}$ comes from the fact that $q'_{12} = -q_{12} \cdot n_i(p_{12})$ occurred in the first coupling. Since $[p_{12}]$ had to be chosen as $[p_{12} \leftarrow p_{123}][p_{123}]$ in order that one might perform the second l–s coupling conveniently, $q'_{12} = -q_{12}[p_{12} \to p_{123}]\, n_i(p_{123}) = -q'_{12} \cdot n_i(p_{123})$.

This is a relativistic effect as well as the cascade of Lorentz transformations which occur in the spin matrices.

Such reductions may be of some use in the study of isobar productions. When isobars corresponding to different coupling ([(12)3], [(13)2] say) are simultaneously produced, it is interesting to know the recoupling coefficients. The solution of this problem will be postponed until later since the symmetrical coupling to be described now makes it essentially trivial.

b) The symmetric coupling[15]

We consider states $|[p_1]\,\sigma_1[p_2]\,\sigma_2[p_3]\,\sigma_3\rangle$ whose total momentum, as we know, is $p_1 + p_2 + p_3 = p_{123}$; let $[p_{123}]$ be an arbitrary frame attached to p_{123} and let $p_{12}^2, p_{23}^2, p_{13}^2, (p_{12}^2 + p_{13}^2 + p_{23}^2 = m_1^2 + m_2^2 + m_3^2 + p_{123}^2)$, be a set of values of invariants formed with the p_i's $(p_{ij}^2 = (p_i + p_j)^2)$. p_i's belonging to such a set of invariants are parametrized for a given p_{123} by a rotation R which takes each p_i to a standard position p_i^s such that $p_{ij}^2 = (p_i^s + p_j^s)^2$.

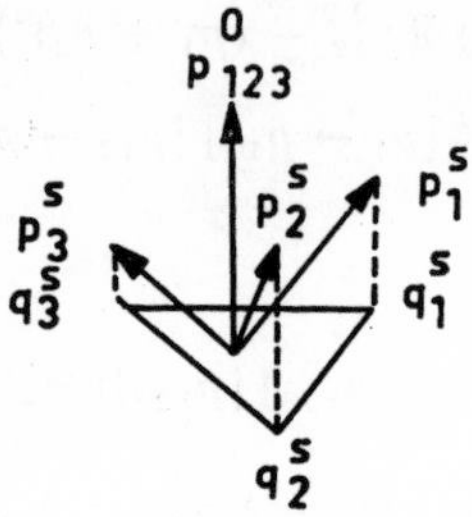

Fig. 4

(Invariants are fixed by the time components $p_i^s \cdot \overset{0}{p}_{123}$, and directions by the triangle with vertices:

$$q_i^s = p_i^s - \frac{p_i^s \cdot \overset{0}{p}_{123}}{\overset{0}{p}{}_{123}^{2}}\,\overset{0}{p}_{123}\Bigg):$$

$$p_i = [p_{123}]\,Rp_i^s.$$

One may then use spin bases $[p_i]$ rigidly attached to the configuration of the p_i's:

$$[p_i] = [p_{123}]\,R[p_i^s]$$

and defines states

$$|[p_{123}], \mu; j_{123}, \lambda, \lambda_1, \lambda_2, \lambda_3, p_{12}^2, p_{23}^2, p_{13}^2\rangle = \int \mathrm{d}R \sqrt{\frac{2j_{123}+1}{4\pi}}\, \mathscr{D}_{\mu\lambda}^{j_{123}*}(R),$$

$$|[p_1]\,(p_{123}, R), \lambda_1; [p_2]\,(p_{123}, R), \lambda_2; [p_3]\,(p_{123}, R)\,\lambda_3\rangle \qquad \text{(III,b,1)}$$

where the λ_i's are spin projections on the above frames, which transform according to

$$U(a, A)\,|[p_{123}]\,\mu; j_{123}, \lambda, \lambda_1, \lambda_2, \lambda_3, p_{12}^2 p_{23}^2 p_{13}^2\rangle = \mathrm{e}^{i(A\cdot p_{123})\cdot a} \qquad \text{(III,b,2)}$$

$$|[Ap_{123}]\,\mu'; j_{123}, \lambda, \lambda_1, \lambda_2, \lambda_3, p_{12}^2 p_{23}^2 p_{13}^2\rangle\, \mathscr{D}_{\mu'\mu}^{j_{123}}([Ap_{123}]^{-1}\,A[p_{123}]).$$

[Note[16]: $[Ap_i] = [Ap_{123}]([Ap_{123}]^{-1}\,A[p_{123}])\,R[p_i^s]$, so that the Wigner rotations computed with the above frames reduce to ± 1, the latter sign being due to the necessity of using SU(2), and j_{123} is thus restricted to be integer or half integer according as $s_1 + s_2 + s_3$ is integer or half integer.]

The quantum number λ can be interpreted as the projection of the total spin on $[p_{123}]\, R\overset{0}{n}_3(p_{123})$, an axis rigidly attached to the three momenta p_i.

The Clebsch–Gordan coefficient is

$$\langle [p_1]\,\sigma_1 [p_2]\,\sigma_2 [p_3]\,\sigma_3\, \| [p_{123}],\, \mu;\, j_{123},\, \lambda,\, \lambda_1,\, \lambda_2,\, \lambda_3 p_{12}^2 p_{13}^2 p_{23}^2 \rangle$$

$$= \frac{2\sqrt{p_{123}^2}}{\sqrt{\pi}}\,\delta^4(p_{123} - p_1 - p_2 - p_3)\,\delta(p_{12}^2 - (p_1 + p_2)^2)\,\delta(p_{13}^2 - (p_1 + p_3)^2)$$

$$\mathscr{D}^{(s_1)}_{\sigma_1\lambda_1}([p_1]^{-1}\,[p_1]_r)\,\mathscr{D}^{(s_2)}_{\sigma_2\lambda_2}([p_2]^{-1}\,[p_2]_r)\,\mathscr{D}^{(s_3)}_{\sigma_3\lambda_3}([p_3]^{-1}\,[p_3]_r)$$

$$\sqrt{\frac{2j_{123} + 1}{4\pi}}\,\mathscr{D}^{j_{123}*}_{\mu\lambda}(R(p_1,\, p_2,\, p_3)) \qquad \text{(III,b,3)}$$

where the $[p_i]_r$ are some frames rigidly tied to the system of 3 momenta as described above. A convenient choice is for instance that where $n_3(p_i)$ are the helicity axes in the overall center of mass:

$$n_3(p_i) = \frac{[p_i \leftarrow p_{123}]\, q_i}{\sqrt{-q_i^2}}$$

and $n_2(p_i) = (p_1 \wedge p_2 \wedge p_3)$ (the normal to the plane of the three momenta).

This coupling scheme is appropriate for the characterization of the decay into three particles of a system of spin j_{123} in terms of the "Dalitz plot variables" p_{ij}^2 and, at each point of the Dalitz plot, of the angles of the normal to the production plane and of the azimuthal angle within this plane, which fixes the orientation of the triangle made up by the three momenta.

One can of course similarly symmetrically couple any number of one particle states

Remark.

The conditions of convergence of angular expansions of transition amplitudes to final states involving three or more particles is very badly known at the moment because of the lack of information on analyticity properties of such amplitudes.

c) Recoupling coefficient between a state labelled by the symmetric coupling and a state labelled by helicities

Let:

$$\langle [p_{123}],\, \mu;\, j_{123} p_{12}^2 j_{12} \lambda_1 \lambda_2 \lambda_{12} \lambda_3\, \| [p'_{123}],\, \mu';\, j'_{123} \lambda'_1 \lambda'_2 \lambda'_3 \lambda p'^2_{12} p'^2_{23} p'^2_{13} \rangle$$

$$= \delta(p_{123} - p'_{123})\,\delta_{\mu\mu'}\delta_{j_{123}}\delta_{j'_{123}} W_{\substack{p^2_{123}\\ j_{123}}}(p_{12}^2 j_{12} \lambda_1 \lambda_2 \lambda_{12} \lambda_3 | \qquad \text{(III,c,1)}$$

$$\cdots | p'^2_{12} p'^2_{23} p'^2_{13} \lambda'_1 \lambda'_2 \lambda'_3 \lambda).$$

All helicity frames are taken to have $(p_1 \wedge p_2 \wedge p_3)$ as axis number 2. This allows us to make a 2 dimensional drawing of the directions of the various vectors involved and read off circular and hyperbolic angles.

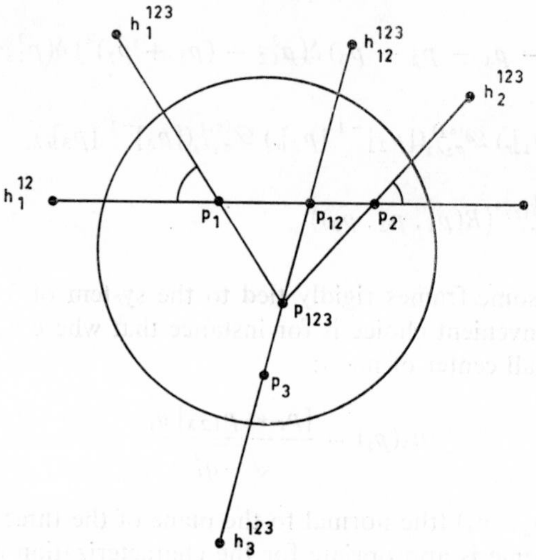

Fig. 5

The circle represents a curve at infinity on the light cone. Time like vectors are represented inside, space like vectors, outside. Two orthogonal vectors are represented by conjugate points.

h_i^j means: helicity axis of particle i in frame of time axis p^j.

One gets factors

$\delta(p_{12}^2 - p_{12}'^2)$	(obvious)
$\delta_{\lambda_3 \lambda'_3}$	(since particle 3 is described in terms of the same helicity frame in both couplings)
$d^{s_2}_{\lambda_2 \lambda'_2}(-\hat{h}_2^{12} \cdot \hat{h}_2^{123})$	describing the change of helicity basis from the symmetric to the unsymmetric coupling,
$d^{s_1}_{\lambda_1 \lambda'_1}(-\hat{h}_1^{12} \cdot \hat{h}_1^{123})$	describing the change of helicity basis from the symmetric to the unsymmetric coupling,
$d^{j_{12}}_{\lambda_{12} \lambda_1 - \lambda_2}(-\hat{q}_{1,2} \cdot \hat{h}_{12}^{123})$	where $q_{1,2}$ is the relative momentum of particles 1 and 2 in their barycentric frame (not $q'_{1,2}$!)

$d^{j_{123}}_{\lambda_{12}-\lambda_3\lambda}(-\hat{q}_{12,3}\cdot n)$ where n is the spin axis rigidly tied up with the triangle of momenta. e.g. $q'_{1,2}$.

All scalar products are evaluated in terms of the invariants p'^{12}_{ij}. The kinematical factors occurring in each Clebsch–Gordan coefficient stay unchanged. Thus we obtain:

$$W_{p^2_{123}}(p^2_{12}j_{12}\lambda_1\lambda_2\lambda_{12}\lambda_3\,|p'^2_{12}p'^2_{23}p'^2_{13}\lambda'_1\lambda'_2\lambda'_3\lambda)_{123}$$

$$= \frac{4\sqrt{p^2_{12}}\sqrt{\pi}\,\delta(p^2_{12}-p'^2_{12})}{\lambda^{1/4}(m^2_1, m^2_2, p^2_{12})\,\lambda^{1/4}(p^2_{12}, m^2_3, p^2_{123})}\sqrt{\frac{2j_{12}+1}{4\pi}}(-1)^{s_2-\lambda_2+s_3-\lambda_3}\,\delta_{\lambda_3\lambda'_3} \tag{III,c,2}$$

$$\times\, d^{s_2}_{\lambda_2\lambda'_2}(-\hat{h}^{12}_2\cdot\hat{h}^{123}_2)\,d^{s_1}_{\lambda_1\lambda'_1}(-\hat{h}^{12}_1\cdot\hat{h}^{123}_1)\times d^{j_{12}}_{\lambda_{12}\lambda_1-\lambda_2}(-\hat{q}_{1,2}\cdot\hat{h}^{123}_{12})$$

$$\times\, d^{j_{123}}_{\lambda_{12}-\lambda_3\lambda}(-\hat{q}_{12,3}\cdot n).$$

The computation of an arbitrary recoupling coefficient (17.18) involves essentially twice as many rotation matrices, as one can see by inserting a complete set of states labelled by the symmetric coupling. Racah coefficients for the rotation group will eventually appear when l–s couplings are considered.

APPENDIX I

BASIC FACTS ABOUT THE LORENTZ GROUP

a) The four sheets of the Lorentz group

Let $x = (x^0, x^1x^2x^3)$ be a vector in Minkowski space.
Transformation matrices L:

$$x \to x' = Lx, \quad \therefore x'Gx' = xGx, \quad G = \begin{pmatrix} 1 & & & \\ & -1 & & \\ & & -1 & \\ & & & -1 \end{pmatrix},$$

such that $L^TGL = G$, form a group: the homogeneous Lorentz group. This group has four connected components:

$$L^\uparrow_+ \quad \det L = +1 \quad L^0_0 > 0 \quad \text{(a subgroup)}$$

$$L^\downarrow_+ \quad \det L = +1 \quad L^0_0 < 0,$$

$$L^\uparrow_- \quad \det L = -1 \quad L^0_0 > 0,$$

$$L^\downarrow_- \quad \det L = -1 \quad L^0_0 < 0$$

The last three components are not subgroups (they do not contain the identity). One has

$$L_+^\downarrow = -\mathbf{1} \times L_+^\uparrow,$$
$$L_-^\uparrow = G \times L_+^\uparrow,$$
$$L_-^\downarrow = -G \times L_+^\downarrow.$$

$L_+^\uparrow$ is not simply connected. Its universal covering group (the smallest Lie group which has the same Lie algebra and is simply connected) is SL(2C), the group of 2×2 complex matrices of determinant one (special linear complex group in two dimensions—or group of 2×2 unimodular complex matrices).

The correspondence is $1 \to 2$:

$$L \to \pm A(L)$$

where $A(L)$ is defined up to a sign by:

$$x' = Lx \to \underset{\sim}{x}' = A\underset{\sim}{x}A^\dagger$$

($\underset{\sim}{x} = x^0 + \boldsymbol{x}\boldsymbol{\sigma}$ where $\boldsymbol{\sigma}$ is the set of Pauli matrices) indeed $\det \underset{\sim}{x} = x^{0^2} - \boldsymbol{x}^2 = \det \underset{\sim}{x}'$ (since $\det A = \det A^\dagger = 1$).

b) Subgroups

The little group $L_+^\uparrow(x)$ of a vector x is the subgroup of Lorentz transformations leaving x invariant.

If x is time-like: $x^2 > 0$ $L_+^\uparrow(x)$ is isomorphic with a rotation group SO(3) in three dimensional space: if $\overset{0}{x} = (1, 0, 0, 0)$ $L_+(\overset{0}{x})$ is just SO(3) in the variables $x_i\, 1 \leqq i \leqq 3$.

The SL(2, C) representative is SU(2) the group of unitary complex 2×2 matrices of determinant 1 ($A\mathbf{1}A^\dagger = \mathbf{1}$).

If x is light-like: $x^2 = 0$ $L_+^\uparrow(x)$ is isomorphic with a euclidean group $E(2)$ in two dimensional space (again a three parameter group):

If $x^0 = (1, 0, 0, -1)$

$$L(x^0) = \begin{bmatrix} 1 + \dfrac{\alpha_1^2+\alpha_2^2}{2}, & \alpha_1\cos\varphi + \alpha_2\sin\varphi, & -\alpha_1\sin\varphi + \alpha_2\cos\varphi, & -\dfrac{\alpha_1^2+\alpha_2^2}{2} \\ \dfrac{\alpha_1}{2}, & \cos\varphi, & -\sin\varphi, & -\dfrac{\alpha_1}{2} \\ \dfrac{\alpha_2}{2}, & \sin\varphi, & \cos\varphi, & -\dfrac{\alpha_2}{2} \\ \dfrac{\alpha_1^2+\alpha_2^2}{2}, & \alpha_1\cos\varphi + \alpha_2\sin\varphi, & -\alpha_1\sin\varphi + \alpha_2\cos\varphi, & 1 - \dfrac{\alpha_1^2+\alpha_2^2}{2} \end{bmatrix}$$

The SL(2C) representative is the subgroup $\begin{pmatrix} e^{\frac{i\Phi}{2}} & z \\ 0 & e^{\frac{-i\Phi}{2}} \end{pmatrix}$; $\overset{0}{\underset{\sim}{x}} = \begin{pmatrix} 2 & 0 \\ 0 & 0 \end{pmatrix}$.

If x is space-like: $x^2 < 0$, $L_+^\uparrow(x)$ is isomorphic with a three dimensional Lorentz group SO(2, 1). The SL(2C) representative is isomorphic with SL(2, R) (unimodular real matrices: take $\overset{0}{x} = (0, 0, 1, 0)$ and use $A\sigma_2 A^\dagger = \sigma_2$ and $\sigma_2 A \sigma_2^{-1} = A^{-1T}$, a general identity) or SU(1, 1) the pseudo unitary group in two dimensions which fulfills $A\begin{pmatrix} 1 & 0 \\ 0 & -1 \end{pmatrix} A^\dagger = \begin{pmatrix} 1 & 0 \\ 0 & -1 \end{pmatrix}$ (pseudo because of the sign!).

Every Lorentz transformation can be written as the product of a particular transformation transforming any four-vector into a vector of equal length (and same sign of the time component if the vector is time-like) by an operation of the little group of this vector.

Thus for instance every Lorentz transformation can be decomposed into a rotation and a pure Lorentz transformation:

$AA^\dagger$ is hermitian positive definite, and has therefore a positive square root H which represents the pure Lorentz transformation:

$$H = h^0 + \boldsymbol{h} \cdot \boldsymbol{\sigma}, \qquad h \text{ real } h^{0^2} - \boldsymbol{h}^2 = 1$$

which represents a Lorentz transformation of velocity in the direction $\hat{h}$ with magnitude $v = \dfrac{2|\boldsymbol{h}|\, h_0}{h_0^2 + |\boldsymbol{h}|^2}$.

Then $AA^\dagger = HH^\dagger \to (H^{-1}A)(H^{-1}A)^\dagger = 1 \to A = HU$ where $U \in \mathrm{SU}(2)$.

c) Representations of SL(2, C)

Let $\begin{pmatrix} \xi \\ \eta \end{pmatrix}$ be a complex two dimensional vector (a "spinor"), transforming according to:

$$A: \begin{pmatrix} \xi \\ \eta \end{pmatrix} \to \begin{pmatrix} \xi' \\ \eta' \end{pmatrix} = A\begin{pmatrix} \xi \\ \eta \end{pmatrix} = \begin{pmatrix} a & b \\ c & d \end{pmatrix}\begin{pmatrix} \xi \\ \eta \end{pmatrix} = \begin{pmatrix} a\xi + b\eta \\ c\xi + d\eta \end{pmatrix}.$$

The $2j + 1$-dimensional vector

$$V_{jm}(\xi, \eta) = \frac{(\xi)^{j+m}(\eta)^{j-m}}{\sqrt{(j+m)!\,(j-m)!}}$$

transforms according to

$$\begin{aligned} \mathscr{D}^j(A)\colon\ V_{jm}(\xi, \eta) \to V'_{jm}(\xi, \eta) &= \mathscr{D}^j_{mm'}(A)\, V_{jm'}(\xi, \eta) \\ &= V_{jm}(a\xi + b\eta, c\xi + d\eta). \end{aligned}$$

Hence:

$$\mathscr{D}^j_{mm'}(A) = \sum_{\substack{p+q=j-m' \\ 0\leq p\leq j+m \\ 0\leq q\leq j-m}} \sqrt{(j+m')!\,(j-m')!\,(j+m)!\,(j-m)!} \times \frac{a^{j+m-p}b^p c^{j-m-q}\,d^q}{(j+m-p)!\,p!(j-m-q)!\,q!}.$$

This representation is labelled $(j, 0)$.
Similarly $\mathscr{D}^j(A^{\dagger-1})$ is labelled $(0, j)$; it is not equivalent to $\mathscr{D}^j(A)$.
This formula defines $\mathscr{D}^j(A)$ for A arbitrary!
One can easily see that

$$\mathscr{D}^j_{mm'}(A^*) = \mathscr{D}^{j*}_{mm'}(A),$$

$$\mathscr{D}^j_{mm'}(A^T) = \mathscr{D}^j_{m'm}(A),$$

$$\mathscr{D}^j_{mm'}(\lambda \mathbf{1}) = \delta_{mm'}\lambda^{2j}.$$

If $A \in \mathrm{SU}(2)$ then $(0, j)$ and $(j, 0)$ become identical ($U = U^{\dagger-1}$).

d) Products of representations[IV-19] Clebsch-Gordan coefficients

Let (ξ_1, η_1), (ξ_2, η_2) be two spinors. From the identity $A\sigma_2 A^T = \sigma_2 \det A$, one finds that $\xi_1'\eta_2' - \xi_2'\eta_1' = (\xi_1\eta_2 - \xi_2\eta_1)(\det A)$; in particular:

$$\frac{(\xi_1\eta_2 - \xi_2\eta_1)^{2j}}{2j!} = \sum_{m=-j}^{m=+j} V_{jm}(\xi_1\eta_1)\,(-)^{j-m}\,V_{j-m}(\xi_2\eta_2)$$

is multiplied by $(\det A)^{2j}$ under the action of A.

The invariant formed with three spinors:

$$I_{j_{12}, j_{23}, j_{31}} = [\xi_2\eta_3 - \xi_3\eta_2]^{j_{23}}\,[\xi_3\eta_1 - \xi_1\eta_3]^{j_{13}}\,[\xi_1\eta_2 - \xi_2\eta_1]^{j_{12}} \times [(j_{12})!\,(j_{13})!\,(j_{23})! \times (j_{12} + j_{13} + j_{23} + 1)!]^{-\frac{1}{2}}$$

is thus multiplied by $(\det A)^{j_{12}+j_{23}+j_{13}}$. It is homogeneous of degree $2j_1 = j_{12} + j_{13}$ in (ξ_1, η_1), $2j_2 = j_{12} + j_{23}$ in (ξ_2, η_2), and $2j_3 = j_{13} + j_{23}$ in (ξ_3, η_3) and can thus be expanded as:

$$\sum_{m_1\, m_2\, m_3} \begin{pmatrix} j_1 & j_2 & j_3 \\ m_1 & m_2 & m_3 \end{pmatrix} V_{j_1 m_1}(\xi_1, \eta_1)\, V_{j_2 m_2}(\xi_2, \eta_2)\, V_{j_3 m_3}(\xi_3, \eta_3).$$

Clebsch–Gordan coefficients are defined by

$$\left(\begin{array}{cc|c} j_1 & j_2 & j_3 \\ m_1 & m_2 & m_3 \end{array}\right) = \sqrt{2j_3 + 1}\begin{pmatrix} j_1 & j_2 & j_3 \\ m_1 & m_2 & -m_3 \end{pmatrix}(-)^{j_1 - j_2 + m_3}$$

they vanish unless $m_1 + m_2 = m_3$; $|j_1 - j_2| < j_3 < j_1 + j_2$, $j_1 + j_2 + j_3$ integer.

The invariance of $I_{j_{12}j_{23}j_{31}}$ then reads

$$(\det A)^{j_1+j_2-j_3}\begin{pmatrix} j_1 & j_2 & j_3 \\ m_1 & m_2 & m_3 \end{pmatrix}\mathscr{D}^{j_3}_{m_3m'_3}(A)$$

$$= \sum_{m'_1+m'_2=m'_3}\begin{pmatrix} j_1 & j_2 & j_3 \\ m'_1 & m'_2 & m'_3 \end{pmatrix}\mathscr{D}^{j_1}_{m_1m'_1}(A)\,\mathscr{D}^{j_2}_{m_2m'_2}(A).$$

Normalizations have been fixed so that the Clebsch–Gordan coefficients fulfill the orthogonality and completeness relations appropriate when $A \in \mathrm{SU}(2)$

$$\sum_{j_3,m_3}\begin{pmatrix} j_1 & j_2 & j_3 \\ m_1 & m_2 & m_3 \end{pmatrix}\begin{pmatrix} j_3 & j_1 & j_2 \\ m_3 & m'_1 & m'_2 \end{pmatrix} = \delta_{m_1m'_1}\delta_{m_2m'_2}$$

$$\sum_{m_1,m_2}\begin{pmatrix} j_3 & j_1 & j_2 \\ m_3 & m_1 & m_2 \end{pmatrix}\begin{pmatrix} j_1 & j_2 & j'_3 \\ m_1 & m_2 & m'_3 \end{pmatrix} = \delta_{j_3j'_3}\delta_{m_3m'_3}$$

so that one also has: e.g.

$$(\det A)^{j_1+j_2-j_3}\mathscr{D}^{j_3}_{m_3m'_3}(A)$$

$$= \sum\begin{pmatrix} j_1 & j_2 & j_3 \\ m_1 & m_2 & m_3 \end{pmatrix}\begin{pmatrix} j_1 & j_2 & j_3 \\ m'_1 & m'_2 & m'_3 \end{pmatrix}\mathscr{D}^{j_1}_{m_1m'_1}(A)\,\mathscr{D}^{j_2}_{m_2m'_2}(A).$$

e) SU(2) versus SL(2, *R*)

Finite dimensional representations of SL(2, *C*) may obviously be restricted to finite dimensional representations both of SU(2) and SL(2, *R*). The restrictions to SU(2) yield the well known *unitary* representations of SU(2). This is not so for SL(2, *R*) because SL(2, *R*) is not a compact group. Unitary representations of SL(2, *R*) have been classified by V. Bargmann[20]. We shall just say, for the purpose of orientation that a convenient basis of representation space can be labelled by integer or half integer eigenvalues of the generator of rotations (corresponding to the subgroup $\begin{pmatrix} \cos\varphi & -\sin\varphi \\ \sin\varphi & \cos\varphi \end{pmatrix}$, which vary by steps of unity over an infinite range either from $-\infty$ to $+\infty$, for some types of representations, or from $(-\infty$ to $-k)$ or $(+k$ to $+\infty)$ where k is a number which characterizes some other types of representations.

f) Fourier analysis

Whether it be for SU(2) or SL(2, *R*) one has the following property: let $f(g)$ be a square integrable function over the group: $\int |f(g)|^2 \mathrm{d}g$ where $\mathrm{d}g$ is the so-called Haar measure on the group ($\mathrm{d}\cos\theta\,\mathrm{d}\varphi\,\mathrm{d}\psi$ for SU(2), $\mathrm{d}\cosh\theta\,\mathrm{d}\varphi\,\mathrm{d}\psi$ for

SL(2, R), then there are sufficiently many unitary representations $\mathscr{D}^j(g)$ with matrix elements $\mathscr{D}^j_{mm'}(g)$ such that:

$$f(g) = \sum_{j,m,m'} C^j_{mm'} \mathscr{D}^j_{m'm}(g)$$

$$\int |f(g)|^2 \, dg = \sum_{j,m,m'} |C^j_{mm'}|^2$$

where the sum may eventually turn into an integral. In the case of SU(2), j just ranges over integers and half integers and the $\mathscr{D}^j(g)$ are just the representations we have previously described.

In the case of SL(2, R) the sum over j becomes an integral plus an infinite discrete sum.

From this, one can deduce the existence of complete sets of functions on "homogeneous spaces" of these groups. For instance, let us rewrite in the case of SU(2):

$$f(\varphi, \theta, \psi) = \sum_{j,m,m'} C^j_{mm'} \mathscr{D}^j_{m'm}(\varphi, \theta, \psi).$$

Consider now functions φ and θ alone, (which label points on the unit sphere). Any function $g(\varphi, \theta)$ can be lifted to a function of (φ, θ, ψ) through $f(\varphi\theta\psi) = g(\varphi, \theta)\, e^{i\lambda\psi}$.

Thus, for such functions, there only survive in the above sum terms where $m = \lambda, j > |\lambda| (\mathscr{D}^j_{m'm}(\varphi, \theta, \psi) = \mathscr{D}^j_{m'm}(\varphi, \theta, 0)\, e^{-im\psi})$. Hence the various complete sets of functions on the sphere $\mathscr{D}^j_{m\lambda}(\varphi, \theta, 0)$ for fixed λ, as mentioned in Chapter II, § b.

A similar result of course holds in the case of SL(2, R), which has been used in attempts to understand the group theoretical origin of Regge's analysis[14].

g) Elements of Minkowski geometry

As one knows, the Lorentz group preserves the light cone $x^2 = 0$. It is convenient to associate with each four vector its direction labelled for instance by the 3-vector $\xi = \dfrac{\boldsymbol{x}}{x^0}$. When x is transformed under a Lorentz transformation L: $x \to x' = Lx$, its direction ξ is transformed under a projective transformation: $\xi \to \xi'$, with $\xi' = \dfrac{\boldsymbol{x}'}{x'^0}$, which preserves the sphere Ω: $\xi^2 = 1$.

Time-like, light-like, and space-like vectors are represented by points respectively, inside, on, and outside Ω. These three regions are preserved globally under any transformation of the group.

The invariant distance between two points:

$$\widehat{AB} = \ln \frac{\overline{AC}}{\overline{AD}} : \frac{\overline{BC}}{\overline{BD}}$$

is a projective invariant, real if A and B are time-like and pure imaginary if A and B are space-like (C and D are then complex conjugate of each other).

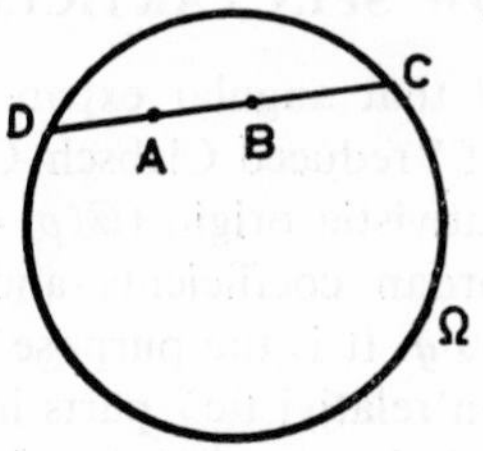

Fig. 6

In particular if the above "anharmonic ratio" is -1 (A and B conjugate with respect to Ω) the corresponding four vectors are orthogonal.

One can similarly define the angle between a pair of two-dimensional planes which intersect, as the logarithm of the anharmonic ratio between their traces on ξ space and the tangents to Ω through their intersection in the plane they determine

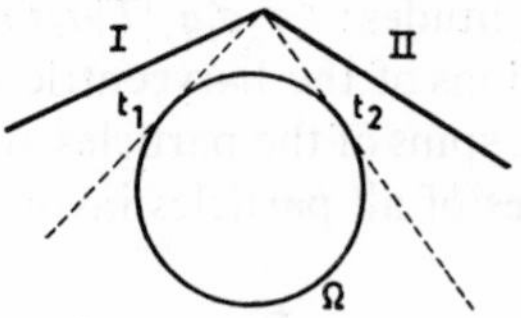

Fig. 7

Invariant volume elements:

if $\xi = \pm 1$ are traces of Ω on a straight line the line element is $\dfrac{d\xi}{1 - \xi^2}$, if $\xi_1^2 + \xi_2^2 = 1$ is the trace of Ω on a two plane, the surface element is

$$\frac{d\xi_1\, d\xi_2}{(1 - \xi_1^2 - \xi_2^2)^2};$$

finally the three dimensional volume element is $\dfrac{d\xi_1\, d\xi_2\, d\xi_3}{(1 - \xi^2)^3}$. As a result the sum of the angles of a triangle is smaller than π (its complement to π is called the defect of the triangle), and is proportional to the surface of the triangle.

This geometry, a hyperbolic analogue of the geometry on the sphere is useful in evaluating recoupling coefficients.

APPENDIX II

ANGULAR EXPANSIONS FOR TWO BODY REACTIONS INVOLVING LOW SPIN PARTICLES

It was found in Chapter II that angular expansions of transition amplitudes could be expressed in terms of "reduced Clebsch–Gordan coefficients" involving spin matrices of a purely relativistic origin ($\mathscr{D}(p_i \leftarrow P)$) multiplying expressions involving SU(2) Clebsch–Gordan coefficients and angular functions of three dimensional (symbolic) vectors $\boldsymbol{q}$. It is the purpose of this appendix to give compact expressions of these "non relativistic" parts in cases where the spins of the particles involved are sufficiently low so that the Clebsch–Gordanry can be treated easily.

The methods used here allow one to quickly write down typical angular distributions or spin correlations. They have a defect, though, that normalization factors, (which often are not useful), have to be computed by a separate calculation. So, reduced matrix elements defined here, and denoted by small letters, will only agree with those defined in the body of the notes, and denoted by capital letters, to within kinematical factors (due to phase space) and $\sqrt{\dfrac{2j+1}{4\pi}}$ factors due to conventional normalization of Clebsch–Gordan coefficients.

We consider transition amplitudes: $\langle \sigma_f \sigma_f' \boldsymbol{q}_f | T | \sigma_i \sigma_i' \boldsymbol{q}_i \rangle$ where only spin variables and angular variables (directions of the barycentric momenta $\boldsymbol{q}_i$, $\boldsymbol{q}_f$ in initial and final states) are indicated. The spins of the particles are s_i, s_i', s_f, s_f' and the product of the relative intrinsic parities of all particles involved is ± 1. The corresponding reaction is denoted by:

$$s_i + s_i' \xrightarrow{\pm} s_f + s_f'.$$

1) $0 + 0 \xrightarrow{\pm} 0 + 0$

$$\langle \boldsymbol{q}_f | T | \boldsymbol{q}_i \rangle = \sum_{\substack{l,m \\ l',m'}} \langle \hat{\boldsymbol{q}}_f | l'm' \rangle \langle l'm' | T | lm \rangle \langle lm | \hat{\boldsymbol{q}}_i \rangle,$$

where $|lm\rangle$ are eigenstates of the total angular momentum operator. From rotational invariance

$$\langle l', m' | T | l, m \rangle = \delta_{ll'} \delta_{mm'} t_l.$$

From parity conservation $(-)^l = \pm(-)^{l'}$, so that only even relative intrinsic parity is allowed. Using

$$\langle l, m | \hat{\boldsymbol{q}}_i \rangle = Y^*_{lm}(\hat{\boldsymbol{q}}_i); \quad \langle \hat{\boldsymbol{q}}_f | l, m \rangle = Y_{lm}(\hat{\boldsymbol{q}}_f)$$

$$\sum_m Y_{lm}(\hat{\boldsymbol{q}}_f)\, Y^*_{lm}(\hat{\boldsymbol{q}}_i) = \frac{2l+1}{4\pi} P_l(\hat{\boldsymbol{q}}_f \cdot \hat{\boldsymbol{q}}_i) \quad \text{(Legendre polynomial)},$$

we obtain:

$$\langle \boldsymbol{q}_f | T | \boldsymbol{q}_i \rangle = \sum_l t_l \frac{2l+1}{4\pi} P_l(\hat{\boldsymbol{q}}_f \cdot \hat{\boldsymbol{q}}_i)$$

where t_l is a function of $|\boldsymbol{q}_i|$ (or $|\boldsymbol{q}_f|$) alone.

$2^+)\ 0 + \frac{1}{2} \xrightarrow{\pm} 0 + \frac{1}{2}$

$$\langle \boldsymbol{q}_f, \sigma_f |T| \boldsymbol{q}_i, \sigma_i \rangle = \sum_{\substack{lm \\ l'm' \\ JM \\ J'M'}} \langle \hat{\boldsymbol{q}}_f | l'm' \rangle \langle l'm'; \tfrac{1}{2}\sigma_f | l', \tfrac{1}{2}, J', M' \rangle$$

$$\times \langle l', \tfrac{1}{2}; J', M' |T| l, \tfrac{1}{2}; J, M \rangle$$

$$\times \langle l, \tfrac{1}{2}; J, M | lm\, \tfrac{1}{2}\sigma_i \rangle \langle l, m | \hat{\boldsymbol{q}}_i \rangle$$

where we have used a slightly more explicit notation for C.G. coefficients.

From rotation and parity invariance

$$\langle l', \tfrac{1}{2}; J', M' |T| l, \tfrac{1}{2}; J, M \rangle = \underset{\text{parity}}{\delta_{ll'}} \ \underset{\text{angular}}{\delta_{JJ'}} \ \underset{\text{momentum}}{\delta_{MM'}} \ t_{J,l}.$$

For each l, J can take up two values, $l \pm \frac{1}{2}$; we call $t_{l\pm 1/2,l} = t_l^{\pm}$ and

$$\sum_M |l, \tfrac{1}{2}; J, M \rangle \langle l, \tfrac{1}{2}; J, M | = \mathscr{P}_{J,l},$$

which is the projection operator on the manifold of states $|\sigma, l\rangle$.

Rule.

Let A be an hermitian operator with eigenvalues a_i, then the projector on the subspace $|a_i\rangle$ is

$$\mathscr{P}_i = \prod_{j \neq i} \frac{A - a_j}{a_i - a_j}$$

and fulfills:

$$\mathscr{P}_i |a_i\rangle = |a_i\rangle, \quad \mathscr{P}_i |a_j\rangle = 0, \quad \mathscr{P}_i \mathscr{P}_j = \delta_{ij} \mathscr{P}_i; \quad \sum \mathscr{P}_i = \mathbf{1}.$$

Take $A = J^2 = (\boldsymbol{l} + \frac{1}{2}\boldsymbol{\sigma})^2$ where $\boldsymbol{l}$ is the orbital angular momentum operator, and $\frac{1}{2}\sigma$, the spin $\frac{1}{2}$ operator.
Then, $a_{l+1/2,l} = (l + \frac{1}{2})(l + \frac{3}{2})$ and $a_{l-1/2,l} = (l - \frac{1}{2})(l + \frac{1}{2})$,

hence

$$\mathscr{P}_{l+1/2,l} = \frac{l + 1 + \boldsymbol{l}\cdot\boldsymbol{\sigma}}{2l + 1} \qquad \mathscr{P}_{l-1/2,l} = \frac{l - \boldsymbol{l}\cdot\boldsymbol{\sigma}}{2l + 1}$$

and

$$\left\langle l, m', \frac{1}{2}, \sigma_f \,|\mathscr{P}_{l+1/2,l}|\, l, m, \frac{1}{2}, \sigma_i \right\rangle$$

$$= \left\langle \sigma_f \right| \int \mathrm{d}\Omega_q Y^*_{lm'}(\hat{q}) \frac{l + 1 + \boldsymbol{l}_q\cdot\boldsymbol{\sigma}}{2l + 1} Y_{lm}(\hat{q}) \left| \sigma_i \right\rangle$$

with a similar formula for $\mathscr{P}_{l-1/2,l}$.

Thus,

$$\langle q_f, \sigma_f |T| q_i, \sigma_i\rangle = \langle\sigma_f| \sum_l t_{l_+} \int d\Omega_q \frac{2l+1}{4\pi} P_l(\hat{q}_f \cdot \hat{q}) \frac{l+1+\boldsymbol{l}_q \cdot \boldsymbol{\sigma}}{2l+1} \frac{2l+1}{4\pi}$$

$$\times P_l(\hat{q}_i \cdot \hat{q}) + t_{l_-} \int d\Omega_q \frac{2l+1}{4\pi} P_l(\hat{q}_f \cdot \hat{q})$$

$$\times \frac{l - \boldsymbol{l}_q \cdot \boldsymbol{\sigma}}{2l+1} \frac{2l+1}{4\pi} P_l(\hat{q}_i \cdot \hat{q}) |\sigma_i\rangle.$$

Using the δ function on the unit sphere:

$$\delta(\hat{q}, \hat{q}') = \sum_l \frac{2l+1}{4\pi} P_l(\hat{q} \cdot \hat{q}'),$$

such that

$$\int \delta(\hat{q}, \hat{q}') f(\hat{q}') \, d\Omega_{\hat{q}'} = f(\hat{q}),$$

and remarking that $\frac{2l+1}{4\pi} P_l(\hat{q}_f \cdot \hat{q})$ can be replaced by $\sum_l \frac{2l+1}{4\pi} P_l(\hat{q}_f \cdot \hat{q})$ because terms which have been added in cancel out through integration over $\hat{q}$ in view of the orthogonality of spherical harmonics, we get:

$$\langle q_f\sigma_f |T| q_i\sigma_i\rangle = \langle\sigma_f| \sum_{l=0}^{\infty} \left[t_{l_+} \frac{l+1+\boldsymbol{l}_{q_f} \cdot \boldsymbol{\sigma}}{2l+1} + t_{l_-} \frac{l - \boldsymbol{l}_{q_f} \cdot \boldsymbol{\sigma}}{2l+1} \right]$$

$$\times \frac{2l+1}{4\pi} P_l(\hat{q}_f \cdot \hat{q}_i) |\sigma_i\rangle.$$

Note that:

$$\boldsymbol{l}_{q_f} = \frac{1}{i} \boldsymbol{q}_f \times \nabla_{q_f}; \quad P_l(\hat{q}_f \cdot \hat{q}_i) = P_l\left(\frac{\boldsymbol{q}_f \cdot \boldsymbol{q}_i}{|q_f|\,|q_i|}\right);$$

since $\nabla_{q_f} \dfrac{1}{|q_f|} \propto \boldsymbol{q}_f$,

$$\boldsymbol{l}_{q_f} P_l(\hat{q}_f \cdot \hat{q}_i) = \frac{1}{i} \hat{q}_f \times \hat{q}_i P_l'(\hat{q}_f \cdot \hat{q}_i)$$

2⁻) $0 + \frac{1}{2} \xrightarrow{-} 0 + \frac{1}{2}$.

Operating as in the previous case, one has to evaluate "projectors" of the type

$$\sum_M |l+1, \tfrac{1}{2}; J = l + \tfrac{1}{2}; M\rangle \langle l, \tfrac{1}{2}; J = l + \tfrac{1}{2}, M|$$

which can be converted into projectors by the use of (Kramer's trick):

$$\langle \boldsymbol{q}, \sigma | \, l+1, \tfrac{1}{2}; J = l + \tfrac{1}{2}, M\rangle = \langle \boldsymbol{q}, \sigma | \boldsymbol{\sigma} \cdot \hat{\boldsymbol{q}} | l, \tfrac{1}{2}; J = l + \tfrac{1}{2}, M\rangle$$

($\boldsymbol{\sigma} \cdot \hat{\boldsymbol{q}}$ being a scalar under rotation leaves J invariant, but, being a pseudoscalar under space reflections, shifts the parity from $(-)^{l+1}$ to $(-)^l$).

The evaluation of e.g.

$$\langle \sigma_f | \int d\Omega_q \frac{2l+3}{4\pi} P_{l+1}(\hat{\boldsymbol{q}}_f \cdot \hat{\boldsymbol{q}}) \, \boldsymbol{\sigma} \cdot \hat{\boldsymbol{q}} \frac{l+1+\boldsymbol{l}_q \cdot \boldsymbol{\sigma}}{2l+1} \frac{2l+1}{4\pi} P_l(\hat{\boldsymbol{q}} \cdot \hat{\boldsymbol{q}}_i) \, |\sigma_i\rangle$$

proceeds as before by replacing $\dfrac{2l+3}{4\pi} P_{l+1}(\hat{\boldsymbol{q}}_f \cdot \hat{\boldsymbol{q}})$ by $\delta(\hat{\boldsymbol{q}}_f, \hat{\boldsymbol{q}})$ which is allowed since the presence of $\boldsymbol{\sigma} \cdot \hat{\boldsymbol{q}}$ and the projection operator ensures that the remainder behaves as a $Y_{l+1}(\hat{\boldsymbol{q}})$.

One finally gets

$$\langle \boldsymbol{q}_f \sigma_f | T | \, \boldsymbol{q}_i \sigma_i\rangle = \langle \sigma_f | \boldsymbol{\sigma} \cdot \hat{\boldsymbol{q}}_f \sum_{l=0}^{\infty} t_{l_+} \frac{l+1+\boldsymbol{l}_{q_f} \cdot \boldsymbol{\sigma}}{2l+1} + t_{l_-} \frac{l - \boldsymbol{l}_{q_f} \cdot \boldsymbol{\sigma}}{2l+1}$$
$$\times \frac{2l+1}{4\pi} P_l(\hat{\boldsymbol{q}}_f \cdot \hat{\boldsymbol{q}}_i) \, |\sigma_i\rangle$$

$3^+) \; \frac{1}{2} + \frac{1}{2} \xrightarrow{+} 0 + 0$

$$\langle \boldsymbol{q}_f | T | \, \boldsymbol{q}_i \sigma_i, \sigma_i'\rangle = \sum_{lm, \hat{\varepsilon}} \langle \hat{\boldsymbol{q}}_f | lm\rangle \, \mathscr{M}_l \langle l, m | \hat{\boldsymbol{q}}_i, \hat{\varepsilon}\rangle \, \langle \hat{\varepsilon} | \sigma_i, \sigma_i'\rangle$$
$$+ \langle \hat{\boldsymbol{q}}_f | l, m\rangle \, \mathscr{S}_l \, \langle l, m | \hat{\boldsymbol{q}}_i\rangle \, \langle 0 | \sigma_i, \sigma_i'\rangle .$$

Here we have first coupled the two spin $\frac{1}{2}$ particles into either a triplet states labelled by the polarization vector $\hat{\varepsilon}$, or into the singlet state $\langle 0|$:

$$\langle \hat{\varepsilon} | \sigma_i \sigma_i'\rangle = \langle \sigma_i' | \hat{\varepsilon} i \sigma_2 \boldsymbol{\sigma} | \, \sigma_i\rangle, \quad \langle 0 | \sigma_i, \sigma_i'\rangle = \langle \sigma_i' | i\sigma_2 | \, \sigma_i\rangle,$$

and then used vector and scalar spherical harmonics:

$\langle l, m | \hat{\boldsymbol{q}}_i, \boldsymbol{\varepsilon}\rangle_{\text{magnetic}} = \dfrac{\hat{\boldsymbol{\varepsilon}} \cdot \boldsymbol{l}_{q_i}}{\sqrt{l(l+1)}} Y_{lm}^*(\hat{\boldsymbol{q}}_i)$ parity $-(-)^l$ if $\boldsymbol{\varepsilon}$ is a true vector

$\langle l, m | \hat{\boldsymbol{q}}_i, \hat{\boldsymbol{\varepsilon}}\rangle_{\text{electric}} = i \dfrac{\hat{\boldsymbol{\varepsilon}} \cdot \hat{\boldsymbol{q}}_i \times \boldsymbol{l}_{q_i}}{\sqrt{l(l+1)}} Y_{lm}^*(\hat{\boldsymbol{q}}_i)$ parity $(-)^l$ (the i factor is useful for time reversal arguments)

$\langle \, m | \hat{q}_i, \hat{\boldsymbol{\varepsilon}}\rangle_{\text{longitudinal}} = \hat{\boldsymbol{\varepsilon}} \cdot \hat{q}_i Y_{lm}^*(\hat{q}_i)$ parity $(-)^l$

$\langle lm | \hat{q}_i, \varepsilon_0\rangle_{\text{scalar}} = \varepsilon_0 Y_{lm}^*(\hat{q}_i)$ parity $-(-)^l$ if ε_0 is a pseudoscalar.

Thus:

$$\langle \boldsymbol{q}_f | T | \, \sigma_i \sigma_i' \boldsymbol{q}_i\rangle = \langle \sigma_i' | i\sigma_2 \sum_l \left(\mathscr{M}_l \frac{\boldsymbol{\sigma} \cdot \boldsymbol{l}_{q_i}}{\sqrt{l(l+1)}} + \mathscr{S}_l \right) \frac{2l+1}{4\pi} P_l(\hat{\boldsymbol{q}}_f \cdot \hat{\boldsymbol{q}}_i) \, |\sigma_i\rangle$$

Similarly:

3⁻)

$$\langle \boldsymbol{q}_f |T| \sigma_i \sigma_i' \boldsymbol{q}_i \rangle = \langle \sigma_i' | i\sigma_2 \sum_l \left[i\mathscr{E}_l \frac{\boldsymbol{\sigma} \cdot \hat{\boldsymbol{q}}_i \times \boldsymbol{l}_{q_i}}{\sqrt{l(l+1)}} + \mathscr{L}_l \boldsymbol{\sigma} \cdot \hat{\boldsymbol{q}}_i \right] \frac{2l+1}{4\pi} \times P_l(\hat{\boldsymbol{q}}_f \cdot \hat{\boldsymbol{q}}_i) |\sigma_i\rangle$$

Exercise.

4) $1 + 0 \to 0 + 0$

(replace $\langle \sigma_i' | i\sigma_2 \sigma | \sigma_i \rangle$ by the polarization vectors of the spin 1 particle).

Note: if the spin 1 particle is a real photon, use gauge invariance to eliminate the scalar and longitudinal parts: $\varepsilon_0 = 0$, $\hat{\varepsilon} \cdot \hat{q}_i = 0$.

5⁺) $1 + \frac{1}{2} \xrightarrow{+} 0 + \frac{1}{2}$.

Using all the previous ingredients, one obtain:

$$\begin{aligned} \langle \sigma_f \boldsymbol{q}_f |T| \sigma_i, \boldsymbol{q}_i, \varepsilon \rangle = \langle \sigma_f | \sum_l \Bigg[& \mathscr{E}_{l_+} \frac{l + 1 + \boldsymbol{l}_{q_f} \cdot \boldsymbol{\sigma}}{2l+1} i \frac{\boldsymbol{\varepsilon} \cdot \hat{\boldsymbol{q}}_i \times \boldsymbol{l}_{q_i}}{\sqrt{l(l+1)}} \\ & + \mathscr{E}_{l_-} \frac{l - \boldsymbol{l}_{q_f} \cdot \boldsymbol{\sigma}}{2l+1} i \frac{\boldsymbol{\varepsilon} \cdot \hat{\boldsymbol{q}}_i \times \boldsymbol{l}_{q_i}}{\sqrt{l(l+1)}} \\ & + \mathscr{M}_{l_+} \boldsymbol{\sigma} \cdot \hat{\boldsymbol{q}}_f \frac{l + 1 + \boldsymbol{l}_{q_f} \cdot \boldsymbol{\sigma}}{2l+1} \frac{\boldsymbol{\varepsilon} \cdot \boldsymbol{l}_{q_i}}{\sqrt{l(l+1)}} \\ & + \mathscr{M}_{l_-} \boldsymbol{\sigma} \cdot \hat{\boldsymbol{q}}_f \frac{l - \boldsymbol{l}_{q_f} \cdot \boldsymbol{\sigma}}{2l+1} \frac{\boldsymbol{\varepsilon} \cdot \boldsymbol{l}_{q_i}}{\sqrt{l(l+1)}} \\ & + \mathscr{L}_{l_+} \frac{l + 1 + \boldsymbol{l}_{q_f} \cdot \boldsymbol{\sigma}}{2l+1} \boldsymbol{\varepsilon} \cdot \hat{\boldsymbol{q}}_i \\ & + \mathscr{L}_{l_-} \frac{l - \boldsymbol{l}_{q_f} \cdot \boldsymbol{\sigma}}{2l+1} \boldsymbol{\varepsilon} \cdot \hat{\boldsymbol{q}}_i \\ & + \mathscr{S}_{l_+} \frac{l + 1 + \boldsymbol{l}_{q_f} \cdot \boldsymbol{\sigma}}{2l+1} \varepsilon_0 \\ & + \mathscr{S}_{l_-} \frac{l - \boldsymbol{l}_{q_f} \cdot \boldsymbol{\sigma}}{2l+1} \varepsilon_0 \Bigg] \frac{2l+1}{4\pi} P_l(\hat{\boldsymbol{q}}_f \cdot \hat{\boldsymbol{q}}_i) |\sigma_i\rangle \end{aligned}$$

$\{\varepsilon_\mu\} = \{\varepsilon_0, \boldsymbol{\varepsilon}\}$ represents the polarization four vector of the spin 1 particle. The transversality condition $\varepsilon \cdot k = 0$: $\boldsymbol{\varepsilon} \cdot \hat{\boldsymbol{q}}_i - \varepsilon_0 = 0$ allows one to eliminate the scalar amplitude.

If the spin 1 particle is a real photon, gauge invariance allows one to choose $\varepsilon_0 = 0$, $\boldsymbol{\varepsilon} \cdot \hat{\boldsymbol{q}}_i = 0$, which eliminates the longitudinal amplitude. If the spin 1 particle is a virtual photon the scalar part can be eliminated by current conservation (invariance under $\varepsilon \to \varepsilon + \lambda k$).

5⁻) $1 + \frac{1}{2} \xrightarrow{-} 0 + \frac{1}{2}$.

Multiply the whole bracket by $\boldsymbol{\sigma}\hat{\boldsymbol{q}}_f$.

6⁺) $\frac{1}{2} + \frac{1}{2} \xrightarrow{+} \frac{1}{2} + \frac{1}{2}$.

a) For each total angular momentum J, the allowed orbital momenta are $J + 1, J, J - 1$. One therefore needs a generalization of Kramer's trick, namely, an operator Q_J (the so called tensor operator) such that

$$\langle \sigma_1, \sigma_1', \hat{\boldsymbol{q}}\, | Q_J |\, J, M; J + 1, 1\rangle = \langle \sigma_1, \sigma_1', \hat{\boldsymbol{q}} | J, M; J - 1, 1\rangle.$$

One finds (see e.g. ref. 21), that

$$Q_J = \frac{2J + 1}{2\sqrt{J(J + 1)}}\left(\boldsymbol{\sigma} \cdot \hat{\boldsymbol{q}}\boldsymbol{\sigma}' \cdot \hat{\boldsymbol{q}} + \frac{1}{2J + 1}\right),$$

and similarly

$$Q_J^{-1} = \frac{2J + 1}{2\sqrt{J(J + 1)}}\left(\boldsymbol{\sigma} \cdot \hat{\boldsymbol{q}}\boldsymbol{\sigma}' \cdot \hat{\boldsymbol{q}} - \frac{1}{2J + 1}\right).$$

b) One may couple spins in the initial state and in the final state as in 3) and match parities of various multipoles in the initial and final states.

6⁻) $\frac{1}{2} + \frac{1}{2} \xrightarrow{-} \frac{1}{2} + \frac{1}{2}$.

a) One now needs to express $|J, M; J, 1\rangle$ in terms of $|J, M; J \pm 1, 1\rangle$ by the use of a pseudoscalar operator.

b) Matching parities is simples as in 6⁺).

Exercises.

7) $1 + \frac{1}{2} \xrightarrow{\pm} 1 + \frac{1}{2}$.

8) $1 + 1 \to \frac{1}{2} + \frac{1}{2}$, $1 + 1 \to 0 + 1$[22].

9) $0 + \frac{1}{2} \to 0 + 3/2 \to 0 + 0 + \frac{1}{2}$[23].

Inversion Formulae.

We have so far obtained amplitudes in the form

$$\langle f | T |\, i\rangle = \sum_{J,\alpha,\beta} t^J_{\beta,\alpha} \langle f\, | \mathscr{P}^J_{\beta,\alpha} |\, i\rangle$$

where J is the total angular momentum, β and α, degeneracy parameters labelling final and initial channels respectively, and the $\mathscr{P}^J_{\beta,\alpha}$'s, operators enjoying the orthogonality properties:

$$\mathscr{P}^J_{\beta\alpha}\mathscr{P}^{J'\dagger}_{\beta'\alpha'} \propto \delta_{J,J'}\delta_{\alpha,\alpha'}\mathscr{P}^J_{\beta\beta'}$$

$$\mathscr{P}^{J\dagger}_{\beta\alpha}\mathscr{P}^{J'}_{\beta'\alpha'} \propto \delta_{J,J'}\delta_{\beta,\beta'}\mathscr{P}^J_{\alpha,\alpha'}$$

$$\mathrm{Tr}\,\mathscr{P}^J_{\alpha\alpha'} \propto \delta_{\alpha\alpha'}.$$

Hence, one obtains the inversion formula, which may be of some use in studies starting from dispersions relations:

$$t^J_{\beta,\alpha} = \frac{\int \mathrm{d}f\,\mathrm{d}i \langle f|T|i\rangle \langle i|\mathscr{P}^{J\dagger}_{\beta\alpha}|f\rangle}{\int \mathrm{d}f\,\mathrm{d}i \langle f|\mathscr{P}^J_{\beta,\alpha}|i\rangle \langle i|\mathscr{P}^{J\dagger}_{\beta\alpha}|f\rangle}$$

Example.

$$\text{photon} + 0 \to 0 + 0$$

$$\begin{aligned}\langle \boldsymbol{q}|T|\hat{\varepsilon}, \boldsymbol{k}\rangle &= (\hat{\varepsilon}\cdot\hat{\boldsymbol{q}}\times\hat{\boldsymbol{k}})f(\hat{\boldsymbol{q}}\cdot\hat{\boldsymbol{k}}, |\boldsymbol{k}|)\\ &= -\sum_l t_l \frac{2l+1}{4\pi}\frac{\hat{\varepsilon}\cdot \boldsymbol{l}_q}{\sqrt{l(l+1)}}P_l(\hat{\boldsymbol{q}}\cdot\hat{\boldsymbol{k}})\\ &= \sum_l t_l \langle \hat{\boldsymbol{q}}|\mathscr{P}_l|\hat{\varepsilon}, \hat{\boldsymbol{k}}\rangle,\end{aligned}$$

$$t_l = \frac{\int \mathrm{d}\Omega_{\hat{q}}\,\mathrm{d}\Omega_{\hat{k}} \sum_{\hat{\varepsilon}\perp\hat{k}} \langle \hat{\varepsilon}, \hat{\boldsymbol{k}}|\mathscr{P}_l|\hat{\boldsymbol{q}}\rangle\, \hat{\varepsilon}\cdot\hat{\boldsymbol{q}}\times\hat{\boldsymbol{k}}f(\hat{\boldsymbol{q}}\cdot\hat{\boldsymbol{k}}, |\boldsymbol{k}|)}{\int \mathrm{d}\Omega_{\hat{q}}\,\mathrm{d}\Omega_{\hat{k}} \sum_{\hat{\varepsilon}\perp\hat{k}} \langle \hat{\varepsilon}, \hat{\boldsymbol{k}}|\mathscr{P}_l|\hat{\boldsymbol{q}}\rangle \langle \hat{\boldsymbol{q}}|\mathscr{P}_l|\hat{\varepsilon}; \hat{\boldsymbol{k}}\rangle}$$

$$= \frac{\int \mathrm{d}\Omega_{\hat{q}}\,\mathrm{d}\Omega_{\hat{k}} \frac{2l+1}{4\pi}\left(-\frac{1}{i}\right)\frac{\hat{\boldsymbol{q}}\times\hat{\boldsymbol{k}}}{\sqrt{l(l+1)}}P_l'(\hat{\boldsymbol{q}}\cdot\hat{\boldsymbol{k}})\cdot\hat{\boldsymbol{q}}\times\hat{\boldsymbol{k}}f(\hat{\boldsymbol{q}}\cdot\hat{\boldsymbol{k}}, |\boldsymbol{k}|)}{\int \mathrm{d}\Omega_{\hat{q}}\,\mathrm{d}\Omega_{\hat{k}} \frac{2l+1}{4\pi}P_l(\hat{\boldsymbol{q}}\cdot\hat{\boldsymbol{k}})\frac{2l+1}{4\pi}P_l(\hat{\boldsymbol{q}}\cdot\hat{\boldsymbol{k}})}$$

$$= \frac{2\pi i}{\sqrt{l(l+1)}}\int_{-1}^{+1} d(\hat{\boldsymbol{q}}\cdot\hat{\boldsymbol{k}})\,[1-(\hat{\boldsymbol{q}}\cdot\hat{\boldsymbol{k}})^2]\,P_l'(\hat{\boldsymbol{q}}\cdot\hat{\boldsymbol{k}})f(\hat{\boldsymbol{q}}\cdot\hat{\boldsymbol{k}}, |\boldsymbol{k}|),$$

where we have used $l^2 = l(l+1)$.

APPENDIX III

REDUCTION FORMULAE

In this appendix we lay down the LSZ[(24)] formalism of a quantum field theory for particles with spin and derive familiar looking expressions for matrix elements of the *S*-matrix which will justify the introduction of spinor amplitudes and of their properties stated in Ch. II, § f.

We will throughout assume that all particles to be described are massive*.

Then the LSZ postulates go as follows:

1) The theory is described in a Hilbert space $\mathscr{H}$ in which a unitary, continuous, up to a phase representation of the Poincaré group acts.

There are in $\mathscr{H}$ two Fock bases the so-called $|\text{in}\rangle$ and $|\text{out}\rangle$ bases constructed from the same vacuum $|0\rangle$ by action of two sets of creation operators labelled by the same quantum numbers (masses, spins, momenta, spin projections, internal quantum numbers) $a^{\dagger}_{\substack{\text{in}\\\text{out}}}([p], \sigma, \mu)$, which describe observed particles.

The vacuum state is the only Lorentz invariant state.

The in and out bases are obtained from each other by means of a unitary operator S:

$$a^{\dagger}_{\text{out}}([p], \sigma, \mu) = S^{\dagger} a^{\dagger}_{\text{in}}([p], \sigma, \mu)\, S$$

hence

$$a_{\text{out}}([p], \sigma, \mu) = S^{\dagger} a_{\text{in}}([p], \sigma, \mu)\, S \tag{A,III,1}$$

and

$$\overset{\text{out}}{\varphi}_{A,\mu}(x) = S^{\dagger} \overset{\text{in}}{\varphi}_{A,\mu}(x)\, S$$

where $\varphi_{A,\mu}(x)$ is any of the local fields constructed from the creation and annihilation operators as in Ch. I, § f, iii).

The vacuum and one particle states are stable:

$$\langle 0_{\text{in}}| = \langle 0_{\text{out}}| = \langle 0_{\text{in}}|\, S$$

$$\langle [p]\, \sigma, \mu, \text{in}| = \langle [p]\, \sigma, \mu, \text{out}| = \langle [p]\, \sigma, \mu, \text{in}|\, S \tag{A,III,2}$$

$$= \langle [p]\, \sigma, \mu, \text{in}|\, S^{\dagger}.$$

2) The asymptotic local fields $\varphi^{\substack{\text{in}\\\text{out}}}_{A,\mu}(x)$ can be interpolated† by a local field $\varphi_{A,\mu}(x)$ in a sense to be shortly made precise (A,III,13) and with the following properties:

$$[\varphi_{A,\mu}(x),\ \ \varphi_{A'\mu'}(x')]_{\pm} = 0, \quad (x - x')^2 < 0 \tag{A,III,3}$$

where the commutator or the anticommutator is taken according as the spin indices A are integer or half integer.

Under Poincaré transformations, the interpolating fields have the same transformation law as the asymptotic fields.

* This restriction has to do with the rather poor understanding one has at present of the meaning of the asymptotic condition stated below, (A,III,13), in the case where there exist massless particles which mediate long range interactions.

† The question of whether one interpolating field has to be associated with each kind of observed particle or whether only a set of interpolating fields is necessary, polynomials in which create asymptotically "composite" particles will not be discussed here. We shall stick to the simplifying assumption made in the text.

This latter property requires a comment. As long as space reflections are not involved, their is no difficulty. But, recall the transformation law under space reflections:

$$U(\Pi)\, \varphi_A^{\overset{\text{in}}{\text{out}}}(x)\, U(\Pi)^{-1} = \eta_\Pi^* \tilde{\varphi}_A^{\overset{\text{in}}{\text{out}}}(\underline{x})$$

$$= \eta_\Pi^* \mathscr{D}^s_{AA'} \left(\frac{\partial_0 - \partial\sigma}{-im}\right) \varphi_{A'}^{\overset{\text{in}}{\text{out}}}(\underline{x}).$$

This transformation law expressed in terms of φ alone cannot be retained for the interpolating field if the latter does not fulfill the Klein–Gordan equation, which is explicitely not assumed, (as, we shall see this would yield a trivial S-matrix).

The set of transformations

$$U(\Pi)\, \varphi_A^{\overset{\text{in}}{\text{out}}}(x)\, U(\Pi)^{-1} = \eta_\Pi^* \tilde{\varphi}_A^{\overset{\text{in}}{\text{out}}}(\underline{x})$$

$$U(\Pi)\, \tilde{\varphi}_A^{\overset{\text{in}}{\text{out}}}(x)\, U(\Pi)^{-1} = \eta_\Pi^* \varphi_A^{\overset{\text{in}}{\text{out}}}(\underline{x})$$

is however perfectly admissible when expressed in terms of the Dirac field

$$\Psi_{\alpha,\mu}^{\overset{\text{in}}{\text{out}}}(x) = \frac{1}{\sqrt{2}} \begin{pmatrix} \varphi_A^{\overset{\text{in}}{\text{out}}}(x) \\ \tilde{\varphi}_A^{\overset{\text{in}}{\text{out}}}(x) \end{pmatrix} \tag{A,III,4}$$

or which one may therefore assume the existence of an interpolating fields which ransforms locally under space reflection:

$$U(\Pi)\, \Psi_{\alpha,\mu}(x)\, U(\Pi)^{-1} = \eta_\Pi^* \gamma_0 \Psi_{\alpha,\mu}(\underline{x}) \tag{A,III,5}$$

where $\gamma_0 = \begin{pmatrix} 0 & 1 \\ 1 & 0 \end{pmatrix}$.

We recall the expressions for the various asymptotic fields:

$$\varphi_{A,\mu}^{as}(x) = \frac{1}{(2\pi)^{3/2}} \int \frac{d^3p}{2\omega_p} [\mathscr{D}^s_{A\sigma}([p])\, a^{as}([p]\,\sigma, \mu)\, e^{-ipx}$$
$$+ \mathscr{D}^s_{A\sigma}([p]\, C^{-1})\, b^{as\dagger}([p]\,\sigma, \mu)\, e^{ipx}]$$
$$\tilde{\varphi}_{A,\mu}^{as}(x) = \frac{1}{(2\pi)^{3/2}} \int \frac{d^3p}{2\omega_p} [\mathscr{D}^s_{A\sigma}([p]^{\dagger -1})\, a^{as}([p]\,\sigma, \mu)\, e^{-ipx}$$
$$+ \mathscr{D}^s_{A\sigma}([p]^{\dagger -1}\, C)\, b^{as\dagger}([p]\,\sigma, \mu)\, e^{ipx}]. \tag{A,III,6}$$

The charge conjugate fields are obtained by the interchange of the a's and b's. We set:

$$\Psi^{as}_{\alpha,\mu}(x) = \frac{1}{(2\pi)^{3/2}} \int \frac{d^3p}{2\omega_p}\, U_{\alpha,\sigma}([p])\, a^{as}([p]\,\sigma,\mu)\, e^{-ipx} + V_{\alpha,\sigma}([p])\, b^{\dagger}([p],\sigma,\mu)\, e^{ipx} \qquad \text{(A,III,7)}$$

with $\alpha = \begin{pmatrix} A \\ \dot{A} \end{pmatrix}$

$$U_{\alpha,\sigma}([p]) = \frac{1}{\sqrt{2}} \begin{pmatrix} \mathscr{D}^s_{A\sigma}([p]) \\ \mathscr{D}^s_{\dot{A}\sigma}([p]^{\dagger-1}) \end{pmatrix} \quad V_{\alpha,\sigma}([p]) = \frac{1}{\sqrt{2}} \begin{pmatrix} \mathscr{D}^s_{A\sigma}([p]\,C^{-1}) \\ \mathscr{D}^s_{\dot{A}\sigma}([p]^{\dagger-1}\,C) \end{pmatrix} \qquad \text{(A,III,8)}$$

with the transformation law

$$U(a,A)\,\Psi_{\alpha,\mu}(x)\,U^{-1}(a,A) = S_{\alpha\alpha'}(A^{-1})\,\Psi_{\alpha',\mu}(A\cdot x + a) \qquad \text{(A,III,9)}$$

with

$$S(A) = \begin{pmatrix} \mathscr{D}(A) & \\ & \mathscr{D}(A^{\dagger-1}) \end{pmatrix}. \qquad \text{(A,III,10)}$$

We note

$$(U^{\dagger})_{\sigma\alpha}([p])\,\gamma^0_{\alpha\beta}U_{\beta\sigma'}([p]) = \delta_{\sigma\sigma'}$$

$$(V^{\dagger})_{\sigma\alpha}([p])\,\gamma^0_{\alpha\beta}V_{\beta\sigma'}([p]) = (-)^{2s}\,\delta_{\sigma\sigma'}$$

and thus define $\bar{U} = U^{\dagger}\gamma^0$, $\bar{V} = V^{\dagger}\gamma^0$.

We can thus solve for the asymptotic creation and annihilation operators.

$$a^{as}([p],\sigma,\mu) = \bar{U}_{\alpha}([p],\sigma)\frac{i}{(2\pi)^{3/2}}\int d^3x\, e^{ipx}\, \overleftrightarrow{\partial_0}\Psi^{as}_{\alpha,\mu}(x)$$

$$a^{\dagger as}([p],\sigma,\mu) = -\frac{i}{(2\pi)^{3/2}}\int d^3x\, e^{-ip\cdot x}\, \overleftrightarrow{\partial_0}\Psi^{C\,as}_{\alpha,\mu}(x)\, U^C_{\alpha}([p],\sigma)$$

where

$$U^C([p],\sigma) = \mathscr{C}V([p],\sigma) \quad \mathscr{C} = \begin{pmatrix} \mathscr{D}(C^{-1}) & \\ & \mathscr{D}(C) \end{pmatrix}. \qquad \text{(A,III,11)}$$

$$b^{as}([p],\sigma,\mu) = \bar{U}_{\alpha}([p],\sigma)\frac{i}{(2\pi)^{3/2}}\int d^3x\, e^{ipx}\, \overleftrightarrow{\partial_0}\Psi^{C\,as}_{\alpha,\mu}(x)$$

$$b^{\dagger as}([p],\sigma,\mu) = -\frac{i}{(2\pi)^{3/2}}\int d^3x\, e^{-ipx}\, \overleftrightarrow{\partial_0}\Psi^{as}_{\alpha,\mu}(x)\, U^C_{\alpha}([p],\sigma)$$

where

$$f\overleftrightarrow{\partial_0}g = f\frac{\partial}{\partial x^0}g - \left(\frac{\partial}{\partial x^0}f\right)g.$$

The integration over x is so arranged that, from each field one only retains the positive or negative frequency part according to the presence of the plane wave function $e^{\pm ipx}$, and that the integral is independent of x^0.

One may define for the interpolating fields similar expressions e.g.:

$$a(f, \mu, t) = \int \frac{d^3p}{2\omega p} f_\sigma^*([p])\, \bar{U}_\alpha([p], \sigma) \times \frac{i}{(2\pi)^{3/2}} \int_{x^0=t} d^3x\, e^{ipx}\, \overleftrightarrow{\partial_0} \Psi_{\alpha,\mu}(x), \tag{A,III,12}$$

which now depend on t and are associated with one particle asymptotic states labelled by the wave function f and internal label μ.

The asymptotic condition now states

$$W - \lim a(f, \mu, t)\Big|_{t\to\pm\infty} = a^{\substack{\text{out}\\ \text{in}}}(\bar{f}, \mu), \tag{A,III,13}$$

(and similar conditions on b, $a^\dagger$, $b^\dagger$), where the W-(eak) limit sign means that the equation holds true for all matrix elements of both sides between sufficiently many normalizable states in $\mathscr{H}$.

Remark.

If we had not had to worry about space reflections, we would have constructed a similar formalism in terms of fields φ and φ^c and the first set of components of the U and V spinors.

Reduction Formulae.

We are now ready to express a matrix element

$$S_{FI} = \langle 0| \prod_{\bar{f}} b^{\text{out}}([p_{\bar{f}}], \sigma_{\bar{f}}, \mu_{\bar{f}}) \prod_{f} a^{\text{out}}([p_f, \sigma_f, \mu_f) \times \prod_i a^{\dagger\text{in}}([p_i], \sigma_i, \mu_i) \prod_{\bar{i}} b^{\dagger\text{in}}([p_{\bar{i}}], \sigma_{\bar{i}}, \mu_{\bar{i}})\, |0\rangle$$

$$= \langle \bar{f}, f\, |S|\, i, \bar{i}\rangle \tag{A,III,14}$$

where bars distinguish antiparticles.

From (A,III,12–13) S_{FI} can be expressed as a certain limit of the expectation value of a product of interpolating fields.

$$W_{FI} = \langle 0| \prod_{\bar{f}} \Psi^C_{\alpha\bar{f},\mu\bar{f}}(x_{\bar{f}}) \prod_f \Psi_{\alpha_f\mu_f}(x_f) \prod_i \Psi^C_{\alpha_i\mu_i}(x_i) \prod_{\bar{i}} \Psi_{\alpha\bar{i}\mu\bar{i}}(x_{\bar{i}})\, |0\rangle \tag{A,III,15}$$

(provided some wave packets f are added in, which we shall not bother to do).

Given the set of indices (FI), it is convenient to introduce "truncated" products W^T_λ according to the recursive definition

$$W_{FI} = \sum (-)^{\sigma(\lambda)}\, W^T_{\lambda_1} \dots W^T_{\lambda_p} \tag{A,III,16}$$

where the sum is taken over all partitions of the set of indices (FI) into subsets $\lambda_1 \dots \lambda_p$ $(\lambda_1 \cup \dots \cup \lambda_p = (FI))$; inside each subset points have to appear in the natural order where they appear in (FI); $\sigma(\lambda)$ is the signature of the permutation of fermion operators appearing in $\lambda_1 \dots \lambda_p$ with respect to that appearing in FI.

Accordingly, connected S-matrix elements are defined by:

$$S_{FI} = \sum (-)^{\sigma(\lambda)}\, S^c_{\lambda_1} \dots S^c_{\lambda_p}. \tag{A,III,17}$$

One then uses repeatedly the formula of integration by parts:

$$\int \frac{d^3p}{2\omega_p} \tilde{f}(p) = \int_{x0=+\infty} d^3x\, e^{ipx} \overleftrightarrow{\partial_0} \varphi(x) - \int_{x0=-\infty} d^3x\, e^{ipx} \overleftrightarrow{\partial_0} \varphi(x)$$

$$= \int d^4x f(x) (\Box_x + m^2)\, \varphi(x) \tag{A,III,18}$$

where $f(x) = \int \frac{d^3p}{2\omega_p} \tilde{f}(p)\, e^{ipx}$, which holds true if $f(\boldsymbol{p})$ decreases fast at infinity in $\boldsymbol{p}$, together with the following identity: Let

$$T(A_1(x_1) \dots A_n(x_n)) = \sum_{P(1\dots n)} (-)^{\sigma(P)} \theta_+(x^0_{P(1)} - x^0_{P(2)}) \dots \theta_+(x^0_{P(n-1)} - x^0_{P(n)})$$

$$\times A_{P(1)}(x_{P(1)}) \dots A_{P(n)}(x_{P(n)}), \tag{A,III,19}$$

be the chronological product of n local field operators.

$$\left[\theta_+(t) = \begin{matrix} 1 & t > 0 \\ 0 & t < 0 \end{matrix}; \quad P = \text{permutation on } (1 \dots n) \right.$$

$$\left. P(i) = \text{transformed of } i \text{ by } P \right]$$

$\sigma(P)$ is the signature of the fermion fields permutation. Then one writes e.g.

$$\int_{x0=+\infty} f(x) \overleftrightarrow{\partial_0} \varphi(x)\, T(A_1(x_1) \dots A_n(x_n))$$

$$= \int_{x0=+\infty} f(x) \overleftrightarrow{\partial_0} T(\varphi(x), A_1(x_1) \dots A_n(x_n)) \tag{A,III,20}$$

since, in view of the θ_+ functions only terms occurring in the left hand side survive.

Hence

$$\left(\int_{x0=+\infty} - \int_{x0=-\infty}\right) d^3x f(x) \overleftrightarrow{\partial_0} \varphi(x)\, T(A_1(x_1) \dots A_n(x_n))$$

$$= \int d^4x f(x) (\Box_x + m^2)\, T(\varphi(x)\, A_1(x_1) \dots A_n(x_n)). \tag{A,III,21}$$

These elementary steps, together with a recursion argument which uses definition (A,III,17), lead to the result.

$$S^c_{FI} = \prod_{\substack{f \\ \bar{f}}} \frac{i}{(2\pi)^{3/2}} \bar{U}_{\alpha_{\underset{\bar{f}}{f}}}([p]_{\underset{\bar{f}}{f}} \sigma_{\underset{\bar{f}}{f}} \mu_{\underset{\bar{f}}{f}}) \, M_{\substack{\alpha_f \alpha_{\bar{f}} \alpha_i \alpha_{\bar{i}} \\ \mu_f \mu_{\bar{f}} \mu_i \mu_{\bar{i}}}} (p_f, p_{\bar{f}}, p_i, p_{\bar{i}})$$

$$\times \prod_{\substack{i \\ \bar{i}}} \frac{-i}{(2\pi)^{3/2}} U^C_{\substack{\alpha_i \\ \alpha_i}}([p]_{\underset{\bar{i}}{i}} \sigma_{\underset{\bar{i}}{i}} \mu_{\underset{\bar{i}}{i}}) \qquad \text{(A,III,22)}$$

where

$$M_{\substack{\alpha_f \alpha_{\bar{f}} \alpha_i \alpha_{\bar{i}} \\ \mu_f \mu_{\bar{f}} \mu_i \mu_{\bar{i}}}}(p_f p_{\bar{f}} p_i p_{\bar{i}}) = \int \prod_{\bar{i} i f \bar{f}} e^{ipjxj} (\Box_j + m_j^2) \, dx_j \qquad \text{(A,III,23)}$$

$$\langle 0| \, T \prod_{\bar{f}} (\Psi_{\substack{\alpha_{\bar{f}} \\ \mu_{\bar{f}}}}(x_{\bar{f}}) \prod_{f} \Psi_{\substack{\alpha_f \\ \mu_f}}(x_f) \prod_{i} \Psi_{\substack{\alpha_i \\ \mu_i}}(x_i) \prod_{\bar{i}} \Psi_{\substack{\alpha_{\bar{i}} \\ \mu_{\bar{i}}}}(x_{\bar{i}}) \, |0\rangle^T,$$

and the truncated chronological product vacuum expectation value is defined from truncated vacuum expectation values of products in the same way as the untruncated chronological product was defined from untruncated vacuum expectation values of products.

Remark.

There is one touchy point here, namely the multiplication of field operators which are in general distributions, by θ functions, which are discontinuous; this defect may lead to an improper handling of the high energy behaviour of the theory, as well as to the possible lack of covariance of chronological products. More work has to be done in this respect.

The definition of the M amplitudes is the starting point of dispersion theory, in this framework, since the locality condition (A,III,3) allows to show[(26)] that M can be obtained as the boundary value of a function of the p_j's holomorphic in a domain, all of which has not been so far determined.

CONCLUSION

We hope to have conveyed the impression that a detailed analysis of elementary systems according to quantum numbers provided by relativistic invariance (momentum, spin) is worthwhile in so far as it makes perfectly precise the understanding of many particle states and the structure of some of their observables. If, at times, computations are lengthy, it is hoped that they do not obscure the general idea. The main reason why we have indulged into so much algebra is precisely to show that they are in principle not so dreadful, although numerical work can become fairly abundant.

From a more lofty point of view, it also is apparent that if some day Lorentz invariance is lost to the benefit of another invariance, the formalism is all set to deal with the new law, provided representation theory is advanced enough for the new group.

We have to apologize for the arbitrary choice of topics, redundancy aswell as omission of some items, and only hope that enough of the basic techniques have been exhibited to allow further applications.

ACKNOWLEDGEMENTS

We wish to thank here all contributors to the ideas expressed in these notes; in particular, Dr. G. Mahoux and Dr. H. Grimmer have detected many errors and made useful suggestions which resulted into corrections over the initial version. Let finally our great master Lobatchewsky* find here the expression of our gratitude for his useful advice.

GENERAL REFERENCES

0 A. Messiah, Mécanique Quantique, Dunod, Paris (1960).
I. A. S. Wightman, Suppl. Nuovo Cimento, Vol. XIV, Xn^{0}1, p. 21 (1959).
II. A. S. Wightman, in Relations de Dispersion et Particules Elémentaires Hermann, Paris (1960), p. 161–226.
III. H. Joos, *Fortschritte der Physik* **10**, p. 65–146 (1962).
IV. E. P. Wigner, Group Theory and its Applications to the Quantum Mechanics of Atomic Spectra, Academic Press (1959).
V. L. Michel, in Group Theoretical Concepts and Methods in Elementary Particle Physics; F. Gürsey Editor, Gordon and Breach, New York, 1964.
Among textbooks which have now appeared and contain numerous examples, we shall only quote:
VI. G. Kallen, Elementary Particle Physics, Addison Wesley, (1964).
VII. J. Werle, Relativistic Theory of Reactions, North Holland, Amsterdam (1966).
VIII. M. Goldberger, and K. M. Watson, Collision Theory, Wiley, New York (1964).

BIBLIOGRAPHY**

1. V. Bargmann, *JMP* 5, n^0 7, 862 (1964) and references therein.
2. The exposition of this chapter follows closely some seminar notes written in collaboration with M. Froissart (Saclay 1963, unpublished). An exposition which uses systematically wave packets—instead of "improper states" whose mathematical existence can be however fully justified—can be found in:
3. P. Moussa, and R. Stora, Lectures in Theoretical Physics, Vol. VIIa, University of Colorado Press, Boulder (1964), p. 37.
4. D. Zwanziger, *Phys. Rev.* 133 B, 65 (1962); D. Zwanziger, same volume as ref. 3, p. 190.
5. E. P. Wigner, (1962) in: Group Theoretical Concepts and Methods in Elementary Particle Physics, F. Gursey Editor, Gordon and Breach, New York (1964).
6. R. F. Streater, and A. S. Wightman, *PCT*, Spin and Statistics and all that, Benjamin, New York (1964), p. 147–157.
Where the so-called Klein transformations, which allow commutation or anticommutation relations to be normal, are constructed.
7. K. Hepp, *Helv. Phys. Acta* **36**, 355 (1963); D. Williams, *UCRL* 11113.

* cf. Tom Lehrer, well known song.
** This list of references is in no way exhaustive. We have just quoted those references which we thought were relevant to the arguments presented here. In most of them, as well as in the general references, the reader will find an ample supply of references to the original articles dealing with the various subjects under consideration.

8. It seems that the fact that $Y^{\Sigma,\varkappa_{\mp}}$ form a basis of covariant tensors has been known by many authors although this result has not been published. We learnt it from M. Froissart. For properties of these functions, see ref. III, appendix.
9. The details of the proof have been provided by G. Cohen-Tannoudji, H. Navelet, and A. Morel, Saclay preprint, to be published in Annals of Physics.
10. G. Szegö, Orthogonal Polynomials, American Mathematical Society Colloquium publications, Vol. XXIII Th. g. 1.1, p. 243.
11. See e.g. articles by G. F. Chew and R. Omnes in the volume quoted in II.
12. The idea of the proof has emerged in the course of a discussion with M. Froissart which essentially yielded the desired result.
13. Such graphs have been already drawn in: A. R. Edmonds, Angular Momentum in Quantum Mechanics; Princeton Univ. Press (1957); and systematized in: A. P. Yutsis, I. B. Levinson, and V. V. Vanagas, Theory of Angular Momentum, translated from Russian by the Israel Program for Scientific Translations, Jerusalem (1962).
14. References to previous work on this question can be found in: The relation of the 0 (2,1) partial wave expansion to the Regge representation by J. F. Boyce *JMP* **8** 675 (1967). For the definition of the spin basis in the Breit system, see also ref. 3.
15. M. Kummer, The most general Clebsch-Gordan coefficients of the Poincaré group, *JMP* **7** 997 (1966), S. M. Berman, and M. Jacob, *Phys. Rev.* **139** B, 1023 (1965).
16. The easiest way to obtain the obvious result that j_{123} is integer or half integer at the same time as $s_1 + s_2 + s_3$, is by following the approach found in 3, c. f. R. Stora, Seminar notes, Institut Henri Poincaré, (1965).
17. Recoupling coefficients for three particle states labelled by helicity degeneracy parameters have been computed by G. C. Wick, *Ann. Phys.* **18**, 65 (1962). See also M. Jacob and G. C. Wick, *Ann. Phys.* **7**, 404 (1959).
18. The case of *l-s* couplings has been treated by: McKerrel, *Nuovo Cimento* XXXIV, 5, 1289 (1964); The answer was known to H. Joos as early as 1962 (private communication).
19. V. Bargmann, *Rev. Mod. Phys.* **34**, 4, 829 (1962), J. Schwinger in: Quantum Theory of Angular momentum, edited by L. C. Biedenharn, and H. van Dam, Academic Press, New York (1965).
20. V. Bargmann, *Ann. Math.* **48**, 569 (1947).
21. The set of formulas collected here first appeared in seminar notes Bologna (1960), and was reproduced and amplified in: University of Maryland, Technical Report n^0 250 (1962). Most of them are widely known, see in particular M. Goldberger, and K. Watson ref. VII.
22. Y. Artru, Thèse de troisième Cycle, Paris (1965).
23. P. Moussa, and R. Stora, Unpublished.
24. H. Lehmann, K. Symanzik, and W. Zimmermann, *Nuovo Cimento I* n^0 1, 205 (1955).
25. K. Hepp, *Comm. Math. Phys.* **1**, n^0 2, 95 (1965).
26. D. Ruelle, *Nuovo Cimento* XIX n^0 2, 356 (1961); H. Araki, *JMP* **2**, 163 (1961).
27. D. Iagolnitzer, "*S*-matrix and Classical Description of Interactions" to be published in J. Math. Phys., A derivation of similar results from basic principles of quantum field theory is now in progress (O. Steinmann, Preprint CERN/Th 789 (1967)).
28. M. Froissart, and R. Taylor, *Phys. Rev.* **153** N^0 5 p 1636 (1967).

Applications of Invariance Principles in the Physics of Elementary Particles

U. Nguyen-Khac

Ecole Polytechnique · Paris · France

and

J. Six

Faculté des Sciences · Orsay · France

CONTENTS

Introduction 179

Chapter I. Laws valid for all interactions 180

I. 1 Space-time conservation laws 180
I. 2 "Spin-statistics" theorem 182
I. 3 Conservation of the electric, baryonic and leptonic charges 183

Chapter II. C, P, T invariances 185

II. 1 Definitions and the CPT theorem 185
II. 2 Invariance under charge conjugation C 186
II. 3 Invariance under space inversion. Parity P 189
II. 4 Invariance under time reversal T 193

Chapter III. Charge symmetry and charge independence. Isotopic spin. Isotopic parity 198

III. 1 Definitions and invariances 198
III. 2 Consequences of charge symmetry and charge independence 201
III. 3 Isotopic parity G 211

Chapter IV. Particular rules for weak interactions 213

IV. 1 Introduction. Strangeness 213
IV. 2 The $|\Delta S| \leqq 1$ rule 215
IV. 3 Rules for leptonic interactions 215
IV. 4 The $|\Delta I| = \frac{1}{2}$ rule for non-leptonic interactions 217

Chapter V. Applications of selection rules in the case of strong and electromagnetic interactions 219

V. 1 2π system 220
V. 2 3π system 221
V. 3 $K\bar{K}$ system 224
V. 4 $N\bar{N}$ system 225

Conclusion 226

References 227

INTRODUCTION

If a physical system is made to undergo a certain transformation and the laws which are applicable to this system remain the same, the physical system is said to be invariant under this transformation. In addition, such an invariance leads in general to the conservation of an observable physical quantity.

The practical importance of these invariances in the physics of elementary particles is obvious. Our purpose will not be to establish the different known invariances but to define them as concisely as possible and, in particular, to draw from them the practical consequences for the reactions of elementary particles. Therefore our study will be extended to the consequences of the general principles of the physics.

We shall first review the different invariances with some examples of selection rules. In conclusion we shall consider their application to particular systems.

In the physics of elementary particles one distinguishes between the three kinds of interaction: strong, electromagnetic and weak, which are very different from the point of view of intensity. They differ from each other also by the fact that the various invariance laws are not applicable to all interactions.

Our study of invariance laws will go from the more general laws to the more particular ones and will be divided into four chapters:

I. General laws valid for all the interactions

Space-time conservation laws: the laws of conservation of momentum, energy, and total angular momentum.

Laws associated with Fermi statistics and with Bose-Einstein statistics.

Gauge invariance: the conservation of electric, baryonic and leptonic charges.

II. Laws valid only for strong and electromagnetic interactions: C, P, T invariances.

The CPT theorem, which is valid for all interactions, will be presented at the same time as the C, P, T invariances. On the other hand, the conservation of strangeness, which is violated only by weak interactions, will be studied for convenience in Chapter IV.

III. Laws valid only for strong interactions: charge independence (I), charge symmetry (R), isotopic parity (G).

IV. Special laws for weak interactions.

Weak interactions violate many invariances, but within well defined limits. These limitations are summarized in the following phenomenological rules: $|\Delta S| \leqq 1$, $|\Delta I| = \frac{1}{2}$, $\Delta S = \Delta Q$.

The general application of the different invariance laws, which will constitute Chapter V, will be restricted to the case of strong or electromagnetic interactions.

CHAPTER I

LAWS VALID FOR ALL INTERACTIONS

I 1 Space-time Conservation Laws

A) *Invariance under space-time translation of a physical system*

These well-known invariances give rise to the conservation of the vector P (space) and the energy E (time) of the system.

The consequences of these are trivial and two remarks suffice here:

1) a particle of mass m_0 can decay neither into a single particle of a different mass nor into 2 particles of a larger mass. In particular, $\gamma \to e^+ + e^-$ cannot occur in vacuum.

2) in the physics of elementary particles one often considers "virtual" processes, i.e. processes in which one of the particles has an imaginary mass: with this convention, the energy-momentum conservation laws are valid.

For example, in the scheme below, the invariance laws may be applied independently to the vertices A and B.

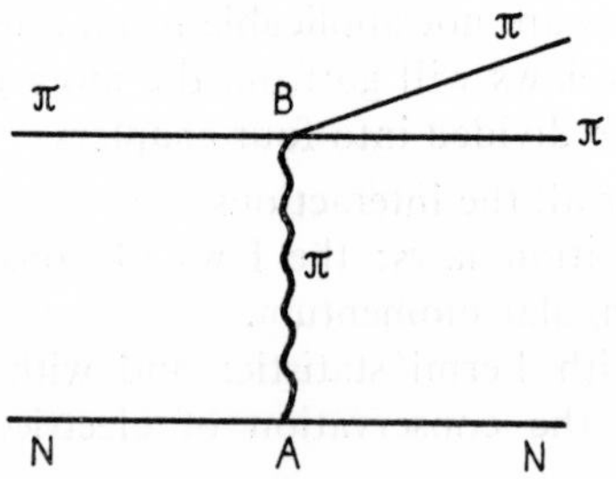

Fig. 1

B) *Invariance under rotation*: conservation of total angular momentum

1) *Laws for particles of non-zero mass*

In a physical system in interaction, the total angular momentum J, and its projection J_z on any axis, are conserved. A priori, J_z can have the values: $-J$, $-J+1, \ldots, +J$.

The combination of two angular momenta J_1 and J_2 gives a momentum J according to this rule: J may have the values $J_1 + J_2, J_1 + J_2 - 1, \ldots, J_1 - J_2$. Moreover, one must have $J_z = J_{1z} + J_{2z}$.

Following these laws, the angular momentum of a particle is obtained by combining:

the intrinsic angular momentum s or the spin of the particle,

and the orbital momentum l defined with respect to an origin ($l = 0, 1, 2, \ldots$)

The orbital momentum is simply the angular momentum $\boldsymbol{l} = \boldsymbol{r} \times \boldsymbol{p}$ and it has, in particular, the property that it is perpendicular to $\boldsymbol{p}$ (the component in the direction of $\boldsymbol{p}$ is zero). This remark is important because it allows simplification of the kinematic analysis. (Thus Adair's[1] method of determining the spin of the Λ^0 is based on the observation of the Λ^0 emitted forward in the reaction $\pi^- p \rightarrow \Lambda^0 K^0$ in such a way that in the direction of the beam one has $J_z = \pm\frac{1}{2}$ (the spin of the proton).)

The angular momentum of two particles is obtained by combining their spins and their orbital momentum l with respect to their $C.M.$

The orbital angular momentum of a system of three particles is obtained by combining the orbital momentum l_1 of two of the particles with respect to their proper $C.M.$ and the orbital momentum l_2 of the third particle with respect to the $C.M.$ of the total system:

schematic representation

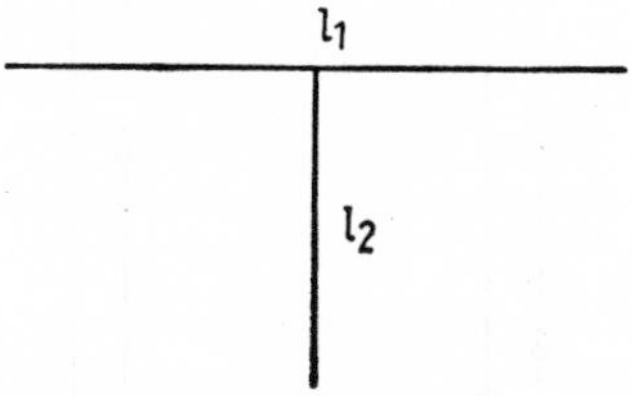

Fig. 2

2) *Particular case of a particle with mass zero*

The case of particles of mass zero must be considered separately. A particle of mass zero and spin s has for the eigenstates of spin along its momentum the values $+s$ and $-s$ only.

The rule of addition of angular momenta (orbital and intrinsic) is no longer valid. Nevertheless, as for any other particle, the projection J_z of the total angular momentum J (for example that of a γ quantum) along its direction of flight is such that: $J_z = L_z + s_z = s_z$ (in addition, $s_z = \pm s$).

3) *Selection rules*

The rules of addition of orbital momenta impose certain obvious restrictions on the possible values. In particular, a system $J = 0$ of 3π must have $l_1 = l_2$ (from the possibles values $l_1 - l_2 \ldots l_1 + l_2$ for J, the value $J = 0$ can be obtained only for $l_1 = l_2$).

The conservation of angular momentum forbids also certain reactions:

$$a)\ A \nleftrightarrow B + \gamma \text{ if } A \text{ and } B \text{ have spin } 0.$$

According to the direction of the γ, the system $B + \gamma$ has in fact $J_z = \pm 1$ instead of $J_z = 0$.

η^0 (spin 0) $\rightarrow \pi^0 + \gamma$ is forbidden,

ω^0 and ϱ^0 (spin 1) $\rightarrow \pi^0 + \gamma$ are allowed,

$K_2^0 \to \pi^+ + \pi^- + \gamma$: the orbital momentum of the 2π cannot be zero (contrary to the decay mode into 3π).

b) $A \nrightarrow 2\gamma$ if A has spin 1[(2)].

The spin of the γ quanta is oriented in their direction of propagation, and in this direction the resultant J_z must be zero ($J_z = 2$ is impossible since $J_A = 1$). The two possible configurations are sketched below.

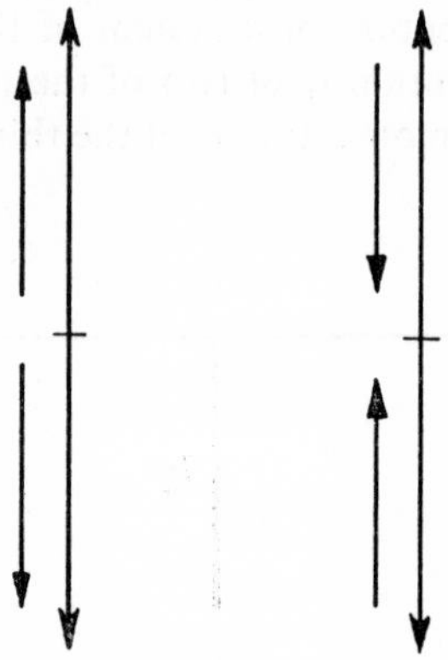

Fig. 3

If the system is rotated around a perpendicular to the direction of propagation, the 2γ are exchanged and hence the wave function of these 2γ must remain the same (spin-statistics theorem). On the contrary, the particle A of spin 1 behaves as a vector in this transformation, and its wave function must be multiplied by -1. So, this particle cannot decays into two gammas.

e. g. ω^0 and $\varrho^0 \to 2\gamma$ are forbidden

$\eta^\circ \to 2\gamma$ is allowed

I. 2 "Spin-statistics" Theorem

The theorem may be stated as follows:

1) The total wave function of n bosons (integer spin) must remain the same when two of these bosons are exchanged (Bose-Einstein statistics).

2) The total wave function of n fermions (half-integer spin) must be multiplied by -1 when two of these fermions are exchanged (Fermi-Dirac statistics). By exchange one means the exchange of all the characteristics of these particles (space coordinates, spin ...). From this theorem the Pauli principle follows: two fermions may not be in the same quantum state, because their wave function should at the same time change sign owing to the "spin-statistics" theorem and remain identical since these fermions are indistinguishable. The most important

consequences for elementary particles are the following:

a) *a system of* $2\pi^0$ *has even orbital momentum* l

When $2\pi^0$ are exchanged the wave function must be multiplied by $(-1)^l$ (the parity of the spherical harmonic Y_m^l) and hence l must be even.

b) within the framework of strong interactions, *a system of* 2π (*no matter what the charges may be*) *must be in a state* $l + I = even$ (I = the isotopic spin of the $\pi\pi$ system).

In effect, in the isotopic spin formalism (see below) the system $\pi^+\pi^-$ may be considered as a system $\pi\pi$ of indistinguishable particles. When 2π are exchanged the wave function is multiplied by $(-1)^{l+I}$, where I is the isotopic spin of the $\pi\pi$ system.

Applications

$2\pi^0$ system: the spin and isotopic spin are even:

e.g. $$f^0 \to \pi^0\pi^0 \; (I = 0, J = 2) \text{ but } \varrho^0 \nleftrightarrow \eta^0\eta^0$$

$\pi^+\pi^-$ system: the spin and isotopic spin are either both even or both odd:

e.g. $$f^0 \to \pi^+\pi^- \quad (I = 0, J = 2).$$

$$\varrho^0 \to \pi^+\pi^- \quad (I = 1, J = 1).$$

As for $2\pi^0$ system, the 2γ system must have an even spin. However, the reasons are not the same as for $2\pi^0$, because the 2γ are not necessarily indistinguishable.

I 3 Conservation of Electric, Baryonic and Leptonic Charges

A) Electric and baryonic charges

The conservation of electric and baryonic charges is well known and well verified.

The concept of electric charge results from classical phenomena, and the conservation of electric charge has been always found to be valid. It is this conservation that ensures in particular the stability of the electron (mean life $> 10^{17}$ years; $e^- \nrightarrow \nu + \gamma$).

The concept of baryonic charge results from the distinction which was established between the "baryons" (baryonic charge +1),

the "antibaryons" (baryonic charge −1),

the other particles (baryonic charge 0) e.g. π, K, γ, ν, e ...

In particular, baryonic charge conservation ensures the stability of the proton (mean life $> 10^{16}$ years; $p \nrightarrow e^+ + \pi^0$) and explains the various reactions of antiprotons:

$$p + p \rightarrow p + \bar{p} + p + p,$$

$$p + \bar{p} \rightarrow \pi^+ + \pi^-,$$

$$p + \bar{p} \rightarrow \Lambda + \bar{\Lambda} \ldots$$

B) *Leptonic charge*

The concept of leptonic charge was originally derived from that of baryonic charge using the following conventions:

$e^-\mu^-\nu$ leptons: leptonic charge $+1$,

$e^+\mu^+\bar{\nu}$ antileptons: leptonic charge -1,
other particles: leptonic charge 0.

The conservation of leptonic charge explains in particular the emission of two leptons in the β radioactivity of nuclei ($e\nu$), the decay $\mu \rightarrow e + \nu + \bar{\nu}$ with two different ν, the absence of double radioactivity, i.e. of the following successive processes:

$$n \rightarrow p + e^- + \bar{\nu},$$

then

$$\bar{\nu} + n \rightarrow p + e^-,$$

i.e. in total

$$n \rightarrow p + e^-.$$

This conservation of leptonic charge, however, is not sufficient, and another selection rule became necessary with the discovery of the difference between the ν associated with the μ and the ν associated with the electron. (Hence the presence of four ν: $\nu_e, \bar{\nu}_e, \nu_\mu, \bar{\nu}_\mu$). Indeed, with the synchrotrons (CERN and Brookhaven) one obtained beams of ν coming from the decay $\pi^+ \rightarrow \mu^+ + \nu$, i.e. ν_μ; the interactions of ν_μ with the nucleons give rise to μ but never to electrons, i.e.:

$$\nu_\mu + n \rightarrow \mu^- + p, \quad \nu_\mu + n \nleftrightarrow e^- + p, \quad \nu_\mu + p \nleftrightarrow e^+ + n.$$

Whatever the convention taken for the definition of leptons may be, the conservation of leptonic charge cannot alone explain the simultaneous absence of the two last processes. One has to distinguish between e, ν_e on the one hand and between μ, ν_μ on the other hand, and there is no transition from one group into the other.

Thus diverse processes, such as the following ones, are forbidden:

$$\mu^- \nleftrightarrow e^- + \gamma,$$

$$\mu^- \nleftrightarrow e^- + e^- + e^+.$$

These selection rules may be interpreted by assigning to the group (μ, ν_μ) a "muonic" charge different from zero, to the group (e, ν_e) a "muonic" charge equal to zero, and by requiring the conservation of this new charge.

Although with the existence of two neutrinos ν_e and ν_μ the definition of leptons becomes more arbitrary (it is possible to call e^- and μ^+ leptons), the old definition seems to be the most natural, since the two neutrinos ν_e and ν_μ of lefthanded helicity (helicity verified by experiment) are leptons.

CHAPTER II

THE *C*, *P*, *T* INVARIANCES

II 1 Definitions and the *CPT* Theorem

A) *Definitions*

A physical system may be defined by three kinds of parameters: space coordinates (r), time coordinates (t), and internal coordinates without any relation with space-time coordinates: electric, baryonic and leptonic charges, strangeness (n_I).

The operations P, T, C act respectively on one, and only one, of these types of coordinates and change only the sign. If $\Psi(n_I, \mathbf{r}, t)$ describes a system, one has:

$$C\Psi(n_I, \mathbf{r}, t) \to \Psi(-n_I, \mathbf{r}, t),$$
$$P\Psi(n_I, \mathbf{r}, t) \to \Psi(n_I, -\mathbf{r}, t),$$
$$T\Psi(n_I, \mathbf{r}, t) \to \Psi(n_I, \mathbf{r}, -t).$$

The effect of the operators C, P, T is to leave unchanged or to change the sign of the different quantities which may be used to described a physical system, as summarised below.

	momentum $\mathbf{p}$	angular momentum l or spin s	energy	magnetic field (or magnetic moment)	electric field (or electric moment)
C	+	+	+	−	−
P	−	+	+	+	−
T	−	−	+	−	+

B) *The CPT theorem*

According to the CPT theorem, established in quantum field theory, if one applies successively the operations C, P, T (in any order) to a physical system, one obtains another physical system which must have the same laws.

The validity of the CPT theorem is associated with:

1) invariance under proper orthochronous Lorentz transformations,
2) the "spin-statistics" theorem (Fermi statistics and Bose-Einstein statistics),
3) the local nature of the interaction, which is assumed to exist at a point.

The first two conditions are quite well established, the last condition is one of the basic assumptions of quantum field theory. Although the CPT theorem does not give rise in general to a conserved quantum number (particle → antiparticle), nevertheless it has been possible to test quite thoroughly some experimental consequences. In short, the CPT theorem relates the properties of a particle and

those of the corresponding antiparticle in the following way:
i) The masses must be equal.

By mass one means the rest energy of the particle. However, the gravitational masses of a particle and its antiparticle are effectively equal, as it was possible to show for the K^0 $\overline{K^0}$ system.

$$\text{Examples:} \quad m_{e^+} = m_{e^-}, \quad m_{K^+} = m_{K^-}$$

ii) The mean lives must be equal: $\tau_\Lambda = \tau_{\Lambda^-}$, $\tau_{K+} = \tau_{K-}$
iii) The spins must be equal.
iv) The magnetic momenta must be equal, but of opposite direction with respect to the spin.

The equality of the mean lives for partial decay rates is found only under well defined conditions. These conditions turn out to be the same for the application of the invariance under T. Because of the time reversal one must consider the possible interactions in the final state. As a very good approximation, one may neglect in general electromagnetic and weak interactions in comparison with strong interaction, and the equality of the transition rates must be verified if the states considered are eigenstates of strong interactions. Thus, according to the *CPT* theorem, the following transition rates must be equal:

$$w(K^0 \to \pi^- \mu^+ \nu) = w(\overline{K^0} \to \pi^+ \mu^- \overline{\nu})$$

but the equality $w(\Lambda^0 \to p\pi^-) = w(\overline{\Lambda^0} \to \overline{p}\pi^+)$ is not predicted by the *CPT* theorem. For this equality, the invariance under C is necessary.

II 2 Invariance under Charge Conjugation *C*

A) *Eigenvalues of charge conjugation*

It may be shown that the charge conjugation operator, which changes particles into antiparticles without affecting the space-time coordinates, may be chosen to be unitary. Thus $C|\Psi\rangle = e^{i\alpha}|\psi>$ since $C^2|\Psi\rangle = |\Psi\rangle$. The phase α is in general arbitrary and one may assume $C|\Psi\rangle = \pm|\Psi\rangle$.

The only possible eigenstates of charge conjugation are evidently the states of zero charge (electric, baryonic, leptonic) and zero strangeness ($C|n\rangle \to |\overline{n}\rangle$). The possible eigenvalues are $C = \pm 1$.

One may consider the different possible neutral systems and their eigenvalue of C (assuming C to be conserved!):

1) For vacuum: $C = +1$ by definition.

2) For the γ photon: $C = -1$.

The γ is represented by the electromagnetic field A_μ which changes sign (electric and magnetic fields change direction) under the operation C.

3) For a system of neutral particles a, b, ... eigenstates of C, it is shown that $\boxed{C = C_a C_b C_c \ldots}$; in particular, for a system of $n\gamma$: $C = (-1)^n$.

4) For the π^0: $C = +1$, because $\pi^0 \to 2\gamma$, C being assumed to be conserved in electromagnetic interactions.

5) For a "neutral" system of 2 fermions, e.g. $p\bar{p}$, e^+e^-, ...

Let l be the orbital momentum of the two particles and s their total spin. If these two particles are exchanged, the total wave function must be multiplied by -1 (system of 2 fermions).

This exchange may be done by three consecutive operations:

– exchange of the charge of the two fermions: the wave function is multiplied by C,

– exchange of the space coordinates: the wave function is multiplied by $(-1)^l$,

– exchange of the spin coordinates: the wave function is multiplied by $(-1)^{s+1}$, (using Table 1 containing Clebsch-Gordan coefficients it is easy to verify that, when two fermions are exchanged, the wave function is antisymmetric for the state $s = 0$, and symmetric for the state $s = 1$).

Thus one must have $C(-1)^l (-1)^{s+1} = -1$, i.e.:

$$\boxed{C = (-1)^{l+s}}$$

6) For a "neutral" system of two or three bosons, e.g.:

$$\pi^+\pi^-, \ \pi^+\pi^-\pi^0, \ K^0\overline{K^0}, \ K^+K^-, \ K^+K^-\pi^0, \ \varrho^+\varrho^-$$

Let l be the orbital momentum of the two particles which are not in an eigenstate of C. When the two particles are completely exchanged the total wave function must remain the same (system of bosons).

The reasoning is the same as for the systems of fermions (nothing that when the spins are exchanged the wave function must now be symmetric for $s = 0$, and antisymmetric for $s = 1$). Hence one has:

$1 = C$	$\times(-1)^l$	$\times(-1)^s$
exchange of particles	exchange of space coordinates	exchange of spins

hence one has the same relation as for the fermions:

$$\boxed{C = (-1)^{l+s}}$$

In particular, for a system of π, $s = 0$, $C = (-1)^l$.

B) *Applications*

Weak interactions do not conserve C. Strong and electromagnetic interactions seem to conserve it, although it has been suggested that in certain cases a slight violation may appear. It is interresting to consider the different predictions of the invariance under C.

1) Selection rules

– e^+e^- annihilation (positronium), which takes place in the state $S(l = 0)$.
If the spin $s = 0$ (singlet state), $e^+e^- \to 2\gamma$ is allowed and observed,
$e^+e^- \to 3\gamma$ is forbidden by C.
If the spin $s = 1$ (triplet state), $e^+e^- \to 2\gamma$ is forbidden (by C and by the spin 1),
$e^+e^- \to 3\gamma$ is allowed and observed.

– $\pi^0 \to 3\gamma$ is forbidden and is not observed.

It should be noted that, if C was violated, the mode $\pi^0 \to 3\gamma$ should in any case be weaker by a factor of 1/137 than the mode $\pi^0 \to 2\gamma$ without taking into account the reduction factor due to phase space.

– Other rules

The C values for different neutral systems may easily be established:

$\eta^0 \to 2\gamma$, hence $C = 1$

$\varrho^0 \to \pi^+\pi^-$ has spin 1, hence $C = -1$

$f^0 \to \pi^+\pi^-$ or $\pi^0\pi^0$, hence $C = 1$,

$\omega^0 \to \pi^+\pi^-\pi^0$ and the relation $G = C(-1)^I$ (see the properties of isotopic parity) gives $C = -1$.

None of the known decay modes (strong or electromagnetic) violates C. From the following list:

$$C = +1 : 2\gamma, \pi^o, 2\pi^o, \eta^o, f^o, \ldots$$

$$C = -1 : \gamma, 3\gamma, \pi^o + \gamma, \varrho^o, \omega^o \ldots$$

it is obvious that certain processes are forbidden such as:

ϱ^0 or $\omega^0 \to \eta^0 + \pi^0$, $f^0 \to \omega^0 + \pi^0$ } these decays are difficult to observe and in any case must be rarer then the usual modes.

The mode $\eta^0 \to \pi^0 + \gamma$ is forbidden by angular momentum conservation and the mode $\eta^0 \to \pi^0 + e^+ + e^-$ by the conservation of C, if it is assumed that the decay proceeds via a virtual γ.

2) Relations between charge conjugate systems

The invariance under C predicts that these systems must have the same laws: equal differential cross-sections, equal energy spectra ... (That the total cross-sections are equal allows simply from the CPT theorem).

Charge conjugate interactions are difficult to investigate experimentally (e.g. π^+p and $\pi^-\bar{p}$), except in the case of $p\bar{p}$ reactions, where C invariance has been tested[(3)]. From C invariance one must have $w(\Lambda^o \to p\pi^-) = w(\overline{\Lambda^o} \to \bar{p}\pi^+)$, i.e. equality between the partial rates, which does not follow from the CPT theorem.

Resonances which decay into more than two particles give interesting predictions. In particular, for the electromagnetic decay $\eta^0 \to \pi^+\pi^-\pi^0$ the spectra of the π^+ and π^- must be identical if C is conserved.

II 3 Invariance under Space Inversion. Parity *P*

A) *Definition. The intrinsic parity of a particle*

The operation of space inversion consists of changing the space coordinates $\boldsymbol{r}$ into $-\boldsymbol{r}$. It may be shown that this operation may be performed by an operator P which is linear and unitary. Applied twice in succession to a system $|\Psi\rangle$ the operator P must be such that $P^2|\Psi\rangle = |\Psi\rangle$; the eigenvalues are hence $P = \pm 1$. The invariance under P is violated in weak interactions but holds with a high degree of accuracy in strong and electromagnetic interactions.

Consider the effect of P on a particle: there is a change in the space coordinates defined with respect to a reference frame. If the reference frame chosen is the system in which the particle is at rest, one obtains a particular operation of space inversion where the associated eigenvalue is called the intrinsic parity of the particle.

The intrinsic parity depends on the nature of the field associated with the particle.

1) Bosons (with non-zero mass) are represented by scalar fields ϕ (spin 0), vector fields (spin 1) or tensor fields (spin 2). On applying the parity operator one has $P\phi = \pm\phi$: the eigenvalues of P are $= \pm 1$ and the particles, according to their spin-parity state, are called scalar (0+), pseudoscalar (0−), pseudovector (1+), vector (1−) ...

2) Fermions of spin $\frac{1}{2}$ are represented by spinors Ψ which, under a 360° rotation, become $-\Psi$. Thus $P^2\Psi = \pm\Psi$ and the eigenvalues are $P = \pm 1$ or $\pm i$. By convention one takes P (proton) $= +1$.

Using the properties of spinors, it may be shown that $P\Psi = \varepsilon\gamma_4\Psi$ and hence that $P_{\bar{p}} = -P_p = -1$.

The π^0 is pseudoscalar (correlation of the decay planes of the $2\gamma s$[4]) and the π^- is pseudoscalar (the capture $\pi^- + d \to n + n$ in the S state,[5] assuming $P_n = P_p$).

Parity is not conserved in weak interactions and strange particles are produced in pairs in strong interactions: hence one can speak only of the relative parity $(\Lambda - K)$, $(\Lambda - \Sigma)$. The intrinsic parities of the strange particles are defined by assuming that $P_\Lambda = P_p = +1$.

With thing convention:

The K meson is pseudoscalar (capture in the S state: $K^- + He^4 \to {}^\Lambda He^4 + \pi^-$[6]). The Σ hyperon has intrinsic parity +1 (study of $K^- + p \to \Sigma + \pi$[7] and of the decay $\Sigma^0 \to \Lambda^0 + e^+ + e^-$[8]).

The parity of the Ξ is not yet established experimentally.

In the theoretical scheme of SU_3 the baryons N, Λ, Σ, Ξ must have the same intrinsic parity.

B) *Parity of the* γ

Strictly speaking, the intrinsic parity of the γ has no meaning, since there is no center of mass. However, one defines the parity of the field $A(x)$ associated with the γ: this parity is -1 because, under operation P, the Hamiltonian $j_\mu A_\mu$ must remain invariant and $\boldsymbol{j}_\mu$ becomes $-\boldsymbol{j}_\mu$.

The emission of a γ is defined by its orbital momentum l with respect to the remaining system of the final state (the parity of the emission is thus $(-1)^{l-1}$) and also by the total angular momentum $\boldsymbol{J} = \boldsymbol{l} + \boldsymbol{S}$ ($\boldsymbol{S}$ is the spin of the γ).

γ radiation is called dipole for $J = 1$, quadrupole for $J = 2$ ..., the multipole order being 2^J. Each multipole emission may be produced by two types of radiation of opposite parities: an electric radiation of parity $(-1)^J$ and a magnetic radiation of parity $(-1)^{J+1}$. These parities are obvious in the case $J = 1$ because it is known that the electric and magnetic dipoles behave respectively as vectors and pseudovectors under operation parity. The different possibilities are summarized below.

J		l	Parity	Name
0	forbidden by angular momentum conservation			
1	dipole	0,2	−	E_1 electric dipole
		1	+	M_1 magnetic dipole
2	quadrupole	1,3	+	E_2 electric quadrupole
		2	−	M_2 magnetic quadrupole

The most important emission is in general that which $l = 0$, that is, electric dipole emission.

C) *The parity of a system of particles*

System of 2 particles (AB)

The total wave function is the product of the proper wave functions and the relative wave function whose parity is $(-1)^l$.

If P_A and P_B are the intrinsic parities of A and B, one has

$$\boxed{P = P_A P_B (-1)^l}$$

System of 3 particles (ABC)

If l_1 and l_2 are the orbital angular momenta defined in the usual way, one has

$$\boxed{P = P_A P_B P_C (-1)^{l_1 + l_2}}$$

D) *Consequences of the conservation of parity*

1) Electromagnetic decays

$0^- \to 0 + \gamma$ is forbidden (angular momentum conservation),
but there are several possible transitions:
$0^- \to 1^- + \gamma$ (M_1 transition)
e.g. $\eta^0 \to \pi^+\pi^- + \gamma$ (the $\pi^+\pi^-$ system must have an angular momentum $l \geqq 1$ and $l = 1$ is favoured by the centrifugal barrier effect).

$1^- \to 0^- + \gamma$ (M_1 transition)
e.g. $\omega^0 \to \pi^0 + \gamma$,
$1^- \to 0^+ + \gamma$ (E_1 transition)
e.g. $\omega^0 \to \pi^+\pi^-\gamma$ or $\pi^0\pi^0\gamma$ (the orbital momentum $l = 0$ is favoured by the centrifugal barrier effect).

2) Momentum and spin distributions

Under the parity operation the momenta (vectors) change sign and the spins (pseudovectors) do not. If the interaction conserves parity, the Hamiltonian consequently cannot contain pseudoscalar terms such as $\boldsymbol{\sigma}.\boldsymbol{p}$, $\boldsymbol{\sigma} \times \boldsymbol{p}$, $\boldsymbol{p}_1(\boldsymbol{p}_2 \times \boldsymbol{p}_3)$ (in particular, the first two terms are invariant under T).

Moreover, it is easily seen that the parity operation ($OM \to OM'$) may be decomposed into a reflection in a plane ($OM \to ON$) followed by a rotation through 180° about the perpendicular to this plane ($ON \to OM'$). The rotation does not change anything in the physical system and from the point of view of invariance, the parity operation may be reduced to a reflection in a plane.

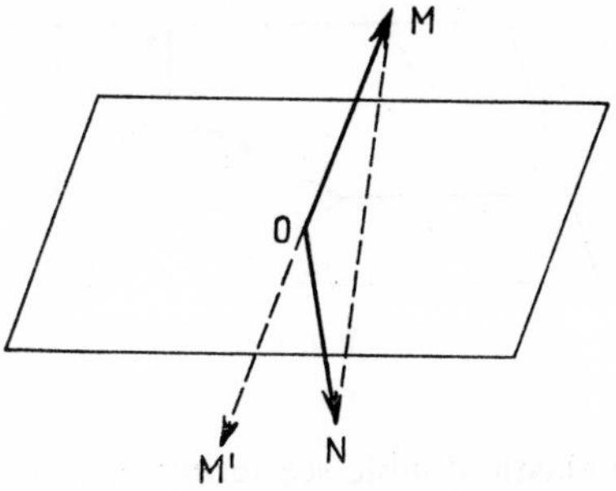

Fig. 4

Many practical applications of the P invariance may be given.

a) In a reaction between unpolarized particles which produces two particles, the outgoing particles may be polarized only in the direction perpendicular to the production plane

e.g.
$$\pi^- + p \to \Lambda^0 + K^0$$
$$\pi^- + p \to \varrho^0 + n$$

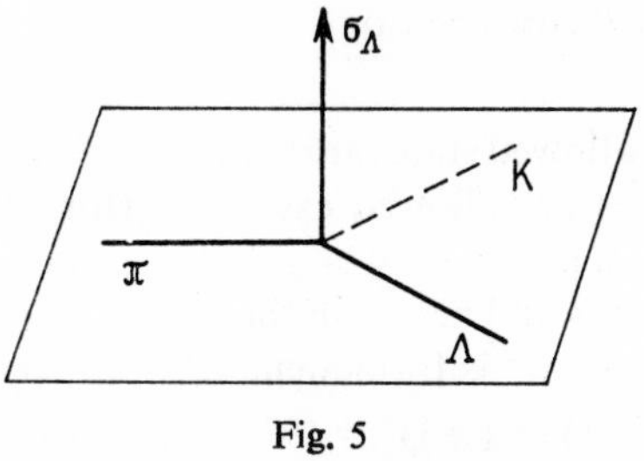

Fig. 5

The parity operation can be applied by a symmetry operation with respect to the production plane: the vectors remain identical, the pseudovectors rotate through 180° about the perpendicular to the plane. In the case where the interacting particles are not polarized, the initial state and the state obtained under the operation P are equally probable and the polarization of the outgoing particles must be perpendicular to the production plane. In the reaction $\pi^- + p \rightarrow \Lambda^0 + K^0$ the polarization of the Λ in the production plane was found experimentally to be compatible with zero(9).

b) Symmetry in a two-stage two-body reaction (double scattering, production and decay of Λ^0 ...).

The distribution of the particles in the second reaction must be symmetric with respect to the production plane of the first reaction. The momenta $\boldsymbol{p}_1$ and $\boldsymbol{p}_2$ define a plane. Each of the particles of the second reaction must go off with equal probability above or below this plane $<(\boldsymbol{p}_1 \times \boldsymbol{p}_2) \cdot \boldsymbol{p}_3> = 0$).

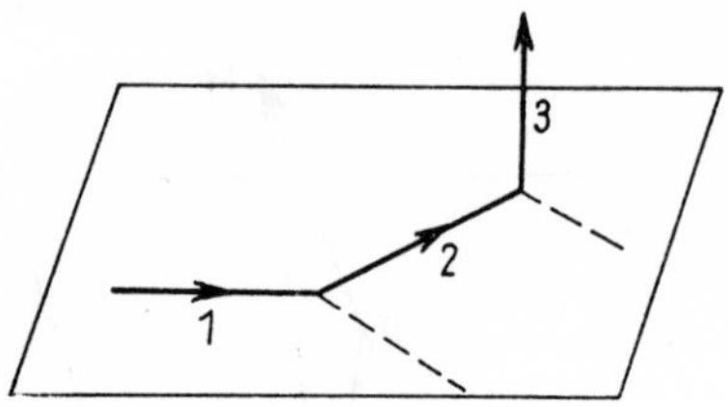

Fig. 6

Thus by means of an elastic double scattering of p on an unpolarized nucleus it was possible to test the P invariance for strong interactions.(10)

By the asymmetry of the π from the decay of the Λ^0 produced in the reaction $\pi^- + p \rightarrow \Lambda^0 + K^0$, one was able to show that P is not conserved in weak interactions.

c) The dielectric moment $\boldsymbol{M}$ of a particle having spin $\boldsymbol{\sigma}$ must be zero.

The terms $\boldsymbol{\sigma} \cdot \boldsymbol{M}$ or $\boldsymbol{\sigma} \times \boldsymbol{M}$ are pseudoscalars under the operation P, and, moreover, it may be shown that an electric field $\boldsymbol{E}$ in the presence of a dielectric moment must give an interaction term proportional to $\boldsymbol{\sigma} \cdot \boldsymbol{E}$ (non-relativistic case). Thus the dielectric moment must be zero both by P invariance and by T invariance ($\boldsymbol{\sigma} \cdot \boldsymbol{E}$ is a pseudoscalar for the operations P and T).

3) Selection rules due to P conservation

a) System of π's

System of 2π: the only allowed states are $0^+, 2^+ \ldots, 1^-, 3^- \ldots$ (because $P = (-1)^l$).

System of 3π: all states are allowed except 0^+ (for spin zero, one must have $l_1 = l_2$ and hence $P = -1$).

π and K are pseudoscalars and hence, in the above, π and K are interchangeable.

b) System of 2γ: the state 3^- is forbidden.(11)

c) System $N\bar{N}$: $P = (-1) \times (-1)^l = (-1)^{l+1}$.

The states may be characterized by the total spin s, the orbital angular momentum l, the total angular momentum J usually written as $2s + 1_{lj}$, $2s + 1$ being the multiplicity of the states due to the spin, and l being represented by the spectroscopic symbols $S, P, D \ldots$

All states are allowed, and have definite parities

$$1S_0 = 0^-, \quad 3P_0 = 0^+$$

$$3S_1 = 1^-, \quad 3P_1 = 1^+$$

$$1P_1 = 1^+, \quad 3P_2 = 2^+$$

II 4 Invariance under Time Reversal *T*

A) *Definition*

It is impossible to define an operator T such as $T\Psi(\boldsymbol{r}, t) = \Psi(\boldsymbol{r}, -t)$, because the Schrödinger equation $H\Psi = \mathrm{i}\, \delta\Psi/\delta t$ would not be satisfied by the new state, as is easily seen in the case of a plane wave: $\Psi \sim e^{i} (pz - Et)$. The equation is satisfied if one assumes the definition:

$$T\Psi(\boldsymbol{r}, t) = \Psi^*(\boldsymbol{r}, -t).$$

The operation of time reversal is thus performed by an operator which is unitary and *antilinear*.

B) *Consequences of T invariance*

Invariance under time reversal seems to be a natural assumption and up to 1964 it was not questioned, since there was much experimental evidence available in the case of strong interactions(12), and the absence of asymmetry in the decay of the polarised neutron(13) seemed to have verified it for weak interactions.

In 1964 the observation of the decay mode $K_2^0 \to 2\pi$(14) $\left(\dfrac{K_2^0 \to 2\pi}{K_2^0 \to \text{all modes}} = 2.0 \pm 0.4.10^{-3}\right)$ yielded proof of non-invariance under T in weak interactions.

The consequences thus become very interesting to study. In fact, the application of T invariance is more delicate than of the P or C invariances. When one reverses the time one should assume that the new physical state is not perturbed by interactions in the final state and that it may be considered as a state of free particles (the Born approximation). With this condition one can establish a symmetry between outgoing waves and incoming waves. In the case of weak interactions, and in general also for electromagnetic interactions, it may be shown that the perturbation is sufficiency weak to be neglected. In the case of particles with strong interactions, tests of T invariance may be done only by taking into account the interactions of the particles in the final state and the phase shifts they produce. Here we shall confine ourselves to particles with weak interactions, and now review the different consequences of T invariance.

1) Momenta and spins distribution

The Hamiltonian cannot contain terms which are pseudoscalar with respect to T, for example:

$$\sigma(p_1 \times p_2), \quad \sigma_1(\sigma_2 \times \sigma_3), \quad p_1(p_2 \times p_3), \quad p(\sigma_1 \times \sigma_2).$$

As was not the case with P invariance, one has here to measure three vectors or pseudovectors, which makes it more difficult to test T invariance experimentally. We may give two examples which indicate the difference between weak interactions and strong interactions.

a) Weak interactions: polarisation of the μ^- in the reaction $\nu + n \rightarrow \mu^- + p$ (unpolarised neutron).

Let the momenta be p_p and p_μ and the spin of the μ be σ_μ. The quantity $<(p_p \times p_\mu) \cdot \sigma_\mu>$ must be zero if there is T invariance, i.e. the polarisation of the μ must be in the plane $(p_p p_\mu)$.

In effect, the operation T makes the transition from the state (1) to the state (2) as sketched below, where the directions of the momenta and spins are reversed.

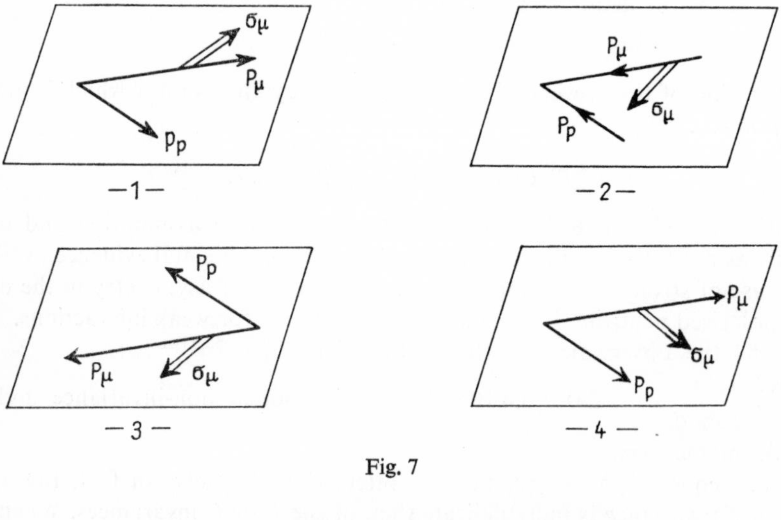

Fig. 7

In this, the incoming and outgoing waves are not perturbed by strong interactions and the states (2) and (3) are identical. A rotation through 180° about an axis perpendicular to the plane $(p_\mu \cdot p_p)$ gives a state (4) where the vectors and the spin σ_μ have rotated through 180° about this axis of rotation.

The momenta obtained in state (4) have the same direction as in state (1), whereas the spin σ_μ has been reflected in the plane $(p_\mu \cdot p_p)$.

Hence the polarization (or the mean of the spins) of the μ must be in the plane $(p_\mu \cdot p_p)$.

It should be noted that the reasoning would not hold if the neutron was polarised, because the states (1) and (4) could not be superposed.

The polarisation of the μ in this reaction has not yet been measured experimentally.

b) Strong interactions: polarization of the Λ^0 in the reaction $\pi^- + p \rightarrow \Lambda^0 + K^0$.

The preceding argument is no longer valid since the incoming and outgoing waves may not be identical because of the strong interactions of Λ^0 and K^0. The Λ^0 is found experimentally to be polarised perpendicular to the production plane.

The following table summarises the situation:

	Invariance under P	Invariance under T
weak interaction $\nu n \rightarrow \mu^- p$	not invariant	The polarisation of the μ, if it exists, must be in the plane $(p_p p_\mu)$
Strong interaction $\pi^- p \rightarrow \Lambda^0 K^0$	The polarisation of the Λ^0 if it exists, must be perpendicular to the plane (ΛK)	No conclusion may be drawn for the polarisation of the Λ^0

Two examples of weak interactions which have led to experimental verification are of the type given above:

– Angular distribution of the decay of the polarised neutron

By T invariance one must have $<\sigma_N \cdot (p_e \times p_\nu)> = 0$. Experimentally[13] measurement of this quantity is described by an associated parameter $A = -0.04 \pm 0.07$.

– Polarisation of the μ in the decay $K^+ \rightarrow \pi^0 \mu^+ \nu$

By T invariance one must have $<\sigma_\mu \cdot (p_{\pi^0} \times p_\mu)> = 0$. Measurement of the transverse component of the polarization of the μ gives[15] $<p_\perp> = 0.04 \pm 0.35$.

2) Decay of $\overline{K^0}$ and K^0

a) Consequences of the non conservation of strangeness in the decay of K^0. It is well known that the decay of $\overline{K^0}$ or K^0 seems as the superposition of two particles K_S^0 and K_L^0 of different mean life:

$$\tau K_S^0 = 0.92 \cdot 10^{-10} \text{ sec.}$$

$$\tau K_L^0 = 5{\cdot}62 \cdot 10^{-8} \text{ sec.}$$

This is associated with the fact that K^0 and $\overline{K^0}$, which are distinguished in production by their different strangeness $S = \pm 1$, have in common the same decay mode of strangeness $S = 0$. Thus the decaying system must be considered as a mixture of K^0 and $\overline{K^0}$, i.e. $\Psi(t) = a(t)\,|K^0\rangle + b(t)|\,\overline{K^0}\rangle$, and the evolution of the system Ψ is given by:

$$\frac{d\Psi}{dt} = (\Gamma + iM)\,\Psi.$$

$\Gamma = \begin{pmatrix}\Gamma_{11} & \Gamma_{12}\\ \Gamma_{21} & \Gamma_{22}\end{pmatrix}$ and $M = \begin{pmatrix}M_{11} & M_{12}\\ M_{21} & M_{22}\end{pmatrix}$ are Hermitian 2×2 matrices; Γ is the decay matrix, and M is the mass matrix.

Diagonalising the matrix $(\Gamma + iM)$, one finds the eigenstates corresponding to two particles of different mean lives K_S^0 and K_L^0:

$$|K_S^0\rangle = \frac{1}{\sqrt{2(1+|\varepsilon_1|^2)}}\{(1+\varepsilon_1)|K^0\rangle + (1-\varepsilon_1)|\bar{K}^0\rangle\},$$
$$|K_L^0\rangle = \frac{1}{\sqrt{2(1+|\varepsilon_2|^2)}}\{(1+\varepsilon_2)|K^0\rangle - (1-\varepsilon_2)|\bar{K}^0\rangle\}. \tag{1}$$

In general, the $K^0\bar{K}^0$ system depends on the 8 independent parameters of the matrix $\Gamma + iM$, which may be expressed in terms of the masses and mean lives of the K_S^0 and K_L^0 and the complex parameters ε_1 and ε_2. (These parameters have an arbitrary phase which cannot be determined by experiment.)

b) Consequences of *CPT* invariance

CPT invariance predicts the equality of the masses and transition rates of the K^0 and $\bar{K}^0$, that is, it predicts the equalities $\Gamma_{11} = \Gamma_{22}$ and $M_{11} = M_{22}$ in the matrices Γ and M. It may then be shown that one must have $\varepsilon_1 = \varepsilon_2$ for $|K_S^0\rangle$ and $|K_L^0\rangle$. The number of parameters is reduced to 6 (including an arbitrary phase). Instead of having the general form (1) $|K^0\rangle = a|K_S^0\rangle + b|K_L^0\rangle$ the *CPT* theorem implies that $a = b$, i.e. that the K^0 or $\bar{K}^0$ desintegrate 50% into K_S^0 and 50% into K_L^0.

c) Consequences of *CP* invariance (or of *T* invariance, assuming *CPT* to be conserved)

It is well known that one of the principal decay modes of K_S^0 (short mean life) is the mode 2π, and it is only recently that the decay mode $K_L^0 \to 2\pi$ has been found:

$$\frac{K_L^0 \to 2\pi}{K_L^0 \to \text{all modes}} = 2.0 \pm 0.4 \times 10^{-3(14)}.$$

For the state 2π one has $C = P = (-1)^l$ and hence $CP = +1$, and if CP is conserved in weak interactions, one should have for K_S^0 $CP = +1$, that is, $\varepsilon = 0$ in the equation (1) i.e.

$$K_S^0 = \frac{|K^0\rangle + |\bar{K}^0\rangle}{\sqrt{2}}$$

(with the arbitrary phase between K^0 and $\bar{K}^0$ such that $CP|K^0\rangle = |\bar{K}^0\rangle$).
In this case K_S^0 and K_L^0 would be two eigenstates K_1^0 and K_2^0 of CP:

$$K_1^0 = \frac{|K^0\rangle + |\bar{K}^0\rangle}{\sqrt{2}} \qquad CP = +1$$

$$K_2^0 = \frac{|K^0\rangle - |\bar{K}^0\rangle}{\sqrt{2}} \qquad CP = -1$$

Since the violation of CP in weak interactions is not large, one can see the consequences for the decays of K_S^0 and K_L^0 by comparing them with K_1^0 and K_2^0.

1) Decay into $2\pi(\pi^+\pi^-$ or $2\pi^0)$
$K_1^0 \to 2\pi$ is allowed,
$K_2^0 \to 2\pi$ is forbidden.
This mode into 2π is favoured by phase space and this explains why the mean life of the K_1^0 is much shorter than that of the K_2^0.

2) Decay into $3\pi(\pi^+\pi^-\pi^0$ or $3\pi^0)$
If l_1 and l_2 are the two orbital momenta, one must have $l_1 = l_2$ (spin of the $K = 0$)

$$C = (-1)^{l_1}, \quad P = (-1)^{l_1 + l_2 + 1}.$$

That is,

$$CP = (-1)^{l_2 + 1}.$$

Hence $K_1^0 \to \pi^+\pi^-\pi^0$ is allowed if $l_2 = 1$ (or odd),
$K_1^0 \to 3\pi^0$ is forbidden (l_2 must be even),

$$\left.\begin{array}{l} K_2^0 \to \pi^+\pi^-\pi^0 \\ K_2^0 \to 3\pi^0 \end{array}\right\} \text{ are allowed, } l_2 = 0 \text{ (or even).}$$

The centrifugal barrier effect favours the state $l_2 = 0$ and thus one must have for the transition rates:

$$w(K_2^0 \to \pi^+\pi^-\pi^0) > w(K_1^0 \to \pi^+\pi^-\pi^0).$$

3) Decay into $\pi \pm l \pm \nu \quad (l = e$ or $\mu)$
By CPT invariance, since there are no strong interactions in the final state, one must have for the transition amplitudes

$$a(K^0 \to \pi^- e^+ \nu) = \bar{a}^*(\overline{K}^0 \to \pi^+ e^- \bar{\nu}),$$

$$a'(K^0 \to \pi^+ e^- \bar{\nu}) = \bar{a}'^*(\overline{K}^0 \to \pi^- e^+ \nu).$$

By CP invariance one has $K_1^0 = (K^0 + \overline{K^0})/\sqrt{2}$ and $K_0^2 = (K^0 - \overline{K^0})/\sqrt{2}$ and by means of the relations between a and a^* it may be shown easily that the following relations exist between the transition rates w:

$$w(K_1^0 \to \pi^- e^+ \nu) = w(K_1^0 \to \pi^+ e^- \bar{\nu}) \sim |a + a'|^2,$$

$$w(K_2^0 \to \pi^- e^+ \nu) = w(K_2^0 \to \pi^+ e^- \bar{\nu}) \sim |a - a'|^2.$$

Stricter relations are found with other hypotheses (for example, the $\Delta S = \Delta Q$ rule).

CHAPTER III

CHARGE SYMMETRY AND CHARGE INDEPENDENCE ISOTOPIC SPIN. ISOTOPIC PARITY

III 1 Definition and Invariances

The forces acting between protons and neutrons are said to be:
a) charge independent if: $(p - p)$ forces $= (n - n)$ forces $= (p - n)$ forces,
b) charge symmetric if: $(p - p)$ forces $= (n - n)$ forces.

In fact, nuclear forces are charge independent and hence charge symmetric. At present, the property of charge independence is valid for all strong interactions.

A) *Isotopic spin*

To account for this law, a new quantity was introduced called isotopic spin (or isospin), which has a mathematical form analogous to spin. The concept of isotopic spin was formulated by Heisenberg(16) to characterize the two charge states of the nucleon. By analogy with the electron (spin $J = \frac{1}{2}$) which has an "up" spin $J_3 = +\frac{1}{2}$ and a "down" spin $J_3 = -\frac{1}{2}$, the nucleon has an isospin $I = \frac{1}{2}$ with an "up" isospin $I_3 = +\frac{1}{2}$ (proton) and a "down" isospin $I_3 = -\frac{1}{2}$ (neutron). The component I_3 of the isotopic spin is connected with the charge Q of the nucleon by the relation

$$Q = I_3 + \frac{B}{2},$$

where B is the baryonic number.

This relation is applicable to π mesons ($B = 0$) and has been generalized for hyperons and K mesons in the form:

$$Q = I_3 + \frac{B + S}{2},$$

where S is the strangeness, which will be discussed later ($S = 0$ for the nucleon and the π meson).

The idea of the isotopic spin formalism hence consists in defining an "isotopic-spin" operator I such that the eigenvalues (2I + 1 states) of its component on the axis of quantization describe the different charge states of the particle. This allows one to infer the value of I for different particles.

The particles of isotopic spin 0, $\frac{1}{2}$, 1 are respectively isoscalars, isospinors and isovectors in isotopic spin space.

The nucleon is an isospinor $N = \begin{pmatrix} p \\ n \end{pmatrix}$.

Isotopic spin	Multiplet	Particle	I_3
$I=0$	Λ hyperon		0
	K meson	K^+	$+\frac{1}{2}$
		K^0	$-\frac{1}{2}$
$I=\frac{1}{2}$	N nucleon	p	$+\frac{1}{2}$
		n	$-\frac{1}{2}$
	Ξ hyperon	Ξ^0	$+\frac{1}{2}$
		Ξ^-	$-\frac{1}{2}$
	π meson	π^+	$+1$
		π^0	0
		π^-	-1
$I=1$	Σ hyperon	Σ^+	$+1$
		Σ^0	0
		Σ^-	-1

The π meson is an isovector

$$\pi = \begin{pmatrix} \pi_1 \\ \pi_2 \\ \pi_3 \end{pmatrix} \quad \text{with} \quad \begin{cases} \pi^+ = \dfrac{\pi_1 + i\pi_2}{\sqrt{2}}, \\ \pi^0 = \pi_3 \\ \pi^- = \dfrac{\pi_1 - i\pi_2}{\sqrt{2}}. \end{cases}$$

Only strong interactions conserve isotopic spin. Hence it is possible to define isotopic spin for particles having strong interactions but this has no meaning for particles having only electromagnetic or weak interactions (photon, leptons).

B) *Charge independence and invariance under rotation in isospace*

In atomic physics, in the absence of an external magnetic field the phenomena observed do not depend on the direction of the axis of quantization of the spin and, thus, there is no distinction between the states $J_3 = +\frac{1}{2}$ and $J_3 = -\frac{1}{2}$. This is the consequence of invariance under rotations in ordinary space. Similarly, in nuclear physics there is no distinction between the states $I_3 = +\frac{1}{2}$ (proton) and $I_3 = -\frac{1}{2}$ (neutron) in the absence of electromagnetic interactions.

Consequently, just as angular momentum conservation results from the invariance of the physical system under rotation in ordinary space, isotopic spin conservation results from the invariance of the physical system under rotations in isotopic spin space (or isospace).

Hence to postulate charge independence means that the physical system depends solely on the value of I and not on the value of I_3.

C) *Charge symmetry* (R)

Charge symmetry is defined by the operator $R = e^{i\pi I_2}$. For the nucleon $I = \tau/2$ where τ represents the Pauli matrices in isotopic spin space (defined as for ordinary spin). Hence

$$R\begin{pmatrix} p \\ n \end{pmatrix} = \left(\cos\frac{\pi}{2} + i\tau_2 \sin\frac{\pi}{2}\right)\begin{pmatrix} p \\ n \end{pmatrix} = \begin{pmatrix} n \\ -p \end{pmatrix},$$

because

$$\tau_2 = \begin{pmatrix} 0 & -i \\ i & 0 \end{pmatrix}.$$

For the π meson, the operation $e^{i\pi I_2}$ is in fact equivalent to a rotation through 180° about the axis 2 of the isospace ($\pi_1 \to -\pi_1, \pi_2 \to \pi_2, \pi_3 \to -\pi_3$), hence

$$R\begin{pmatrix} \pi^+ \\ \pi^0 \\ \pi^- \end{pmatrix} = R\begin{pmatrix} \dfrac{\pi_1 + i\pi_2}{2} \\ \pi_3 \\ \dfrac{\pi_1 - i\pi_2}{2} \end{pmatrix} = -\begin{pmatrix} \pi^- \\ \pi^0 \\ \pi^+ \end{pmatrix}$$

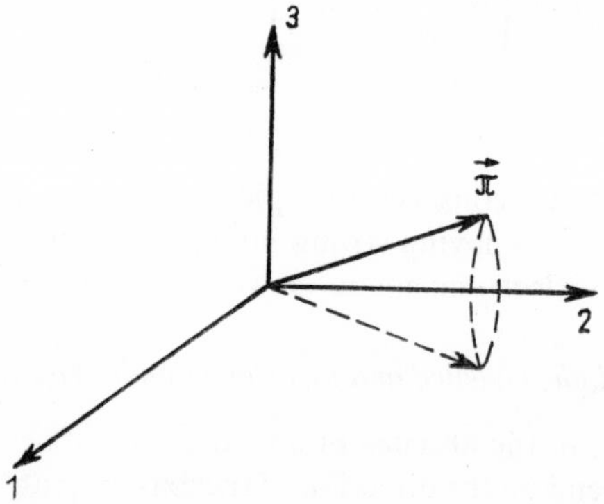

Fig. 8

D) *Isotopic spin wave functions*

Isospin plays in isospace the same role as spin in ordinary space, and the addition rules are identical with those already given for angular momenta.

One may wish to obtain from two particles of isotopic spin I^a and I^b a definite state of isotopic spin I^c and component I_3^c. This may be done in general for many combinations of (I_3^a, I_3^b). The state obtained, normalized, is a linear superposition of these different states which are themselves normalized, where the relative weight are called Clebsch-Gordan coefficients:[17]

$$|I^c I_3^c\rangle = \sum_{I_3^a}\sum_{I_3^b}^{I_3^a + I_3^b = I_3^c} c_{I^a b_I}(I^c I_3^c;\, I_3^a I_3^b)\,|I^a I_3^a\rangle\,|I^b I_3^b\rangle.$$

In the physics of elementary particles we have often to deal with a system made up of two or three isospins of the following types:

$$\frac{1}{2} \times \frac{1}{2} \qquad \text{(e.g. } N - N\text{)},$$

$$1 \times \frac{1}{2} \qquad \text{(e.g. } \pi - N\text{)},$$

$$2 \times \frac{1}{2} \qquad \text{(e.g. } (2\pi) - N\text{)},$$

$$\frac{3}{2} \times 1 \qquad \text{(e.g. } N^* - \pi\text{)},$$

$$1 \times 1 \qquad \text{(e.g. } \pi - \pi\text{)},$$

$$1 \times 1 \times 1 \quad \text{(e.g. } \pi - \pi - \pi\text{)}.$$

Thus it would appear useful to give here the tables of the Clebsch-Gordan coefficients corresponding to these systems and involving the different states $|I, I_3 >$. They allow one, (as we shall see later), to write down immediately the isotopic spin wave functions of well defined states and to infer the relations existing between them.

For the 3π system one can use the tables (1×1) and (2×1), adding first the isospins of two of the three π's ($I_{\pi\pi} = 0, 1, 2$) and then the isospin of the system of 2π and that of the third $\pi(I_\pi = 1)$.

III 2 Consequences of Charge Symmetry and Charge Independence

A) *Consequences of charge symmetry*

For charge symmetric reactions invariance under charge symmetry implie that the modulis (and only the modulis) of the transition amplitudes, and henc

Table 1 — 1/2 × 1/2

	(1, 1)	(1, 0)	(0, 0)	(1, −1)
$(\frac{1}{2}, \frac{1}{2})$ $(\frac{1}{2}, \frac{1}{2})$	1			
$(\frac{1}{2}, \frac{1}{2})$ $(\frac{1}{2}, -\frac{1}{2})$		$\frac{1}{\sqrt{2}}$	$\frac{1}{\sqrt{2}}$	
$(\frac{1}{2}, -\frac{1}{2})$ $(\frac{1}{2}, \frac{1}{2})$		$\frac{1}{\sqrt{2}}$	$-\frac{1}{\sqrt{2}}$	
$(\frac{1}{2}, -\frac{1}{2})$ $(\frac{1}{2}, -\frac{1}{2})$				1

Table 2 — 1 × 1/2

	$(\frac{3}{2}, \frac{3}{2})$	$(\frac{3}{2}, \frac{1}{2})$	$(\frac{1}{2}, \frac{1}{2})$	$(\frac{3}{2}, -\frac{1}{2})$	$(\frac{1}{2}, -\frac{1}{2})$	$(\frac{3}{2}, -\frac{3}{2})$
$(1, 1)\ (\frac{1}{2}, \frac{1}{2})$	1					
$(1, 1)\ (\frac{1}{2}, -\frac{1}{2})$		$\sqrt{\frac{1}{3}}$	$\sqrt{\frac{2}{3}}$			
$(1, 0)\ (\frac{1}{2}, \frac{1}{2})$		$\sqrt{\frac{2}{3}}$	$-\sqrt{\frac{1}{3}}$			
$(1, 0)\ (\frac{1}{2}, -\frac{1}{2})$				$\sqrt{\frac{2}{3}}$	$\sqrt{\frac{1}{3}}$	
$(1, -1)\ (\frac{1}{2}, \frac{1}{2})$				$\sqrt{\frac{1}{3}}$	$-\sqrt{\frac{2}{3}}$	
$(1, -1)\ (\frac{1}{2}, -\frac{1}{2})$						1

Table 5 – 1 × 1

	(2, 2)	(2, 1)	(1, 1)	(2, 0)	(1, 0)	(0, 0)	(2, −1)	(1, −1)	(2, −2)
(1, 1) (1, 1)	1								
(1, 1) (1, 0)		$\sqrt{\frac{1}{2}}$	$\sqrt{\frac{1}{2}}$						
(1, 0) (1, 1)		$\sqrt{\frac{1}{2}}$	$-\sqrt{\frac{1}{2}}$						
(1, 1) (1, −1)				$\sqrt{\frac{1}{6}}$	$\sqrt{\frac{1}{2}}$	$\sqrt{\frac{1}{3}}$			
(1, 0) (1, 0)				$\sqrt{\frac{2}{3}}$	0	$-\sqrt{\frac{1}{3}}$			
(1, −1) (1, 1)				$\sqrt{\frac{1}{6}}$	$-\sqrt{\frac{1}{2}}$	$\sqrt{\frac{1}{3}}$			
(1, 0) (1, −1)							$\sqrt{\frac{1}{2}}$	$\sqrt{\frac{1}{2}}$	
(1, −1) (1, 0)							$\sqrt{\frac{1}{2}}$	$-\sqrt{\frac{1}{2}}$	
(1, −1) (1, −1)									1

Table 3 — 2 × 1/2

	$(\frac{5}{2}, \frac{5}{2})$	$(\frac{5}{2}, \frac{3}{2})$	$(\frac{3}{2}, \frac{3}{2})$	$(\frac{5}{2}, \frac{1}{2})$	$(\frac{3}{2}, \frac{1}{2})$	$(\frac{5}{2}, -\frac{1}{2})$	$(\frac{3}{2}, -\frac{1}{2})$	$(\frac{5}{2}, -\frac{3}{2})$	$(\frac{3}{2}, -\frac{3}{2})$	$(\frac{5}{2}, -\frac{5}{2})$
$(2, 2)\,(\frac{1}{2}, \frac{1}{2})$	1									
$(2, 2)\,(\frac{1}{2}, -\frac{1}{2})$		$\sqrt{\frac{1}{5}}$	$\sqrt{\frac{4}{5}}$							
$(2, 1)\,(\frac{1}{2}, \frac{1}{2})$		$\sqrt{\frac{4}{5}}$	$-\sqrt{\frac{1}{5}}$							
$(2, 1)\,(\frac{1}{2}, -\frac{1}{2})$				$\sqrt{\frac{2}{5}}$	$\sqrt{\frac{3}{5}}$					
$(2, 0)\,(\frac{1}{2}, \frac{1}{2})$				$\sqrt{\frac{3}{5}}$	$-\sqrt{\frac{2}{5}}$					
$(2, 0)\,(\frac{1}{2}, -\frac{1}{2})$						$\sqrt{\frac{3}{5}}$	$\sqrt{\frac{2}{5}}$			
$(2, -1)\,(\frac{1}{2}, \frac{1}{2})$						$\sqrt{\frac{2}{5}}$	$-\sqrt{\frac{3}{5}}$			
$(2, -1)\,(\frac{1}{2}, -\frac{1}{2})$								$\sqrt{\frac{4}{5}}$	$\sqrt{\frac{1}{5}}$	
$(2, -2)\,(\frac{1}{2}, \frac{1}{2})$								$\sqrt{\frac{1}{5}}$	$-\sqrt{\frac{4}{5}}$	
$(2, -2)\,(\frac{1}{2}, \frac{1}{2})$										1

Table 4 — 3/2 × 1

	$(\frac{5}{2},\frac{5}{2})$	$(\frac{5}{2},\frac{3}{2})$	$(\frac{3}{2},\frac{3}{2})$	$(\frac{5}{2},\frac{1}{2})$	$(\frac{3}{2},\frac{1}{2})$	$(\frac{1}{2},\frac{1}{2})$	$(\frac{5}{2},-\frac{1}{2})$	$(\frac{3}{2},-\frac{1}{2})$	$(\frac{1}{2},-\frac{1}{2})$	$(\frac{5}{2},-\frac{3}{2})$	$(\frac{3}{2},-\frac{3}{2})$	$(\frac{5}{2},-\frac{5}{2})$
$(\frac{3}{2},\frac{3}{2})(1,1)$	1											
$(\frac{3}{2},\frac{3}{2})(1,0)$		$\sqrt{\frac{2}{5}}$	$\sqrt{\frac{3}{5}}$									
$(\frac{3}{2},\frac{1}{2})(1,1)$		$\sqrt{\frac{3}{5}}$	$-\sqrt{\frac{2}{5}}$									
$(\frac{3}{2},\frac{3}{2})(1,-1)$				$\sqrt{\frac{1}{10}}$	$\sqrt{\frac{2}{5}}$	$\sqrt{\frac{1}{2}}$						
$(\frac{3}{2},\frac{1}{2})(1,0)$				$\sqrt{\frac{3}{5}}$	$\sqrt{\frac{1}{15}}$	$-\sqrt{\frac{1}{3}}$						
$(\frac{3}{2},-\frac{1}{2})(1,1)$				$\sqrt{\frac{3}{10}}$	$-\sqrt{\frac{8}{15}}$	$\sqrt{\frac{1}{6}}$						
$(\frac{3}{2},\frac{1}{2})(1,-1)$							$\sqrt{\frac{3}{10}}$	$\sqrt{\frac{8}{15}}$	$\sqrt{\frac{1}{6}}$			
$(\frac{3}{2},\frac{1}{2})(1,0)$							$\sqrt{\frac{3}{5}}$	$-\sqrt{\frac{1}{15}}$	$-\sqrt{\frac{1}{3}}$			
$(\frac{3}{2},-\frac{3}{2})(1,1)$							$\sqrt{\frac{1}{10}}$	$-\sqrt{\frac{2}{5}}$	$\sqrt{\frac{1}{2}}$			
$(\frac{3}{2},-\frac{1}{2})(1,-1)$										$\sqrt{\frac{3}{5}}$	$\sqrt{\frac{2}{5}}$	
$(\frac{3}{2},-\frac{3}{2})(1,0)$										$\sqrt{\frac{2}{5}}$	$-\sqrt{\frac{3}{5}}$	
$(\frac{3}{2},-\frac{3}{2})(1,-1)$												1

Table 6 − 2 × 1

	(3, 3)	(3, 2)	(2, 2)	(3, 1)	(2, 1)	(1, 1)	(3, 0)	(2, 0)	(1, 0)	(3, −1)	(2, −1)	(1, −1)	(3, −2)	(2, −2)	(3, −3)
(2, 2) (1, 1)	1														
(2, 2) (1, 0)		$\sqrt{\frac{1}{3}}$	$\sqrt{\frac{2}{3}}$												
(2, 2) (1, 1)		$\sqrt{\frac{2}{3}}$	$-\sqrt{\frac{1}{3}}$												
(2, 2) (1, −1)				$\sqrt{\frac{1}{15}}$	$\sqrt{\frac{1}{3}}$	$\sqrt{\frac{3}{5}}$									
(2, 1) (1, 0)				$\sqrt{\frac{8}{15}}$	$\sqrt{\frac{1}{6}}$	$-\sqrt{\frac{3}{10}}$									
(2, 0) (1, 1)				$\sqrt{\frac{6}{15}}$	$-\sqrt{\frac{1}{2}}$	$\sqrt{\frac{1}{10}}$									
(2, 1) (1, −1)							$\sqrt{\frac{1}{5}}$	$\sqrt{\frac{1}{2}}$	$\sqrt{\frac{3}{10}}$						
(2, 0) (1, 0)							$\sqrt{\frac{3}{5}}$	0	$-\sqrt{\frac{2}{5}}$						
(2, −1) (1, 1)							$\sqrt{\frac{1}{5}}$	$-\sqrt{\frac{1}{2}}$	$\sqrt{\frac{3}{10}}$						
(2, 0) (1, −1)										$\sqrt{\frac{6}{15}}$	$\sqrt{\frac{1}{2}}$	$\sqrt{\frac{1}{10}}$			
(2, −1) (1, 0)										$\sqrt{\frac{8}{15}}$	$-\sqrt{\frac{1}{6}}$	$-\sqrt{\frac{3}{10}}$			
(2, −2) (1, 1)										$\sqrt{\frac{1}{15}}$	$-\sqrt{\frac{1}{3}}$	$\sqrt{\frac{3}{5}}$			
(2, −1) (1, −1)													$\sqrt{\frac{2}{3}}$	$\sqrt{\frac{1}{3}}$	
(2, −2) (1, 0)													$\sqrt{\frac{1}{3}}$	$-\sqrt{\frac{2}{3}}$	
(2, −2) (1, −1)															1

the cross-sections, must be equal. For example, one must have:

$$\sigma(\pi^+ + p \to \pi^+ + p) = \sigma(\pi^- + n \to \pi^- + n),$$

$$\sigma(K^+ + p \to K^+ + p) = \sigma(K^0 + n \to K^0 + n),$$

$$\sigma(K^+ + n \to K^+ + n) = \sigma(K^0 + p \to K^0 + p).$$

B) *Consequences of charge independence*

Charge independence gives relations of three types:

ratios of different decay modes
relations between cross-sections
relations between polarisations.

In these different applications the tables of Clebsch-Gordan coefficients play an essential role.

1) Ratios between different decay modes

For a particle of given isotopic spin, decaying by strong interaction into a system of particles, it is in general easy to calculate the ratios between the different possible states of this system.

Example 1 $N^* \to N + \pi, \quad N^{*+} \to \begin{cases} p\ \pi^0 \\ n\ \pi^+ \end{cases}$

The two possible states of N^{*+} are $I = 1/2,\ 3/2$ and Table 2 allows one to write:

$$\left|\frac{1}{2}, \frac{1}{2}\right\rangle = \sqrt{\frac{2}{3}}\,|n\pi^+\rangle - \sqrt{\frac{1}{3}}\,|p\pi^0\rangle,$$

$$\left|\frac{3}{2}, \frac{1}{2}\right\rangle = \sqrt{\frac{1}{3}}\,|n\pi^+\rangle + \sqrt{\frac{2}{3}}\,|p\pi^0\rangle,$$

hence the decay ratios:

$$\frac{p\pi^0}{n\pi^+} = \frac{1}{2} \quad \text{if} \quad I = \frac{1}{2}$$

$$= 2 \quad \text{if} \quad I = \frac{3}{2}$$

Example 2: $Y^\pm \to \Sigma + \pi, \quad Y^{\pm 0} \to \Sigma^+\pi^-,\ \Sigma^-\pi^+,\ \Sigma^0\pi^0.$

Table 5 gives immediately:

$$\frac{Y^{*0} \to \Sigma^0\pi^0}{Y^{*0} \to \Sigma^+\pi^- \text{ or } \Sigma^-\pi^+} = \frac{1}{2} \quad \text{if} \quad I = 0$$

$$= 0 \quad \text{if} \quad I = 1$$

$$= 2 \quad \text{if} \quad I = 2.$$

In fact there exists a *selection rule* for neutral states of isotopic spin 1 or 2. This rule derives from the zero values of the Clebsch-Gordan coefficients. It is

$$(1, 0) \rightleftarrows (1, 0) + (1, 0) \quad \text{forbidden},$$

$$(2, 0) \rightleftarrows (2, 0) + (1, 0) \quad \text{forbidden}.$$

If, for example, a $\varrho^0\pi^0$ or $\Sigma^0\pi^0$ resonance exists, it cannot have isotopic spin 1 (The $\pi^0\pi^0$ system with $I = 1$ is in any case forbidden by Bose statistics).

$$\left.\begin{array}{l} A_1^0 \nleftrightarrow \varrho^0\pi^0 \\ Y_{1(1660)}^* \nleftrightarrow \Sigma^0\pi^0 \end{array}\right\} \quad \text{If} \quad I = 1$$

2) Relations between cross-sections

The relations which we are going to obtain here arise when one has a system $A + B$ which may be in different isotopic spin states. In particular, that is the case for strong interactions involving two particles, and one gets relations between the cross-sections. However, relations of the same kind may be obtained for weak interactions where the $|\Delta I| = 1/2$ rule allows one formally to transform the decay of a particle A into the interaction of A with a hypothetical spurion of isotopic spin 1/2 such that this interaction conserves isotopic spin.

Two classical cases will be discussed here: K-nucleon and π-nucleon interaction.

a) K-nucleon interaction

Consider, for example, the production of the (ΞK) system (the conclusions draw will hold also for the KN system).
The possible reactions are:

$$K^- + n \to \Xi^- + K^0,$$

$$K^- + p \to \Xi^- + K^+,$$

$$K^- + p \to \Xi^0 + K^0.$$

The particels K, $\overline{K}$, N and Ξ have isotopic spin 1/2 and, consequently, the total isotopic spin of the system is either $I = 0$ or $I = 1$. One obtains according to Table 1:

$$|K^-n\rangle = |1, -1\rangle,$$

$$|K^-p\rangle = \sqrt{\frac{1}{2}}\,|1, 0\rangle - \sqrt{\frac{1}{2}}\,|0, 0\rangle,$$

$$|K^0\Xi^-\rangle = |1, -1\rangle,$$

$$|K^+\Xi^-\rangle = \sqrt{\frac{1}{2}}\,|1, 0\rangle + \sqrt{\frac{1}{2}}\,|0, 0\rangle,$$

$$|K^0\Xi^0\rangle = \sqrt{\frac{1}{2}}\,|1, 0\rangle - \sqrt{\frac{1}{2}}\,|0, 0\rangle.$$

By charge independence one has two independent amplitudes $f_0(I = 0)$ and $f_1(I = 1)$:

$$f_0 = \langle 0, 0| M |0, 0\rangle,$$
$$f_1 = \langle 1, -1| M |1, -1\rangle = \langle 1, 0| M |1, 0\rangle,$$

where M is the transition matrix.

The amplitudes corresponding to the 3 reactions are then expressed as functions of f_0 and f_1:

$$f_{K^0\Xi^-} = \langle K^0\Xi^-| M |K^-n\rangle = f_1$$
$$f_{K^+\Xi^-} = \langle K^+\Xi^-| M |K^-p\rangle = \frac{1}{2}(f_1 + f_0),$$
$$f_{K^0\Xi^0} = \langle K^0\Xi^0| M |K^-p\rangle = \frac{1}{2}(f_1 - f_0).$$

From this one obtains the relation:

$$\boxed{f_{K^0\Xi^-} = f_{K^+\Xi^-} + f_{K^0\Xi^0}}$$

The matrix elements f_0 and f_1 are in general complex, hence the amplitudes $f_{K^0\Xi^-}$, $f_{K^+\Xi^-}$ and $f_{K^0\Xi^0}$ form a triangle in the complex plane. In other words, the cross-sections $\sigma_{K^0\Xi^-}$, $\sigma_{K^+\Xi^-}$, $\sigma_{K^0\Xi^0}$ must satisfy the triangular relation:

$$\sqrt{\sigma_1} \leqq \sqrt{\sigma_2} + \sqrt{\sigma_3},$$

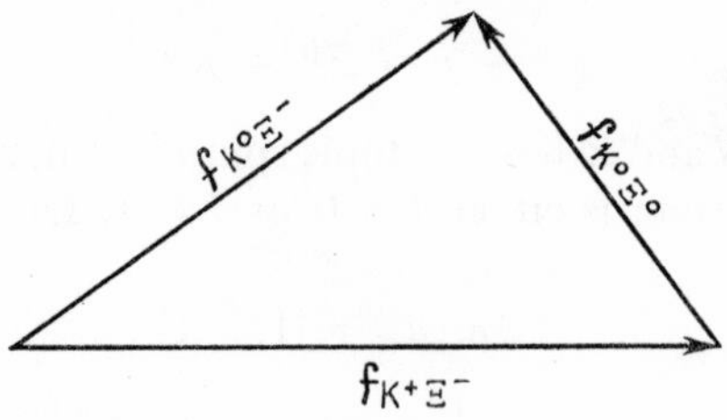

Fig. 9

in particular

$$\sqrt{\sigma_{K^+\Xi^-}} \leqq \sqrt{\sigma_{K^0\Xi^-}} + \sqrt{\sigma_{K^0\Xi^0}}$$

Up to now, this triangular relation has not been verified, because identification of the Ξ^0 is difficult and the statistics still very limited.

b) π-nucleon interaction

In an analogous way one can interrelate the three cross-sections σ^+, σ^-, σ^0 for the following processes:

$$\sigma^+ \text{ for } \pi^+ + p \to \pi^+ + p \quad (\text{or } \Sigma^+ + K^+),$$

$$\sigma^- \text{ for } \pi^- + p \to \pi^- + p \quad (\text{or } \Sigma^- + K^+),$$

$$\sigma^0 \text{ for } \pi^- + p \to \pi^0 + n \quad (\text{or } \Sigma^0 + K^0).$$

Using Table 2, one has:

$$|\pi^+ p\rangle = |3/2, 3/2\rangle,$$

$$|\pi^- p\rangle = \sqrt{\frac{1}{3}}\,|3/2, -1/2\rangle - \sqrt{\frac{2}{3}}\,|1/2, -1/2\rangle,$$

$$|\pi^0 n\rangle = \sqrt{\frac{2}{3}}\,|3/2, -1/2\rangle + \sqrt{\frac{1}{3}}\,|1/2, -1/2\rangle.$$

One obtains, as in the preceding case, a relation between amplitudes,

$$\boxed{f_+ + \sqrt{2} f_0 = f_-,}$$

and hence between cross-sections

$$\sqrt{\sigma^+} + \sqrt{2\sigma^0} \geqq \sqrt{\sigma^-} \text{ or } \sqrt{\sigma^+} + \sqrt{\sigma^-} \geqq \sqrt{2\sigma^0} \qquad (1)$$

In the region of $N^*_{3/2,3/2}$ production, one has $f_{3/2} \gg f_{1/2}$ and in this case one obtains the simple relations:

$$\sigma(\pi^+ p \to \pi^+ p) \sim 1,$$

$$\sigma(\pi^- p \to \pi^- p) \sim 1/9,$$

$$\sigma(\pi^- p \to \pi^0 n) \sim 4/9,$$

and hence:

$$\sigma(\pi^+ p \to \pi^+ p) = 9\sigma(\pi^- p \to \pi^- p),$$

$$\sigma(\pi^- p \to \pi^0 n) = 4\sigma(\pi^- p \to \pi^- p).$$

The experimental results are in good agreement with these relations. It should be noted that the relation (1) turns out to be identical (using the $|\Delta I| = \frac{1}{2}$ rule) for the Σ, if one specifies $\sigma^+ = w(\Sigma^+ \to n\pi^+)$, $\sigma_0 = w(\Sigma^+ \to p\pi^0)$ and $\sigma^- = w(\Sigma^- \to n\pi^-)$.

c) Relation between polarisations

If the total isotopic spin of a produced system has only one value, for given values of momentum and energy, the polarisation of the particles do not depend on their charge state. This results directly from the charge independence law. For example, the polarisation of the recoil nucleons are equal, in the two processes:

$$\pi^- + p \to \pi^- + p,$$

$$\pi^- + p \to \pi^0 + n$$

at the energy of the resonance $I = 3/2$, $J = 3/2$.

In the case where there are two possible values of the total isotopic spin I (this is the case which is most often encountered in practice), the polarisatons of the different production processes are in general not identical but may be related.

For example, consider the polarisations of the Ξ in the following processes:

$$K^- + n \to K^0 + \Xi^- \quad (1)$$

$$K^- + p \to K^+ + \Xi^- \quad (2)$$

$$K^- + p \to K^0 + \Xi^0 \quad (3)$$

Let σ_μ be the cross-section for the production of the Ξ, and let η_μ be the polarisation of the Ξ,

$\mu = 1, 2, 3$ for the reactions (1), (2) and (3).

If $\sigma_\mu{}^{(+)}$ and $\sigma_\mu{}^{(-)}$ are respectively the cross-sections for the production of the Ξ of the "up" spin and the "down" spin, one can write:

$$\sigma_\mu = \sigma_\mu^{(+)} + \sigma_\mu^{(-)},$$

$$\eta_\mu = \frac{\sigma_\mu^{(+)} - \sigma_\mu^{(-)}}{\sigma_\mu}$$

This shows that there must exist a relation between the polarisations which are due to the charge independence, since there is a relation between the cross-sections.

If one denotes by α_3 the quantity

$$\alpha_3 = \frac{\sigma_1 + \sigma_2 - \sigma_3}{2\sqrt{\sigma_1}\sqrt{\sigma_2}}$$

it may be shown that[18]

$$\eta_1^2 + \eta_2^2 - 2\eta_1\eta_2 \cos 2\alpha_3 - \sin^2 2\alpha_3 \leqq 0.$$

Consequently, the experimental point $(\eta_1 . \eta_2)$, representing the values of the polarisations of the Ξ associated with K^0 and K^+ mesons, must be located inside an ellipse.

III 3 The Isotopic Parity G

A) *Definition*

The isotopic parity operator G is defined to be the product of the charge conjugation operator C and the charge symmetry operator R:

$$G = CR.$$

Since charge symmetry is a particular case of charge independence, G must consequently be conserved in strong interactions.

The operator G was introduced by Michel and by Lee and Yang[19] for very simple reasons. In fact, if one considers the systems having $B = S = 0$ (for example, the π meson or a grouping of π mesons such as the ϱ or the ω) one notes that $Q = I_3$ and, consequently, only the neutral state of the system is an eigenstate of C, since the operator C changes the sign of the charge of the system. Now, we have seen that rotation through 180° about the second axis of isospace (R) also changes the sign of the system. Hence under two successive operations C and R the system conserves its initial charge state and may be an eigenstate of G.

For example, one has for the π meson:

$$G\begin{pmatrix}\pi^+\\ \pi^0\\ \pi^-\end{pmatrix} = CR\begin{pmatrix}\pi^+\\ \pi^0\\ \pi^-\end{pmatrix} = -C\begin{pmatrix}\pi^-\\ \pi^0\\ \pi^+\end{pmatrix} = -\begin{pmatrix}\pi^+\\ \pi^0\\ \pi^-\end{pmatrix}$$

i.e. $G\pi = -\pi$.

The π meson is an eigenstate of G with eigenvalue -1. There is a resemblance between the role of G in isospace on the isovector π and the role of P in ordinary space on a vector. The name "isotopic parity" given to G by Wick[20] derives from this.

Thus the isotopic parity of a system may be found by determining the isotopic parity of its neutral state ($I_3 = 0$): C is then well determined and it is sufficient to consider the effect of the operator R.

The importance of G is obvious, because it can give selection rules whereas C cannot (if $Q \neq 0$). G is particularly important in the case of bosons resonances.

B) *Values of G for various common systems*

The values of G may often be obtained by applying the two following remarks:

1) For a system of particles a, b, c, eigenstates of G, it may be shown that $G = G_a \cdot G_b \cdot G_c$ (the same property as for the operator C).

2) Every system $B = S = 0$ has integral isotopic spin and hence exists in the neutral state ($I_3 = 0$), which is the eigenstate of C. The isotopic parity G may be calculated more easily for this neutral state for which one has:

$$\boxed{G_{\text{neutral system}} = C(-1)^I}$$

This is a consequence of the definition $G = CR$, since the isotopic spin wave function for $I_3 = 0$ transforms as the spherical harmonic Y_I^0 which changes into $(-1)^I Y_I^0$ under the operation R.

The isotopic parity of various interesting systems follows easily:

1) System of π

For one π: $G = -1$

For $n\pi$: $G_{n\pi} = (-1)^n$.

2) $K\bar{K}$ system

We have already shown that for the neutral state K^+K^- or $K^0\bar{K}^0$ $C = (-1)^l$, hence for a $K\bar{K}$ system:

$$\boxed{G_{K\bar{K}} = (-1)^{l+I}}$$

It should be noted that for the $\pi\pi$ system (indistinguishable particles) $l + I$ must always be even and hence $G = +1$.

3) $N\bar{N}$ system

The nucleon-antinucleon system is an eigenstate of G. For the neutral state $(1/2(p\bar{p} \pm n\bar{n}))$ one has $C = (-1)^{l+s}$, where s is the sum of the spins.

Hence for a $N\bar{N}$ system

$$\boxed{G_{N\bar{N}} = (-1)^{l+s+I}}$$

C) *Selection rules*

1) If a particle decays by strong interactions into an even number of π, it cannot decay also into an odd number of π (and vice versa), since $G_{n\pi} = (-1)^n$,

e.g. ϱ or $f^0 \to 2\pi$, hence ϱ or $f^0 \not\to 3\pi$

$\omega^0 \to 3\pi$, hence $\omega^0 \not\to 2\pi$

The $\pi^+\pi^-$ mode of ω^0, if it exists must be produced electromagnetically.

G conservation in strong interactions implies that in a Feynman diagram, for vertices involving only pions or pion resonances, the total number of π must be even.

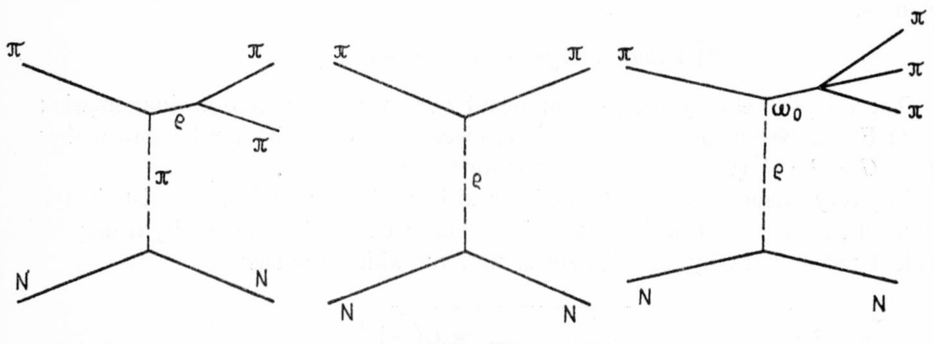

Fig. 10

Thus, the ϱ found in $\pi - N$ reactions with a small momentum transfer to the nucleon may be produced in a peripheral collision with the exchange of an intermediate π.

On the other hand, the π or ω^0 produced in the same $\pi - N$ reactions cannot be interpreted by the same mechanism. However, the exchange of a dipion, such as the ϱ, is possible.

2) Consider the production of π by antiprotons:

$$\bar{p} + p \rightarrow n\pi$$

One must have:

$$G(\bar{p}p) = (-1)^{l+s+I}$$

$$G(n\pi) = (-1)^n$$

$$l + s + I = n' \quad (n' \text{ being even or odd according to } n).$$

Hence $(\bar{p}p)$ states with even $l + s + I$ may give only an even number of π, while $(\bar{p}p)$ states with odd $l + s + I$ may give only an odd number of π.

In particular, the $\bar{p}n$ annihilation ($I = 1$ since $I_3 = -1$) in the S state ($l = 0$) gives for the number of π:

$$n' = s + 1 \begin{cases} 1S_0 \text{ state: odd number of } \pi, \\ 3S_1 \text{ state: even number of } \pi. \end{cases}$$

CHAPTER IV

RULES PARTICULAR TO WEAK INTERACTIONS

IV 1 Introduction. Strangeness

The relation $Q = I_3 + B/2$, which connects charge, the third component of isotopic spin and baryonic number for the nucleon and the π meson, was generalized to the case of the K mesons and hyperons:

$$Q = I_3 + \frac{B + S}{2},$$

where S is a quantum number called "strangeness".

This relation was obtained in a phenomenological way by Gell-Mann and Nishijima[21]. The quantity $B + S = Y$ is called hypercharge. One of the successes of this scheme was the prediction of the Σ^0 forming a triplet with Σ^+ and Σ^- and also of the Ξ^0 forming a doublet with the Ξ^-.

The K (K^+, K^0)	has	$S = +1$
the Λ^0	has	$S = -1$
the Σ $(\Sigma^+, \Sigma^0, \Sigma^-)$	has	$S = -1$
the Ξ (Ξ^0, Ξ^-)	has	$S = -2$
the Ω^-	has	$S = -3$

The strangeness of an antiparticle is opposite to that of the particle. Thus, the K^- and $\overline{K^0}$ mesons—the antiparticles of the K^+ and K^0—must have strangeness -1.

While strangeness is not necessarily conserved in weak interactions (therefore one does not define the strangeness of leptons), experiment shows that it is always conserved in strong and electromagnetic interactions. Thus:

$$\left.\begin{aligned} \pi^- p &\to \Sigma^- K^+ \\ K^- p &\to \Xi^- K^+ \\ K^- p &\to \Omega^- K^+ K^0 \\ p\bar{p} &\to \Lambda^0 \bar{\Lambda}^0 \\ \gamma p &\to \Lambda^0 K^+ \end{aligned}\right\} \quad \begin{array}{l}\text{reactions: } \Delta S = 0, \\ \text{which have been observed}\end{array}$$

$$\left.\begin{aligned} \pi^- p &\to \Sigma^+ K^- \\ \pi^- p &\to \Xi^- K^+ \\ K^- p &\to \Xi^- \pi^+ \end{aligned}\right\} \quad \begin{array}{l}\text{reactions: } \Delta S \neq 0, \\ \text{which have not been observed}\end{array}$$

The strangeness scheme explains well the difference between K^--nucleon and K^+-nucleon interactions. The $K^-(S = -1)$ can interact with a nucleon to give the hyperons Λ^0, $\Sigma^+(S = -1)$ etc., whereas the K^+ can give only elastic scattering or charge exchange for the two body final states.

Strange particles are produced up to now by strong or electromagnetic interactions. They decay by weak interactions. The only electromagnetic decay which conserves strangeness is that of $\Sigma^0 \to \Lambda^0 + \gamma$. Other decays are at the same time weak and electromagnetic and are thereby rarer (e.g. $\Sigma^+ \to p + \gamma$, $K^\pm_- \to \pi^\pm_- \pi^0$ ...).

Weak interactions, contrary to strong interactions, conserve neither the quantum numbers C, P, T not strangeness S nor isotopic spin I. Nevertheless, as far as the two last quantities are concerned, it seems that there are limitations in their violation. It is these rules, some of which are still dubious, that we are going to consider now.

Before beginning, two observations must be made:

1) We shall distinguish between two classes of weak interactions

a) leptonic interactions (involving leptons)

$$\mu \to e\nu\nu, \quad K^+ \to \pi^0 e^+ \nu, \quad \Lambda^0 \to p e^- \bar{\nu},$$

b) non-leptonic interactions (without leptons)

$$\Lambda^0 \to p\pi^-, \quad K^+ \to \pi^+ \pi^0.$$

According to Fermi's hypothesis, a weak interaction may be interpreted as the product of "currents" between two particles. The current between leptonic particles seems to be well known, which simplifies the interpretation of leptonic interactions.

2) The following rules refer particularly to the "hadronic" part of the currents, for which S and I in particular are defined. In a reaction the changes proposed concerne only particles with strong interactions.

Example

	$K^+ \to \pi^0 e^+ \nu$	$\Lambda^0 \to p \pi^-$
change in strangeness $\Delta S = S_f - S_i$	$\Delta S = -1$	$\Delta S = 1$
change in charge $\Delta Q = Q_f - Q_i$	$\Delta Q = -1$	$\Delta Q = 0$
change in isotopic spin	$\Delta I = 1/2, 3/2$	$\Delta I = 1/2, 3/2$

IV 2 The $|\Delta S| \leqq 1$ rule

Many weak interactions having $\Delta S = 0$ or $|\Delta S| = 1$ are known.

$$\left.\begin{array}{l} n \to pe^-\bar{\nu} \\ \Sigma^+ \to \Lambda^0 e^+ \nu \\ \Sigma^- \to \Lambda^0 e^- \nu \end{array}\right\} \Delta S = 0, \quad \left.\begin{array}{l} \Lambda^0 \to pe^-\bar{\nu} \\ K^+ \to \pi^+\pi^0 \\ \Xi^- \to \Lambda^0 \pi^- \end{array}\right\} \quad |\Delta S| = 1.$$

No decay $|\Delta S| = 2$ has been observed up to the present. These decays could occur in the case of the Ξ:

$$\Xi^- \to n\pi^-$$
$$\Xi^- \to ne^-\bar{\nu}$$
$$\Xi^0 \to p\pi^-$$

The decay $\Xi^- \to n\pi^-$, which has not been observed, should be favoured by phase space in comparison with decay $\Xi^- \to \Lambda^0\pi^-$.

The relative rarity of Ξ's and the difficulty of their analysis strengthens another argument for the $|\Delta S| \geqq 1$ rule: if $|\Delta S| = 2$ transitions existed, they would give the virtual transitions $\overline{K^0} \rightleftarrows K^0$ which would produce a $K_1^0 - K_2^0$ mass difference exceeding the observed one by a factor of about 10^7 (22).

Thus the $|\Delta S| \leqq 1$ rule is quite well established.

In fact, $\Delta S = 0$ transitions exist only for leptonic interactions. For non-leptonic decays the rule thus reduces to $|\Delta S| = 1$ which is equivalent to $|\Delta I_3| = \frac{1}{2}$ because of the definition of S and the conservation of charge and baryonic number.

IV 3 Rules for Leptonic Interactions

A) *The* $|\Delta Q| = 1$ *rule*

This rule is principally a rule concerning the leptonic current; leptons occur always in pairs having always an electric charge ± 1 ($e\nu$, $\mu\nu$). Indeed, neutral currents ($\nu\nu$), (e^+e^-) have never been found, as proved by the non-observance of certain reactions such as:

$$K^+ \to \pi^+ + \nu + \bar{\nu},$$
$$K^0 \to e^+ + e^-$$
$$\nu + p \to \nu + p \text{ (23)}.$$

Consequently, one has the same rule for hadronic current.

B) *The $\Delta S = \Delta Q$ rule or the $|\Delta I_3| = \frac{1}{2}$ rule for $|\Delta S| = 1$ transitions*

Minimal rules have been proposed for the violation of isotopic spin.

Because of the relation $Q = I_3 + \dfrac{B+S}{2}$ and the $|\Delta Q| = 1$ rule one has:

$$\text{if } \Delta S = 0, \quad \Delta Q = \pm 1 \quad \Delta I_3 = \pm 1$$
$$\text{if } \Delta S = \pm 1, \quad \Delta Q = \pm 1 \quad \Delta I_3 = \pm 1/2, \pm 3/2$$

A minimal violation rule was proposed by Feynman and Gell-Mann[24] assuming the transitions $|\Delta I_3| = 3/2$ to be non-existent, which requires, as is easily seen, the relation $\Delta S = \Delta Q$.

The consequences are the following:

$$\left.\begin{array}{l} \Lambda^0 \to p e^- \bar{\nu} \\ \Sigma^- \to n e^- \bar{\nu} \\ \Xi^- \to \Lambda^0 e^- \bar{\nu} \\ \Xi^0 \to \Sigma^+ e^- \bar{\nu} \\ K^0 \to \pi^- e^+ \nu \\ \bar{K^0} \to \pi^+ e^- \bar{\nu} \\ K^+ \to \pi^+ \pi^- e^+ \nu \end{array}\right\} \begin{array}{l}\text{allowed} \\ \text{reactions;} \\ \Delta S = \Delta Q\end{array} \quad \left.\begin{array}{l} \Sigma^+ \to n e^+ \nu \\ \Xi^0 \to \Sigma^- e^+ \nu \\ K^0 \to \pi^+ e^- \bar{\nu} \\ \bar{K^0} \to \pi^- e^+ \nu \\ K^+ \to \pi^+ \pi^+ e^- \bar{\nu} \end{array}\right\} \begin{array}{l}\text{forbidden} \\ \text{reactions;} \\ \Delta S = -\Delta Q\end{array}$$

Up to present, while reactions where $\Delta S = \Delta Q$ have been observed, there is virtually no evidence for $\Delta S = -\Delta Q$ transitions. For example, only a single event $\Sigma^+ \to n\mu^+\nu$ has been observed, and no $K^+ \to \pi^+\pi^+e^-\bar{\nu}$ events have been seen.[26] Experiments on the decay of K^0 and $\overline{K^0}$ into $\pi \mp e \pm \nu$ also show that the violation of the $\Delta S = \Delta Q$ rule, if it exists, is in any case weak.[27]

C) *The $|\Delta I| = \frac{1}{2}$ rule*

This rule obviously includes the preceding rule $|\Delta I_3| = 1/2$, but is more restrictive than the latter. In particular it gives predictions concerning the transition amplitudes of the K mesons.

The conservation of CP gave the relations:

$$w(K_1^0 \to \pi^- e^+ \nu) = w(K_1^0 \to \pi^+ e^- \bar{\nu}),$$
$$w(K_2^0 \to \pi^- e^+ \nu) = w(K_2^0 \to \pi^+ e^- \bar{\nu}).$$

The $|\Delta I| = \frac{1}{2}$ rule gives in addition:

$$w(K^0 \to \pi^- e^+ \nu) = 2w(K^+ \to \pi^0 e^+ \nu),$$
$$w(K_1^0 \to \pi^\pm e^\mp \nu) = w(K_2^0 \to \pi^\pm e^\mp \nu) = w(K^+ \to \pi^0 e^+ \nu).$$

To obtain these relations it is convenient to make use of the spurion, a fictitious particle of isotopic spin 1/2 which with the K meson (K + spurion $\to \pi e \nu$) gives a reaction which conserves isotopic spin. Using Table 1 of Clebsch-Gordan coefficients and the definition of K_1^0 and K_2^0 as functions of $\overline{K^0}$ and K^0, one easily obtains the preceding relations.

The experimental measurements are compatible with the $|\Delta I| = 1/2$ rule, but the accuracy of these measurements nevertheless does not allow one to exclude other contributions such as $|\Delta I| = 3/2$.

IV 4 The $|\Delta I| = 1/2$ rule for non-leptonic interactions

We have seen above that non-leptonic decays obey the $|\Delta S| = 1$ rule which implies automatically the $|\Delta I_3| = \frac{1}{2}$ rule. The suggestion of Gell-Mann and Pais[28] was to assume a more general rule, $|\Delta I| = 1/2$.

This rule predicts branching ratios which are calculated using the tables of Clebsch-Gordan coefficients and in some cases an intermediary spurion

1) Decay $K^0 \to 2\pi$

The isotopic spin of the K is 1/2, that of the 2π system is 0, 1 or 2.

For the 2π system one must have $I + l$ = even (symmetric wave function). The spatial part is symmetric, $l = 0$ (the spins of the K and π are equal to zero) hence I is even ($I = 0$ or 2). If one assumes the $|\Delta I| = 1/2$ rule, only the state $I = 0$ is allowed for the final system.

In this case, according to Table 5:

$$|0, 0\rangle = \frac{|\pi^+\pi^-\rangle - |\pi^0\pi^0\rangle + |\pi^-\pi^+\rangle}{\sqrt{3}}$$

Hence

$$\frac{K^0 \to \pi^0\pi^0}{K^0 \to \pi^0\pi^0 \text{ and } \pi^+\pi^-} = \frac{1}{3}$$

2) Decay $\Lambda^0 \to \pi N$

The isotopic spin of the Λ^0 is 0, that of the πN system is 1/2 or 3/2. With the $|\Delta I| = 1/2$ rule, only the state $I = 1/2$ is allowed. Hence from Table 2 one may write:

$$\left|\frac{1}{2}, -\frac{1}{2}\right\rangle = \frac{|\pi^0 n\rangle - \sqrt{2}\,|\pi^- p\rangle}{\sqrt{3}} \tag{1}$$

Hence

$$\frac{\Lambda^0 \to \pi^- p}{\Lambda^0 \to \pi^0 n \text{ and } \pi^- p} = \frac{2}{3}$$

Because of the non conservation of parity in the decay, the πN system may be in the states $l = 0$ or $l = 1$, to which there correspond two amplitudes, S and P. Experimentally one measures the parameter $\alpha = \dfrac{2 \operatorname{Re} S^*P}{|S|^2 + |P|^2}$. According to (1) one has the following relation between amplitudes, A:

$$A(\Lambda^0 \to n\pi^0) = \sqrt{2}A(\Lambda^0 \to p\pi^-)$$

which is valid separately for the waves S and P. Thus the $|\Delta I| = 1/2$ rule gives

$$\alpha_{\Lambda^0 \to n\pi^0} = \alpha_{\Lambda^0 \to p\pi^-}$$

and this relation should be true also for a pure transition $|\Delta I| = 3/2$

3) Decay $\Sigma^{\pm} \rightarrow \pi N$

The isotopic spin of the Σ is 1. The $|\Delta I| = 1/2$ rule requires that the $(N\pi)$ system have $I = 1/2$ or $I = 3/2$.

The three decays $\Sigma^{+} \rightarrow n\pi^{+}$, $\Sigma^{+} \rightarrow p\pi^{0}$ and $\Sigma^{-} \rightarrow n\pi^{-}$ are hence related by a relation, since there exist only two possible states of $(N\pi)$. This relation may be found by the technique of a spurion s of isotopic spin 1/2 such that the "reaction" $\Sigma + s \rightarrow N + \pi$ conserves isotopic spin. This reaction is formally identical with the case of $\pi + N \rightarrow \pi + N$ which has already considered, and for the transition amplitudes f_{+}, f_{0}, f_{-} for the processes giving respectively $n\pi^{+}$, $p\pi^{0}$, $n\pi^{-}$ one obtains the relation:

$$f_{+} + \sqrt{2} f_{0} = f_{-}$$

These amplitudes, which are a priori complex, make this a relation between vectors f_{+}, f_{0}, f_{-}. The transition rates w, the moduli of these vectors, must then obey the rule:

$$\sqrt{w_{+}} + \sqrt{2w_{0}} \geqq \sqrt{w_{-}} \quad \text{or} \quad \sqrt{w_{+}} + \sqrt{w_{-}} \geqq \sqrt{2w_{0}}$$

Experimentally: $w_{+} \sim w_{0} \sim w_{-}$

4) Decays $\Xi \rightarrow \Lambda + \pi$

The isotopic spins are $I = 1/2$ for the Ξ and $I = 1$ for the $\Lambda\pi$ system (because the Λ has $I = 0$). So there is only one wave $f_{1}(I = 1)$ for the $\Lambda\pi$ system. The $|\Delta I| = 1/2$ rule is applied by considering the system Ξ + spurion, and Table 1 of Clebsch-Gordan coefficients gives the following relations between amplitudes:

$$A(\Xi^{0} \rightarrow \Lambda^{0}\pi^{0}) = \frac{1}{\sqrt{2}} f_{1}$$

$$A(\Xi^{-} \rightarrow \Lambda^{0}\pi^{-}) = f_{1}$$

Thus one obtains predictions for the mean lives τ and the parameters α:

$$\alpha_{\Xi^{0} \rightarrow \Lambda^{0}\pi^{0}} = \alpha_{\Xi^{-} \rightarrow \Lambda^{0}\pi^{-}}$$

$$\tau_{\Xi^{0}} = 2\tau_{\Xi^{-}}.$$

5) The $K_{\pi 3}$ decay

The K has isotopic spin $I = 1/2$. The $|\Delta I| = 1/2$ rule implies $I = 1$ for the 3π, as is seen in chapter V, where the 3π system is studied in detail. Simple relations are given in this chapter for the different modes of decay of the K_{2}^{0} and K^{+} into 3π.

The various relations given above seem to be well verified, some with very good accuracy, which gives strength to the $|\Delta I| = 1/2$ rule which up to now does not follow the usual theoretical schemes.

If the diverse rules for leptonic and non-leptonic interactions proved eventually to be well verified—probably they are in part—weak interactions, in spite of their violation of the usual quantum numbers, would be governed by rather strict rules.

CHAPTER V

APPLICATIONS OF THE SELECTION RULES FOR STRONG AND ELECTROMAGNETIC INTERACTIONS

We have already defined in the preceding sections the different invariance principles of the physics of elementary particles. We have seen that the following quantum numbers arise from these considerations of invariance:

Spin	$= J$
Electric charge	$= Q$ (or I_3)
Baryonic charge	$= B$
Leptonic charge	$= L$
Charge conjugation	$= C$ (if $S = Q = B = L = 0$)
Space parity	$= P$
Isotopic spin	$= I$
Isotopic parity	$= G$ (if $S = 0$)
Strangeness	$= S$

A particle or a system of particles is characterized by a certain number of these quantum numbers.

At present there exist essentially three types of interaction between particles:

strong interactions	(mean life $\sim 10^{-23}$ sec),
electromagnetic interactions	(mean life $\sim 10^{-19}$ sec),
weak interactions	(mean life $\sim 10^{-10}$ sec).

For strong interactions, all these quantum numbers must be conserved separately.

For electromagnetic interactions, I and G are not necessarily conserved.

For weak interactions, the only quantum numbers which are conserved are J, Q and L. Strangeness S and isotopic spin I are in general not conserved, but it seems that one has the selection rules $|\Delta S| \leqq 1$ and perhaps $|\Delta I| = 1/2$.

To establish the quantum numbers of a particle or a system of particles, the quantum numbers of the decay products, the branching ratios of the different modes of decay, the invariance laws are very useful.

Table 7 summarizes the eigenvalues of J, P, C, I and G (which are conserved in strong interactions) for the common systems which we are going to study.

To find selection rules for strong and electromagnetic decays, it is convenient to classify the particles or the systems of particles according to their quantum numbers JPG. Thus one writes the states: 0^{++}, 0^{+-} ...

$$\uparrow\uparrow\uparrow$$
$$JPG$$

For example, the π meson is a 0^{--} state.

Table 7

	J	P	C*	I	G
γ	1		-1		
π	0	-1	$+1$	1	-1
$\pi\pi$	l	$(-1)^l$	$(-1)^l$	0, 1, 2	$+1$
$\pi\pi\pi$	$l_1 - l_2$ to $l_1 + l_2$	$(-1)^{l_1+l_2+1}$	$(-1)^{l_1}$	0, 1, 2, 3	-1
$K\bar{K}$	l	$(-1)^l$	$(-1)^l$	0, 1	$(-1)^{l+1}$
$N\bar{N}$	$l-s$ to $l+s$	$(-1)^{l+1}$	$(-1)^{l+s}$	0, 1	$(-1)^{l+s+1}$

For strong decays, one has selection rules by *JPGI*, (and also by *C*, but only for a neutral system).

For electromagnetic decays, one has selection rules by *JP* and also by *C* for a neutral system.

V 1 2π System

A) *Restrictions on the quantum numbers*

1) system of 2 different pions: $\pi^+\pi^-$, $\pi^+\pi^0$, $\pi^-\pi^0$.

One has: $J = l$, $P = (-1)^l \cdot G = +1$, $l + I = J + I =$ even (Bose statistics). Hence the only possible states are:

0^{++} $I = 0, 2$

1^{-+} $I = 1$

2^{++} $I = 0, 2$

. . .

For the neutral system $\pi^+\pi^-$, $C = (-1)^l$ and $CP = +1$

2) System of 2 identical pions: $\pi^+\pi^+$, $\pi^0\pi^0$, $\pi^-\pi^-$

The above conclusions apply, with the restriction that l and I must be even (Bose statistics). Thus no $J = 1, 3 \ldots$ states are possible.

B) *Existing systems*

1) $I = 0$

This is the case of the $f_0(m \sim 1250$ MeV) and the 2π system of the K_1^0 within the framework of the $|\Delta I| = 1/2$ rule.

For $I = 0$ one must have $$\frac{f_0 \to \pi^0\pi^0}{f^0 \to \pi^+\pi^-} = \frac{K_1^0 \to \pi^0\pi^0}{K_1^0 \to \pi^+\pi^-} = \frac{1}{2}$$

The 2π of the K_1^0 are in the 0^{++} state, while those of the f_0 are probably in the 2^{++} state.

* Valid only for the neutral system (e.g. $\pi^+\pi^-\pi^0$)

2) $I = 1$

This is the case of the ϱ ($m \sim 760$ MeV). The ϱ has been found in the states $\pi^+\pi^0$, $\pi^+\pi^-$, $\pi^-\pi^0$ but not in the state $\pi^+\pi^+$, which excludes isotopic spin 2. Thus the spin must be odd.

The analysis of the angular distributions and the values of the cross-sections are in good agreement with spin 1 and exclude spin 3. The ϱ is thus 1^{-+}.

Possible decays by strong interactions:

$$\varrho \to 2\pi$$
$$\varrho \to 4\pi \quad \text{(not observed)}$$

but the state 3π is forbidden by G conservation

Possible decays by electromagnetic interactions:

$$\varrho^{\overset{\circ}{\pm}} \to \pi^{\overset{\circ}{\pm}} + \gamma$$
$$\varrho \quad \to 3\pi \qquad \text{(except } 3\pi^0 \text{ forbidden by } C)$$
$$\varrho^0 \to e^+e^- \quad \text{or} \quad \mu^+\mu^-$$

Forbidden transitions:

$$\varrho^0 \to \eta^0 + \pi^0 \quad \text{forbidden by } C,$$
$$\varrho^0 \to 2\gamma \qquad \text{forbidden by the spin 1}$$

V 2 The 3π System

Since $P = (-1)^{l1+l2+1}$ and the orbital momenta l_1 and l_2 must be such that $l_1 = l_2$ in order to have spin 0, it is clear that the 0^+ state is forbidden. All other states are possible.

Moreover $G = -1$. For the neutral system the relation $G = C(-1)^I$ gives $C = -1$ if I is even, $C = +1$ if I is odd.

The isotopic spin may be 0, 1, 2, 3, given by the following possible combinations:

$$\pi + 2\pi$$
$$I = 1 \pm \begin{cases} 0 & I = 1 \\ 1 & I = 0, 1, 2 \\ 2 & I = 1, 2, 3 \end{cases}$$

One has three independent functions giving $I = 1$, two giving $I = 2$ and only one for $I = 0$ or 3.

It is necessary to distinguish between the different possibilities:

A) $I = 0$

One must have $I_1(1\pi) = I_2(2\pi) = 1$. The orbital momentum between any two of the pions must be odd ($l + I =$ even). The state is totally antisymmetric in the exchange of 2π.

The state $3\pi^0$ is thus forbidden. It is forbidden also because $C = (-1)^{l_1} = -1$.

The ω^0 resonance ($m \sim 785$ MeV) is an example of this case. It exists only in the neutral mode (hence $I = 0$) and analysis of the distributions of the pions (Dalitz plot) shows that the ω^0 is a 1^{--} state.

The situation for the decays in π is the following:

$\omega^0 \to \pi^+\pi^-\pi^0$ is allowed

$\omega^0 \to 2$ or $3\pi^0$ is forbidden by C

$\omega^0 \to 2\pi$ or 4π is forbidden by G for strong interactions

The others electromagnetic decays can be:

$$\left.\begin{array}{l}\omega^0 \to \pi^+\pi^-\gamma \quad \text{or} \quad \pi^0\pi^0\gamma \\ \omega^0 \to \pi^0\gamma \quad \text{or} \quad \eta^0\gamma \\ \omega^0 \to e^+e^- \quad \text{or} \quad \mu^+\mu^-\end{array}\right\} \text{allowed}$$

$\omega^0 \to 2\gamma$ forbidden by spin 1

$\omega^0 \to \eta^0\pi^0$ forbidden by C

B) $I = 1$

We have seen that a priori the wave function for I $= 1$ depends on 3 independent parameters. This may shown in another way. If a, b, c represent the three isovectors π, one may form an isovector $I = 1$ using the quantity $a(b \cdot c)$ where (b. c.) is an isoscalar. The most general isovector is of the form $Aa(b \cdot c) + Bb(c \cdot a) + Cc(a \cdot b)$, where A, B, C are independent parameters.

The components a_1, a_2, a_3 of the isovector a are given as functions of the charged components a_-, a_0, a_+ by the relations $a_1 = (a_- + a_+)/\sqrt{2}\, a_2 = i(a_- - a_+)/\sqrt{2}$, $a_3 = a_0$, correspondant to the usual definition of the π. Thus one has:

$$(a \cdot b) = a_1b_1 + a_2b_2 + a_3b_3 = a_-b_+ + a_0b_0 + a_+b_- .$$

The states $\pi^+\pi^+\pi^-$ and $\pi^0\pi^0\pi^+$ of charge $+1$ and $\pi^+\pi^-\pi^0$ and $\pi^0\pi^0\pi^0$ of charge 0 are represented by:

$$M_{\overset{+}{\circ}} = Aa_{\overset{+}{\circ}}(b_-c_+ + b_0c_0 + b_+c_-) + Bb_{\overset{+}{\circ}}(c_-a_+ + c_0a_0 + c_+a_-)$$
$$+ Cc_{\overset{+}{\circ}}(a_-b_+ + a_0b_0 + a_+b_-).$$

where the superscript stands for the mode of charge $+1$, while the subscript stands for the neutral mode.

Thus for a particle of isotopic spin 1 decaying into 3π (of isotopic spin 1) the transition rates R are given by $|M|^2$, that is, taking into account the fact that pions of the same charge are indistinguishable, by:

$$R(\pi^+\pi^+\pi^-) = |A + B|^2 + |B + C|^2 + |C + A|^2,$$
$$R(\pi^0\pi^0\pi^+) = |A|^2 + |B|^2 + |C|^2,$$
$$R(\pi^+\pi^-\pi^0) = 2(|A|^2 + |B|^2 + |C|^2),$$
$$R(\pi^0\pi^0\pi^0) = |A + B + C|^2.$$

The branching ratios $R_+ = R(\pi^+\pi^0\pi^0)/R(\pi^+\pi^+\pi^-)$ and $R_0 = R(\pi^+\pi^-\pi^0)/R(\pi^0\pi^0\pi^0)$ thus satisfy $1/4 \leqq R_+ \leqq 1$ and $R_0 \geqq 3/2$.

1) The case of the 0^- state

The simplest orbital momenta $l_1 = l_2$, favoured by the centrifugal barrier effect, are $l_1 = l_2 = 0$. In this case the state is completely symmetric in the 3π and in order that the isotopic spin wave function may be completely symmetric one must have $A = B = C$. The ratios R_+ and R_0 are then $R_+ = 1/4$, $R_0 = 2/3$.

a) The K meson

For $K_2^0 \to 3\pi \quad CP = -1 = (-1)^{l2+1}$, l_2 is even.

Since $l_1 = l_2$, the 3π have $C = (-1)^{l1} = +1$. The relation $G = C(-1)^I$ indicates that the isotopic spin of the 3π is odd.

Hence the isotopic spin of the 3π cannot be zero (it is odd for the neutral mode, and, obviously, non-zero for the charged mode). The $|\Delta I| = \frac{1}{2}$ rule for weak interactions hence implies isotopic spin 1 for the 3π.

From the preceding general relations one obtains the following relations between the transition rates:

$$w(K_2^0 \to \pi^+\pi^-\pi^0) = 2w(K^+\pi^+\pi^0\pi^0),$$

$$w(K_2^0 \to \pi^0\pi^0\pi^0) = w(K^+ \to \pi^+\pi^+\pi^-) - w(K^+ \to \pi^+\pi^0\pi^0).$$

Analysis of the Dalitz plot shows that for the K_2^0 and K^+ the 3π are in a quasi-pure $l_1 = l_2 = 0$ state, in agreement with the centrifugal barrier effect. Hence one must have the following branching ratios:

$$\frac{K^+ \to \pi^+\pi^0\pi^0}{K^+ \to \pi^+\pi^+\pi^-} = \frac{1}{4}$$

$$\frac{K_2^0 \to \pi^+\pi^-\pi^0}{K_2^0 \to \pi^0\pi^0\pi^0} = \frac{2}{3}$$

b) the η^0 meson ($m \sim 500$ MeV)

The modes $\eta^0 \to \pi^+\pi^-\pi^0$ and $\eta^0 \to 2\gamma$ are well known. The 2γ mode implies that $C = +1$. The 2γ mode and analysis of the Dalitz plot of the 3π give spin 0^- for the η^0. As for the 3π, one has $C = (-1)^{l_1} = +1$ and the values $l_1 = l_2 = 0$ are favoured.

The isotopic spin of the η^0 is 0 ($\eta^\pm$ has not been detected) and that of the 3π is odd (G and C are of opposite sign) and probably $I = 1$ to have an electromagnetic transition $|\Delta I| = 1$. Thus one must have

$$\frac{\eta^0 \to \pi^+\pi^-\pi^0}{\eta^0 \to 3\pi^0} = \frac{2}{3}$$

The decay of the η^0 is electromagnetic (change of isotopic spin, large amplitude for decay into 2γ, small resonance width). Assuming $G = +1$ for the η, the 3π decay is thus forbidden for strong interactions whereas the 2π mode is always forbidden by parity (0^- state) and the 4π mode is below the mass limit.

The possible electromagnetic decays are in particular:

$$\eta \rightarrow \pi^+\pi^-\pi^0$$

$$\eta \rightarrow \pi^0\pi^0\pi^0$$

$$\eta \rightarrow 2\gamma$$

$$\eta \rightarrow \pi^0\gamma\gamma$$

$$\eta \rightarrow \pi^+\pi^-\gamma$$

and the following decays are forbidden:

$$\eta \rightarrow \pi^0\gamma \quad \text{(forbidden by spin 0 and by } C\text{)}$$

$$\eta \rightarrow \pi^0\pi^0\gamma \quad \text{(forbidden by C).}$$

2) The case of the state $\varrho + \pi$

Two resonances of isotopic spin 1 decaying into $\varrho + \pi$ are proposed at present: the $A_1(m \sim 1080$ MeV, spin $1^+)$ whose situation is not clear, and the $A_2(m \sim 1320$ MeV, spin $2^+)$.

From the point of view of isotopic spin, the ϱ is analogous to the π and hence one must have $\dfrac{A^+ \rightarrow \varrho^+\pi^0}{A^+ \rightarrow \varrho^0\pi^+} = 1$ (no matter what the isotopic spin of the A may be). Moreover, for $I = 1$ $A^0 \nrightarrow \varrho^0\pi^0$ (forbidden by the Clebsch-Gordan coefficients).

V 3 $K\bar{K}$ System

A) *General properties*

As for the $\pi\pi$ system: $J = l$, $P = (-1)^l$ and the only possible states are $0^+, 1^- \ldots$ The isotopic spin is $I = 0, 1$. For the neutral state $C = (-1)^l$ and $CP = +1$. The isotopic parity G is then $G = (-1)^{l+I}$(($l + I$) was required to be even for the $\pi\pi$ system).

B) *Neutral system*: K^+K^-, $K^0\bar{K}^0$, $K_1^0K_1^0$, $K_2^0K_2^0$, $K_1^0K_2^0$

In the production of these systems one has K^+K^- or $K^0\bar{K}^0$, and the branching ratio $\dfrac{K^0\bar{K}^0}{K^+K^-}$ is 1 whatever the values of I (0 or 1).

In the decay one can have the systems:

$$K^+K^-, \quad K_1^0K_1^0, \quad K_2^0K_2^0 \quad \text{and} \quad K_1^0K_2^0,$$

which must have $CP = +1$ (assuming CP conservation)

The restrictions imposed on spin are the following:

K^+K^-, $P = (-1)^l$: states $0^+, 1^-, 2^+ \cdots$

$K_1^0K_1^0$ or $K_2^0K_2^0$, l is even (Bose statistics): : states $0^+, 2^+ \cdots$

$K_1^0K_2^0$, $CP_{K_1K_2} = (-1)(-1)^l = CP_{K_0\bar{K}_0} = +1$: states $1^-, 3^- \cdots$

Obviously, there exist other restrictions according to the modes of production of $K\bar{K}$ or according to the existence of other decay modes besides $K\bar{K}$.

One of the best known resonances decaying into $K\bar{K}$ is the Φ meson ($m \sim 1020$ MeV), a 1^{--} state of isotopic spin 0; one has $\Phi \to K^+K^-$ or $K_1^0K_2^0$, $\Phi \nrightarrow K_1^0K_1^0$ or $K_2^0K_2^0$.

It should be noted that the Φ has the same quantum numbers 1^{--} as the ω^0. The fact that the $\Phi \to 3\pi$ decay, if it exists is rarer than the $K\bar{K}$ mode may perhaps be explained by the role played by a new quantum number suggested by Bronzan and Low[(30)]. Moreover, one may predict electromagnetic decays analogous to those of the ω^0.

V 4 $N\bar{N}$ System

The total spin of the system—combination of the spins of the two nucleons may be $s = 0$ (singlet state) or $s = 1$ (triplet state).

The parity is $P = (-1)^{l+1}$
The isotopic spin is $I = 0, 1$.
The isotopic parity is $G = (-1)^{l+s+I}$
The charge conjugation is $C = (-1)^{l+s}$ (for the neutral state).

There is no strict selection rule in the general case. We shall discuss now a case which is frequently encountered in practice: the annihilation of $\bar{p}$ at rest.

A) *Annihilation of $\bar{p}$ at rest*

1) *Annihilation taking place in the state $S(l = 0)$*

A theoretical argument[(31)] was given for this and the experimental verification was done by the study of the reaction $p + \bar{p} \to K^0 + \bar{K}^0$.

For the $K^0\bar{K}^0$ system $CP = +1$, for the $p\bar{p}$ system $CP = (-1)^{s+1}$, which implies $s = 1$ (triplet state). Comparison of P shows that the orbital angular momenta are different (even $\leftrightarrow$ odd) for the $K^0\bar{K}^0$ and $p\bar{p}$ system. If one compares the modes $K_1^0K_1^0$ (or $K_2^0K_2^0$) and $K_1^0K_2^0$, one obtains:

$$p + \bar{p} \to K_1^0 + K_1^0 \quad l_{K_1K_1} = \text{even} \to l_{p\bar{p}} = \text{odd}$$

$$p + \bar{p} \to K_1^0 + K_2^0 \quad l_{K_1K_2} = \text{odd} \to l_{p\bar{p}} = \text{even}$$

The first mode has not been found experimentally, which is in agreement with the restriction $l_{p\bar{p}} =$ even and with the most reasonable hypothesis $l = 0$.

All annihilations of antiprotons at rest are thus assumed to occur in the state $1S_0(l = s = 0)$ or $3S_1(l = 0, s = 1)$.

2) *Restrictions for the* $p\bar{p}$ *system with* $l = 0$

We have $P = -1$ and $C = (-1)^S$, where $s = 0, 1$. $G = (-1)^{S+I}$, where $I = 0, 1$.

The different possible states are summarised below:

name	*JPG*	I	C
$1S_0$	0^{-+}	0	+
	0^{--}	1	+
$3S_1$	1^{-+}	1	−
	1^{--}	0	−

G or *I* give no selection rule. *P* forbids the following processes:

$$p + \bar{p} \nrightarrow \pi^0 + \pi^0$$

$$p + \bar{p} \nrightarrow K_1^0 + K_1^0 \quad \text{(as above)}$$

C is different for the states $1S_0$ or $3S_1$, for example:

$$p + \bar{p} \rightarrow \begin{cases} K_1^0 + K_1^0 + \pi^0 \\ K_1^0 + K_1^0 + \eta^0 \end{cases} \quad C = +1, \text{ state } 1S_0$$

$$p + \bar{p} \rightarrow \begin{cases} K_1^0 + K_2^0 + \pi^0 \\ K_1^0 + K_1^0 + \omega^0 \end{cases} \quad C = -1, \text{ state } 3S_1$$

In the production of $K^*{}_0 + \bar{K}^0$ (or $\bar{K}^{*0} + K^0$), if the spin of the K^* was 0, the conservation of parity would impose an odd orbital momentum l_{K^*K} and hence a state $3S_1$, i.e. production of the system $K_1^0K_2^0\pi^0$. This argument was used to eliminate spin 0 for the K^*.

B) *Annihilation of a* $\bar{p}$ *at rest with a neutron*

Here we have a pure state of isotopic spin $I = 1$ (because $I_3 = -1$). If one assumes that the annihilation takes place in the state *S*, $P = -1$, $G = (-1)^{S+1}$ ($\bar{p}n$ is not an eigenstate of *C*).

We have the two possible states: $1S_0$ and $3S_1$

name	*JPG*
$1S_0$	0^{--}
$3S_1$	1^{-+}

Production of 2π or $K\bar{K}$ must take place in the state $3S_1$, and that of 3π in the state $1S_0$

CONCLUSION

Our study has been based on the invariance principles and the selection rules in the physics of elementary particles. We have deliberately omitted the studies of angular distributions and Dalitz plots which allow one to determine the spins of particles, in order to concentrate on the most immediate applications of the invariance principles. There exist excellent reviews of the problems which we have considered, in particular, the work of Marshak and Sudarshan and of Sakurai[(32)].

We have confined to examples of particles or resonances which are well known. In the last few years a large number of new resonances have been discovered, and this domain is in constant development. On the other hand, different models have been proposed in order to group particles having the same characteristics. The introduction of the concept of isotopic spin, which allowed one to group proton and neutron into a single particle, the nucleon, also allowed one to establish other isotopic spin multiplets for the strange particles. Recently, a new symmetry group SU_3, various consequences of which have been verified, has classified different particles of different isotopic spin but having the same quantum numbers J, P, C.

The main aim of these theories is to put order into the vast collection of particles, and it probable that in the years to come the idea of unitary symmetry lead to considerable progress.

ACKNOWLEDGMENTS

We wish to express here our gratitude to Professor A. Lagarrigue, who gave us precious help in conceiving this text. Our thanks are due to him also for advice and discussions on the various subjects treated.

REFERENCES

1. R. K. Adair, *Phys. Rev.* **100**, 1540 (1955).
2. C. N. Yang, *Phys. Rev.* **77**, 242 (1950).
3. N. H. Xuong, G. R. Lynch, and C. K. Hinrichs, *Phys. Rev.* **124**, 575 (1961); and B. C. Maglic, G. R. Kalbfleisch, M. L. Stevenson, *Phys. Rev. Lett.* **7**, 137 (1961).
4. R. Plano, A. Prodell, N. Samios, M. Schwartz, J. Steinberger, *Phys. Rev.* **119**, 1400 (1959).
5. W. K. H. Panofsky, R. L. Aamodt, and J. Hadley, *Phys. Rev.* **81**, 565 (1951); W. Chinowski, and J. Steinberger, *Phys. Rev.* **95**, 1561 (1954).
6. M. M. Block, L. Lendinara, and L. Morari, Proceedings of the 1962 International Conference on High Energy Physics (CERN), p. 371.
7. M. Ferro-Luzzi, R. D. Tripp, and M. B. Watson, *Phys. Rev. Lett.* **8**, 28 (1962); R. D. Tripp, M. B. Watson, and M. Ferro-Luzzi, *Phys. Rev. Lett.* **8**, 175 (1962).
8. H. Courant, H. Filthuth, P. Franzini, R. G. Glasser, A. Minguzzi-Ranzi, A. Segar, W. Willis, R. A. Burnstein, T. B. Day, B. Kehoe, A. J. Herz, M. Sakitt, B. Sechi-Zorn, N. Seeman, and G. A. Snow, Proceeding of the Sienna International Conference on Elementary Particles—1963—Vol. 1, p. 73.
9. F. S. Crawford Jr, M. L. Good, F. T. Solmitz, and M. L. Stevenson, *Phys. Rev. Lett.* **1**, 209 (1958).
10. O. Chamberlain, E. Segrè, R. Tripp, C. Wiegand, and T. Ypsilantis, *Phys. Rev.* **93**, 1430 (1954).
11. C. N. Yang, *Phys. Rev.* **77**, 242 (1950).
12. Y. Eisenberg, *Phys. Rev.* **96**, 541 (1954), T. Yamanouchi, *Phys. Rev. Lett.* **3**, 480 (1959).
13. M. T. Burgey, V. E. Krohn, J. B. Novey, G. R. Ringo, and V. L. Teledgi, *Phys. Rev.* **110**, 1214 (1958).
14. J. H. Christenson, J. W. Cronin, V. L. Fitch, and R. Turlay, *Phys. Rev. Lett.* **13**, 138 (1964).
15. U. Camerini, R. L. Hautman, R. H. March, D. Murphree, G. Gidal, G. E. Kalmus, W. M. Powell, R. T. Pu, C. L. Sandler, S. Natali, and M. Villani, *Phys. Rev. Lett.* **14**, 989 (1965).
16. W. Heisenberg, Z. Physik 77, 1 (1932).

17. A. R. Edmonds: Angular momentum in quantum mechanics (Princeton University Press 1957).
18. L. Michel, *Nuovo Cimento* **22**, 203 (1961).
19. L. Michel, *Nuovo Cimento* **10**, 319 (1953), T. D. Lee and C. N. Yang, *Nuovo Cimento* **3**, 749 (1956).
20. G. Wick, *Ann. Rev. Nucl. Sci.* **8**, 1 (1958).
21. M. Gell-Mann, *Phys. Rev.* 92, 833 (1953); *Suppl. Nuovo Cimento* **4**, 848 (1956); T. Nakano, and K. Nishijima, *Progr. Theoret. Phys.* **10**, 581 (1953); K. Nishijima, *Progr. Theoret. Phys.* **13**, 285 (1955).
22. L. Okun, and B. Pontecorvo, *Sov. Phys. JETP* **5**, 1297 (1957); F. Muller, R. W. Birge, W. B. Fowler, R. H. Good, W. Hirsch, R. P. Matsen, L. Oswald, W. M. Powell, H. S. White, and O. Piccioni, *Phys. Rev.. Lett.* **4**, 418 (1960).
23. J. S. Bell, J. Løvseth, and M. Veltman, Proceedings of the Sienna International Conference on Elementary Particles (1963) Vol. 1, p. 587.
24. R. P. Feynman, and M. Gell-Mann, *Phys. Rev.* **109**, 193 (1958).
25. A. Barbaro-Galtieri, W. H. Barkas, H. H. Heckmann, J. W. Patrick, and F. M. Smith, *Phys. Rev. Lett.* **9**, 26 (1962).
26. R. W. Birge, R. P. Ely, G. Gidal, G. E. Kalmus, A. Kernan, W. M. Powell, U. Calmerini, W. F. Fry, J. Gaidos, R. H. March, and S. Natali, *Phys. Rev. Lett*, **11**, 35 (1963).
27. B. Aubert, L. Behr, J. P. Lowys, P. Mittner, and C. Pascaud, *Physies Letters* **10**, 215 (1964).
28. M. Gell-Mann, and A. Pais, Proceeding of the 1954 Glasgow Conference on Nuclear and Mesons Physics (Pergamon Press, London, 1955).
29. C. Zemach, *Phys. Rev.* **133**, 1201 (1964).
30. J. B. Bronzan, and F. E. Low, *Phys. Rev. Lett.* **12**, 522 (1964).
31. T. B. Day, G. A. Snow, and J. Sucher, *Phys. Rev. Lett.* **3**, 61 (1959).
32. R. E. Marshak, and E. C. G. Sudarshan, Introduction to Elementary Particles Physics. Interscience Publishers, Inc., New York, 1961; J. J. Sakurai, Invariance Principles and Elementary Particles. Princeton University Press. Princeton, New Jersey, 1964.

Some Methods of Spin Analysis in Elementary Particle Physics

W. Koch

CERN, Geneva, Switzerland

CONTENTS

Preface 231

I. Recapitulation of Quantum Mechanical Spin Description 231
- a) Spin Eigenstates and Eigenvalues 231
- b) Pure and Mixed Spin States 233
- c) Operators and Matrix Elements 234
- d) Spherical Harmonics 240
- e) Vector Coupling 244
- f) Rotations of Spin States 247

II. Some Simple Treatments of Decay Processes 259
- a) Decay of a Boson into 2 Spinless Particles 259
- b) Decays of Fermions into a Spin 1/2 Fermion plus a Spin 0 Boson 260
  - 1) General Aspects 260
  - 2) Adair Analysis 266
- c) Weak Decays of Hyperons 269

III. The Spin Density Matrix 276
- a) The General Formalism 276
- b) Symmetry Properties of the Density Matrix due to Parity Conservation in the Production Process 280

IV. Determination of the Spin Density Matrix from Decay Processes and Spin Tests 286
- a) Decays of Bosons into 2 Spinless Particles 286
- b) 3π Decay of the ω^0 Meson 290
- c) Decay of a Fermion into a Spin 1/2 Fermion plus a Spinless Particle (Method of Byers and Fenster) 298
- d) Decay of a Boson into a Boson of Spin 1 plus a Spinless Boson 309
- e) Photons as Decay Products 318

Appendix: Relativistic Generalization of the Spin Analysis 325

References 331

PREFACE

This article on a somewhat theoretical subject is written by an experimentalist and therefore, by definition, not for theoreticians. It arose from a contribution to the Herceg Novi Easter School 1964[42] and from a series of lectures held at CERN in Spring 1965. The aim is to make the student or the newcomer to this field familiar with some current methods of spin analysis in particle reactions. Emphasis is laid on explicit calculations rather than on a complete review of the subject because it is felt that the detailed presentation of a few problems is of higher didactic value than a condensed summary of many results. Moreover, all the different spin analysis methods proposed, are in fact rather similar. This is, of course, not purely accidental but closely related to the fact that everything in this subject follows just from angular momentum conservation and from the superposition principle in quantum mechanics; and quantum mechanical spin treatment has been standardized for many years. Therefore, if the reader has once understood the density matrix formalism (section III) and for instance the analysis method of Byers and Fenster (section IVc) he will read most of the quoted literature without difficulties or be able to solve his spin problems by the "do it yourself" method. In section I he will find most of the relevant formulae.

Phaseshift analysis is not included in this paper as it is already a standard subject in many textbooks. Nor are genuine 3-particle decays (not stepwise decays) treated here (with the exception of the particularly simple ω^0 decay) because the detailed presentation of their analysis is somewhat lengthy. The 3-particle decay analysis may well be studied in the original papers by C. Zemach[19] and S. M. Berman and M. Jacob[30].

ACKNOWLEDGEMENTS

The author is very indepted to Professor L. van Hove for his aid in questions of relativistic spin states and to Dr. D. C. Potter for valuable criticism and for checking the manuscript. Clarifying discussions with Dr. F. Wagner are gratefully appreciated.

I. RECAPITULATION OF QUANTUM MECHANICAL SPIN DESCRIPTION

a) Spin Eigenstates and Eigenvalues

In analogy to the classical definition of angular momentum

$$\boldsymbol{L} = \boldsymbol{r} \times \boldsymbol{p}$$

quantum mechanical spin operators, J_x, J_y, J_z for the components of the total angular momentum and $\boldsymbol{J}^2$ for the square, can be defined which obey the commutation relations:

$$[J_x, J_y] = i\hbar J_z, \quad [J_y, J_z] = i\hbar J_x, \quad [J_z, J_x] = i\hbar J_y.$$

From this follows

$$[J_2, J_{x,y,z}] = 0. \tag{I.1}$$

As all the spin components commute with $\boldsymbol{J}^2$ but do not commute with one another, only one component can have simultaneous eigenstates with $\boldsymbol{J}^2$. It is customary to choose representations where J_z and $\boldsymbol{J}^2$ have the same eigenstates.

Eigenstates and eigenvalue of the spin operators are defined by the eigenvalue equations

$$\begin{aligned} J^2\Psi_J &= C_{J^2}\Psi_J \\ J_z\Psi_J &= C_{J_z}\Psi_J. \end{aligned} \tag{I.2}$$

Applying the commutation relations to these operator equations one finds as possible eigenvalues for $\boldsymbol{J}^2$ and J_z

$$C_{J^2} = \hbar j(\mathrm{j} + 1), \quad j = {}^1/_2, 1, {}^3/_2, 2 \ldots \tag{I.3}$$

$$C_{J_z} = \hbar m, \quad m = -j, -j + 1, \ldots +j.$$

Only integer or half integer values are allowed for j, the (quantum number of) total angular momentum. Each angular momentum j has $(2j + 1)$ possible integer or half integer values for the magnetic quantum number m which runs from $m = -j$ to $m = +j$.

At the same time the eigenvalue equations define an eigenfunction

$$\Psi_J = \Psi(j, m)$$

for every pair j, m, so that the solution of Eq. (I.2) is

$$\begin{aligned} J^2\Psi(j, m) &= \hbar j(j + 1)\,\Psi(j, m) \\ J_z\Psi(j, m) &= \hbar m\Psi(j, m) \\ j = {}^1/_2, 1, {}^3/_2 \ldots, &\quad m = -j, -j + 1 \ldots +j. \end{aligned} \tag{I.4}$$

So far the symbol $\Psi(j, m)$ is a rather abstract object, a so-called "basis vector in Hilbert space", specifying an eigenstate of angular momentum. Instead of $\Psi(j, m)$ we shall use as well the Dirac ket vector notation

$$|j, m\rangle = \Psi(j, m).$$

Once a specific spin representation is chosen, $|j, m\rangle$ will be a well defined mathematical object, e.g. a column vector or, for integer spin states, a spherical harmonic.

Examples

$$\psi\left(\frac{1}{2}, \frac{1}{2}\right) = \left|\frac{1}{2}, \frac{1}{2}\right\rangle = \begin{bmatrix} 1 \\ 0 \end{bmatrix}$$

$$\psi\left(\frac{3}{2}, -\frac{1}{2}\right) = \left|\frac{3}{2}, -\frac{1}{2}\right\rangle = \begin{bmatrix} 0 \\ 0 \\ 1 \\ 0 \end{bmatrix}$$

$$\psi(1, 1) = |1, 1\rangle = \begin{bmatrix} 1 \\ 0 \\ 0 \end{bmatrix} = -\frac{1}{\sqrt{4\pi}}\sqrt{\frac{3}{2}} \sin\theta \, e^{i\varphi}$$

For any basis vector $\psi(j, m)$ a conjugate vector

$$\psi^*(j, m) \equiv \langle j, m|$$

can be defined together with an operation

$$(\psi^*(j_1 . m_1), \quad \psi(j_2, m_2)) \equiv \langle j_1 m_1 | j_2 m_2 \rangle$$

which we call the scalar product of two eigenstates.

This product is 1 for indentical basis vectors and 0 for different basis vectors:

$$\langle j_1, m_1 | j_2 m_2 \rangle = \delta_{j_1 j_2} \delta_{m_1 m_2} . \tag{I.5}$$

This property is called orthonormality. It can be shown that the $|j, m\rangle$ form a complete orthonormal set of basis vectors.

b) Pure and Mixed Spin States

Consider a quantum mechanical system of spin j. The most general pure state is defined by a linear superposition of basis vector belonging to the same j.

$$\psi_a = |a\rangle = \sum_{m=-j}^{m=+j} a_m |j, m\rangle \tag{I.6}$$

In the matrix representation this state is a $2j + 1$ dimensional column vector

$$\psi_a = \begin{bmatrix} \vdots \\ a_m \\ \vdots \end{bmatrix}$$

The conjugate state is

$$\psi_a^* = \langle a| = \sum_{m=-j}^{m=+j} a_m^* \langle j, m| \tag{I.7}$$

and in the matrix representation a $2j + 1$ dimensional row vector

$$\psi_a^* = [\dots a_m^* \dots]$$

The a_m are complex numbers and a_m^* their complex conjugates. It is useful to consider normalized states with

$$\sum_{m=-j}^{j} a_m^* a_m = \sum_{m=-j}^{j} |a_m|^2 = 1 \tag{I.8}$$

A scalar product of 2 pure states $|a\rangle$ and $|b\rangle$ of spin j and j' can be defined as follows:

$$\langle b|a\rangle = \left(\sum_{m'} b_{m'}^* \langle j', m'|\right) \left(\sum_m a_m |j, m\rangle\right)$$

$$= \sum_{m'} \sum_m b_{m'}^* a_m \underbrace{\langle j' m' | j, m\rangle}_{\delta_{jj'}\delta_{mm'}}; \tag{I.9}$$

$$\langle b|a\rangle = \sum_{m=-j}^{j} b_m^* a_m = [\dots b_m^* \dots] \begin{bmatrix} \vdots \\ a_m \\ \vdots \end{bmatrix}$$

With the normalization condition Eq. (I.8), the scalar product of a pure state with itself is clearly 1.

So far we have considered only pure states which are described by a linear superposition of basis vectors. This mode of description implies that maximum information possible in a quantum mechanical framework is actually available, which amounts to knowing not only the magnitudes of the eigenstates involved but also their relative phases.

There also exist, however, mixed states with less than maximum information which are statistical mixtures of pure states.

Example: In a system of spin $\frac{1}{2}$ particles one knows that 30 per cent of the particles are in the pure state ψ_1 and 70 per cent of the particles are in the pure state ψ_2 but one does not know in which of the 2 possible states is each individual particle of the system. A description of this state in terms of the probabilities $p_1 = 0.7$, $p_2 = 0.3$ could be e.g.

$$\left\{\begin{aligned} \psi_1 &= \left|\frac{1}{2}, \frac{1}{2}\right\rangle; & p_1 &= 0.7 \\ \psi_2 &= \sqrt{\frac{1}{2}}\left|\frac{1}{2}, \frac{1}{2}\right\rangle + i\sqrt{\frac{1}{2}}\left|\frac{1}{2}, -\frac{1}{2}\right\rangle; & p_2 &= 0.3 \end{aligned}\right\}.$$

Mixed states will be treated in detail in connection with the density matrix.

c) Operators and Matrix Elements

One may define linear operators Q which acting on a spin state $|a\rangle$ will produce another spin state $|b\rangle$

$$|b\rangle = Q|a\rangle$$

Q may be written explicitly in the form

$$Q = \sum_{m'm} Q_{m'm} |j', m'\rangle \langle j, m| \tag{I.10}$$

where in the most general case $j' \neq j$, m runs from $-j$ to $+j$ and m' from $-j'$ to $+j'$ respectively. Applying Q to the state

$$|a\rangle = \sum_m a_m |j, m\rangle$$

we have

$$\begin{aligned} |b\rangle = Q|a\rangle &= \sum_{m'm} Q_{m'm} a_m |j', m'\rangle \underbrace{\langle j, m|j, m\rangle}_{1} \\ &= \sum_{m'} b_{m'} |j'm'\rangle \end{aligned} \tag{I.11}$$

with

$$b_{m'} = \sum_m Q_{m'm} a_m$$

This can be written in matrix form

$$\begin{bmatrix} \vdots \\ b_{m'} \\ \vdots \end{bmatrix} = \begin{bmatrix} \\ Q_{m'm} \\ \\ \end{bmatrix} \begin{bmatrix} \vdots \\ a_m \\ \vdots \end{bmatrix}$$

where the operator Q is simply a matrix of dimensions $(2j + 1) \times (2j' + 1)$. Correspondingly we have for the conjugate state

$$\langle b| = \langle a|Q^+$$

$$b^*_{m'} = \sum_m a^*_m Q^*_{mm'} \tag{I.12}$$

or

$$[\ldots\, b^*_{m'} \,\ldots] = \begin{bmatrix} \\ Q^*_{mm'} \\ \\ \end{bmatrix} [\ldots\, a^*_m \,\ldots]$$

where Q^+ is the Hermitian conjugate of Q (transposed complex conjugate matrix) Furthermore, one can define matrix elements of the operator Q acting between 2 states $|a\rangle$ and $|c\rangle$:

$$\langle c|Q|a\rangle = c|b\rangle = \sum_{mm'} c^*_{m'} Q_{m'm} a_m$$

$$= [\ldots\, c^*_{m'} \,\ldots] \begin{bmatrix} \\ Q_{m'm} \\ \\ \end{bmatrix} \begin{bmatrix} \vdots \\ a_m \\ \vdots \end{bmatrix} \tag{I.13}$$

If $|a\rangle$ and $\langle c|$ are eigenstates normalized to 1, one has the identity

$$Q_{m'm} = \langle j'm'|Q|jm\rangle$$

Let us anticipate some examples of operators to be used later on. Consider for instance the transition operator T which describes the decay of a spin $^3/_2$ baryon into a spin $^1/_2$ baryon plus a pion. It will generate from the initial spin $^3/_2$ state

$$\psi_{\text{in}} = \sum_m a_m \left|\frac{3}{2}, m\right\rangle$$

the spin $\frac{1}{2}$ state of the daughter fermion

$$\psi_{\text{fin}} = \sum_{m'} b_{m'} \left|\frac{1}{2}, m'\right\rangle$$

where the $b_{m'}$ will be functions of the decay angles θ, ϕ of the daughter baryon (more precisely, they will be spherical harmonics). In matrix notation we have

$$b_{m'}(\theta, \phi) = \sum_m T_{m'm}(\theta, \phi)\, a_m$$

Another example of operators creating new spin states of the same j are the rotation matrices to be discussed below.

Hermitian or self conjugate operators satisfying the relation

$$Q = Q^+$$

have a special role in quantum mechanics. From the general concept of quantum mechanics it is well known that to every physical observable q there corresponds a Hermitian operator Q, such that the expectation $\langle Q\rangle$ of the observable q in a system specified by a state vector $|a\rangle$ is

$$\begin{aligned}\langle Q\rangle &= \langle a\,|Q|\,a\rangle \\ &= \sum_{m'm} a^*_{m'} Q_{m'm} a_m \\ &= \sum_{m'm} a^*_{m'} a_m \langle jm'\,|Q|\,jm\rangle \end{aligned} \tag{I.14}$$

For the Hermitian operators J_x, J_y, J_z, J^2 the matrix elements $\langle jm'\,|Q|\,j, m\rangle$ can be derived from the commutation relations. The result is

$$\begin{aligned}\langle j, m+1\,|J_x|\,j, m\rangle &= {}^1/_2\sqrt{(j-m)(j+m+1)} \\ \langle j, m-1\,|J_x|\,j, m\rangle &= {}^1/_2\sqrt{(j+m)(j-m+1)} \\ \langle j, m+1\,|J_y|\,j, m\rangle &= -{}^1/_2 i\sqrt{(j-m)(j+m+1)} \\ \langle j, m-1\,|J_y|\,j, m\rangle &= {}^1/_2 i\sqrt{(j+m)(j-m+1)} \\ \langle j, m\,|J_z|\,j, m\rangle &= m \\ \langle j, m\,|J^2|\,j, m\rangle &= j(j+1). \end{aligned} \tag{I.15}$$

All other matrix elements are 0. The factor $\hbar$ on the right side has been omitted.

As is seen from Eq. (I.15) the J_x and J_y matrix elements are connected by the relation

$$\langle j, m' |J_y| j, m\rangle = e^{i\frac{\pi}{2}(m-m')} \langle j, m |J_x| j, m'\rangle. \tag{I.16}$$

Let us now calculate the spin expectation values in x, y, z direction for a general pure state of spin j

$$|a\rangle = \sum_{m=-j}^{j} a_m |j, m\rangle.$$

From the matrix elements given in Eq. (I.15) and the definition of an expectation value Eq. (I.14), follows immediately

$$\langle a |J_z| a\rangle = \langle J_z\rangle = \sum_{m=-j}^{+j} m\, |a_m|^2$$

Furthermore

$$\begin{aligned}
\langle a |J_x| a\rangle &= \langle J_x\rangle \\
&= \sum_{m=-j}^{j-1} a^*_{m+1} a_m \langle j, m+1 |J_x| j, m\rangle + \sum_{m=-j}^{j-1} a^*_m a_{m+1} \langle j, m |J_x| j, m+1\rangle \\
&= \sum_{m=-j}^{j-1} a^*_{m+1} a_m \, {}^1/_2 \sqrt{(j-m)(j+m+1)} \\
&\quad + \sum_{m=-j}^{j-1} a^*_m a_{m+1} \, {}^1/_2 \sqrt{(j-m)(j+m+1)} \\
&= {}^1/_2 \sum_{m=-j}^{j-1} (a^*_m a_{m+1} + a_m a^*_{m+1}) \sqrt{(j-m)(j+m+1)} \\
&= \sum_{m=-j}^{j-1} \mathrm{Re}(a^*_{m+1} a_m) \sqrt{(j-m)(j+m+1)}.
\end{aligned}$$

A similar calculation yields a corresponding expression for $\langle J_y\rangle$. So the expectation values for the three spin components are:

$$\begin{aligned}
\langle J_x\rangle &= \sum_{m=-j}^{j-1} \mathrm{Re}\,(a^*_{m+1} a_m) \sqrt{(j-m)(j+m+1)} \\
\langle J_y\rangle &= \sum_{m=-j}^{j-1} \mathrm{Im}\,(a^*_{m+1} a_m) \sqrt{(j-m)(j+m+1)} \qquad \text{(I.17)} \\
\langle J_z\rangle &= \sum_{m=-j}^{j+1} m\, |a_m|^2.
\end{aligned}$$

Let us now introduce the concept of the polarization vector $\boldsymbol{P}(P_x, P_y, P_z)$.

Definition:

$$P_x = \frac{\langle J_x \rangle}{j}, \quad P_y = \frac{\langle J_y \rangle}{j}, \quad P_z = \frac{\langle J_z \rangle}{j}$$

or

$$\boldsymbol{P} = \frac{1}{j} \langle \boldsymbol{J} \rangle. \tag{I.18}$$

This means that the component of the polarization vector in a certain direction is given by the spin expectation value in this direction divided by the maximum spin expectation value, which is $|m| = j$.

Inspecting the expressions for $\langle J_x \rangle$, $\langle J_y \rangle$ in Eq. (I.17), one sees that only the interference of adjacent eigenstates

$$a_m |j, m\rangle, \quad a_{m+1} |j, m+1\rangle$$

produces polarization in x or y direction. For example the states

$$\psi = \sqrt{\frac{1}{2}}\, |1, 1\rangle + \sqrt{\frac{1}{2}}\, |1, -1\rangle$$

or

$$\psi = \sqrt{\frac{1}{2}} \left| \frac{3}{2}, \frac{3}{2} \right\rangle + \sqrt{\frac{1}{2}} \left| \frac{3}{2}, -\frac{1}{2} \right\rangle$$

have

$$P_x, P_y = 0.$$

So at least one pair of neighbouring amplitudes a_m in the expression for the general pure state $|j\rangle$ has to be different from 0 in order to give non-vanishing polarization in x or y direction. This criterion for polarization P_x, $P_y \neq 0$, however, is only necessary but not sufficient, as the following example shows.

Consider the state

$$\psi = \mathrm{e}^{i\varphi} \left[\sqrt{\frac{1}{3}}\, |1, 1\rangle + \sqrt{\frac{1}{3}}\, |1, 0\rangle - \sqrt{\frac{1}{3}}\, |1, -1\rangle \right]$$

Applying Eq. (I.17) yields

$$\langle J_x \rangle = \mathrm{Re}\, \underbrace{(\mathrm{e}^{-i\varphi}\, \mathrm{e}^{i\varphi})}_{1} \left[-\frac{1}{3} \underbrace{\sqrt{(1+1)(1-1+1)}}_{\sqrt{2}} + \frac{1}{3} \underbrace{\sqrt{(1-0)(1+0+1)}}_{\sqrt{2}} \right] = 0$$

$$\langle J_y \rangle = 0 \quad \text{because} \quad \mathrm{Im}\, (\mathrm{e}^{-i\varphi}\, \mathrm{e}^{+i\varphi}) = 0$$

$$\langle J_z \rangle = \frac{1}{3} \cdot 1 + \frac{1}{3}(-1) = 0.$$

As we shall often deal with spin $\frac{1}{2}$ particles in the following, let us rewrite relations Eq. (I.17) for $j = \frac{1}{2}$.

General $j = \frac{1}{2}$ state: $|\frac{1}{2}\rangle = a|\frac{1}{2}, \frac{1}{2}\rangle + b|\frac{1}{2}, -\frac{1}{2}\rangle$
with

$$|a|^2 + |b|^2 = 1$$

$$\begin{aligned} P_x &= 2\langle J_x\rangle = 2 \operatorname{Re} a^*b \\ P_y &= 2\langle J_y\rangle = 2 \operatorname{Im} a^*b \\ P_z &= 2\langle J_z\rangle = |a|^2 - |b|^2 \end{aligned} \tag{I.19}$$

One can easily verify

$$|\boldsymbol{P}|^2 = (2 \operatorname{Re}(a^*b))^2 + (2 \operatorname{Im}(a^*b))^2 + (|a|^2 - |b|^2)^2 = 1.$$

As a consequence, pure spin $\frac{1}{2}$ states, e.g. nucleons or electrons in pure states, are always completely polarized. This is an exclusive property of spin $\frac{1}{2}$ which is clearly no longer true for higher spins. Generally valid, also for spin $\frac{1}{2}$, is the following statement:

Completely polarized are only the states

$$\psi = |j, j\rangle \quad \text{and} \quad \psi = |j, -j\rangle$$

and those which result from them by rotation of the coordinate system. All other pure states are only partially polarized or have no vector polarization at all, as for instance the integer spin states $|j, 0\rangle$. On the other hand, for $j > \frac{1}{2}$ all incompletely polarized *pure spin states* or even such with 0 vector polarization, have a so-called tensor polarization or spin alignment, where alignment means here every spin configuaration which is not invariant under rotations and thus gives rise to detectable anisotropies. For instance, in the eigenstates $|j, m\rangle$ the spin is aligned along cones around the z axis.

Let us anticipate the corresponding properties of mixed spin states, which will become clearer in connection with the density matrix. There again spin $\frac{1}{2}$ states are an exception. Mixed states with $j > \frac{1}{2}$ can be spin aligned without having any vector polarization, for instance an equal mixture of the states

$$|{}^3/_2, {}^1/_2\rangle \quad \text{and} \quad |{}^3/_2, -{}^1/_2\rangle.$$

In the case of spin $\frac{1}{2}$ particles, however, no mixture with resulting polarization 0 is aligned.

Let us finally write down some matrices of the operators J_x, J_y, J_z. For a given j, the matrix elements are defined in relations Eq. (I.15).

$j = {}^1/_2$:

$$J_x = \frac{1}{2}\begin{bmatrix} 0 & 1 \\ 1 & 0 \end{bmatrix} \quad J_y = \frac{1}{2}\begin{bmatrix} 0 & -i \\ i & 0 \end{bmatrix} \quad J_z = \frac{1}{2}\begin{bmatrix} 1 & 0 \\ 0 & -1 \end{bmatrix} \quad \text{or} \quad \boldsymbol{J} = \frac{1}{2}\boldsymbol{\sigma}$$

$j = 1$:

$$J_x = \frac{1}{\sqrt{2}}\begin{bmatrix} 0 & 1 & 0 \\ 1 & 0 & 1 \\ 0 & 1 & 0 \end{bmatrix} \quad J_y = \frac{1}{\sqrt{2}}\begin{bmatrix} 0 & -i & 0 \\ i & 0 & -i \\ 0 & i & 0 \end{bmatrix} \quad J_z = \begin{bmatrix} 1 & 0 & 0 \\ 0 & 0 & 0 \\ 0 & 0 & -1 \end{bmatrix} \tag{I.20}$$

$j- = {}^3/_2$:

$$J_x = \frac{1}{2}\begin{bmatrix} 0 & \sqrt{3} & 0 & 0 \\ \sqrt{3} & 0 & 2 & 0 \\ 0 & 2 & 0 & \sqrt{3} \\ 0 & 0 & \sqrt{3} & 0 \end{bmatrix} \quad J_y = \frac{1}{2}\begin{bmatrix} 0 & -\sqrt{3i} & 0 & 0 \\ \sqrt{3i} & 0 & -2i & 0 \\ 0 & 2i & & -\sqrt{3i} \\ 0 & 0 & \sqrt{3i} & 0 \end{bmatrix}$$

$$J_z = \frac{1}{2}\begin{bmatrix} 3 & 0 & 0 & 0 \\ 0 & 1 & 0 & 0 \\ 0 & 0 & -1 & 0 \\ 0 & 0 & 0 & -3 \end{bmatrix}$$

The corresponding matrix for $\boldsymbol{J}^2$ is always given by a $(2j + 1)$ dimensional unit matrix multiplied by $j(j + 1)$

$$\boldsymbol{J}^2 = j(j + 1)\, \mathbb{1}_{2j+1}.$$

d) Spherical Harmonics

Whereas the matrix representation is applicable to all integer and half integer spin states, an analytic representation can be found only for integer spins. In the abstract operator representation, the eigenstates are found from pure operator algebra, defined by the commutation relations. In the analytic representation one does not make use of the commutation relations at all (though they are of course still valid) but only solves the eigenvalue equation defined by differential spin operators. The solutions of these partial differential equations are the spherical harmonics which can represent only the eigenstates of systems with integer spin.

In terms of polar coordinates the angular momentum operators are

$$\begin{aligned} L_x &= i\hbar\left(\sin\varphi\frac{\partial}{\partial\theta} + \cot\theta\cos\varphi\frac{\partial}{\partial\varphi}\right) \\ L_y &= i\hbar\left(-\cos\varphi\frac{\partial}{\partial\theta} + \cot\theta\sin\varphi\frac{\partial}{\partial\varphi}\right) \\ L_z &= -i\hbar\frac{\partial}{\partial\varphi} \\ \boldsymbol{L}^2 &= -\hbar^2\left[\frac{1}{\sin\theta}\frac{\partial}{\partial\theta}\left(\sin\theta\frac{\partial}{\partial\theta}\right) + \frac{1}{\sin^2\theta}\frac{\partial^2}{\partial\varphi^2}\right] \end{aligned} \tag{I.21}$$

The eigenvalue equations

$$L^2\psi = C_L\,\psi \quad \text{and} \quad L_z\psi = C_{L_z}\psi$$

are

$$-\left[\frac{1}{\sin\theta}\frac{\partial}{\partial\theta}\left(\sin\theta\frac{\partial}{\partial\theta}\right)+\frac{1}{\sin^2\theta}\frac{\partial^2}{\partial\varphi^2}\right]\psi = l(l+1)\,\psi$$

$$-\,i\frac{\partial}{\partial\varphi}\psi = m\psi \tag{I.22}$$

Solutions $\psi_{lm}(\theta,\varphi)$ exist for integer l and m

$$l = (0, 1, 2, 3 \ldots \; m = -l, -l+1, \ldots l)$$

$$\psi_{lm}(\theta,\varphi) = Y_l^m(\theta,\varphi) = \Theta_{lm}(\theta)\,\phi_m(\varphi) \tag{I.23}$$

The function Θ_{lm} can be calculated by the recursion formula

$$\Theta_{lm} = (-1)^l\sqrt{\frac{2l+1}{2}\frac{(l+m)!}{(l-m)!}}\,\frac{1}{2^l l!}\,\frac{1}{\sin^m\theta}\,\frac{d^{(l-m)}(\sin^{2l}\theta)}{(d\cos\theta)^{(l-m)}} \tag{I.24}$$

or in terms of the associated Legendre functions $P_l^m(\cos\theta)$.

$$\Theta_{lm} = (-1)^m\sqrt{\frac{(2l+1)}{2}\frac{(l-|m|)!}{(l+|m|)!}}\,P_l^m(\cos\theta) \tag{I.25}$$

The functions ϕ_m are

$$\phi_m = \frac{1}{\sqrt{2\pi}}\,e^{im\varphi}. \tag{I.26}$$

The Y_l^m have the property of orthonormality:

$$\langle l_1, m_1|l_2, m_2\rangle = \int_0^{2\pi}\int_0^{\pi} Y_{l_1}^{m_1 *}Y_{l_2}^{m_2}\sin\theta\,d\theta\,d\phi = \delta_{l_1 l_2}\,\delta_{m_1 m_2} \tag{I.27}$$

Furthermore the following relations are valid

$$Y_l^{-m} = (-1)^m\,Y_l^{m*} \tag{I.28}$$

$$\sum_{m=-l}^{+l} Y_l^{m*}Y_l^m = \frac{2l+1}{4\pi} \tag{I.29}$$

Table 1

Spherical harmonics in the form

$$Y_l^m = (-1)^m\sqrt{\frac{1}{4\pi}}\sqrt{(2l+1)\frac{(l-|m|)!}{(l+|m|)!}}\,P_l^m(x)\,e^{im\varphi}; \quad x = \cos\theta$$

$$l = 0 \quad Y_0^0 = \sqrt{\frac{1}{4\pi}}\cdot 1$$

$$l = 1 \quad Y_1^0 = \sqrt{\frac{1}{4\pi}}\sqrt{3}\cdot x$$

$$Y_1^{\pm 1} = \mp\sqrt{\frac{1}{4\pi}}\sqrt{\frac{3}{2}}\cdot\sqrt{1-x^2}\,\mathrm{e}^{\pm i\varphi}$$

$$l = 2 \quad Y_2^0 = \sqrt{\frac{1}{4\pi}}\sqrt{5}\cdot\frac{1}{2}(3x^2-1)$$

$$Y_2^{\pm 1} = \mp\sqrt{\frac{1}{4\pi}}\sqrt{\frac{5}{6}}\cdot 3x\sqrt{1-x^2}\,\mathrm{e}^{\pm i\varphi}$$

$$Y_2^{\pm 2} = \sqrt{\frac{1}{4\pi}}\sqrt{\frac{5}{24}}\cdot 3(1-x^2)\,\mathrm{e}^{\pm 2i\varphi}$$

$$l = 3 \quad Y_3^0 = \sqrt{\frac{1}{4\pi}}\sqrt{7}\cdot\frac{1}{2}(5x^3-3x)$$

$$Y_3^{\pm 1} = \mp\sqrt{\frac{1}{4\pi}}\sqrt{\frac{7}{12}}\cdot\frac{3}{2}(5x^2-1)\sqrt{1-x^2}\,\mathrm{e}^{\pm i\varphi}$$

$$Y_3^{\pm 2} = \sqrt{\frac{1}{4\pi}}\sqrt{\frac{7}{120}}\cdot 15x(1-x^2)\,e^{\pm 2i\varphi}$$

$$Y_3^{\pm 3} = \mp\sqrt{\frac{1}{4\pi}}\sqrt{\frac{7}{120}}\cdot 15(1-x^2)\sqrt{1-x^2}\,\mathrm{e}^{\pm 3i\varphi}$$

$$l = 4 \quad Y_4^0 = \sqrt{\frac{1}{4\pi}}\cdot 3\cdot\frac{1}{8}(35x^4-30x^2+3)$$

$$Y_4^{\pm 1} = \mp\sqrt{\frac{1}{4\pi}}\cdot\sqrt{\frac{9}{20}}\cdot\frac{5}{2}(7x^2-3)\,x\sqrt{1-x^2}\,\mathrm{e}^{\pm i\varphi}$$

$$Y_4^{\pm 2} = \sqrt{\frac{1}{4\pi}}\cdot\sqrt{\frac{1}{40}}\cdot\frac{15}{2}(7x^2-1)(1-x^2)\,\mathrm{e}^{\pm 2i\varphi}$$

$$Y_4^{\pm 3} = \mp\sqrt{\frac{1}{4\pi}}\cdot\frac{1}{4}\sqrt{\frac{1}{35}}\cdot 105x(1-x^2)^{3/2}\,\mathrm{e}^{\pm 3i\varphi}$$

$$Y_4^{\pm 4} = \sqrt{\frac{1}{4\pi}}\cdot\frac{1}{8}\sqrt{\frac{1}{70}}\cdot 105(1-x^2)^2\,\mathrm{e}^{\pm 4i\varphi}$$

Table 1 contains the spherical harmonics for $l = 0$ to 4.

Let us briefly sketch how to calculate spin expectation values in this representation. Take as an example the state

$$\psi = \sqrt{\frac{1}{2}}\,|1,1\rangle + \sqrt{\frac{1}{2}}\,|1,0\rangle = \sqrt{\frac{1}{2}}\,Y_1^1 + \sqrt{\frac{1}{2}}\,Y_1^0$$

and calculate the angular momentum in x direction. This is done by performing the integral

$$\langle L_x\rangle = \int \psi^* L_x \psi \, \mathrm{d}\Omega$$

$$= \int_0^{2\pi}\int_0^{\pi} \frac{1}{2}(Y_1^{1*} + Y_1^{0*})\left[i\left(\sin\phi\frac{\partial}{\partial\theta} + \cot\theta\cos\phi\frac{\partial}{\partial\phi}\right)\right]$$

$$\times\, (Y_1^1 + Y_1^0)\sin\theta\,\mathrm{d}\theta\cdot 2\pi\,\mathrm{d}\phi$$

This is a tiresome job, but it gives of course the same result as the matrix method

$$\langle L_x\rangle = \left[\sqrt{\frac{1}{2}}, \sqrt{\frac{1}{2}}, 0\right]\cdot\sqrt{\frac{1}{2}}\begin{bmatrix}0 & 1 & 0\\ 1 & 0 & 1\\ 0 & 1 & 0\end{bmatrix}\begin{bmatrix}\sqrt{\frac{1}{2}}\\ \sqrt{\frac{1}{2}}\\ 0\end{bmatrix} = \frac{1}{2}\sqrt{\frac{1}{2}}\,[1,1,0]\cdot\begin{bmatrix}1\\1\\1\end{bmatrix} = \sqrt{\frac{1}{2}}$$

Clearly the matrix method is a much more efficient tool to calculate spin components than the analytic method.

Nevertheless, in the spin analysis we shall always deal with spherical harmonics when analysing angular distributions of decays. This can be best explained by an example. Let us assume a particle of spin 1, for instance a ϱ meson, is produced in some reaction with its spin completely polarized along a direction z. So the ϱ is in the spin state $|1, 1\rangle$.

Afterwards the particle decays into 2π mesons which both have spin 0. The decaying system is described by a wave function

$$\psi(\boldsymbol{r}_1, \boldsymbol{r}_2)$$

where $\boldsymbol{r}_1, \boldsymbol{r}_2$ are the position vectors of the two particles. As a decay into two particles is collinear in the c.m. system we can write

$$\psi(\boldsymbol{r}_1, \boldsymbol{r}_2) = R(r)\,f(\theta, \phi)$$

where θ, ϕ indictae the emission direction and $R(r)$ is the expression for an outgoing wave

$$R(r) = \frac{e^{ikr}}{r}$$

As the spin of the two daughter pions is 0, the orbital angular momentum state of the final 2π system is the same as the spin state $|l, m\rangle$ of the mother particle. The angular part of the wave function is therefore the spherical harmonic $Y_l^m(\theta, \phi)$:

$$\psi = \frac{e^{ikr}}{r} Y_l^m(\theta, \phi) \tag{I.30a}$$

The probability of finding one of the outgoing particles at a point with coordinates (r, θ, ϕ) is clearly

$$\psi^*\psi = \frac{1}{r^2} f^* f = \frac{1}{r^2} |Y_l^m|^2$$

therefore the angular distribution of the decay is

$$I(\theta, \phi) = \frac{dN}{d\Omega} = f^*(\theta, \phi) f(\theta, \phi) \tag{I.30b}$$

For the state $|1, 1\rangle$ for instance

$$I(\theta, \phi) = Y_1^{1*} Y_1^1 = \frac{1}{4\pi} \frac{3}{2} \sin^2 \theta$$

e) Vector Coupling

In this section we deal with the following two problems:

1) Consider two systems in the eigenstates $|j_1, m_1\rangle$ and $|j_2, m_2\rangle$. Together they form one state specified by

$$|j_1 j_2 m_1 m_2\rangle = |j_1 m_1\rangle |j_2, m_2\rangle$$

Express this state in terms of possible eigenstates $|J, M\rangle$ of the resulting angular momentum. The result is of the form

$$|j_1 j_2 m_1 m_2\rangle = \sum_{JM}\sum C_{JM} |J, M\rangle \tag{I.31}$$

2) Consider a system in the eigenstate $|J, M\rangle$. Decompose this system into two sub-systems of well specified spins j_1 and j_2 respectively. Express the state $|J, M\rangle$ in terms of eigenstates $|j_1 j_2 m_1 m_2\rangle$:

$$|J, M\rangle = \sum_{m_1 m_2}\sum C_{m_1 m_2} |j_1 j_2 m_1 m_2\rangle. \tag{I.32}$$

The rules of angular momentum combination require

$$m_1 + m_2 = M \tag{I.33}$$

and allow for given $j_1 j_2$, the following values for the total spin J

$$\begin{aligned} J &= |j_1 - j_2| \\ &= |j_1 - j_2| + 1 \\ &\;\vdots \\ &\;\; j_1 + j_2 \end{aligned}$$

The condition Eq. (I.33) reduces the two summation indices in Eq. (I.31) and (I.32) to one index only.

The C_{JM} and $C_{m_1 m_2}$ are the so-called vector coupling or Clebsch-Gordan coefficients. We shall use for them the notation

$$C_{JM} = (JM|j_1 j_2 m_1 m_2)$$

$$C_{m_1 m_2} = (j_1 j_2 m_1 m_2|JM).$$

Let us re-write the coupling relations in this notation:

$$|j_1 j_2 m_1 m_2\rangle = \sum_{J=|j_1-j_2|}^{j_1+j_2} |JM\rangle (JM|j_1 j_2 m_1 m_2)$$

$$|JM\rangle = \sum_{m_1=-j_1}^{+j_1} |j_1 j_2 m_1 M - m_1\rangle (j_1 j_2 m_1 M - m_1|JM). \tag{I.34}$$

We shall use a representation where all vector coupling coefficients are real and where

$$(JM|j_1 j_2 m_1 m_2) = (j_1 j_2 m_1 m_2|JM).$$

Furthermore we have the orthonormality relations

$$\sum_{JM} (j_1 j_2 m_1 m_2|JM)(JM|j_1 j_2 m_1' m_2') = \delta_{m_1 m'} \delta_{m_2 m'}$$

$$\sum_{m_1 m_2} (JM|j_1 j_2 m_1 m_2)(j_1 j_2 m_1 m_2|J'M') = \delta_{JJ'} \delta_{MM'}. \tag{I.35}$$

Formulae to calculate general Clebsch-Gordan coefficients are rather complicated so that we prefer to copy the tables of the most frequent types of spin coupling (Table 2).[41] The different nomenclature in Table 2 is related to ours by

$$U_{J_1}^{m_1} V_{J_2}^{m_2} = |j_1 j_2 m_1 m_2\rangle \quad \text{and} \quad W_J^M = |JM\rangle.$$

The phase convention adopted here for Clebsch-Gordan coefficients and for spherical harmonics is that of Condon and Shortley.[5]

Tables II

$D_l \times D_{1/2}$

	$W_{l+1/2}^m$	$W_{l-1/2}^m$
$U_l^{m+1/2} V_{1/2}^{-1/2}$	$\sqrt{\dfrac{l-m+{}^1/_2}{2l+1}}$	$\sqrt{\dfrac{l+m+{}^1/_2}{2l+1}}$
$U_l^{m-1/2} V_{1/2}^{1/2}$	$\sqrt{\dfrac{l+m+{}^1/_2}{2l+1}}$	$-\sqrt{\dfrac{l-m+{}^1/_2}{2l+1}}$

$$D_l \times D_{3/2}$$

	$W^m_{l+3/2}$	$W^m_{l+1/2}$
$U_l^{m+3/2}V_{3/2}^{-3/2}$	$\sqrt{\dfrac{(l-m-{}^1/_2)(l-m+{}^1/_2)(l-m+{}^3/_2)}{(2l+1)(2l+2)(2l+3)}}$	$\sqrt{\dfrac{3(l-m-{}^1/_2)(l-m+{}^1/_2)(l+m+{}^3/}{(2l+3)(2l+1)(2l)}}$
$U_l^{m+1/2}V_{3/2}^{-1/2}$	$\sqrt{\dfrac{3(l+m+{}^3/_2)(l-m+{}^1/_2)(l-m+{}^3/_2)}{(2l+1)(2l+2)(2l+3)}}$	$(l+3m+{}^3/_2)$ $\times\sqrt{\dfrac{(l-m+{}^1/_2)}{(2l+3)(2l+1)(2l)}}$
$U_l^{m-1/2}V_{3/2}^{1/2}$	$\sqrt{\dfrac{3(l-m+{}^3/_2)(l+m+{}^1/_2)(l+m+{}^3/_2)}{(2l+1)(2l+2)(2l+3)}}$	$-(l-3m+{}^3/_2)$ $\times\sqrt{\dfrac{(l+m+{}^1/_2)}{(2l+3)(2l+1)(2l)}}$
$U_l^{m-3/2}V_{3/2}^{3/2}$	$\sqrt{\dfrac{(l+m-{}^1/_2)(l+m+{}^1/_2)(l+m+{}^3/_2)}{(2l+1)(2l+2)(2l+3)}}$	$-\sqrt{\dfrac{3(l+m-{}^1/_2)(l+m+{}^1/_2)(l-m+{}^3/}{(2l+3)(2l+1)(2l)}}$

	$W^m_{l-1/2}$	$W^m_{l-3/2}$
$U_l^{m+3/2}V_{1/2}^{-3/2}$	$\sqrt{\dfrac{3(l+m+{}^1/_2)(l+m+{}^3/_2)(l-m-{}^1/_2)}{(2l-1)(2l+1)(2l+2)}}$	$\sqrt{\dfrac{(l+m-{}^1/_2)(l+m+{}^1/_2)(l+m+{}^3/}{(2l-1)(2l)(2l+1)}}$
$U_l^{m+1/2}V_{3/2}^{-1/2}$	$-(l-3m-{}^1/_2)$ $\times\sqrt{\dfrac{(l+m+{}^1/_2)}{(2l-1)(2l+1)(2l+2)}}$	$-\sqrt{\dfrac{3(l+m-{}^1/_2)(l+m+{}^1/_2)(l-m-{}^1/}{(2l-1)(2l)(2l+1)}}$
$U_l^{m-1/2}V_{3/2}^{1/2}$	$-(l+3m-{}^1/_2)$ $\times\sqrt{\dfrac{(l-m+{}^1/_2)}{(2l-1)(2l+1)(2l+2)}}$	$\sqrt{\dfrac{3(l-m-{}^1/_2)(l-m+{}^1/_2)(l+m-{}^1/}{(2l-1)(2l)(2l+1)}}$
$U_l^{m-3/2}V_{3/2}^{3/2}$	$\sqrt{\dfrac{3(l-m+{}^1/_2)(l-m+{}^3/_2)(l+m-{}^1/_2)}{(2l-1)(2l+1)(2l+2)}}$	$-\sqrt{\dfrac{(l-m-{}^1/_2)(l-m+{}^1/_2)(l-m+{}^3/}{(2l-1)(2l)(2l+1)}}$

$D_l \times D_1$

	W_{l+1}^m	W_l^m	W_{l-1}^m
$U_l^{m+1} V_1^{-1}$	$\sqrt{\frac{(l-m+1)(l-m)}{(2l+1)(2l+2)}}$	$\sqrt{\frac{(l-m)(l+m+1)}{l(2l+2)}}$	$\sqrt{\frac{(l+m)(l+m+1)}{(2l)(2l+1)}}$
$U_l^m V_1^0$	$\sqrt{\frac{2(l+m+1)(l-m+1)}{(2l+1)(2l+2)}}$	$\sqrt{\frac{m}{l(l+1)}}$	$-\sqrt{\frac{2(l-m)(l+m)}{(2l)(2l+1)}}$
$U_l^{m-1} V_1^1$	$\sqrt{\frac{(l+m+1)(l+m)}{(2l+1)(2l+2)}}$	$-\sqrt{\frac{(l+m)(l-m+1)}{l(2l+2)}}$	$\sqrt{\frac{(l-m)(l-m+1)}{(2l)(2l+1)}}$

The following symmetry relations between Clebsch-Gordan coefficients will be usefull for further application

$$(jjm, -m|j0) = (-1)^{j-m}\frac{1}{\sqrt{2j+1}} \tag{I.36a}$$

$$(j0m0|j0) = 1 \tag{I.36b}$$

$$(j_1 j_2 m_1 m_2|jm) = (-1)^{j_1+j_2-j}(j_2 j_1 m_2 m_1|jm) \tag{I.36c}$$

$$(j_1 i_2, -m_1, -m_2|j-m) = (-1)^{j_1+j_2-j}(j_1 j_2 m_1 m_2|jm) \tag{I.36d}$$

$$(j_1 j_2 m_1 m_2|j_3 m_3) = (-1)^{j_2+m_2}\left(\frac{2j_3+1}{2j_1+1}\right)^{1/2}(j_2 j_3, -m_2 m_3|j_1 m_1) \tag{I.36e}$$

$$(j_1 j_2 m_1 m_2|j_3 m_3) = (-1)^{j_1-m_1}\left(\frac{2j_3+1}{2j_1+1}\right)^{1/2}(j_3 j_1 m_3, -m_1|j_2 m_2) \tag{I.36f}$$

Between Clebsch-Gordan coefficients and spherical harmonics one has the relation

$$Y_{l_1}^{m_1}(\theta,\phi)\, Y_{l_2}^{m_2}(\theta,\phi)$$

$$= \sqrt{\frac{(2l_1+1)(2l_2+1)}{4\pi}}\sum_l \sqrt{\frac{1}{2l+1}}\, Y_l^m(\theta,\phi)\,(l_1 l_2 m_1 m_2|lm)\,(l_1 l_2 00|l0) \tag{I.36g}$$

f) Rotations of Spin States

Consider a scalar field

$$\psi = \psi(x, y, z)$$

defined in the coordinate system $S(x, y, z)$. Rotate the coordinate system by an angle α around the z axis, in the negative sense, to a new frame $S'(x', y', z')$. The coordinate transformation is

$$\begin{aligned} x &= x' \cos\alpha + y' \sin\alpha \\ y &= -x' \sin\alpha + y' \cos\alpha \\ z &= z' \end{aligned} \tag{I.37}$$

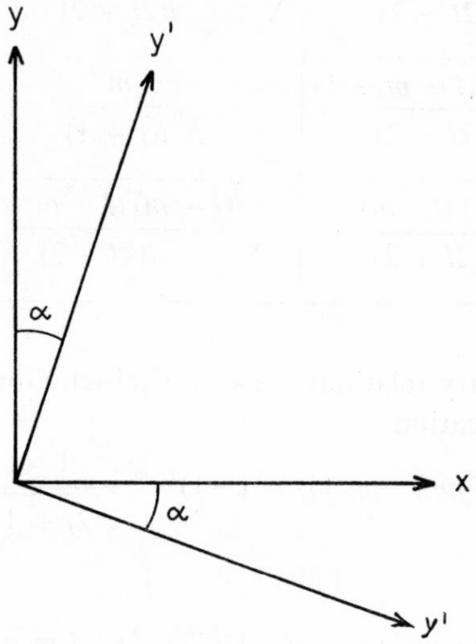

Fig. 1

Now keep the field ψ fixed in space and express it in terms of x', y', z'. This is simply done by inserting the substitution Eq. (I.37) in $\psi(x, y, z)$. So

$$\psi(x, y, z) \to \psi'(x', y', z').$$

An infinitesimal transformation by an angle $d\alpha$ leads to corresponding relations:

$$\begin{aligned} x &= x' + y'\,d\alpha = x' + dx' \\ y &= y' - x'\,d\alpha = y' + dy' \\ z &= z' \qquad\quad\;\; = z' \end{aligned}$$

and

$$\begin{aligned} \psi(x, y, z) \to \psi'(x', y', z') &= \psi(x' + dx', y' + dy', z') \\ &= \psi(x', y', z') + \frac{\partial\psi}{\partial x'}\,dx' + \frac{\partial\psi}{\partial y'}\,dy' \\ &= \psi(x', y', z') + \frac{\partial\psi}{\partial x'}(+y'\,d\alpha) + \frac{\partial\psi}{\partial y'}(-x'\,d\alpha) \\ &= \psi(x', y', z') + \frac{d\psi}{d\alpha}\,d\alpha \end{aligned}$$

where the derivative $d\psi/d\alpha$ is

$$\frac{d\psi}{d\alpha} = \left(-x'\frac{\partial}{\partial y'} + y'\frac{\partial}{\partial x'}\right)\psi(x', y', z') = r_z\psi$$

The infinitesimal rotation operator around the z axis

$$r_z = -\left(x\frac{\partial}{\partial y} - y\frac{\partial}{\partial x}\right)$$

is proportional to the operator of the angular momentum in z direction

$$L_z = i\hbar\left(x\frac{\partial}{\partial y} - y\frac{\partial}{\partial x}\right)$$

so that

$$r_z = -\frac{i}{\hbar}L_z \tag{I.38}$$

and for rotations around the x and y axis:

$$r_x = -\frac{i}{\hbar}L_x; \quad r_y = -\frac{i}{\hbar}L_y.$$

The operators $r_{x,y,z}$ were defined as rotating the *coordinate system* in the *mathematically negative sense.* This is equivalent to keeping the coordinate system fixed and rotating ψ *in the positive sense.* The rotation of ψ in a fixed coordinate system we shall call an active rotation. The rotation of the coordinate system with respect to ψ fixed in space is called a passive rotation. Our r's are here defined as active rotation operators.

A finite rotation by an angle α can be constructed by repeated application of the infinitesimal operator r. From the infinitesimal rotation

$$\psi \to \psi' = \psi + d\psi = (1 + r\,d\alpha)\,\psi$$

one constructs the finite rotation

$$\psi \to \psi' = R(\alpha)\,\psi = \lim_{n\to\infty}\left(1 + r\frac{\alpha}{n}\right)^n$$

$$= e^{r\alpha}\psi = \left(\sum_0^\infty \frac{1}{n!}(r\alpha)^n\right)\psi.$$

$$R(\alpha) = e^{r\alpha} = \sum_0^\infty \frac{1}{n!}(r\alpha)^n$$

is the operator of a finite rotation by the angle α.

The operators $r_{x,y,z}$ and the corresponding finite rotation operators $R_{x,y,z}(\alpha)$ can clearly be applied to the wave functions of integer spin representations. For half integer spin states where only the matrix representation is available, one has to construct matrix operators. It can be shown that for any integer or half integer spin state with total spin J, relations Eq. (I.38) become

$$r_x = -\frac{i}{\hbar} J_x; \quad r_y = -\frac{i}{\hbar} J_y; \quad r_z = -\frac{i}{\hbar} J_z \tag{I.39}$$

independently of a specific representation. From Eqs. (I.39) one constructs the finite rotation operators for rotations around the x, y, z axis

$$R_x(\alpha) = e^{-\frac{i\alpha}{\hbar}J_x}, \quad R_y(\alpha) = e^{-\frac{i\alpha}{\hbar}J_y}, \quad R_z(\alpha) = e^{-\frac{i\alpha}{\hbar}J_z}. \tag{I.40}$$

It is customary to describe the most general rotation as a product of three rotations: a first rotation around the z axis by an angle γ, a second rotation about the y axis by an angle β and a third rotation again around the z axis by an angle α

$$R(\alpha, \beta, \gamma) = R_z(\alpha)\, R_y(\beta)\, R_z(\gamma)$$

$$= \left(e^{-\frac{i\alpha}{\hbar}J_x}\right)\left(e^{-\frac{i\beta}{\hbar}J_y}\right)\left(e^{-\frac{i\gamma}{\hbar}J_z}\right). \tag{I.41}$$

In the following $\hbar$ will always be put equal to 1.

Let us now rotate an eigenstate $|j, m\rangle$ around the z axis. The resulting spin state ψ' is

$$\psi' = R_z(\alpha)\,|j, m\rangle$$

$$= e^{-i\alpha J_z}|j, m\rangle = \sum_0^\infty \frac{1}{n!}(-i\alpha J_z)^n\,|j, m\rangle.$$

As J_z is diagonal, cf. (I.15),

$$J_z^n|j, m\rangle = m^n|j, m\rangle,$$

$$\psi' = \sum_0^\infty \frac{1}{n!}(-i\alpha m)^n\,|j, m\rangle,$$

and

$$R_z(\alpha)\,|j, m\rangle = e^{-i\alpha m}|j, m\rangle. \tag{I.42a}$$

Therefore in the matrix representation the operator $R_z(\alpha)$ is a diagonal matrix of the form

$$(D_z^{(J)}(\alpha))_{m,n} = e^{-i\alpha m}\delta_{m,n} \tag{I.42b}$$

Rotations around the y axis are more complicated, because J_y is not a diagonal operator. Let us first take the spin state $|\frac{1}{2}, \frac{1}{2}\rangle$

$$R_y(\beta)\left|\frac{1}{2}, \frac{1}{2}\right\rangle = \sum_0^\infty \frac{1}{n!}(-i\beta J_y)^n\left|\frac{1}{2}, \frac{1}{2}\right\rangle. \tag{I.43}$$

From the matrix representation of J_y Eq. (I.20) one verifies immediately

$$J_y\left|\frac{1}{2}, \pm\frac{1}{2}\right\rangle = \pm\frac{i}{2}\left|\frac{1}{2}, \mp\frac{1}{2}\right\rangle.$$

From this follows

$$J_y^n|{}^1/_2, +{}^1/_2\rangle = ({}^1/_2)^n\,|{}^1/_2, {}^1/_2\rangle \quad \text{for } n \text{ even}$$
$$= ({}^1/_2)_i^n\,|{}^1/_2, -{}^1/_2\rangle \quad \text{for } n \text{ odd}.$$

So one can split the summation in Eq. (I.43):

$$\begin{aligned} R_y(\beta)\left|\frac{1}{2}, \frac{1}{2}\right\rangle &= \sum_{k=0}^{\infty}\frac{1}{(2k)!}\left(-\frac{i\beta}{2}\right)^{2k}\left|\frac{1}{2}, \frac{1}{2}\right\rangle \\ &\quad + \sum_{k=0}^{\infty}\frac{1}{(2k+1)!}\left(-\frac{i\beta}{2}\right)^{2k+1} i\left|\frac{1}{2}, -\frac{1}{2}\right\rangle \\ &= \cos\frac{\beta}{2}\left|\frac{1}{2}, \frac{1}{2}\right\rangle + \sin\frac{\beta}{2}\left|\frac{1}{2}, -\frac{1}{2}\right\rangle \end{aligned} \tag{I.44}$$

Correspondingly one finds

$$R_y(\beta)\left|\frac{1}{2}, -\frac{1}{2}\right\rangle = -\sin\frac{\beta}{2}\left|\frac{1}{2}, \frac{1}{2}\right\rangle + \cos\frac{\beta}{2}\left|\frac{1}{2}, -\frac{1}{2}\right\rangle \tag{I.45}$$

The coefficients of the eigenstates in Eqs. (I.44) and (I.45) are the matrix elements

$$\langle \tfrac{1}{2}, m|\, R_y(\beta)|\, \tfrac{1}{2}, m'\rangle$$

which build up the y rotation matrix for spin $\frac{1}{2}$

$$D_y^{(1/2)}(\beta) = \begin{bmatrix} \cos\frac{\beta}{2} & -\sin\frac{\beta}{2} \\ \sin\frac{\beta}{2} & \cos\frac{\beta}{2} \end{bmatrix} \tag{I.46}$$

Applied to a pure state it rotates the state by β around the y axis, so that the z direction moves towards the x direction. Rotation around the x axis is effected by the matrix

$$D_x^{(1/2)}(\beta) = \begin{bmatrix} \cos\frac{\beta}{2} & -i\sin\frac{\beta}{2} \\ -i\sin\frac{\beta}{2} & \cos\frac{\beta}{2} \end{bmatrix}$$

Here the y direction moves towards the z direction.

In a similar way one constructs the y rotation matrix for spin 1

$$D_y^{(1)}(\beta) = \begin{bmatrix} \frac{1}{2}(1+\cos\beta) & -\sqrt{\frac{1}{2}}\sin\beta & \frac{1}{2}(1-\cos\beta) \\ \sqrt{\frac{1}{2}}\sin\beta & \cos\beta & -\sqrt{\frac{1}{2}}\sin\beta \\ \frac{1}{2}(1-\cos\beta) & \sqrt{\frac{1}{2}}\sin\beta & \frac{1}{2}(1+\cos\beta) \end{bmatrix} \tag{I.47}$$

The matrix elements $D_y(\beta)_{mm'}$ obey the symmetry relation $D_y(\beta)_{mm'} = D_y(-\beta)_{m'm}$. The y rotation matrices have a particularly simple structure for rotations of 90°. Therefore it is sometimes advantageous to decompose an arbitrary rotation $D_y(\beta)$ into rotations around the z axis and 90° rotations around y. $D_y(\beta)$ may be written as

$$D_y(\beta) = D_z\left(\frac{\pi}{2}\right) D_y\left(\frac{\pi}{2}\right) D_z(\beta)\, D_y\left(-\frac{\pi}{2}\right) D_z\left(-\frac{\pi}{2}\right) \tag{I.48}$$

$D_y(-\pi/2)\, D_z(-\pi/2)$ transforms the y axis into the z direction. Then $D_z(\beta)$ effects a rotation by β around the z axis. Finally the z axis is transformed back into the y axis by $D_z(\pi/2)\, D_y(\pi/2)$.

Table 3 gives the matrices $D_y^{(j)}(\pi/2)$ for $j = {}^1/_2, 1, {}^3/_2, 2$.

Table III

y rotation matrices for $\beta = \pi/2$

$$D_y^{(1/2)}(\pi/2) = \begin{bmatrix} \sqrt{1/2} & -\sqrt{1/2} \\ \sqrt{1/2} & \sqrt{1/2} \end{bmatrix} \qquad D_y^{(1)}(\pi/2) = \begin{bmatrix} 1/2 & -\sqrt{1/2} & 1/2 \\ \sqrt{1/2} & 0 & -\sqrt{1/2} \\ 1/2 & \sqrt{1/2} & 1/2 \end{bmatrix}$$

$$D_y^{(3/2)}(\pi/2) = 1/2 \cdot \begin{bmatrix} \sqrt{1/2} & -\sqrt{3/2} & \sqrt{3/2} & -\sqrt{1/2} \\ \sqrt{3/2} & -\sqrt{1/2} & -\sqrt{1/2} & \sqrt{3/2} \\ \sqrt{3/2} & \sqrt{1/2} & -\sqrt{1/2} & -\sqrt{3/2} \\ \sqrt{1/2} & \sqrt{3/2} & \sqrt{3/2} & \sqrt{1/2} \end{bmatrix}$$

$$D_y^{(2)}(\pi/2) = 1/2 \cdot \begin{bmatrix} 1/2 & -1 & \sqrt{3/2} & -1 & 1/2 \\ 1 & -1 & 0 & 1 & -1 \\ \sqrt{3/2} & 0 & -1 & 0 & \sqrt{3/2} \\ 1 & 1 & 0 & -1 & -1 \\ 1/2 & 1 & \sqrt{3/2} & 1 & 1/2 \end{bmatrix}$$

The most general active rotation $R_a(\alpha, \beta, \gamma)$ of a spin j state is effected by applying the rotation matrix

$$D^{(j)}_{m'm}(\alpha, \beta, \gamma) = (D^{(j)}_z(\alpha))_{m'k}\,(D^{(j)}_y(\beta))_{kl}\,(D^{(j)}_z(\gamma))_{lm} \tag{I.49}$$

to the row vector a_m of the spin state.

We have for active rotations $R_a(\alpha, \beta, \gamma)$:

$$R_a(\alpha, \beta, \gamma)\,|j, m\rangle = \sum_{m'} D^{(j)}_{m'm}(\alpha, \beta, \gamma)\,|jm'\rangle \tag{I.50}$$

or

$$\begin{bmatrix} \vdots \\ b \\ \vdots \end{bmatrix} = \begin{bmatrix} D \end{bmatrix} \begin{bmatrix} \vdots \\ a \\ \vdots \end{bmatrix}$$

$$b_{m'} = \sum_m D_{m'm} a_m$$

and

$$\langle j, m|R_a(\alpha, \beta, \gamma) = \sum_{m'} \langle j, m'|D^{(j)*}_{mm'}(\alpha, \beta, \gamma) \tag{I.51}$$

or

$$[\ldots\, b^* \ldots] = [\ldots\, a^* \ldots]\,[D^+]$$

$$b^*_{m'} = \sum_m a^*_m D^*_{mm'}.$$

For passive rotations $R_p(\alpha, \beta, \gamma)$, i e. rotations of the coordinate system, we have to apply the matrix $D^{-1} = D^+$ (orthogonality)

$$R_p(\alpha, \beta, \gamma)\,|j, m\rangle = \sum_{m'} D^{(j)*}_{mm'}(\alpha, \beta, \gamma)\,|j, m'\rangle$$

$$[b] = [D^+]\,[a] \tag{I.52}$$

$$b_{m'} = \sum_m D^*_{mm'} a_m$$

and

$$\langle j, m|R_p(\alpha, \beta, \gamma) = \sum_{m'} \langle j, m'|D^{(j)}_{m'm}(\alpha, \beta, \gamma)$$

$$[\ldots\, b^* \ldots] = [\ldots\, a^* \ldots]\,[D] \tag{I.53}$$

$$b^*_{m'} = \sum_m a^*_m D_{m'm}$$

The most general rotation matrix for a certain spin j is obtained from the factorization

$$D^{(j)}_{m'm}(\alpha, \beta, \gamma) = \mathrm{e}^{-i(m'\alpha + m\gamma)}\,\mathrm{d}^{(j)}_{m'm}(\beta) \tag{I.54}$$

where the d's are the y-rotation matrices called $D^{(j)}_y$ before. They are all real and obey the relations

$$\mathrm{d}^{(j)}_{m'm}(\beta) = (-1)^{m-m'}\,\mathrm{d}^{(j)}_{-m',-m}(\beta) \tag{I.55a}$$

$$\mathrm{d}^{(j)}_{m'm}(\beta) = (-1)^{m-m'}\,\mathrm{d}^{(j)}_{mm'}(\beta) \tag{I.55b}$$

$$d^{(j)}_{m'm}(\beta) \quad = d^{(j)}_{mm'}(-\beta) \tag{I.55c}$$

$$d^{(j)}_{m'm}(\pi) \quad = (-1)^{j+m'}\,\delta_{m',-m} \tag{I.55d}$$

$$d^{(j)}_{m'm}(-\pi) \quad = (-1)^{j-m'}\,\delta_{m',-m} \tag{I.55e}$$

$$d^{(j)}_{m'm}(\beta+\pi) = (-1)^{j+m'}\,d^{(j)}_{-m'm}(\beta) \tag{I.55f}$$

$$d^{(j)}_{m'm}(\pi-\beta) = (-1)^{j+m'}\,d^{(j)}_{m,-m'}(\beta) \tag{I.55g}$$

The d-matrix elements may be related to Jacobi polynomials[25]. For spins from $^1/_2$ to $^5/_2$ they are given in Table 4. The missing elements may be obtained by relations (I.55a, b).

The elements of the rotation matrices $D^{(j)}(\alpha, \beta, \gamma)$ obey the orthogonality relations:

$$\int D^{(j)*}_{m\mu}(\alpha, \beta, \gamma)\, D^{(j')}_{m'\mu'}(\alpha, \beta, \gamma)\, d\Omega = \frac{8\pi^2}{2j+1}\,\delta_{jj'}\,\delta_{mm'}\,\delta_{\mu\mu'}$$

with

$$\int d\Omega = \int_0^{2\pi} d\alpha \int_0^{2\pi} d\gamma \int_{-1}^{1} d\cos\beta \tag{I.56}$$

A product of two D matrices may be expanded according to the relation

$$D^{(j_1)}_{m_1m_1'}D^{(j_2)}_{m_2m_2'} = \sum_j D^{(j)}_{mm'}(j_1 j_2 m_1 m_2|jm)\,(j_1 j_2 m_1' m_2'|jm') \tag{I.57}$$

Example

Construct a spin $\frac{1}{2}$ state completely polarized in the direction (θ, ϕ).

$$\psi(\theta,\phi) = R_z(\phi)\,R_y(\theta)\left|\frac{1}{2},\frac{1}{2}\right\rangle$$

$$= \sum_{m'} D^{(1/2)}_{m'1/2}(\phi,\theta,0)\left|\frac{1}{2}, m'\right\rangle$$

$$= \begin{bmatrix} e^{-\frac{i\phi}{2}} & 0 \\ 0 & e^{\frac{i\phi}{2}} \end{bmatrix} \cdot \begin{bmatrix} \cos\frac{\theta}{2} & -\sin\frac{\theta}{2} \\ \sin\frac{\theta}{2} & \cos\frac{\theta}{2} \end{bmatrix} \cdot \begin{bmatrix} 1 \\ 0 \end{bmatrix}$$

$$= \begin{bmatrix} e^{-\frac{i\phi}{2}}\cos\frac{\theta}{2} \\ e^{\frac{i\phi}{2}}\sin\frac{\theta}{2} \end{bmatrix}$$

$$\psi(\theta,\phi) = e^{-\frac{i\phi}{2}}\cos\frac{\theta}{2}\left|\frac{1}{2},\frac{1}{2}\right\rangle + e^{\frac{i\phi}{2}}\sin\frac{\theta}{2}\left|\frac{1}{2},-\frac{1}{2}\right\rangle$$

Table IV

d-matrices

$$d^{(J)}_{m'm}(\beta) = (-1)^{m-m'}\, d^{(J)}_{-m'-m}(\beta)$$

$$d^{(J)}_{m'm}(\beta) = (-1)^{m-m'}\, d^{(J)}_{mm'}(\beta)$$

Spin $\frac{1}{2}$

$d_{1/2\,1/2}(\beta) = \cos\frac{\beta}{2}$ $\qquad$ $d_{1/2\,1/2}(\beta) = \sin\frac{\beta}{2}$

Spin 1

$d_{11}(\beta) = \frac{1+\cos\beta}{2}$ $\qquad$ $d_{01}(\beta) = \frac{\sin\beta}{\sqrt{2}}$

$d_{1-1}(\beta) = \frac{1-\cos\beta}{2}$ $\qquad$ $d_{00}(\beta) = \cos\beta$

Spin $\frac{3}{2}$

$$d_{3/2\ 3/2}(\beta) = \frac{1+\cos\beta}{2} \qquad d_{3/2\ 1/2}(\beta) = -\sqrt{3}\,\frac{1+\cos\beta}{2}\sin\frac{\beta}{2}$$

$$d_{3/2\ -1/2}(\beta) = \sqrt{3}\,\frac{1-\cos\beta}{2}\cos\frac{\beta}{2} \qquad d_{3/2\ -3/2}(\beta) = -\frac{1-\cos\beta}{2}\sin\frac{\beta}{2}$$

$$d_{1/2\ 1/2}(\beta) = \frac{3\cos\beta-1}{2}\cos\frac{\beta}{2} \qquad d_{1/2\ -1/2}(\beta) = -\frac{1+3\cos\beta}{2}\sin\frac{\beta}{2}$$

Spin 2

$$d_{22}(\beta) = \left(\frac{1+\cos\beta}{2}\right)^2 \qquad d_{21}(\beta) = -\frac{1+\cos\beta}{2}\sin\beta$$

$$d_{20}(\beta) = \frac{\sqrt{6}}{4}\sin^2\beta \qquad d_{2-1}(\beta) = -\frac{1-\cos\beta}{2}\sin\beta$$

$$d_{2-2}(\beta) = \left(\frac{1-\cos\beta}{2}\right)^2 \qquad d_{11}(\beta) = \frac{1+\cos\beta}{2}(2\cos\beta-1)$$

$$d_{10}(\beta) = -\sqrt{\frac{3}{2}}\sin\beta\cos\beta \qquad d_{1-1}(\beta) = \frac{1-\cos\beta}{2}(2\cos\beta+1)$$

$$d_{00}(\beta) = \frac{3\cos^2\beta-1}{2}$$

Spin $\frac{5}{2}$

$$d_{5/2\,5/2}(\beta) = \left(\frac{1+\cos\beta}{2}\right)^2 \cos\frac{\beta}{2} \qquad d_{5/2\,3/2}(\beta) = -\sqrt{5}\left(\frac{1+\cos\beta}{2}\right)^2 \sin\frac{\beta}{2}$$

$$d_{5/2\,1/2}(\beta) = \frac{\sqrt{10}}{4}\sin^2\beta\cos\frac{\beta}{2} \qquad d_{5/2\,-1/2}(\beta) = -\frac{\sqrt{10}}{4}\sin^2\beta\sin\frac{\beta}{2}$$

$$d_{5/2\,-3/2}(\beta) = \sqrt{5}\left(\frac{1-\cos\beta}{2}\right)^2 \cos\frac{\beta}{2} \qquad d_{5/2\,-5/2}(\beta) = -\left(\frac{1+\cos\beta}{2}\right)^2 \sin\frac{\beta}{2}$$

$$d_{3/2\,3/2}(\beta) = \frac{5\cos\beta-3}{2}\cos^3\frac{\beta}{2} \qquad d_{3/2\,1/2}(\beta) = \frac{-(5\cos\beta-1)}{\sqrt{2}}\cos^2\frac{\beta}{2}\sin\frac{\beta}{2}$$

$$d_{3/2\,-1/2}(\beta) = \frac{1+5\cos\beta}{\sqrt{2}}\sin^2\frac{\beta}{2}\cos\frac{\beta}{2} \qquad d_{3/2\,-3/2}(\beta) = -\frac{5\cos\beta+3}{2}\sin^3\frac{\beta}{2}$$

$$d_{1/2\,1/2}(\beta) = \frac{5\cos^2\beta-2\cos\beta-1}{2}\cos\frac{\beta}{2} \qquad d_{1/2\,-1/2}(\beta) = -\frac{5\cos^2\beta+2\cos\beta-1}{2}\sin\frac{\beta}{2}$$

Spin 3

$$d_{33}(\beta) = \left(\frac{1+\cos\beta}{2}\right)^3 \qquad d_{32}(\beta) = -\frac{\sqrt{6}}{8}\sin\beta(1+\cos\beta)^2$$

$$d_{31}(\beta) = \frac{\sqrt{15}}{8}\sin^2\beta(1+\cos\beta) \qquad d_{30}(\beta) = -\frac{\sqrt{5}}{4}\sin^3\beta$$

$$d_{3-1}(\beta) = \frac{\sqrt{15}}{8}\sin^2\beta(1-\cos\beta) \qquad d_{3-2}(\beta) = -\frac{\sqrt{6}}{8}\sin\beta(1-\cos\beta)^2$$

$$d_{3-3}(\beta) = \left(\frac{1-\cos\beta}{2}\right)^3 \qquad d_{22}(\beta) = \left(\frac{1+\cos\beta}{2}\right)^2(3\cos\beta-2)$$

$$d_{21}(\beta) = -\frac{\sqrt{5}}{4\sqrt{2}}\sin\beta(3\cos^2\beta+2\cos\beta-1) \qquad d_{20}(\beta) = \frac{\sqrt{15}}{2\sqrt{2}}\cos\beta\sin^2\beta$$

$$d_{2-1}(\beta) = \frac{\sqrt{5}}{4\sqrt{2}}\sin\beta(3\cos^2\beta-2\cos\beta-1) \qquad d_{2-2}(\beta) = \left(\frac{1-\cos\beta}{2}\right)^2(3\cos\beta+2)$$

$$d_{11}(\beta) = \frac{1+\cos\beta}{8}(15\cos^2\beta-10\cos\beta-1) \qquad d_{10}(\beta) = -\frac{\sqrt{3}}{4}\sin\beta(5\cos^2\beta-1)$$

$$d_{1-1}(\beta) = \frac{1-\cos\beta}{8}(15\cos^2\beta+10\cos\beta-1) \qquad d_{00}(\beta) = \frac{5\cos^3\beta-3\cos\beta}{2}$$

As any state is determined only up to a phase factor $e^{i\alpha}$ we can choose for that $e^{\frac{i\phi}{2}}$ and obtain in another gauge convention

$$\psi(\theta, \phi) = \cos\frac{\theta}{2}\left|\frac{1}{2}, \frac{1}{2}\right\rangle + e^{i\phi}\sin\frac{\theta}{2}\left|\frac{1}{2}, -\frac{1}{2}\right\rangle \tag{I.56}$$

References to section I: 1, 2, 3, 4, 5, 6.

II. SOME SIMPLE TREATMENTS OF DECAY PROCESSES

a) Decay of a Boson into 2 Spinless Particles

Let us consider a boson decay of the type

$$B_1(j) \to B_2(0) + B_3(0)$$

where B_1 is a boson of spin j, B_2 and B_3 are bosons of spin 0. Here the total spin j of B_1 becomes the orbital angular momentum $l = j$ of the outgoing particles. Therefore, if the initial spin state is

$$\psi_{\text{in}} = \sum_{m=-j}^{+j} a_m|j, m\rangle$$

the angular part of the final state wave function will be according to (I.30)

$$\psi_{\text{fin}} = \sum_m a_m Y_j^m(\theta, \phi)$$

and the decay angular distribution

$$I(\theta, \phi) = \psi_{\text{fin}}^* \psi_{\text{fin}} = \sum_{m,n} a_m^* a_n Y_j^{m*} Y_j^n$$

One may introduce a transition operator T which transforms the initial state ψ_{in} into the final state. If ψ_{in} is defined by the column vector a_m then the transition operator is in this particular case *a* $(2j + 1) \times 1$ dimensional matrix, i.e. a row vector. As we are only interested in the decay angular distribution and not in the absolute decay rate, we need not care about coupling constants and can simply write

$$T_m = Y_j^m(\theta, \phi)$$

One verifies immediately

$$\psi_{\text{fin}} = \sum_m T_m a_m = \sum a_m Y_j^m(\theta, \phi)$$

The usefulness of this operator T will become evident in cases where there are particles with spin $\neq 0$ in the final state.

Looking only at the θ dependence of the decay distribution we find that for spin j the highest possible power in $\cos\theta$ is $(\cos\theta)^{2j}$. Observe, however, that according to Eq. (I.29) an equal mixture of all eigenstates from $|j, -j\rangle$ to $|j, +j\rangle$ results in an isotropic angular distribution.

b) Decays of Fermions into a Spin $^1/_2$ Fermion plus a Spin O Boson

1) *General Aspects*

Now we treat the decays

$$F_1(j) \rightarrow F_2(\tfrac{1}{2}) + B(0)$$

where $F(j)$ denotes a fermion of spin j. We start with a particular case and assume that F_1 is in the state $|^3/_2, {}^1/_2\rangle$ and decays over a P wave ($l = 1$) into $F(^1/_2)$ and $B(0)$. From the decomposition rules of angular momentum we have

$$\begin{aligned}|\tfrac{3}{2}, \tfrac{1}{2}\rangle \rightarrow \psi_{\text{fin}} &= (\tfrac{1}{2}\ 1\ \tfrac{1}{2}\ 0|\tfrac{3}{2}\ \tfrac{1}{2})\, |\tfrac{1}{2}, \tfrac{1}{2}\rangle\, Y_1^0(\theta, \phi) \\ &\quad + (\tfrac{1}{2}\ 1, -\tfrac{1}{2}\ 1|\tfrac{3}{2}\ \tfrac{1}{2})\, |\tfrac{1}{2}, -\tfrac{1}{2}\rangle\, Y_1^1(\theta, \phi) \\ &= \sqrt{\tfrac{2}{3}}\, Y_1^0(\theta, \phi)\, |\tfrac{1}{2}, \tfrac{1}{2}\rangle + \sqrt{\tfrac{1}{3}}\, Y_1^1(\theta, \phi)\, |\tfrac{1}{2}, -\tfrac{1}{2}\rangle\end{aligned}$$

where the Y's describe the orbital angular momentum and $|\tfrac{1}{2} \pm \tfrac{1}{2}\rangle$ the spin of the daughter fermion F_2 whose spin state is now angle dependent

$$\psi_{F_2} = \begin{bmatrix}\sqrt{^2/_3}\, Y_1^0(\theta, \phi) \\ \sqrt{^1/_3}\, Y_1^1(\theta, \phi)\end{bmatrix}$$

The decay angular distribution is, when summing over the spin states of F_2,

$$I(\theta, \phi) = \psi_{\text{fin}}^* \psi_{\text{fin}} = \tfrac{2}{3}\, |Y_1^0|^2 + \tfrac{1}{3}\, |Y_1^1|^2$$

For the general case of spin j when the decay proceeds over a wave with orbital angular momentum $l (l = j + \tfrac{1}{2}$ or $j - \tfrac{1}{2})$, the initial state $|j, m\rangle$ will lead to the final state

$$\begin{aligned}\psi_{\text{fin}} &= (\tfrac{1}{2} l\, \tfrac{1}{2}, m - \tfrac{1}{2}|jm)\, |\tfrac{1}{2}, \tfrac{1}{2}\rangle\, Y_l^{m-1/2} \\ &\quad + (\tfrac{1}{2} l, -\tfrac{1}{2}, m + \tfrac{1}{2}|jm)\, |\tfrac{1}{2}, -\tfrac{1}{2}\rangle\, Y_l^{m+1/2}\end{aligned}$$

From this we see that we can define a transition operator T which will produce from the initial spin state of F_1 the angle dependent spin state of F_2. This operator is a $(2j + 1) \times 2$ dimensional matrix:

$$T_{sm} = (\tfrac{1}{2} ls, m - s|jm)\, Y_l^{m-s}(\theta, \phi) \tag{II.1}$$

which, when applied to the $2j + 1$ dimensional row vector of the initial state a_m, will give the 2 dimensional row vector b_s of the final state. We have

$$b_s(\theta, \varphi) = \sum_m T_{sm}(\theta, \varphi)\, a_m \tag{II.2}$$

For spin $\tfrac{3}{2}$ this is a matrix multiplication of the type

$$\begin{bmatrix}\cdot \\ \cdot\end{bmatrix} = \begin{bmatrix}\cdot & \cdot & \cdot & \cdot \\ \cdot & \cdot & \cdot & \cdot\end{bmatrix} \begin{bmatrix}\cdot \\ \cdot \\ \cdot \\ \cdot\end{bmatrix}$$

The angular distribution of the decay averaged over the spin states of F_2 is

$$I(\theta, \phi) = \sum_s^m b_s^*(\theta, \phi)\, b_s(\theta, \phi) \qquad \text{(II.3)}$$

Depending on the parity of the parent state F_1, the decay wave will be either $l = j + \frac{1}{2}$ or $l = j - \frac{1}{2}$. Only when parity is violated will both waves be present and interfere with one another. It can be shown that the decay angular distributions for $l = j + \frac{1}{2}$ and $j = j - \frac{1}{2}$ are identical. This property is called Minami ambiguity and is proved section IV C. However the polarization distribution of the daughter fermion is different for the two cases. This we shall now demonstrate in an example: Assume a Y^* in the spin state $|3/2, 3/2\rangle$ It can decay into $\Lambda + \pi$ via a P or a D wave depending on its parity.

1) P wave decay:

$$\left|\frac{3}{2}, \frac{3}{2}\right\rangle \rightarrow \psi = Y_1^1(\theta, \phi)\left|\frac{1}{2}, \frac{1}{2}\right\rangle = \begin{bmatrix} a(\theta, \phi) \\ 0 \end{bmatrix}$$

$$I(\theta, \phi) = \psi^*\psi = |Y_1^1(\theta, \phi)|^2 = \frac{3}{2}(1 - x^2)$$

with $x = \cos\theta$. (A factor $\sqrt{1/4\pi}$ in the spherical harmonics and, correspondingly, $1/4\pi$ in angular and palarisation distributions has been omitted throughout this section.)

The Λ is fully polarized in z direction and we have

$$P_z = 1; \quad P_x = P_y = 0$$

or

$$I(\theta, \phi)\, P_z = \tfrac{3}{2}(1 - x^2)$$

2) D wave decay:

$$|{}^3/_2, {}^3/_2\rangle \rightarrow \psi = +\sqrt{{}^1/_5}\, Y_2^1|{}^1/_2, {}^1/_2\rangle - \sqrt{{}^4/_5}\, Y_2^2|{}^1/_2, -{}^1/_2\rangle$$

$$\psi = -\sqrt{{}^1/_6}\, 3x\sqrt{1 - x^2}\, e^{i\phi}|{}^1/_2, {}^1/_2\rangle - \sqrt{{}^1/_6}\, 3(1 - x^2)\, e^{2i\phi}|{}^1/_2, -{}^1/_2\rangle$$

$$\psi = a(\theta, \phi)\left|\frac{1}{2}, -\frac{1}{2}\right\rangle + b(\theta, \phi)\left|\frac{1}{2}, -\frac{1}{2}\right\rangle = \begin{bmatrix} a(\theta, \phi) \\ b(\theta, \phi) \end{bmatrix}$$

This row vector denotes the Λ spin state. It is not normalized to 1 but to

$$\psi^*\psi = I(\theta, \phi) = |a|^2 + |b|^2 = \tfrac{3}{2}(1 - x^2)$$

According to Eq. (I.19) we have

$$I(\theta, \phi)\, P_z = |a|^2 - |b|^2 = \tfrac{3}{2}(-1 + 3x^2 - 2x^4)$$

$$I(\theta, \phi)\, P_x = 2\,\mathrm{Re}\,(a^*b) = 3x(1 - x^2)^{3/2}\cos\phi$$

$$I(\theta, \phi)\, P_y = 2\,\mathrm{Im}\,(a^*b) = 3x(1 - x^2)^{3/2}\sin\phi$$

So the polarization vector has no ϕ dependence. The radial component in the xy-plane is

$$I(\theta, \phi)\, P_r = 3x(1 - x^2)^{3/2}$$

One may as well split the polarization $\boldsymbol{P}$ into a longitudinal component $P_{\parallel}$ parallel to the emission direction of the Λ and a transversal component $P_{\perp}$ perpendicular to $P_{\parallel}$ and lying in the plane defined by the z axis and the emission direction of the Λ in the Y^* system. According to Fig. 2 one has the following

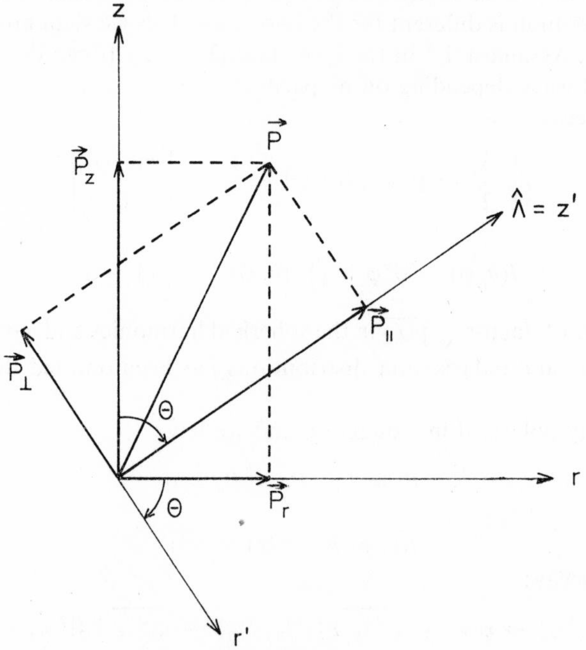

Fig. 2

relations between the polarization components

$$P_{\parallel} = P_z \cos\theta + P_r \sin\theta$$

$$P_{\perp} = -P_z \sin\theta + P_r \cos\theta$$

Applying this to the above example one obtains:

$$\psi^*\psi P_{\parallel} = I(\theta, \phi)\, P_{\parallel} = (\tfrac{3}{2} - \tfrac{3}{2}x^2)\, x$$

$$\psi^*\psi P_{\perp} = I(\theta, \phi)\, P_{\perp} = (\tfrac{3}{2} - \tfrac{3}{2}x^2)\sqrt{1 - x^2}$$

Carrying through analogous calculation for all diagonal spin states $|J, M\rangle$ of mother particles with spin $J = {}^1/_2, {}^3/_2$ and treating each case with the two possible parity assignments leads to the results quoted in Table 5.

Table V

Angular and Polarization Distributions of fermions in state $|J, M\rangle$ decaying into a spin $^1/_2$ fermion and a spinless boson.
$x = \cos\theta$

Initial state	Decay wave L	$I(\theta, \phi)$	$\pm I(\theta, \phi)\, P_z$	$\pm I(\theta, \phi)\, P_r$	$\pm I(\theta, \phi)\, P_\parallel$	$\pm I(\theta, \phi)\, P_\perp$	$\pm I(\theta, \phi)\, P_m$
$\left\lvert\frac{1}{2}, \pm\frac{1}{2}\right\rangle$	0	1	1	0	x	$+\sqrt{1-x^2}$	$-1+2x^2$
	1	1	$-1+2x^2$	$2x\sqrt{1-x^2}$	x	$-\sqrt{1-x^2}$	1
$\left\lvert\frac{3}{2}, \pm\frac{3}{2}\right\rangle$	1	$\frac{3}{2}-\frac{3}{2}x^2$	$\frac{3}{2}-\frac{3}{2}x^2$	0	$\left(\frac{3}{2}-\frac{3}{2}x^2\right)x$	$+\left(\frac{3}{2}-\frac{3}{2}x^2\right)\sqrt{1-x^2}$	$-\frac{3}{2}+\frac{9}{2}x^2-3x^4$
	2	$\frac{3}{2}-\frac{3}{2}x^2$	$-\frac{3}{2}+\frac{9}{2}x^2-3x^4$	$3(1-x^2)\,x\sqrt{1-x^2}$	$\left(\frac{3}{2}-\frac{3}{2}x^2\right)x$	$-\left(\frac{3}{2}-\frac{3}{2}x^2\right)\sqrt{1-x^2}$	$\frac{3}{2}-\frac{3}{2}x^2$
$\left\lvert\frac{3}{2}, \pm\frac{1}{2}\right\rangle$	1	$\frac{1}{2}+\frac{3}{2}x^2$	$-\frac{1}{2}+\frac{5}{2}x^2$	$-2x\sqrt{1-x^2}$	$\left(-\frac{5}{2}+\frac{9}{2}x^2\right)x$	$-\left(\frac{1}{2}-\frac{9}{2}x^2\right)\sqrt{1-x^2}$	$\frac{1}{2}-\frac{15}{2}x^2+9x^4$
	2	$\frac{1}{2}-\frac{3}{2}x^2$	$\frac{1}{2}-\frac{15}{2}x^2+9x^4$	$3(3x^2-1)\,x\sqrt{1-x^2}$	$\left(-\frac{5}{2}+\frac{9}{2}x^2\right)x$	$+\left(\frac{1}{2}-\frac{9}{2}x^2\right)\sqrt{1-x^2}$	$-\frac{1}{2}+\frac{5}{2}x^2$

As seen from Table 5 the parallel polarization $P_{\parallel}$ is the same for opposite parities of the same spin state, whereas transverse polarization changes sign, so it is easy to find for a polarization $\boldsymbol{P}^{+}(\theta)$ that of the opposite parity state $\boldsymbol{P}^{-}(\theta)$ as illustrated in Fig. 3.

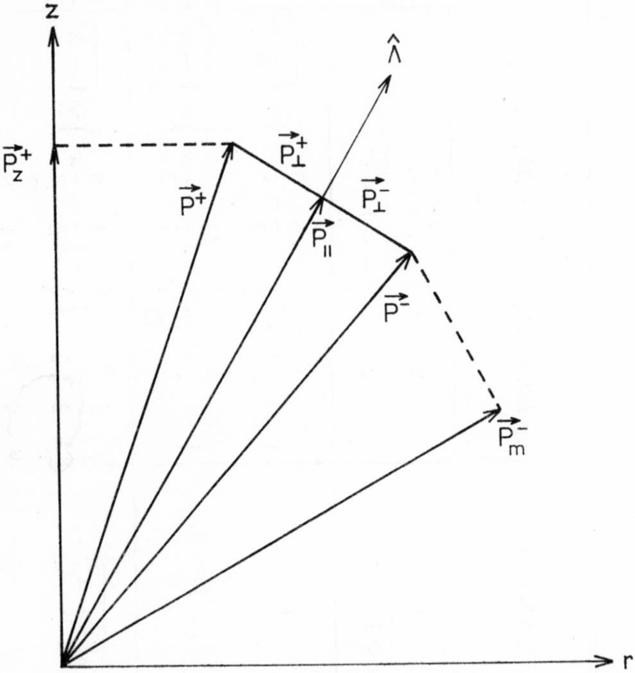

Fig. 3

P^{-} is obtained from P^{+} by a rotation of 180° around the Λ emission direction $\hat{\Lambda}$. By this rotation the spin quantization axis $\hat{n}\|z$ becomes the indicated direction $\hat{m}$. the so-called "magic direction", and can be written as

$$\hat{m} = -\hat{n} + 2(\hat{n}\hat{\Lambda})\,\hat{\Lambda}. \tag{II.4}$$

It is evident now that for a certain spin-parity final state, the distribution of the polarization component P_m along the magic direction $\hat{m}$ is the same as the component in the direction $\hat{n} = z$ of the opposite parity state. From Fig. 3 $P_z^{+} = P_m^{-}$. $I(\theta, \phi)\, P_m$ is tabulated in the last column of Table 5.

From inspection of Table 5 one can state a series of properties of the angular and polarization distribution which have been proved here only for spin $^1/_2$, $^3/_2$, though it may be shown that they are valid for arbitrary spin $J = n/2$.

1) The decay angular distributions are even polynomials in $\cos\theta$, therefore symmetric about 90°. The highest power of $\cos\theta$ is $2J - 1$, if J is the spin of the initial state.

2) Opposite parity decays of the same initial spin state $|J, M\rangle$ have identical angular distributions (Minami-ambiguity).

3) The angular distributions of any two states $|J, M\rangle$ and $|J, -M\rangle$ are identical.

4) For a given J, a statistical mixture of states $|J, M\rangle$ with equal population in all possible $|M|$ give an isotropic decay distribution.

5) If the polarization (of the daughter fermion) coming from a state $|J, M\rangle$ is $\boldsymbol{P}(\theta)$, the corresponding polarization for the state $|J, -M\rangle$ with the same parity is $-\boldsymbol{P}(\theta)$.

6) The polarization lies in a plane defined by the axis of spin alignment $\hat{n}$ and the emission direction $\hat{\Lambda}$ of the fermion.

7) The polarization functions

$$I(\theta, \phi)\, P_z = \frac{\mathrm{d}N}{\mathrm{d}\cos\theta}\, P_z \quad \text{and} \quad I(\theta, \phi)\, P_r = \frac{\mathrm{d}N}{\mathrm{d}\cos\theta}\, P_r$$

depend on the parity of the state $|J, M\rangle$.

8) $I(\theta, \phi)\, P_z$ is an even polynomial in $\cos\theta$.

9) $I(\theta, \phi)\, P_r$ has the form $f(\cos^2\theta)\cos\theta\sin\theta$, i.e. an odd function of $\cos\theta$.

10) The polarization component $P_{\parallel}$ in the fermion emission direction does not depend on the parity of the state $|J, M\rangle$.

11) The perpendicular polarization component $P_{\perp}$ of the state $|JM\rangle$ changes sign for the opposite parity state.

12) $I(\theta, \phi)\, P_{\parallel}$ has the form $f_1(\cos^2\theta)\cos\theta$.

13) $I(\theta, \phi)\, P_{\perp}$ has the form $f_2(\cos^2\theta)\sin\theta$.

14) If a state $|JM\rangle$ leads to a certain polarization distribution in the z direction $P_z^+(\theta)$, the opposite parity state shows the same polarization distribution with respect to the magic direction et v.v.

$$P_z^+(\theta) = P_m^-(\theta).$$

All these properties of the decay distributions are valid only for the case that the parent fermion is in one spin eigenstate $|J, M\rangle$ in a statistical mixture of eigenstates. If however, the parent spin state is a linear superposition of eigenstates the decay distributions will show ϕ dependence. Then statements 1) to 14) are still valid when integration over ϕ is carried out in the decay angular distributions $I(\theta, \phi)$ and the polarization distributions $I(\theta, \phi)\, P$. Note that for fixed J, an equal statistical mixture of all eigenstates $|J, M\rangle$ will lead to an isotropic decay distributions and 0 polarization of the daughter fermion.

How can this knowledge be used for spin determination? Let us consider a Y^* produced in the process

$$K^- + p \to \pi + Y^*$$

As spin quantization axis one chooses the production normal, because by parity conservation this is the only direction in which the Y^* can be polarized. From the above results it follows that the spin of the Y^* can be determined, at least in principle, from the decay angular distribution, if the contributing states do not happen to add up to isotropy. The parity of the Y^* should follow from the Λ

polarization distribution, if the Y^* is produced polarized. This type of analysis was applied, e.g. by Shafer *et al.*[7] to determine the spin and parity of the 1385 MeV Y_1^* resonance produced in the reaction

$$\begin{array}{l} K^- + p \to Y^{\pm *} + \pi^{\mp} \\ \qquad\qquad \hookrightarrow \Lambda + \pi^{\pm} \end{array}$$

They obtained for the angular distribution

$$I(\theta) = 1 + (0.69 \pm 0.22)\,(\hat{\Lambda}\hat{n})^2; \quad \cos\theta = (\hat{\Lambda}\hat{n})$$

and for the Λ polarization components in the normal and magic direction

$$I(\theta)\,P_n = -1 + 3.5(\hat{\Lambda}\hat{n})^2$$

$$I(\theta)\,P_m = 1 - 9.7(\hat{\Lambda}\hat{n})^2 + 11.2(\hat{\Lambda}\hat{n})^4.$$

Comparing these results to the theoretical distributions in Table 4 the conclusion was that the most likely spin parity assignment is $P_{3/2}$ i.e. $J = {}^3/_2$, P wave decay. (How the Λ polarization is measured will be explained in detail in section II C.)

If the sample of events is large enough it may be advantageous to consider separate subsamples corresponding to different production angles because for a small interval of production angle the particle produced is less likely to be in a statistical mixture of many pure spin states which could average out the angular distribution to isotropy. This is because for a fixed production angle the spin state of the Y^* produced in the reaction $K^- + p \to Y^* + \pi$ is an equal mixture of exactly 2 pure states corresponding to the 2 pure initial spin states of the nucleons which build up the unpolarized target. (The incident plane wave plus a fully polarized nucleon is a pure quantum mechanical state which by the interaction is transformed into another pure state.)

2) *Adair Analysis*

These 2 pure states of the outgoing fermion can immediately be visualized for the so-called Adair case, i.e. at production angles of 0° or 180° with respect to the incident beam. In our case we consider the configuration of Fig. 4.

Initial and final state configurations are collinear. From classical arguments it follows that the orbital angular momentum of the initial state L_{in} and that of the final state L_{fin} lie in a plane perpendicular to the beam direction. Choosing the beam direction as spin quantization axis, orbital angular momenta are in the states $|L, 0\rangle$

The quantum mechanical argument for this is the fact that the expansion of a plane wave in terms of angular momentum eigenfunctions contains only spherical harmonics with $m = 0$ if the plane wave direction is the spin quantization axis. As π, K, L_{in}, L_{fin} all have spin component 0 in z direction the Y^* must have the same m as the proton, namely $m = \pm{}^1/_2$. Therefore in the Adair case fermions are produced in the eigenstates $|J, \pm{}^1/_2\rangle$ and show the corresponding angular distribution of Table 5 with respect to the beam direction. The decay distributions are strictly valid only for particles emitted at 0° or 180°. In practice however, one

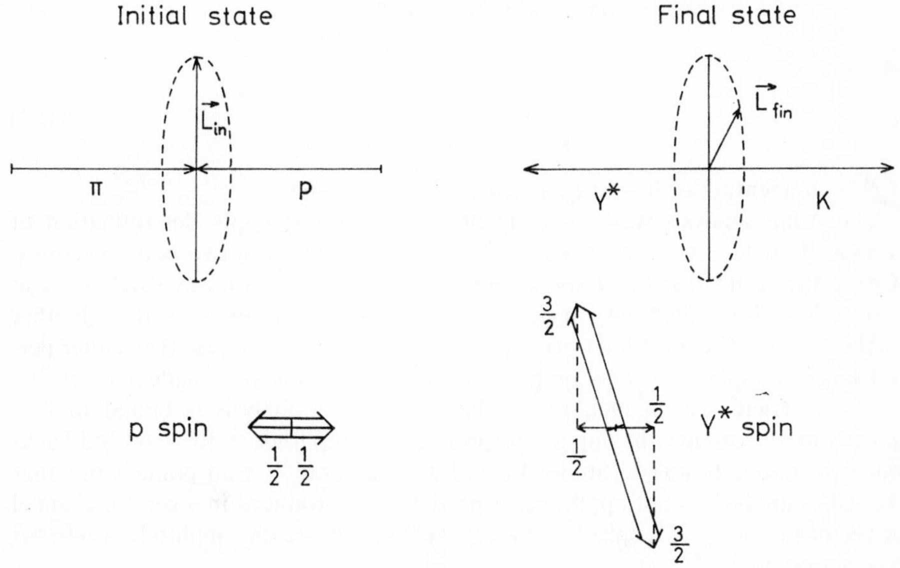

Fig. 4

has to choose a finite acceptance angle. How large may it be so that the decay distribution is still significant for the spin of the produced particle? The requirement is of course, that nearly all produced particles are in the states $|J, {}^1/_2\rangle$ or $|J, -{}^1/_2\rangle$. One easily verifies that all other states $|J, m\rangle$, $m \neq {}^1/_2, -{}^1/_2$ are associated with production orbital momentum states Y_l^m $(m \neq 0)$. The Y_l^m $(m \neq 0)$ are 0 at 0° and 180°, which is the crucial requirement for the Adair analysis to work, and rise with $\sin^m \theta$. So the cutoff angle should be reasonably chosen smaller or equal to the angle θ_{max} of the first maximum of all substantially contributing Y_l^m $(m \neq 0)$. Looking at tables of the adjoint Legendre functions e.g. in Jahnke-Emde, one finds that for fixed l, Y_l^1 reaches the maximum first and in the same time covers a larger area from 0° to θ_{max} than the other Y_l^m of the same l. So Y_l^1 is the most dangerous term for the Adair analysis for a given l. θ_{max} is roughly $1/l$, so the highest l contributing substantially to the production—call it l_{max}—determines the cutoff angle which corresponds to the first maximum of $Y_{l\,max}^1$. Thus we have

$$\theta_{cutoff} \approx \frac{1}{l_{max}}. \tag{II.5}$$

If one assumes that the range of the interaction is given by the Compton wavelength of the π meson

$$\lambda_\pi = \frac{\hbar}{m_\pi c} \tag{II.6}$$

an estimate of l_{max} can easily be obtained regarding λ_π as the maximum impact parameter. Applying the classical definition of angular momentum one finds the relation

$$\hbar l_{max} = p_{inc}^{CM} \lambda_\pi = p_{inc}^{CM} \cdot \frac{\hbar}{m_\pi c}$$

or

$$l_{max} = \frac{p_{inc}^{CM}}{m_\pi c} \tag{II.7}$$

p_{inc}^{CM} = momentum of incident particle in the c.m. system.

The Adair analysis was originally proposed[8] for the spin determination of strange particles. Applied to Λ and Σ hyperons produced in two body reactions, it gave the result that the Λ and Σ spins are $^1/_2$[9]. Later on it was widely used in connection with excited baryon states and meson-meson resonances, though other methods to be discussed later often proved more efficient because they either permit larger samples of events or because the Adair analysis is inadequate to the problem. There are, in fact, cases where the Adair analysis is bound to fail, namely in all reactions having a zero production amplitude in forward and backward direction. It was L. Stodolsky and J. J. Sakurai[11] who pointed out that the Adair analysis is not applicable if particles are produced in a certain channel of vector meson (ϱ, K^*, spin 1^- bosons) exchange where the amplitude is zero for production angles $\theta = 0, \pi$.

For instance the reactions

$$\pi^+ + p \to N_{3/2}^{*++} + \pi^0$$

$$K^+ + p \to N_{3/2}^{*++} + K^0$$

$$\pi^+ + p \to Y_1^{*+} + K^+$$

$$K^- + p \to Y_1^{*+} + \pi^-$$

are most likely to proceed via ϱ or K^* exchange, because π or K exchange are forbidden by parity conservation. In fact it seems that in none of these reactions the Adair analysis has given satisfactory results for the spin determination of the baryons[11].

An important result of Stodolsky's and Sakurai's calculations was that the decay distribution of an $N_{3/2}^*$ produced in the most probable magnetic dipole transition $M1 \to p_{3/2}$ of vector meson exchange, should be of the form

$$\frac{dN}{d\cos\theta} = \frac{1}{2}[1 + 3(\hat{n}\hat{\pi})^2] \tag{II.8}$$

where $\hat{n}$ is the *production normal* and $\hat{\pi}$ the direction of the π in the N^* decay, measured in the N^* c.m.

This angular distribution corresponds to the eigenstate

$$\psi_{N^*} = |\tfrac{3}{2}, \tfrac{1}{2}\rangle$$

with respect to the production normal. Let us see what the angular distribution would be if measured with respect to the Adair direction. First we rotate the coordinate system by 90° so that the beam direction becomes the spin quantization direction. Applying the y rotation matrix of Table 3

$$\psi'_{N*} = R_y(\pi/2)\,\psi_{N*} = \sqrt{{}^1/_8}\begin{bmatrix} 1 & -\sqrt{3} & \sqrt{3} & -1 \\ \sqrt{3} & -1 & -1 & \sqrt{3} \\ \sqrt{3} & 1 & -1 & -\sqrt{3} \\ 1 & \sqrt{3} & \sqrt{3} & 1 \end{bmatrix}\begin{bmatrix} 0 \\ 1 \\ 0 \\ 0 \end{bmatrix}$$

$$\psi'_{N*} = \sqrt{{}^1/_8}\,[-\sqrt{3}\,|{}^3/_2, {}^3/_2\rangle' - |{}^3/_2, {}^1/_2\rangle' + |{}^3/_2, -{}^1/_2\rangle' + \sqrt{3}\,|{}^3/_2 - {}^3/_3\rangle']$$

where the states $|\rangle'$ are quantized along the beam direction. Averaging over the azimuthal angular distribution we can neglect the interference of different eigenstates $|\rangle'$, so that the resulting angular distribution is given by

$$\frac{\mathrm{d}N}{\mathrm{d}\cos\theta} = \frac{3}{4}(\psi^*\psi)_{3/2,\pm 3/2} + \frac{1}{4}(\psi^*\psi)_{3/2,\pm 1/2}$$

where the two terms may be taken from Table 5. So

$$\frac{\mathrm{d}N}{\mathrm{d}\cos\theta} = \frac{3}{4}\left(\frac{3}{2} - \frac{3}{2}x^2\right) + \frac{1}{4}\left(\frac{1}{2} + \frac{3}{2}x^2\right) = \frac{5}{4}\left(1 - \frac{3}{5}x^2\right)$$

whereas the expected Adair distribution is ${}^1/_2(1 + 3x^2)$.

In the Adair case the daughter fermions show no polarization at all if the decay is strong. This can be seen from the polarization distributions in Table 5. Thus a polarization measurement of the daughter fermions of Adair selected events gives no answer about the parity.

Problem

Discuss the Adair analysis of a spin ${}^5/_2$ particle A strongly decaying into a spin ${}^3/_2$ particle B and a π meson. Try to find a method to determine the relative parity A, B.

c) Weak Decays of Hyperons

Consider a two-body decay of a particle ($A \to B + C$). If the decay interaction is strong, parity is conserved, i e

$$\xi_A = \xi_B\xi_C(-1)^L \tag{II.9}$$

where the ξ's are the instrinsic parities of the particles involved, L is the angular momentum of the final state, and (-1^L) its contribution to the parity.
As can be seen from Eq. (II.9), only either odd or even L are allowed for the final state. If, however, as is usual in weak interactions, parity is not conserved, rela-

tion (1) breaks down and both even *and* odd angular momenta are permitted, as far as the total spin can be conserved.

We choose the Ξ decay

$$\Xi \to \Lambda + \pi$$

as a specific example to discuss how the wave function describing a nonleptonic weak two-body decay can be found experimentally. It will turn out that this wave function (of the decay products) is most conveniently described in terms of the so-called "decay parameters" which are more closely related to measurable quantities than the wave equation's amplitudes themselves. We shall assume that both Ξ and Λ have spin $\frac{1}{2}$ (well established now).

As initial state we choose a Ξ in its c.m. with the spin pointing into the positive z direction of the reference frame:

$$\psi_{\text{in}} = |\tfrac{1}{2}, \tfrac{1}{2}\rangle_\Xi$$

Angular momentum conservation in the decay allows only S or P wave. S wave decay leads to the final state wave function*

$$\psi_S = |{}^1/_2, {}^1/_2\rangle_\Lambda \, Y_0^0(\theta, \phi) \tag{II.10}$$

and P wave decay to

$$\psi_P = \sqrt{{}^1/_3}\, |{}^1/_2, {}^1/_2\rangle_\Lambda \, Y_1^0(\theta, \phi) - \sqrt{{}^2/_3}\, |{}^1/_2, -{}^1/_2\rangle \, Y_1^1(\theta, \phi) \tag{II.11}$$

As the decay is parity non-conserving both S and P wave is contained in the final state

$$\begin{aligned}\psi_{\text{fin}} &= A_S\psi_S + A_P\psi_P \\ &= (A_S + A_P\cos\theta)\,|\tfrac{1}{2}, \tfrac{1}{2}\rangle_\Lambda + A_P\,e^{i\phi}\sin\theta\,|\tfrac{1}{2}, -\tfrac{1}{2}\rangle_\Lambda\end{aligned} \tag{II.12}$$

where the complex amplitudes A_s and A_p are normalized to 1

$$|A_S|^2 + |A_p|^2 = 1 \tag{II.13}$$

A_S and A_P completely describe the decaying state. They are defined only up to a common phase factor $e^{i\varphi}$. Alternatively one may describe the decay in terms of the real decay parameters

$$\begin{aligned}\alpha &= 2\,\mathrm{Re}\,(A_S^* A_P) \\ \beta &= 2\,\mathrm{Im}\,(A_S^* A_P) \\ \gamma &= |A_S|^2 - |A_P|^2\end{aligned} \tag{II.14}$$

From (II.14) follows

$$\alpha^2 + \beta^2 + \gamma^2 = 1 \tag{II.15}$$

Thus the decay is determined by 2 parameters and the sign of the third one.

* The relative sign between S and P wave is a matter of convention and depends on the choice of Clebsch-Gordan coefficients: $({}^1/_2 l..|..)$ or $(l\,{}^1/_2..|..)$.

The decay angular distribution of the Ξ completely polarized in positive z direction is

$$I(\theta, \phi) = \psi^*_{\text{fin}}\psi_{\text{fin}} = 1 + 2 \operatorname{Re} A_S A_P \cos\theta$$
$$= 1 + \alpha_\Xi \cos\theta . \qquad \text{(II.16)}$$

If the Ξ is not completely polarized but has the polarization P_Ξ in z direction we have

$$I(\theta, \phi) = 1 + P\alpha_\Xi \cos\theta \qquad \text{(II.17)}$$

α_Ξ shows up in the decay angular distribution, β_Ξ and γ_Ξ are related to the polarization of the Λ, $\boldsymbol{P}_\Lambda$.
If ψ_{fin} has the form

$$\psi_{\text{fin}} = a(\theta, \phi)\, |\tfrac{1}{2}, \tfrac{1}{2}\rangle_\Lambda + b(\theta, \phi)\, |\tfrac{1}{2}, -\tfrac{1}{2}\rangle_\Lambda \qquad \text{(II.18)}$$

one has according to Eq. (I.19)

$$\begin{aligned} I(\theta, \phi)\, P_{\Lambda x} &= 2 \operatorname{Re} a^* b \\ I(\theta, \phi)\, P_{\Lambda y} &= 2 \operatorname{Im} a^* b \\ I(\theta, \phi)\, P_{\Lambda z} &= |a|^2 - |b|^2 \end{aligned} \qquad \text{(II.19)}$$

Inserting Eq. (II.12) into Eq. (II.19) gives for a Ξ completely polarized in $(\pm)$ z direction

$$\begin{aligned} (1(\pm)\, \alpha_\Xi \cos\theta)\, P_{\Lambda x} &= \alpha_\Xi \sin\theta (\pm)\, 2\, |A_P|^2 \cos\theta \sin\theta \\ (1(\pm)\, \alpha_\Xi \cos\theta)\, P_{\Lambda y} &= (\pm)\, \beta_\Xi \sin\theta \\ (1(\pm)\, \alpha_\Xi \cos\theta)\, P_{\Lambda z} &= (\pm)\, \gamma_\Xi + \alpha_\Xi \cos\theta (\pm)\, 2\, |A_P|^2 \cos^2\theta \end{aligned} \qquad \text{(II.20)}$$

Note that not all terms in Eq. (II.20) change sign with inversion of the Ξ polarization. Therefore for Ξ's only partially polarized in $+z$ direction only the $(\pm)$ terms get the factor P_Ξ. The Λ polarization is described more conveniently in a coordinate system which depends on the decay angle θ. In Fig. 5 it is defined by the unit vectors $\hat{e}_1$,$\hat{e}_2$,$\hat{e}_3$.

$\hat{e}_3$ is the Λ emission direction $\hat{\Lambda}$, $\hat{e}_2$ is parallel to $\hat{e}_z \times \hat{e}_3$ and $\hat{e}_1 = \hat{e}_2 \times \hat{e}_3$ such that for $\theta = 0, \phi = 0$ $\hat{e}_1 = \hat{e}_x, \hat{e}_2 = \hat{e}_y, \hat{e}_3 = \hat{e}_z$.

Since in our case the decay angular distributions is independent of ϕ we may put $\phi = 0$ and obtain for the Λ polarization in the new coordinate system

$$\begin{aligned} P_{\Lambda 1} &= -P_{\Lambda z} \sin\theta + P_{\Lambda x} \cos\theta \\ P_{\Lambda 2} &= P_{\Lambda y} \\ P_{\Lambda 3} &= P_{\Lambda z} \cos\theta + P_{\Lambda x} \sin\theta \end{aligned} \qquad \text{(II.21)}$$

Inserting Eq. (II.20) one obtains

$$
\begin{aligned}
I(\theta, \phi)\, P_{\Lambda 1} &= -P_{\Xi}\gamma_{\Xi} \sin\theta \\
I(\theta, \phi)\, P_{\Lambda 2} &= P_{\Xi}\beta_{\Xi} \sin\theta \\
I(\theta, \phi)\, P_{\Lambda 3} &= P_{\Xi} \cos\theta + \alpha_{\Xi}
\end{aligned}
\tag{II.22}
$$

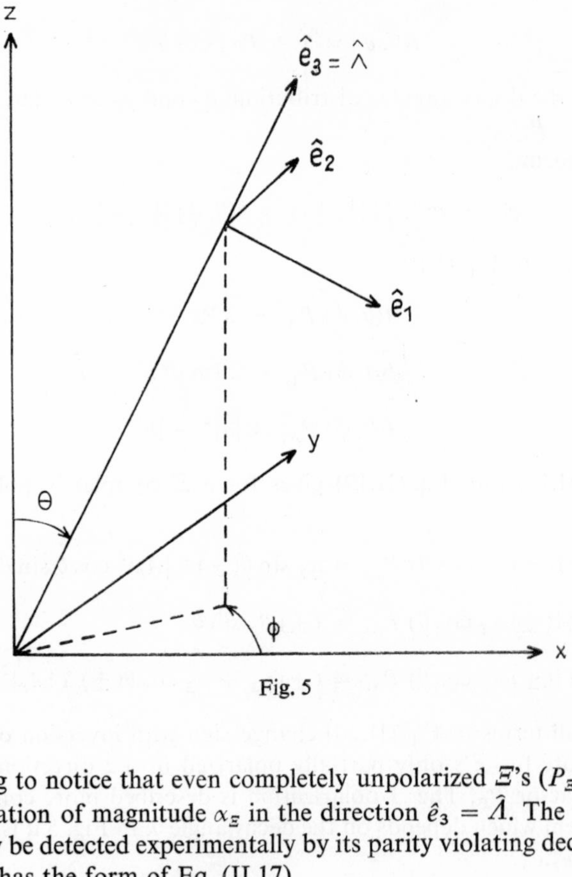

Fig. 5

It is interesting to notice that even completely unpolarized Ξ's ($P_{\Xi} = 0$) will lead to a Λ polarization of magnitude α_{Ξ} in the direction $\hat{e}_3 = \hat{\Lambda}$. The polarization of the Λ, $\boldsymbol{P}_{\Lambda}$, may be detected experimentally by its parity violating decay $\Lambda \to p + \pi^-$ which in turn has the form of Eq. (II.17).

$$I(\vartheta, \varphi) = 1 + P_{\Lambda}\alpha_{\Lambda} \cos\vartheta \tag{II.23}$$

where ϑ is the angle between the Λ polarization vector $\boldsymbol{P}_{\Lambda}$ and the direction of flight $\hat{p}$ of the proton in the decay $\Lambda \to p + \pi^-$. With

$$\cos\vartheta = (\hat{P}_{\Lambda} \cdot \hat{p})$$

or

$$I(\vartheta, \varphi) = 1 + \alpha_{\Lambda}(\boldsymbol{P}_{\Lambda} \cdot \hat{p}) \tag{II.24}$$

How can we determine the polarization vector of the Λ, $\boldsymbol{P}_\Lambda$ from its decay angular distribution? From simple geometrical arguments it may be shown that Eq. (II.23) or Eq. (II.24) are valid for every individual Λ polarization *component* ($P_{\Lambda i} = P_{\Lambda 1}, P_{\Lambda 2}, P_{\Lambda 3}$) when averaging over the azimuth φ is done:

$$I(\vartheta_i) = \int d\varphi_i I(\vartheta_i \varphi_i) = 1 + \alpha_\Lambda P_{\Lambda i} \cos \vartheta_i \tag{II.25}$$

with

$$\cos \vartheta_i = (\hat{P}_{\Lambda i} \cdot \hat{p})$$

ϑ_i is the angle between the proton emission direction $\hat{p}$ and the direction of the i'th Λ spin component $\hat{P}_{\Lambda i}$. Equation (II.25) permits us to determine the polarization vector P_Λ of any given sample of Λ decays simply by fitting 3 angular distributions of type (II.25) to the 3 parameters $P_{\Lambda i}$ assuming that α_Λ is known. $P_{\Lambda i}$ may be expressed in terms of the average value of $\cos \vartheta_i$.

$$\langle \cos \vartheta_i \rangle = \frac{\int I(\vartheta_i) \cos \vartheta_i \, d \cos \vartheta_i}{\int I(\vartheta_i) \, d \cos \vartheta_i}$$

$$= \frac{1}{3} \alpha_\Lambda P_{\Lambda i}$$

or

$$P_{\Lambda i} = \frac{3}{\alpha_\Lambda} \langle \cos \vartheta_i \rangle = \frac{3}{\alpha_\Lambda} \langle \hat{e}_i \hat{p} \rangle \tag{II.26}$$

where the polarization component $P_{\Lambda i}$ is parallel to the unit vector $\hat{e}_i$. Experimentally for a sample of N events with the angles $\vartheta_{i\nu}$ one has

$$\langle \cos \vartheta_i \rangle = \frac{1}{N} \sum_{\nu=1}^{N} \cos \vartheta_{i\nu}$$

Now let us apply this to the polarization of Λ's coming from Ξ decays. Their polarization components $P_{\Lambda 1}, P_{\Lambda 2}, P_{\Lambda 3}$ in the directions $\hat{e}_1, \hat{e}_2, \hat{e}_3$ as indicated in Fig. 5 depend on the Λ emission angle θ. For a fixed angle θ the protons of the subsequent Λ decay will obey distributions

$$I(\vartheta_i) = 1 + \alpha_\Lambda P_{\Lambda i}(\theta) \cos \vartheta_i \tag{II.27}$$

with respect to the Λ polarization components $P_{\Lambda i}(\theta)$ as defined in Eq. (II.22). Adding up corresponding distributions (II.27) for all Ξ decay angles θ will give the resulting distribution

$$I(\vartheta_i) = 1 + \alpha_\Lambda \langle P_{\Lambda i} \rangle \cos \vartheta_i \tag{II.28}$$

where $\langle P_{\Lambda i} \rangle$ is the statistical average of the polarization components $P_{\Lambda i}(\theta)$ over the Ξ decay angle θ.

$$\langle P_{\Lambda i} \rangle = \frac{1}{4\pi} \int P_{\Lambda i}(\theta) \, I(\theta, \phi) \, d\Omega \tag{II.29}$$

where $P_{\Lambda i}(\theta)$ are the expressions of Eq. (II.22) with $I(\theta,\phi)$ normalized to 4π when integrated over the full solid angle.

So one obtains

$$\langle P_{\Lambda 3}\rangle = \frac{1}{2}\int_{-1}^{+1} (P_\Xi \cos\theta + \alpha_\Xi)\,\mathrm{d}\cos\theta = \alpha_\Xi \tag{II.30}$$

$$\langle P_{\Lambda 1}\rangle = \frac{1}{2}\int_{0}^{\pi} -P_\Xi\gamma_\Xi \sin^2\theta\,\mathrm{d}\theta = -\frac{\pi}{4}P_\Xi\beta_\Xi$$

and correspondingly

$$\langle P_{\Lambda 2}\rangle = \frac{\pi}{4}P_\Xi\beta_\Xi$$

The distributions (II.28) of the decay protons of the Λ decays are explicitly

$$I(\vartheta_1 = 1 - \frac{\pi}{4}P_\Xi\gamma_\Xi\alpha_\Lambda\cos\vartheta_1;\quad \cos\vartheta_3 = \hat{p}\cdot\hat{e}_1$$

$$I(\vartheta_2) = 1 + \frac{\pi}{4}P_\Xi\beta_\Xi\alpha_\Lambda\cos\vartheta_2;\quad \cos\vartheta_2 = \hat{p}\cdot\hat{e}_2 \tag{II.31}$$

$$I(\vartheta_3) = 1 + \alpha_\Xi\alpha_\Lambda\cos\vartheta_3;\quad \cos\vartheta_3 = \hat{p}\cdot\hat{e}_3$$

Furthermore one has the Ξ decay distribution

$$I(\theta,\phi) = 1 + P_\Xi\alpha_\Xi\cos\theta \tag{II.31 a}$$

In the definitions of the angles, $\hat{p}$ is the emission direction of the p in the Λ rest frame and $\hat{n}$ is the direction of the Ξ polarization. The $\hat{e}_k$ have been defined before as

$$\hat{e}_3 = \hat{\Lambda}$$

$$\hat{e}_2 = \frac{\hat{n}\times\hat{e}_3}{|\hat{n}\times\hat{e}_3|} \tag{II.32}$$

$$\hat{e}_1 = \frac{\hat{e}_2\times\hat{e}_3}{|\hat{e}_2\times\hat{e}_3|}$$

Relations, Eq. (II.31) have first been given by Teutsch *et al.*[12].

How is the situation experimentally? If the Ξ's produced in some reaction, e.g.

$$K^- + p \to \Xi^- + K^+ + n\pi$$

are unpolarized, one can, nevertheless determine the α_Ξ parameter from the asymmetry coefficient $a_3 = \alpha_\Xi\alpha_1$ in the third angular distribution Eq. (II.31) if α_Λ is known from other experiments ($\alpha_\Lambda = 0.62 \pm 0.02$)[13]. For the other decay parameters, polarized Ξ's are required. Polarized fermions can be produced either in elastic scattering or in inelastic two-body reactions, such as

$$K^- + p \to \Xi^- + K^+$$

where the polarization has to be normal to the production plane, i.e. parallel to the direction

$$\hat{n} = \hat{K}^- \times \hat{\Xi}^-$$

Any other direction is forbidden by parity conservation. The polarization depends on the production angle $\theta_{pr.}$ in the c.m. of the colliding particles.
$P_\Xi(\theta_{pr.})$ tends to 0 for $\theta_{pr.} \to 0°, 180°$. If the average polarization in an angle interval $\theta_1 < \theta_{pr.} < \theta_2$ is different from 0, the method described above can be applied. The four asymmetry coefficients in the angular distributions Eq. (II.31),

$$\begin{aligned} a_1 &= -\frac{\pi}{4} P_\Xi \gamma_\Xi \alpha_\Lambda \\ a_2 &= \frac{\pi}{4} P_\Xi \beta_\Xi \alpha_\Lambda \\ a_3 &= \alpha_\Xi \alpha_\Lambda \\ a_4 &= P_\Xi \alpha_\Xi \end{aligned} \tag{II.33}$$

are determined experimentally which allows Eq. (II.33) to be solved for P_Ξ, α_Ξ, β_Ξ, γ_Ξ, if α_Λ is known. Actually α, β, γ are overdetermined because they have to obey the relation $\alpha^2 + \beta^2 + \gamma^2 = 1$.

Alternatively these parameters may be obtained by a maximum likelihood method applied to the combined probability W of the Ξ decay and the successive Λ decay in terms of these parameters.

$$\begin{aligned} W_\Xi &= 1 + \alpha_\Xi P_\Xi \cos\theta \\ W_\Lambda &= 1 + \alpha_\Lambda \hat{p} \cdot \boldsymbol{P}_\Lambda(\theta, P_\Xi, \alpha_\Xi, \beta_\Xi, \gamma_\Xi) \\ W &= W_\Xi \cdot W_\Lambda \end{aligned} \tag{II.34}$$

where $\boldsymbol{P}_\Lambda(\theta)$ is obtained from Eq. (II.22).
The best values for the Ξ decay parameters at the moment are[13]

$$\alpha_\Xi = -0.391 \pm 0.032, \quad \beta_\Xi \approx 0, \quad \gamma_\Xi = 0.92$$

It can be shown that by time reversal invariance of weak interactions the β decay parameter must be 0. In other words A_s and A_p must be relatively real because of $\beta = 2 \,\mathrm{Im}\, A_s^* A_p = 0$. By strong final state interactions the phases of the S and P wave may, however, be shifted by different amounts δ_S and δ_P respectively.

$$A_S \to A'_S = A_S\, e^{i\delta_S}$$

$$A_P \to A'_P = A_P\, e^{i\delta_P}$$

So in the case of final state interactions the observed decay parameters are with $\delta = \delta_P - \delta_S$

$$\alpha = 2\,\mathrm{Re}\,A_S'^*A_P' = 2\,\mathrm{Re}\,(A_S^*A_P)\cos\delta - 2\,\mathrm{Im}\,(A_S^*A_P)\sin\delta$$

$$\beta = 2\,\mathrm{Im}\,A_S'^*A_P' = 2\,\mathrm{Re}\,(A_S^*A_P)\sin\delta + 2\,\mathrm{Im}\,(A_S^*A_P)\cos\delta$$

$$\gamma = |A_S'|^2 - |A_P'|^2$$

If the phase shifts are known the influence of the final state interaction may be subtracted.

The treatment of the Ξ decay as presented in this section is purely non-relativistic. As a spin is defined primarily only in the rest system of a particle, especially the meaning of the spin state of the Λ moving in the Ξ rest frame remains vague. This question is discussed in the appendix. Here we only state that all relations remain true for particles in relativistic motion, if in the analysis the following procedure is applied: One first transforms all decay products of the Ξ and Λ from the laboratory system to the Ξ rest frame and subsequently the Λ decay products from there to the Λ rest frame. Then the angles (θ, ϕ) are evaluated in the Ξ rest fame and (ϑ_i, φ_i) in the Λ rest frame.

T. D. Lee and C. N. Yang(43) have developed a system of test functions which permits the spin determination of hyperons decaying weakly into a spin 0 boson and a spin $\frac{1}{2}$ fermion (Ξ, Ω^- decay) from the decay angular distribution (42).

III. THE SPIN DENSITY MATRIX

a) The General Formalism

In practice it is very rare that one deals with particles in pure spin states. Mostly one has statistical mixtures of pure states.

Take as an example the hypothetical case of a system of spin $\frac{1}{2}$ particles where $\frac{1}{3}$ is completely polarized in z direction the other $\frac{2}{3}$ in x direction. Furthermore, for an individual particle it is not known to which cathegory it belongs. It has probabilities $p_1 = \frac{1}{3}$ and $p_2 = \frac{2}{3}$ of being in one or the other pure state. Nevertheless, it is possible to calculate expectation values of physical observables for the entire sample. The natural procedure is to calculate the expectation values for both contributing pure states and to add them up with their relative probabilities.

There is a convenient mathematical tool to do this, namely, the formalism of the density matrix.

For a pure state

$$\psi = \sum_m a_m |j, m\rangle \tag{III.1}$$

the expectation value $\langle Q\rangle$ of an operator Q is, according to Eq. (I.14), a bilinear expression of the coefficients a_m^* and a_k. So if the system under consideration is a mixture of N pure states $\psi^{(i)}$ with prohabilities $p^{(i)}$, the expectation value $\langle Q\rangle$ will be a linear function of the *average values* of $a_k a_m^*$ which are clearly defined as

$$\varrho_{km} = \sum_{i=1}^{N} p^{(i)} a_k^{(i)} a_m^{(i)*}, \qquad \text{(III.2)}$$

the density matrix elements.

This can be shown more mathematically in the following way. For a pure state we have according to (I.14)

$$\langle Q \rangle = \sum_{m,k} a_m^* a_k \langle j, m | Q | j, k \rangle$$
$$= \sum_{m,k} a_m^* a_k Q_{mk}$$

where $\langle j, m | Q | j, k \rangle$ is the matrix element Q_{mk} of the operator Q.

For a statistical mixture of states $\psi^{(i)}$ with probabilities $p^{(i)}$, the expectation value is

$$\langle Q \rangle = \sum_i p^{(i)} \langle Q \rangle^{(i)} = \sum_i p^{(i)} \Big\{ \sum_{m,k} a_m^{*(i)} a_k^{(i)} Q_{mk} \Big\} \qquad \text{(III.3)}$$

Defining the density matrix ϱ as

$$\varrho_{km} = \sum_i p^{(i)} a_m^{*(i)} a_k^{(i)} \qquad \text{(III.2)}$$

$\langle Q \rangle$ can be written as

$$\langle Q \rangle = \sum_{m,k} Q_{mk} \varrho_{km} = \sum_m (Q\varrho)_{mm}$$
$$= \mathrm{Tr}\,(Q\varrho) \quad = \mathrm{Tr}\,(\varrho Q) \qquad \text{(III.4)}$$

Equation (III.4) can be regarded as a definition of the density matrix in terms of a set of measurable quantities $\langle Q \rangle$.

Let us quote some important properties of the density matrix which can easily be verified from the definition (III.2).

1) It is hermitian

$$\varrho_{mk} = \varrho_{km}^* \qquad \text{(III.5a)}$$

2) The sum of the diagonal elements is 1

$$\mathrm{Tr}\,(\varrho) = \mathrm{Tr}\,(\varrho^*) = \sum_m \varrho_{mm} = 1 \qquad \text{(III.5b)}$$

3) The diagonal elements are positive

$$\varrho_{mm} \geqq 0 \qquad \text{(III.5c)}$$

4) A system of spin j has $2j + 1 = N$ orthogonal basis vectors. The $N \times N$ complex elements of the density matrix correspond to $2N^2$ real parameters which are subject to different constraints:

a) hermiticity $\varrho_{mk} = \varrho_{km}^*$ gives N^2 constraints,

b) one constraint on the trace

$$\sum_{1}^{N} \varrho_{mm} = 1$$

so there are left

$$n = 2N^2 - N^2 - 1 = N^2 - 1 \tag{III.5d}$$

real parameters which determine the density matrix.

5) Under a unitary transformation U of the system of orthogonal basis vectors the density matrix transforms as an operator

$$\varrho' = U\varrho U^{-1}.$$

Expectations values $\langle Q\rangle$ stay invariant under this transformation.

$$\begin{aligned}\langle Q'\rangle &= \mathrm{Tr}\,(Q'\varrho') = \mathrm{Tr}\,(UQU^{-1}U\varrho U^{-1}) \\ &= \mathrm{Tr}\,(UQ\varrho U^{-1}) = \mathrm{Tr}\,(Q\varrho) = \langle Q\rangle\end{aligned}$$

because the trace is invariant under unitary transformations.

6) As the density matrix can be regarded as a hermitian operator there exists always a unitary transformation that makes the density matrix diagonal. This transformation corresponds to a new choice of basis vectors. As a consequence a pure spin state can always be described by a density matrix having all elements 0 but one diagonal element which is 1. Together with (III.5c) it follows that the density matrix is positive definite, i.e. for any vector a_m one has

$$\sum_{km} a_k\, a_m^*\, \varrho_{km} \geqq 0 \tag{III. 5e}$$

7) $\mathrm{Tr}\,(\varrho^2) = \sum_{km} |\varrho_{km}|^2 \leqq 1$ (III. 5f)

8) If the density matrix describes a mixture of N pure states

$$N\,\mathrm{Tr}\,(\varrho^2) \geqq \mathrm{Tr}\,(\varrho) = 1 \tag{III.5g}$$

9) $|\varrho_{km}| \leq \sqrt{\varrho_{kk}\varrho_{mm}}$ (III.5h)

10) One may specify a random mixture of states with spin j by requiring that all possible pure states in the mixture are equally probable, or that the probability of the mixture to be in a definite pure spin state ψ_j is the same for all possible states $\psi_j^{(i)}$. This probability is

$$p = \psi_j^* \varrho \psi_j \tag{III.5i}$$

where the state ψ_j is represented by a column vector a_m and ψ_j^* by the corresponding row vector. The expression Eq. (III.5i) is independent of the particular ψ_j (i.e. the normalized coefficients a_m) only if ϱ is a multiple of the unit matrix. Because of the normalization requirement of the density matrix, all diagonal elements have the value

$$\varrho_{mm} = \frac{1}{2j+1}.$$

Therefore a *random mixture* of spin j particles is described by an *equal mixture* of all eigenstates $|j, m\rangle$.

The special structure of the density matrix for the random spin state can also be derived by the requirement that it be invariant under any rotation D:

$$\varrho' = D\varrho D^{-1} = \varrho. \tag{III.5j}$$

As the D matrices are irreducible representations of the rotation group, by Schur's lemma [20] Eq. (III.5j) is valid for arbitrary D's only if ϱ is a multiple of the unit matrix.

As an example let us construct the density matrix for the system defined at the beginning of this chapter.

$$\psi_1 = \begin{bmatrix} 1 \\ 0 \end{bmatrix}; \qquad ; \quad p_1 = \tfrac{1}{3}$$

$$\psi_2 = \sqrt{\tfrac{1}{2}}\begin{bmatrix} 1 \\ 0 \end{bmatrix} + \sqrt{\tfrac{1}{2}}\begin{bmatrix} 0 \\ 1 \end{bmatrix}; \quad p_2 = \tfrac{2}{3}$$

In the terminology of Eq. (III.1) we have

$$a^{(1)}_{1/2} = 1 \qquad a^{(2)}_{1/2} = \sqrt{{}^1/_2}$$

$$a^{(1)}_{-1/2} = 0 \qquad a^{(2)}_{-1/2} = \sqrt{{}^1/_2}$$

$$p_1 = {}^1/_3 \qquad p_2 = {}^2/_3$$

and calculate

$$\varrho = \tfrac{1}{3}\begin{bmatrix} 1 & 0 \\ 0 & 0 \end{bmatrix} + \tfrac{2}{3}\begin{bmatrix} \frac{1}{2} & \frac{1}{2} \\ \frac{1}{2} & \frac{1}{2} \end{bmatrix} = \begin{bmatrix} \frac{2}{3} & \frac{1}{3} \\ \frac{1}{3} & \frac{1}{3} \end{bmatrix}$$

The polarization of this mixed state is with (III.4)

$$\langle P_x \rangle = \mathrm{Tr}\,(P_x\varrho) = \mathrm{Tr}\,(\sigma_x\varrho)$$

$$= \mathrm{Tr}\left\{\begin{bmatrix} 0 & 1 \\ 1 & 0 \end{bmatrix} \cdot \begin{bmatrix} \frac{2}{3} & \frac{1}{3} \\ \frac{1}{3} & \frac{1}{3} \end{bmatrix}\right\} = \mathrm{Tr}\begin{bmatrix} \frac{1}{3} & \frac{1}{3} \\ \frac{2}{3} & \frac{1}{3} \end{bmatrix} = \tfrac{2}{3}$$

Correspondingly one finds

$$\langle P_y \rangle = 0; \quad \langle P_z \rangle = \tfrac{1}{3}$$

as was expected from the construction of the example.

The density matrix of spin $\frac{1}{2}$ particles depends on $2^2 - 1 = 3$ real parameters, so it is presumably possible to express the density matrix in terms of the three polarization components P_x, P_y, P_z. To this end one expands the 2×2 density matrix in terms of the unit matrix $\mathbb{1}$ and the matrices σ_x, σ_y, σ_z which are all linearly independent. From the condition

$$P = 2\langle J\rangle = \langle \sigma\rangle = \mathrm{Tr}\,(\sigma\varrho) \tag{III.6}$$

one calculates ϱ in terms of σ

$$\begin{aligned}\varrho &= \tfrac{1}{2}(\mathbb{1} + P_x\sigma_x + P_y\sigma_y + P_z\sigma_z)\\ &= \tfrac{1}{2}(\mathbb{1} + P\sigma) = \tfrac{1}{2}\begin{bmatrix}1 + P_z & P_x - iP_y\\ P_x + iP_y & 1 - P_z\end{bmatrix}\end{aligned} \tag{III.7}$$

One verifies immediately that Eq. (III.7) satisfies Eq. (III.6). So the measurement of the three polarization components of spin $^1/_2$ particles completely determines the spin density matrix of the system.

Generally, for systems with spin j, having $N = 2j + 1$ eigenstates, $N^2 - 1$ linear independent observables will determine the density matrix.

References: 34, 35, 36, 37.

b) Symmetry Properties of the Density Matrix due to Parity Conservation in the Production Process.

We consider the reaction

$$A + B \to C + D$$

where all particles may have different and arbitrary spins but particles A and B are required to represent a random mixture of pure spin states. D may even be a particle system. We ask for the most general structure of the density matrix of particle C.

To this purpose we first consider one particular pure initial state out of the mixture: $\psi_{\text{in}}^{(1)}$ which leads to one particular final state $\psi_{\text{fin}}^{(1)}$. ψ_{in} and ψ_{fin} are chosen to be plane wave states in the directions x and r, respectively. So we have

$$\psi_{\text{in}}^{(1)} = e^{ik_{\text{in}}x} S_A^{(1)} S_B^{(1)}$$

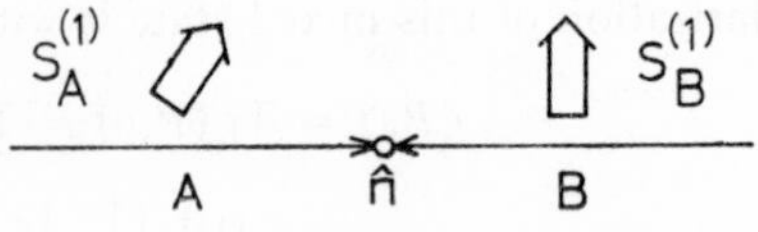

Fig. 6a

$$\psi_{\text{fin}}^{(1)} = e^{ik_{\text{fin}}r} S_C^{(1)} S_D^{(1)}$$

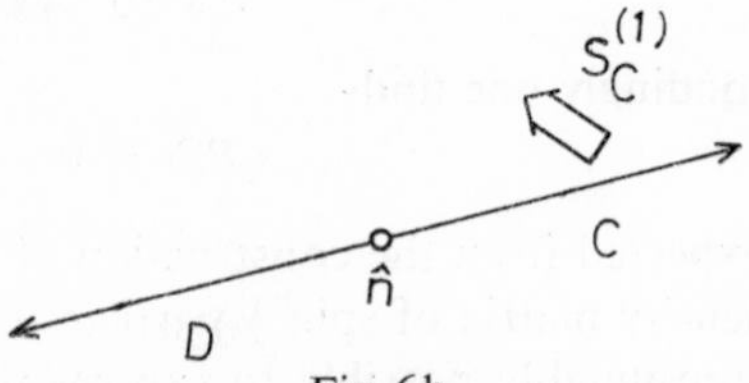

Fig. 6b

where the S denote the spin part of the wave functions. Now we apply a space reflection or parity operation P to the states $\psi^{(1)}$ and obtain

$$\psi_{\text{in}}^{(2)} = P\psi_{\text{in}}^{(1)} = e^{-ik_{\text{in}}x} S_A^{(2)} S_B^{(2)}$$

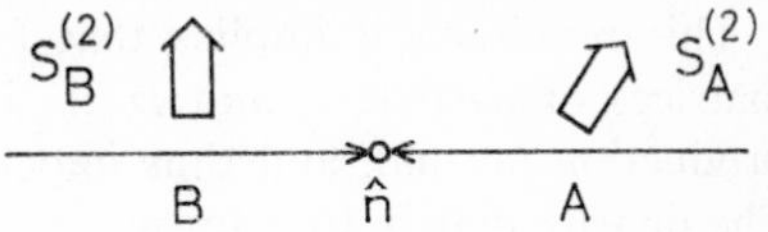

Fig. 6c

$$\psi_{\text{fin}}^{(2)} = P\psi_{\text{fin}}^{(1)} = e^{-ik_{\text{fin}}r} S_C^{(2)} S_D^{(2)}$$

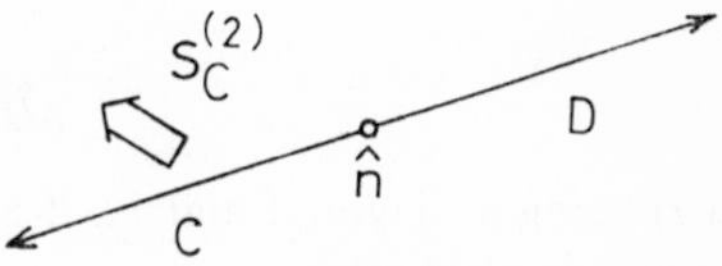

Fig. 6d

As the spin is an axial vector it remains unchanged under space reflection and we have

$$S^{(1)} = S^{(2)}$$

(up to may be a sign factor due to intrinsic parities).

Subsequently we rotate the states $\psi^{(2)}$ by 180° around the production normal $\hat{n}$. Defining $\tilde{\psi} = R_{\hat{n}}(\pi)\, P\psi$, we have

$$\tilde{\psi}_{\text{in}}^{(1)} = \psi_{\text{in}}^{(3)} = R_{\hat{n}}(\pi)\, \psi_{\text{in}}^{(2)} = e^{ik_{\text{in}}x} S_A^{(3)} S_B^{(3)}$$

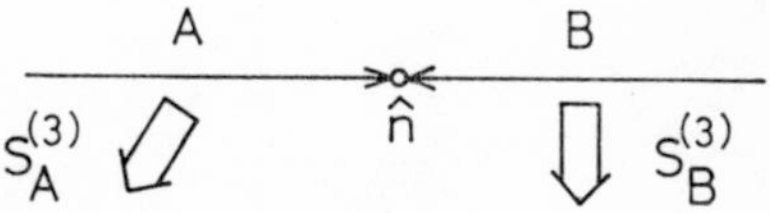

Fig. 6e

$$\tilde{\psi}_{\text{fin}}^{(1)} = \psi_{\text{fin}}^{(3)} = R_{\hat{n}}(\pi)\, \psi_{\text{fin}}^{(2)} = e^{ik_{\text{fin}}r} S_C^{(3)} S_D^{(3)}$$

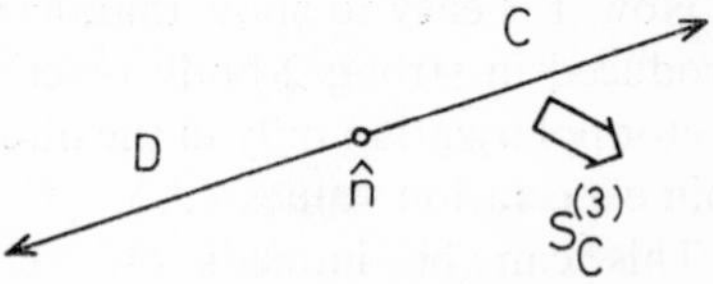

Fig. 6f

Parity conservation in an interaction means that to every process the mirror image is also possible and equally likely. Now if in our case the initial state is a random mixture of pure states then it contains the states $\psi_{\text{in}}^{(1)}$ and $\psi_{\text{in}}^{(3)}$ (which result from one another by $R_{\hat{n}}(\pi)\, P$) with equal probability. So the processes

$$\psi_{\text{in}}^{(1)} \rightarrow \psi_{\text{fin}}^{(1)}$$

and

$$\tilde{\psi}_{\text{in}}^{(1)} = \psi_{\text{in}}^{(3)} \rightarrow \psi_{\text{fin}}^{(3)} = \tilde{\psi}_{\text{fin}}^{(1)}$$

occur equally frequent and thus the final pure states $S_C^{(1)}$ and $S_C^{(3)}$ are equally populated[38]. This consideration is true, of course, for any pure state $S_C^{(i)}$ contained in the mixed state of C. So, for any pure state $S_C^{(i)}$ contained in the mixed spin state of particle C another state $\tilde{S}_C^{(i)} = R_{\hat{n}}(\pi)\, PS_C^{(i)}$ is contained with equal probability. As all $\tilde{\psi}^{(i)}$ and $\psi^{(i)}$ are transformed into one another under $R_{\hat{n}}(\pi)\, P$ it follows that the spin density matrix of C is invariant under $R_{\hat{n}}(\pi)\, P$.

This requirement implies that for every production angle the spin density matrices of particle C and D are invariant under a rotation of 180° about the production normal, and thus imposes a special structure on the density matrix. The density matrix transforms as an operator, so one requires, when choosing $\hat{n}$ in z direction,

$$\tilde{\varrho} = D_z(\pi)\, \varrho D_z^{-1}(\pi) = \varrho$$

or

$$\varrho D_z(\pi) = D_z(\pi)\, \varrho \tag{III.8}$$

$D_z(\pi)$ being a diagonal matrix, if z is the spin quantization direction we have for one matrix element ϱ_{km}

$$\begin{aligned} \varrho_{km} D_{mm} &= D_{kk} \varrho_{km} \\ \varrho_{km}\, \mathrm{e}^{-im\pi} &= \mathrm{e}^{-ik\pi} \varrho_{km} \\ \varrho_{km} &= \mathrm{e}^{i(m-k)\pi} \varrho_{km}\,. \end{aligned} \tag{III.9a}$$

As a consequence all matrix elements ϱ_{km} with $|m - k| = 2n + 1$ $(n = 0, 1, 2, \ldots)$ are 0 so that the density matrix shows a checker board pattern[14]:

$$\varrho = \begin{bmatrix} x & 0 & x & 0 \\ 0 & x & 0 & x \\ x & 0 & x & 0 \\ 0 & x & 0 & x \end{bmatrix} \tag{III.9b}$$

Now it is easy to show that, as a corollary to this more general result, particles produced in strong 2-body reactions from random initial spin states can have a vector polarization only in the direction of the production normal (z direction), the spin expectation values $\langle J_x \rangle$, $\langle J_y \rangle$ being 0.

This can be immediately verified, recalling that in the J_x, J_y matrices (cf. Eq. I.20) only the elements $C_{k,k+1}$ are different from 0; so

$$\begin{aligned} \langle J_{x,y} \rangle &= \mathrm{Tr}\,(J_{x,y} \varrho) \\ &= \mathrm{Tr} \left\{ \underset{J_{x,y}}{\begin{bmatrix} 0 & x & 0 & 0 \\ x & 0 & x & 0 \\ 0 & x & 0 & x \\ 0 & 0 & x & 0 \end{bmatrix}} \underset{\varrho}{\begin{bmatrix} x & 0 & x & 0 \\ 0 & x & 0 & x \\ x & 0 & x & 0 \\ 0 & x & 0 & x \end{bmatrix}} \right\} = 0 \end{aligned}$$

If one chooses e.g. the momentum direction of particle A or C as seen in the rest system of C) as spin quantization axis z and the production normal $\hat{n}$ as y axis, ϱ has to be invariant under $R_y(\pi)$.

With

$$[D_y(\pi)]_{mk} = D_{mk}^{(j)}(0, \pm\pi, 0) = (-1)^{j\pm m}\,\delta_{m,-k} \tag{I.55d, e}$$

we require for the density matrix

$$\varrho = D_y(\pi)\,\varrho D_y^{-1}(\pi) = D_y(\pi)\,\varrho D_y(-\pi)$$

or for the individual matrix element

$$\begin{aligned}\varrho_{mm'} &= \sum_{kl} D_{mk}\,\varrho_{kl} D_{lm'}^{-1}\\ &= \sum_{kl} (-1)^{j+m}\,\delta_{m,-k}\,\varrho_{kl}(-1)^{j-l}\,\delta_{l,-m'}\\ \varrho_{mm'} &= (-1)^{2j+m+m'}\,\varrho_{-m-m'}\\ &= (-1)^{m-m'}\,\varrho_{-m-m'}\end{aligned} \tag{III.10}$$

With (III.9) and (III.10) we find, e.g. for the spin 1 case, the general shape of the density matrix for parity conserving production processes. If the y axis is the production normal we have

$$\varrho_{\hat{n}=y} = \begin{bmatrix} \varrho_{11} & \varrho_{10} & \varrho_{1-1} \\ \varrho_{10}^{*} & (1-2\varrho_{11}) & -\varrho_{10}^{*} \\ \varrho_{1-1} & -\varrho_{10} & \varrho_{11} \end{bmatrix} \tag{III.11}$$

where ϱ_{11} is real by definition and ϱ_{1-1} because of (III.10) and the hermiticity of the density matrix. Thus we are left with 4 real parameters: ϱ_{11}, ϱ_{1-1}, Re ϱ_{10}, Im ϱ_{10}.

As will be shown in the next section, Im ϱ_{10}, which is related to the vector polarization of the particle (along $\hat{n}$), cannot be determined in parity conserving decays.

Correspondignly we have for the case that z is the production normal

$$\varrho_{\hat{n}=z} = \begin{bmatrix} \varrho_{11} & 0 & \varrho_{1-1} \\ 0 & \varrho_{00} & 0 \\ \varrho_{1-1}^{*} & 0 & (1-\varrho_{11}-\varrho_{00}) \end{bmatrix} \tag{III.12}$$

Here the 4 real parameters are ϱ_{11}, ϱ_{00}, Re ϱ_{1-1}, Im ϱ_{1-1}. ϱ_{11} cannot be determined from strong decay processes, only $\varrho_{11} + \varrho_{-1-1}$ which, by definition of ϱ, is equal to $1 - \varrho_{00}$.

The symmetry properties of the density matrix (III.9), (III.10) were derived for particles produced in parity conserving 2-body processes from an unpolarized initial state. In the derivation spin averaging over particle D was tacitly assumed. Now we ask whether this symmetry of the density matrix remains valid for particles in 3- or more-body final states. For simplicity we study the situation in detail in a 3-body final state. The calculation presented for this case is also likely to clarify questions that remained open in the more intuitive than rigorous treatment of the 2-body case. As indicated in Fig. 7 the initial state is formed by particles A and B, the final state by C, E and F. E and F may be assumed to form a pseudo-particle D without definite spin and parity. In the c.m. of the reaction the momentum vectors of A, B, C and D all lie in the production plane with normal $\hat{n} = z$. The particles may have arbitrary spins j_A, j_B, j_C, j_E, j_F. For fixed c.m. energy the kinematics is completely defined by the masses of all particles involved (also the invariant mass of $D = (E + F)$), the production angle ϕ and the decay angles ϑ, φ of particle E in the $(E + F) = D$ rest system.

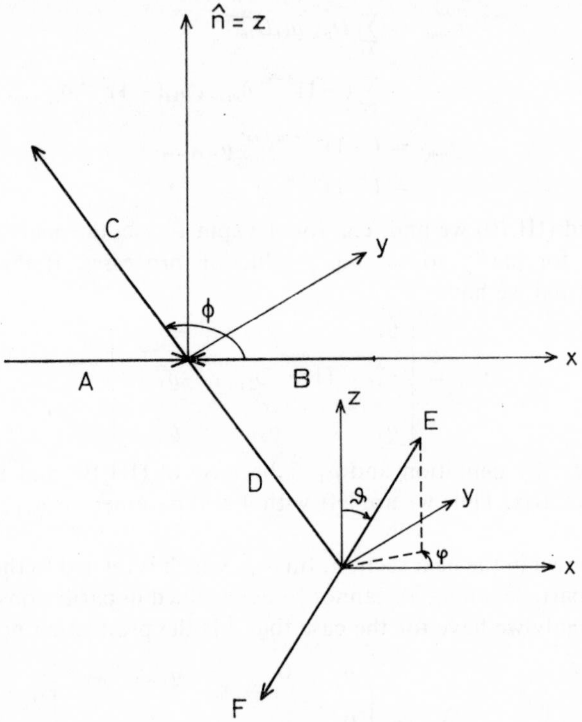

Fig. 7

Now we consider one particular pure initial state

$$\psi_{\text{in}}^{(1)} = \mathrm{e}^{ikx} \sum C_{mn} |j_A m\rangle\, |j_B n\rangle \tag{III.13}$$

By the operation

$$Z = R_z(\pi)\, P, \quad \text{with} \quad Z^2 = 1 \tag{III.14}$$

which is equivalent to a reflection on the xy-plane $(z \to -z)$ $\psi_{\text{in}}^{(1)}$ becomes

$$\tilde{\psi}_{\text{in}}^{(1)} = Z\psi_{\text{in}}^{(1)} = \xi_{\text{in}}\, \mathrm{e}^{ikx} \sum C_{mn}\, \mathrm{e}^{-i\pi(m+n)}\, |j_A m\rangle\, |j_B n\rangle \tag{III.15}$$

where ξ_{in} is the product of intrinsic parities of A and B. If the actual initial state ϱ_{in} contains $\psi_{\text{in}}^{(1)}$ and $\tilde{\psi}_{\text{in}}^{(1)}$ with equal probabilities, then

$$\varrho_{\text{in}} = \psi_{\text{in}}^{(1)} \oplus Z\psi_{\text{in}}^{(1)} \tag{III.16}$$

is invariant under Z:

$$\varrho_{\text{in}} = Z\varrho_{\text{in}} = Z\psi_{\text{in}}^{(1)} \oplus \psi_{\text{in}}^{(1)} = \varrho_{\text{in}} \tag{III.17}$$

$\oplus$ denotes statistical superposition.

If the target particles A, B are in random spin states, condition (III.16) is certainly satisfied for every pure state in the mixture.

The pure initial state $\psi_{\text{fin}}^{(1)}$ gives rise to the final state $\psi_{\text{fin}}^{(1)}$ which we write in its most general form

$$\psi_{\text{fin}}^{(1)} = \sum_{\mu\nu\lambda} a_{\mu\nu\lambda}(\phi, x, \varphi) \, |j_C\mu\rangle_C \, |j_E\nu\rangle_E \, |j_F\lambda\rangle_F \tag{III.18}$$

The $a_{\mu\nu\lambda}(\phi, x, \varphi)$ are angle dependent complex amplitudes, x stands for $\cos\vartheta$. Under the operation Z one has

$$Za_{\mu\nu\lambda}(\phi, x, \varphi) = a_{\mu\nu\lambda}(\phi, -x, \lambda),$$

as may be seen from Fig. 7., and

$$Z|j_C\mu\rangle \, |j_E\nu\rangle \, |j_F\lambda\rangle = \xi_{\text{fin}} \, e^{-i\pi(\mu+\nu+\lambda)} \, |j_C\mu\rangle \, |j_E\nu\rangle \, |j_F\lambda\rangle$$

where ξ_{fin} is the intrinsic parity product of all final state particles. Applying Z to $\psi_{in}^{(1)}$ gives

$$\tilde{\psi}^{(1)} = Z\psi_{\text{fin}}^{(1)} = \xi_{\text{fin}} \sum a_{\mu\nu\lambda}(\phi, -x, \varphi) \, e^{-i\pi(\mu+\nu+\lambda)} \, |j_C\mu\rangle \, |j_E\nu\rangle \, |j_F\lambda\rangle \tag{III.19}$$

The combined density matrix of particles C, E, F is

$$\varrho^{(1)}_{\mu\mu'\nu\nu'\lambda\lambda'} = a_{\mu\nu\lambda}(\phi, x, \varphi) \, a^*_{\mu'\nu'\lambda'}(\phi, x, \varphi) \tag{III.20}$$

Summing over the spins of particles E and F gives the density matrix of C alone:

$$\varrho^{(1)}_{\mu\mu'} = \sum_{\nu\lambda} a_{\mu\nu\lambda}(\phi, x, \varphi) \, a^*_{\mu'\nu\lambda}(\phi, x, \varphi) \tag{III.21}$$

Correspondingly one finds with (III.19) for $\tilde{\psi}_{\text{fin}}^{(1)} = Z\psi_{\text{fin}}^{(1)}$

$$\tilde{\varrho}^{(1)}_{\mu\mu'} = e^{-i\pi(\mu-\mu')} \sum_{\nu\lambda} a_{\mu\nu\lambda}(\phi, -x, \varrho) \, a^*_{\mu'\nu\lambda}(\phi, -x, \varrho) \tag{III.22}$$

The density matrix for the complete final state $\psi_{\text{fin}}^{(1)} \oplus \tilde{\psi}_{\text{fin}}^{(1)}$ is of course

$$\varrho_{\mu\mu'} = \varrho^{(1)}_{\mu\mu'} + \tilde{\varrho}^{(1)}_{\mu\mu'}. \tag{III.23}$$

Now we split all matrices into 2 parts, ϱ^+ and ϱ^- which, in $x = \cos\vartheta$, are even or odd, respectively

$$\varrho^+(\phi, -x, \varphi) = \varrho(\phi, x, \varphi) \tag{III.24}$$

$$\varrho^-(\phi, -x, \varphi) = -\varrho(\phi, x, \varphi)$$

From (III.21) and (III.22) we obtain

$$\overset{+}{\varrho}_{\mu\mu'} = \varrho^{(1)+}_{\mu\mu'} + \tilde{\varrho}^{(1)+}_{\mu\mu'} = \varrho^{(1)+}_{\mu\mu'} + e^{-i\pi(\mu-\mu')} \varrho^{(1)+}_{\mu\mu'} \tag{III.25}$$

$$\overset{-}{\varrho}_{\mu\mu'} = \varrho^{(1)-}_{\mu\mu'} + \tilde{\varrho}^{(1)-}_{\mu\mu'} = \varrho^{(1)-}_{\mu\mu'} - e^{-i\pi(\mu-\mu')} \varrho^{(1)-}_{\mu\mu'} \tag{III.26}$$

As

$$e^{-i\pi(\mu-\mu')} = (-1)^{\mu-\mu'}$$

ϱ^+ contains non-vanishing terms only for $\mu - \mu'$ even and ϱ^- only for $\mu - \mu'$ odd. So one can split the density matrix ϱ into 2 non-overlapping parts ϱ^+, ϱ^- whose elements have the property (III.24) and form a checker-board pattern:

$$\varrho = \varrho^+ + \varrho^- = \begin{bmatrix} + & - & + & - \\ - & + & - & + \\ + & - & + & - \\ - & + & - & + \end{bmatrix} \qquad \text{(III.27)}$$

which becomes the $R_{\hat{n}}(\pi)$ – invariant pattern (III.9b) if the ϱ^- elements vanish.

ϱ^- always vanishes according to (III.24) when summing the density matrix over two emission directions of particles E, namely (x, φ) and $(-x, \varphi)$ which are transformed into one another by reflection on the production plane (x, y plane).

The result is easily extended to a many-body final state and can be put as follows. The density matrix of a particle produced in a parity conserving interaction with an unpolarized 2-body initial state and a many-body final state, is invariant under rotations by π about the production normal (defined by the beam direction and the particle considered) if integration is carried out over the emission directions of the remaining particles. The integration may be reduced to a sum over 2 decay configuration of the remaining system which are mirror symmetric with respect to the production plane. This result is important to know if a density matrix analysis is done in an experiment where the detector cuts out part of the decay angular region of the remaining system.

IV. DETERMINATION OF THE SPIN DENSITY MATRIX FROM DECAY PROCESSES AND SPIN TESTS

a) Decays of Bosons into 2 Spinless Particles

In section IIa we have seen that a pure state of spin j

$$\psi = \sum a_m |j, m\rangle \qquad \text{(IV.1)}$$

which decays into 2 spinless particles is transformed into the final state by application of the transition operator

$$T_m = Y_j^m(\theta, \phi)$$

so that we have

$$\psi_{\text{fin}} = \sum a_m Y_j^m(\theta, \phi). \qquad \text{(IV.2)}$$

Now a mixed state is described by a density matrix

$$\varrho_{mn} = \sum_i p^{(i)} a_m^{(i)} a_n^{*(i)} \qquad \text{(IV.3)}$$

This is transformed to the final state density matrix which in this case is one-dimensional (because the particles in the final state have spin 0) and identical to the angular distribution, by the relation

$$\varrho_{\text{fin}} = I = T\varrho T^{+}$$

$$= \sum_{mn} T_m \varrho_{mn} T_n^*$$

$$I(\theta, \phi) = \sum_{mn} Y_j^m(\theta, \phi)\, \varrho_{mn} Y_j^{n*}(\theta, \phi) \tag{IV.4}$$

One way to obtain the density matrix elements ϱ_{mn} for a given experimental angular distribution $I(\theta, \phi)$ is to fit the observed distribution to Eq. (IV.4) with ϱ_{mn} as free parameters. There is, however, another way to determine the density matrix. For this purpose we first expand the observed angular distribution in spherical harmonics. If j is the spin of the decaying particle we have

$$I(\theta, \phi) = \sum_{L=0}^{2j} \sum_{M=-L}^{L} t_L^M Y_L^{M*} \tag{IV.5}$$

The expansion coefficients t_M can be simply obtained from the integral

$$\int I(\theta, \phi)\, Y_L^M(\theta, \phi)\, d\Omega = t_L^M = \langle Y_L^M \rangle \tag{IV.6}$$

which follows from the orthonormality of spherical harmonics Eq. (I.27).

$\langle Y_L^M \rangle$ denotes the average of Y_L^M over the distribution $I(\theta, \phi)$ and is called a moment.

As $I(\theta, \phi)$ is real by definition, it follows from Eq. (IV.6) that the t_L^M have the same reality property (I.28) as spherical harmonics, namely

$$t_L^{-M} = (-1)^M\, t_L^{M*} \tag{IV.7}$$

So every t_L^M corresponds to just 1 real parameter which one could choose to be

$$\text{Re}\, t_L^M \quad \text{and} \quad \text{Im}\, t_L^M \quad \text{for} \quad M \geqq 0$$

For a given j in the most general case (e.g. parity violating decays of baryons) there are altogether $(2j + 1)^2$ different t_L^M and therefore just as many real parameters which determine the angular distribution. This number is of course equal to the number of independent parameters in the density matrix. In our case of a parity conserving decay, however, (the decay into 2 spinless bosons could not even be parity violating without violating angular momentum conservation) only t_L^M with L even are present, as will be shown subsequently, so that the density matrix cannot be fully determined by the decay angular distrubution.

For a given sample of N experimental events with decay angles θ_i, ϕ_i and weights (reciprocal observation probability) w_i we can write according to (IV.6)

$$t_L^M = \langle Y_L^M \rangle = \frac{1}{W} \sum_{i=1}^{N} Y_L^M(\theta_i \phi_i)\, w_i \tag{IV.8}$$

where

$$W = \sum_{i=1}^{N} w_i$$

Note that this method does not work if there is a solid angle region where no events can be observed.

To evaluate the error matrix of the expansion parameters one introduces real quantities

$$\tau_\alpha \text{ stands for } \operatorname{Re} t_L^M \quad \text{or} \quad \operatorname{Im} t_L^M, \quad M \geqq 0$$

$$y_\alpha \text{ stands for } \operatorname{Re} Y_L^M \quad \text{or} \quad \operatorname{Im} Y_L^M, \quad M \geqq 0$$

Then the error matrix is[15]

$$E_{\alpha\beta} = \langle \Delta\tau_\alpha \Delta\tau_\beta \rangle = \frac{1}{WN} \sum_{i=1}^{N} (y_\alpha(i) - \tau_\alpha)(y_\beta(i) - \tau_\beta)\, w_i \tag{IV.9}$$

The χ^2 for the hypothesis that a set of experimental moments τ_α results from a population with moments τ_α^0 is

$$\chi^2 = \sum_{\alpha\beta} (\tau_\alpha - \tau_\alpha^0)(E^{-1})_{\alpha\beta}(\tau_\beta - \tau_\beta^0) \tag{IV.10}$$

For a given spin j of the decaying particle the density matrix elements can be expressed in terms of the experimentally determined t_L^M. For this purpose one expands the products $Y_j^m Y_j^{n*}$ in Eq. (IV.4) into a sum of spherical harmonics by relation (I.36g) which can be found in many textbooks, e,g, Blatt-Weisskopf:

$$Y_{l_1}^{m_1}(\theta, \phi)\, Y_{l_2}^{m_2}(\theta, \phi)$$

$$= \sum_{L,M} \left[\frac{(2l_1 + 1)(2l_2 + 1)}{4\pi(2L + 1)}\right]^{1/2} (l_1 l_2 00|L0)(l_1 l_2 m_1 m_2|LM)\, Y_L^M(\theta, \phi) \tag{IV.11}$$

(Note that from now on when dealing with more complicated subjects we will always assume the spherical harmonics as properly normalized to 1

$$\int Y_L^M Y_L^{M*}\, d\Omega = 1$$

and not to 4π as was occasionally done before for reasons of simpler writing.)

First we shall treat the case of spin $j = 1$ more explicitly. Here Eq. (IV.11) reads with $l_1 = 1, l_2 = 1$

$$Y_1^m Y_1^n = \frac{3}{\sqrt{4\pi}} \sum_{L,M} (1100|L0)(11mn|LM)\, Y_L^M \tag{IV.12}$$

Inserting this into the decay angular distribution

$$I(\theta, \phi) = \sum \varrho_{mn} Y^m Y^{n*} \tag{IV.4}$$

yields

$$\sqrt{4\pi}\, I(\theta, \phi) = (\varrho_{11} + \varrho_{-1-1})\left[Y_0^{0*} - \sqrt{\frac{1}{5}}\, Y_2^{0*}\right]$$

$$+ \varrho_{00}\left[Y_0^{0*} + 2\sqrt{\frac{1}{5}} Y_2^{0*}\right]$$

$$+ \varrho_{1-1}\left[-3\sqrt{\frac{2}{15}}\, Y_2^{-2*}\right]$$

$$+ \varrho_{-11}\left[-3\sqrt{\frac{2}{15}}\, Y_2^{2*}\right]$$

$$+ (\varrho_{10} - \varrho_{0-1})\left[-3\sqrt{\frac{1}{15}}\, Y_2^{-1*}\right]$$

$$+ (\varrho_{01} - \varrho_{-10})\left[3\sqrt{\frac{1}{15}}\, Y_2^{1*}\right] \qquad \text{(IV.13)}$$

Multiplying this expression by $Y_L^M(\theta, \phi)$ and integrating over θ, ϕ gives the moments $\langle Y_L^M \rangle = t_L^M$.

$$\sqrt{4\pi}\, t_0^0 = \varrho_{11} + \varrho_{00} + \varrho_{-1-1} = 1$$

$$\sqrt{4\pi}\, t_2^0 = -\sqrt{\frac{1}{5}}(\varrho_{11} + \varrho_{-1-1}) + 2\sqrt{\frac{1}{5}}\varrho_{00}$$

$$\sqrt{4\pi}\, t_2^2 = -3\sqrt{\frac{2}{15}}\varrho_{-11}$$

$$\sqrt{4\pi}\, t_2^{-2} = -3\sqrt{\frac{2}{15}}\varrho_{1-1}$$

$$\sqrt{4\pi}\, t_2^1 = 3\sqrt{\frac{1}{15}}(\varrho_{01} - \varrho_{-10})$$

$$\sqrt{4\pi}\, t_2^{-1} = 3\sqrt{\frac{1}{15}}(\varrho_{0-1} - \varrho_{10}) \qquad \text{(IV.14)}$$

All other t_L^M are 0, i.e. those with L odd. The parameter $\sqrt{4\pi}\, t_0^0$ is equal to the trace of the density matrix and therefore an invariant $= 1$. Equations (IV.14) can be easily solved for the ϱ's.

Note however that only the matrix elements on the second diagonal can be determined individually, i.e. ϱ_{1-1}, ϱ_{00}, ϱ_{-11}. For the rest of the matrix elements only the sum

$$\varrho_{nm} + (-1)^{n-m} \varrho_{-m-n} \tag{IV.15}$$

is obtained from the decay angular distribution.

Now we shall carry out this calculation for arbitrary integer spin j. In the angular distribution

$$I(\theta, \phi) = \sum_{nm} \varrho_{nm} Y_j^n(\theta, \phi) Y_j^{m*}(\theta, \phi) = \sum_{LM} t_L^{M*} Y_L^M(\theta, \phi) \tag{IV.16}$$

we substitute according to Eq. (IV.11)

$$Y_j^n Y_j^{m*} = (-1)^m Y_j^n Y_j^{-m} = (-1)^m \sum_{LM} \frac{2j+1}{\sqrt{4\pi(2L+1)}} (jj00|L0)(jjn, -m|LM) Y_L^M \tag{IV.17}$$

where $M = n - m$ and $(jj00|L0) = 0$ for L odd.

Comparison of the coefficients of the Y_L^M gives immediately

$$t_L^{M*} = \frac{2j+1}{\sqrt{4\pi(2L+1)}} (jj00|L0) \sum_{n,m} (-1)^m (jjn, -m|LM) \varrho_{nm}$$

or

$$t_L^M = \frac{2j+1}{\sqrt{4\pi(2L+1)}} (jj00|L0) \sum_{n,m} (-1)^m (jjn, -m|LM) \varrho_{mn} \tag{IV.18}$$

This relation may be solved for $\varrho_{mn} + (-1)^{m-n} \varrho_{-n-m}$. Defining

$$f_{Lj} = \frac{\sqrt{4\pi(2L+1)}}{(2j+1)(jj00|L0)}$$

we have from (IV.18) for even L (L_e)

$$t_{L_e}^M f_{L_e j} = \sum_{m,n} (-1)^m (jjn, -m|L_e M) \varrho_{mn}$$

Multiplying both sides with $(jjn', -m'|L_e M)$ and summing over L_e, M gives

$$\sum_m (-1)^m \varrho_{mn} \left\{ \sum_{L_e M} (jjn, -m|L_e M)(jjn', -m'|L_e M) \right\}$$
$$= \sum_{L_e M} t_{L_e}^M f_{L_e j} (jjn', -m'|L_e M)$$

Adding on both sides the sum over odd L (L_0)

$$\sigma(m' n') = \sum_{mn} (-1)^m \varrho_{mn} \left\{ \sum_{L_0 M} (jjn, -m|L_0 M)(jjn', -m'|L_0 M) \right\}$$

leads to

$$\sum_{mn} (-1)^m \varrho_{mn} \left\{ \sum_{LM} (jjn, -m|LM)(jjn', -m'|LM) \right\}$$
$$= \sum_{L_e M} t_{L_e}^M f_{L_e j} (jjn', -m'|L_e M) + \sigma(m', n')$$

The expression in the bracket on the left side is, by the orthogonality relation (I.35), equal to $\delta_{nn'} \cdot \delta_{mm'}$. Therefore the left side reduces to $\varrho_{m'n'}$:

$$\varrho_{m'n'} = (-1)^{m'} \sum_{L_e M} t^M_{L_e} f_{L_e j}(jjn' \, -m'|L_e M) + (-1)^{m'} \sigma(m', n') \quad \text{(IV.19a)}$$

Correspondingly one has

$$\varrho_{-n'-m'} = (-1)^{n'} \sum_{L_e M} t^M_{L_e} f_{L_e j}(jj, -m'n'|L_e M) + (-1)^{n'} \sigma(-n', -m') \quad \text{(IV.19b)}$$

Since with (I.36d)

$$(jj, -mn|LM) = (jjn, -m|LM)(-1)^L$$

and therefore

$$\sigma(-n', -m') = -\sigma(m', n')$$

we obtain from (IV.19)

$$\varrho_{mn} + (-1)^{m-n} \varrho_{-n-m} = \frac{(-1)^m \cdot 2 \cdot \sqrt{4\pi}}{2j+1} \sum_{L_e M} \frac{\sqrt{2L_e+1}}{(jj00|L0)} (jjn, -m|L_e M)\, t^M_{L_e} \quad \text{(IV.20)}$$

This relation permits us to calculate the density matrix elements from the observed decay angular distribution analyzed in terms of moments $t^M_L = \langle Y^M_L \rangle$.

For the case of spin 1, 5 independent parameters could, in principle, be determined from the decay angular distribution. This number is, however, reduced to 3 when taking into account the restrictions imposed by parity conservation in the production process as was discussed earlier. These additional constraints to the density matrix are reflected in constraints to the moments t^M_L. If the production normal $\hat{n}$ is chosen to be the z axis we have

$$t^M_L = 0 \quad \text{for } M \text{ odd} \quad z = \hat{n} \quad \text{(IV.21)}$$

If the y axis is the production normal one has

$$t^M_L = (-1)^M t^{-M}_L = \text{real} \quad y = \hat{n} \quad \text{(IV.22)}$$

These relations will be proved below. Let us finally write down explicitly the angular distribution for the decay of a spin 1 particle produced in a parity conserving reaction.

With $x = \cos\theta$ we have

for $\hat{n} = z$

$$\begin{aligned} 4\pi I(\theta, \phi) = 1 &+ (3\varrho_{00} - 1) \cdot \tfrac{1}{2}(3x^2 - 1) \\ &- 3 \operatorname{Re} \varrho_{1-1}(1 - x^2) \cos 2\phi \\ &- 3 \operatorname{Im} \varrho_{1-1}(1 - x^2) \sin 2\phi \end{aligned} \quad \text{(IV.23)}$$

For $\hat{n} = y$

$$\begin{aligned} 4\pi I(\theta, \phi) = 1 &+ (3\varrho_{00} - 1) \cdot \tfrac{1}{2}(3x^2 - 1) \\ &- 3\varrho_{1-1}(1 - x^2) \cos 2\phi \\ &- 6\sqrt{2} \operatorname{Re} \varrho_{10} x \sqrt{1 - x^2} \cos \phi \end{aligned} \quad \text{(IV.24)}$$

How can the spin of a particle be determined from its decay angular distribution? The most general method is to assume a certain hypothesis of spin j and to calculate under this assumption the density matrix elements which have to form a positive definite matrix. Necessary conditions are:

$$0 < \varrho_{mm} < 1$$

$$|\varrho_{mn}| \leqq \sqrt{\varrho_{mm}\varrho_{nn}} \qquad \text{(IV.25)}$$

To this purpose it is advantageous to first project all the information about the angular distribution into the expansion coefficients t_L^M and to calculate the ϱ's from them. The presence of a moment $t_L^M \neq 0$ indicates that the spin j of the particle satisfies the relation $2j \geqq L$. Whether a moment is 0 or not can be tested with the χ^2 method indicated above. It could happen that the highest possible moment for a spin j is suppressed by a special structure of the density matrix or it may be statistically insignificant. In this case it may help to calculate the density matrix elements for competing spin hypotheses and to look whether the relations (IV.25) are satisfied.

On the basis of these arguments Wolters[16] has developed a system of spin test functions which the angular distribution $I(\theta)$ has to satisfy under a certain spin hypothesis. He especially treats the question under which conditions a spin assignment is unique.

So far we have always assumed that the particle has a fixed spin j and decays isolated. In practice, however, short living particles like all resonances may interfere with a background of other angular momentum states yielding the same particles in the final state as the decaying resonance. If there is interference of two angular momentum states with spin j_1 and j_2 moments t_L^M with odd L will occur in the angular distribution if $j_1 - j_2$ is odd. This can be verified immediately for the case

$$\Psi = aY_0^0 + bY_1^0$$

Nevertheless not all moments t_L^M are allowed due to parity conservation in the production process. Let us now find out the allowed moments for background interference.

We assume that in the collision of particles A and B, which are both in random spin states, we produce particles C and D (which may have any spin) plus the rest system of particles X. C and D may come from the decay of a resonance or not. In any case we can combine C and D to a decaying particle M and consider its decay angular distribution in its own rest frame. The production normal $\hat{n}$ is defined by the directions of flight of particles A and M. As discussed before the initial state is invariant under the parity operation P and a successive rotation of 180° around the production normal $R_{\hat{n}}(\pi)$. If parity is conserved in the interaction the same must be true for the final state. As we do not know any details about the system $C + D = M$ we cannot write down its density matrix and require its invariance under $R_{\hat{n}}(\pi)\, P$. All we can do is to require that the decay angular distribution of M is invariant under $R_{\hat{n}}(\pi)\, P$. In Fig. 8 a certain decay

direction of particle C, $(\theta_1\phi_1)$, is transformed by P into $(\theta_2\phi_2)$ and successively by $R_{\hat{n}}(\pi)$ into $(\theta_3\phi_3)$. The production normal is chosen as z axis.
As can be seen from Fig. 8, $I(\theta, \phi)$ is invariant under $R_{\hat{n}}(\pi)\, P$ only if configurations

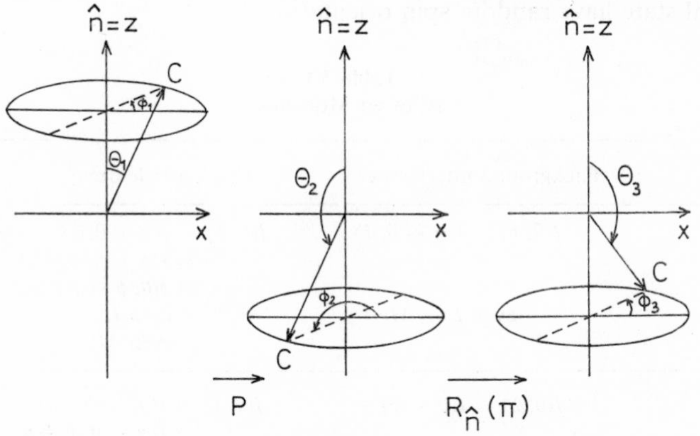

Fig. 8

$I(\theta_1, \phi_1)$ and $I(\theta_3, \phi_3)$ are equally probable. This implies for

1) $\hat{n} = z$ $\quad I(\theta, \phi) = I(\pi - \theta, \phi)$ (IV.26)

From the general relation

$$Y_L^M(\theta, \phi) = (-1)^{L+M}\, Y_L^M(\pi - \theta, \phi) \quad \text{(IV.26a)}$$

it follows immediately that only t_L^M with even $(L + M)$ are $\neq 0$. All M are allowed.

2) $\hat{n} = y$ $\quad I(\theta, \phi) = I(\theta, -\phi)$ (IV.27)

This can be shown in a similar way by drawing the corresponding configurations for $\hat{n}$ as y direction. The most general angular distribution is built up from terms

$$I_L^M(\theta, \phi) = f(\theta)\,[\cos(M\phi) + i \sin(M\phi)]\, t_L^M + (-1)^M f(\theta)\,[\cos(M\phi) - i \sin(M\phi)]\, t_L^{-M}$$

Relation (IV.27) is satisfied only if the $\sin(M\phi)$ term vanishes. This is only the case when

$$t_L^M = (-1)^M\, t_L^{-M}.$$

From the reality property $t_L^M = (-1)^M\, t_L^{-M*}$ it follows that all t_L^M are real for the case that $\hat{n}$ is the y axis. All L and M are allowed.

For the case that we deal with the *free parity conserving decay* of a particle the angular distribution has, in addition, to fulfill the relation

$$I(\theta, \phi) = I(\pi - \theta, \phi + \pi) \quad \text{(IV.28)}$$

which puts further constraints to the allowed t_L^M.

In table VI we have summarized the allowed moments for the general case of a parity conserving decay with background interference and the parity conserving decay of a free particle. These rules are valid for all parity conserving 2 body decays regardless of the spin of all particles involved as long as the 2 incident particles in the initial state have random spin orientation.

Table VI
Allowed Moments

	Background interference	Free particle decay
$\hat{n} = z$	$I(\theta, \phi) = I(\pi - \theta, \phi)$ even $L + M$	$I(\theta, \phi) = I(\pi - \theta, \phi)$ $= I(\pi - \theta, \phi + \pi)$ $= I(\theta, \phi + \pi)$ even L even M
$\hat{n} = y$	$I(\theta, \phi) = I(\theta, -\phi)$ all L all M real $t_L{}^M$	$I(\theta, \phi) = I(\theta, -\phi)$ $= I(\pi - \theta, \phi + \pi)$ $= I(\pi - \theta, \pi - \phi)$ even L all M real $t_L{}^M$

Let us now discuss a specific case of background interference namely the well known interference of the P wave $\varrho^0 \to \pi^+\pi^-$ decay with an S wave background which leads to a forward-backward assymmetry.

Assume there is in the final state mixture a pure state

$$\psi = a_1 Y_1^1 + a_0 Y_1^0 + a_{-1} Y^{-1} + a_s Y_0^0 \tag{IV.29}$$

From previous arguments the state

$$\psi' = R_{\hat{n}}(\pi)\, P\psi$$

is contained in the mixture with the same probability. When using the y axis as production normal we have

$$\psi = (a_1, a_0, a_{-1}, a_s)$$

$$P\psi = (-a_1, -a_0, -a_{-1}, a_s)$$

$$R_y(\pi)\, P\psi = (-a_{-1}, a_0, -a_1, a_s) = \psi'$$

$$= (a'_1, a'_0, a'_{-1}, a'_s) \tag{IV.30}$$

One can define a density matrix for the 2 states ψ and ψ'

$$\varrho_{mn} = {}^1/_2\{a_m a_n^* + a'_m a'^*_n\} \tag{IV.31}$$

with $m, n = 1, 0, -1, S$

When writing it down explicitly it reveals immediately its general symmetry properties:

$$\varrho = \begin{bmatrix} \varrho_{11} & \varrho_{10} & \varrho_{1-1} & \varrho_{1s} \\ \varrho_{10}^{*} & \varrho_{00} & -\varrho_{10}^{*} & \varrho_{0s} \\ \varrho_{1-1} & -\varrho_{10} & \varrho_{11} & -\varrho_{1s} \\ \varrho_{1s}^{*} & \varrho_{0s}^{*} & -\varrho_{1s}^{*} & \varrho_{ss} \end{bmatrix} \tag{IV.32}$$

The diagonal is normalized to 1

$$2\varrho_{11} + \varrho_{00} + \varrho_{ss} = 1, \tag{IV.33}$$

ϱ_{1-1} is real.

For the angular distribution

$$I(\theta, \phi) = \sum_{mn} \varrho_{mn} Y^{m}(\theta, \phi)\, Y^{n*}(\theta, \phi)$$

one obtains with $x = \cos\theta$

$$\begin{aligned} 4\pi I(\theta, \phi) = 1 & \\ & + (\varrho_{00} - \varrho_{11})(3x^2 - 1) \\ & - 3(\varrho_{1-1})(1 - x^2)\cos 2\phi \\ & - 6\sqrt{2}\,(\mathrm{Re}\,\varrho_{10})\, x\sqrt{1 - x^2}\cos\phi \\ & + 2\sqrt{3}\,(\mathrm{Re}\,\varrho_{0s})\, x \\ & - 2\sqrt{6}\,(\mathrm{Re}\,\varrho_{1s})\sqrt{1 - x^2}\cos\phi \end{aligned} \tag{IV.34}$$

Note that neither of the diagonal elements can be determined individually, i.e. the absolute amount of background ϱ_{ss} is not measurable, only a lower limit can be found from the interference terms, e.g. Re ϱ_{0s}.

The experimental determination of density matrices has become important since models for peripheral resonance production were able to calculate it or, as in the one-particle exchange model, to draw conclusions from the experimental values of the ϱ parameters to the nature of the exchanged particle.[17] We shall demonstrate the idea for the case of the simple one-particle exchange model.

Assume the reaction

$$K + p \to K^{*} + p; \quad K^{*} \to K + \pi \tag{IV.35}$$

is described by the graph in Fig. 9a) where X is the exchanged particle. Figure 9b) shows the K^* production and decay in its own c.m. system. We assume that the K^* has spin 1^-($K^*(890)$) and that X is a π meson. As π and K have spin 0 the K^* has to take its spin entirely from the orbital angular momentum between K and π which has clearly 0 component along the K beam direction in the c.m. of the K^*.

Thus if the beam direction is the z axis, the K^* is produced in the eigenstate $|1, 0\rangle$ i.e. $\varrho_{00} = 1$ and its decay distribution is $\sim\cos^2\theta$.

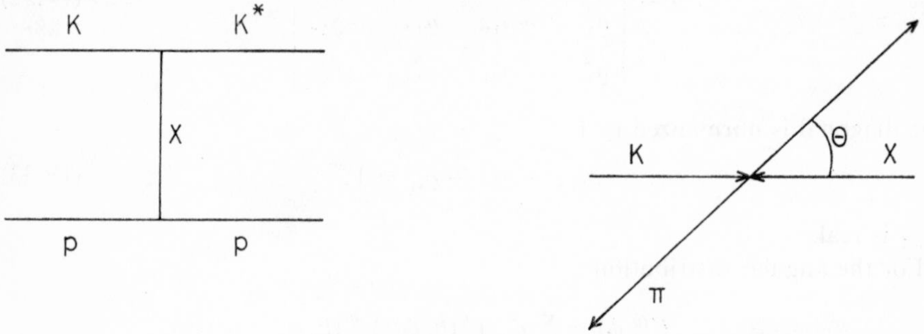

a) Fig. 9 b)

If X is a ϱ or ω meson (spin 1) the situation is different. Spin conservation would allow as initial angular momenta $L = 0, 1, 2$ between K and ϱ (or ω). Parity conservation, however, restricts these possibilities. With the intrinsic parities $\xi_K = -1$, $\xi_\varrho = -1$, $\xi_{K^*} = -1$ and the orbital parity $(-1)^L$ we have

$$\xi_K \xi_\varrho (-1)^L = \xi_{K^*}$$

and find $L = 1$ as the only allowed angular momentum which is again in the eigenstate $|1, 0\rangle$. The spins of ϱ and K^* are coupled to the orbital angular momentum $|1, 0\rangle_L$ in the following way

$$|1, 0\rangle_L = \alpha|1, 1\rangle_{K^*}|1, -1\rangle_\varrho + \beta|1, 0\rangle_{K^*}|1, 0\rangle_\varrho + \gamma|1, -1\rangle_{K^*} 1, 1\rangle_\varrho$$

where α, β, γ are Clebsch-Gordan Coefficients. β however is 0 like all coefficients

$$(L_1 L_2 00|L_3 0) = 0 \quad \text{for} \quad L_1 + L_2 + L_3 \quad \text{odd} \tag{IV.36}$$

so that with ϱ or ω exchange the K^* is only produced in the eigenstates $|1, 1\rangle$ and $|1 - 1\rangle$. With $\varrho_{00} = 0$, $\varrho_{11} = \varrho_{-1-1} = \frac{1}{2}$ the angular distribution is $\sim\sin^2\theta$.

However experimental results do not obey the simple graph in Fig. 9a) to which in the so-called "absorption-model"[18] elastic scattering in the initial and final state was added to obtain better agreement with the experiment. This scattering also smears out the simple form of the density matrix obtained in the primitive model though its qualitative features still seem to remain valid.

b) 3π Decay of the ω^0-Meson

Although we do not discuss 3 particle decays on a broader base in this paper we would like nevertheless to point out how the density matrix of the ω can be obtained from its decay

$$\omega^0 \to \pi^+\pi^-\pi^0 \tag{IV.37}$$

because this is particularly simple.

First some fundamentals[20]: States of integer spin j transform under rotations like irreducible tensors of rank j (i.e. tensors which are traceless and symmetric in every pair of indices). Those tensors consist of $2j + 1$ independent components. In order to have the tensor components represent spin eigenstates they should be defined in a spherical base. A vector in a spherical base (V_+, V_0, V_-) is related to a Cartesian vector (V_x, V_y, V_z) by the relations

$$\begin{bmatrix} V_x \\ V_y \\ V_z \end{bmatrix} = \sqrt{\tfrac{1}{2}} \begin{bmatrix} -1 & 0 & 1 \\ i & 0 & i \\ 0 & \sqrt{2} & 0 \end{bmatrix} \cdot \begin{bmatrix} V^+ \\ V^0 \\ V^- \end{bmatrix}, \quad \begin{bmatrix} V^+ \\ V^0 \\ V^- \end{bmatrix} = \sqrt{\tfrac{1}{2}} \begin{bmatrix} -1 & -i & 0 \\ 0 & 0 & \sqrt{2} \\ 1 & -i & 0 \end{bmatrix} \cdot \begin{bmatrix} V_x \\ V_y \\ V_z \end{bmatrix} \tag{IV.38}$$

From the vector, which is the irreducible tensor describing spin 1, higher rank irreducible tensors can be constructed e.g. for spin 2

$$T_{ij} = \tfrac{1}{2}(u_i v_j + v_i u_j) - \tfrac{1}{3}\delta_{ij} u_i v_j$$

where u and v are Cartesian vectors.

If now a particle is in a certain spin state such that it transforms under rotations like the tensor $T^{(P)}$, where P denotes the parity of the tensor, then the entire final state after decay has also to transform under rotations like $T^{(P)}$ because of angular momentum and parity conservation. Therefore, in order to calculate a decay process one has to construct from all the tensors contained in the final state (intrinsic spin tensors of the decay products and momentum vectors) a tensor $T^{(P)}_{\text{fin}}$ of the final state which has to have the same rank and parity as the tensor of the initial state $T^{(P)}_{\text{in}}$. As the tensor components are conserved in the decay, the matrix element has to project out, from the most general final state tensor, those components which are contained in the initial state, i.e. the decay matrix element will be proportional to the tensor contraction of the product $T^{(P)}_{\text{in}}\, T^{(P)*}_{\text{fin}}$:

$$M = \sum_{i,j\ldots} (T^{(P)}_{\text{fin}})^*_{i,j\ldots} (T^{(P)}_{\text{in}})_{i,j\ldots} \tag{IV.39}$$

For the ω decay we have in the initial state the spherical vector (a, a_0, a_{-1}) which can be transformed to a Cartesian one $\boldsymbol{V}_{in}^{(-)} = (V_x, V_y, V_z) = (V_i)$.

The final state vector has to be constructed from the 3 pseudoscalars $S^{(-)}_\pi$ corresponding to the 3π's and 2 independent momentum vectors which can be chosen e.g. to be the π^+ and π^- momenta in the ω c.m. system $\boldsymbol{p}_{\pi^+}, \boldsymbol{p}_{\pi^-}$. There is only one possibility to construct from all these quantities the final state vector with negative parity, namely[19]

$$\boldsymbol{V}^{(-)}_{\text{fin}} = S^{(-)}_{\pi^+} S^{(-)}_{\pi^-} S^{(-)}_{\pi^0} (\boldsymbol{p}_{\pi^+} \times \boldsymbol{p}_{\pi^-})^{(+)} \quad \text{for} \quad \omega \to \pi^+\pi^-\pi^0 \tag{IV.40}$$

where $\boldsymbol{p}_1 \times \boldsymbol{p}_2 = \boldsymbol{q}$ has the direction of the decay normal. The matrix element is then

$$M(\omega) = \sum_i V_i (p_{\pi^+} \times p_{\pi^-})_i = \boldsymbol{V}\boldsymbol{q} \tag{IV.41}$$

If we treat in the same way the decay into $\pi^+\pi^0$ of the ϱ^+ which is also a vector particle described by V_i, we obtain the final state vector

$$V_{\text{fin}}^{(-)} = \boldsymbol{p}_{\pi^+} \quad \text{for} \quad \varrho \to \pi^+\pi^0 \tag{IV.42}$$

where $\boldsymbol{p}_{\pi^+}$ is the π momentum in the ϱ rest frame. The decay matrix element is

$$M(\varrho) = \sum_i V_i p_{\pi i} = \boldsymbol{V}\boldsymbol{p}_\pi \tag{IV.43}$$

From this it follows immediately that the angular distribution of the normal to the 3π decay plane of the ω is identical to the angular distribution of the $\varrho \to \pi\pi$ decay assuming the ϱ has the same density matrix as the ω. So the ω density matrix can be determined with the angular analysis described in the previous section when θ and ϕ now define the direction of the ω decay normal.

At last we show how one calculates angular distributions from the matrix element for the ϱ-decay $M = \boldsymbol{V}\boldsymbol{p}$. Assume, for example, that the ϱ is in the state

$$\psi = \sqrt{\tfrac{1}{2}}\,|1, 1\rangle + \sqrt{\tfrac{1}{2}}\,|1, 0\rangle = \begin{bmatrix} \sqrt{\tfrac{1}{2}} \\ \sqrt{\tfrac{1}{2}} \\ 0 \end{bmatrix}$$

This spherical vector is first transformed to a Cartesian one by relation (IV.38) giving

$$\boldsymbol{V} = \left(-\frac{1}{2}, \frac{i}{2}, \sqrt{\frac{1}{2}}\right)$$

$$M = \boldsymbol{V}\boldsymbol{p} = -\frac{1}{2}p_x + \frac{i}{2}p_y + \sqrt{\frac{1}{2}}\,p_z$$

$$= p\left(-\frac{1}{2}\sin\theta\cos\phi + \frac{i}{2}\sin\theta\sin\phi + \sqrt{\frac{1}{2}}\cos\theta\right)$$

$$I(\theta, \phi) \sim |M|^2 = p^2\left(\frac{1}{4} + \frac{1}{4}\cos^2\theta - \sqrt{\frac{1}{2}}\cos\theta\sin\theta\cos\phi\right).$$

c) Decay of a Fermion into a Spin $^1/_2$ Fermion plus a Spinless Particle (Method of Byers and Fenster)[21, 40]

The method of Byers and Fenster completely analyzes the decay

$$F_1(j) \to F_2(\tfrac{1}{2}) + B(0) \tag{IV.44}$$

which we shall identify with the processes

$$Y^* \to \Lambda + \pi$$

or

$$\Xi \to \Lambda + \pi \tag{IV.44a}$$

In the decay, to every j there are 2 different orbital angular momenta l possible

$$\text{namely,} \quad l = j + \tfrac{1}{2} \quad \text{and} \quad l = j - \tfrac{1}{2}$$

corresponding to different parities of the Y^*. From the decomposition of the Y^* eigenstate $|j, m\rangle$ into orbital angular momentum and Λ spin

$$\begin{aligned} |jm\rangle = & \left({}^1/_2 l\, {}^1/_2, m - {}^1/_2 | jm\right) Y_l^{m-1/2}(\theta, \phi) \, |{}^1/_2, {}^1/_2\rangle_\Lambda \\ & + \left({}^1/_2 l, -{}^1/_2, m + {}^1/_2 | jm\right) Y_l^{m+1/2}(\theta, \phi) \, |{}^1/_2, -{}^1/_2\rangle_\Lambda \end{aligned} \tag{IV.45}$$

we can, for fixed l, immediately write down the transition matrix which transforms the Y^* spin state into the angle dependent Λ spin state:

$$T_{s,m}(\theta, \phi) = \left({}^1/_2 ls, m - s | jm\right) Y_l^{m-s}(\theta, \phi) \, A_l \tag{IV.46}$$

where s denotes the z component of the Λ spin.

A_l is the amplitude of a transition with angular momentum l. It may be put $= 1$ if only one l is present. Consider now the case that the Λ is emitted along the z axis, i.e. $\theta = 0$, $\phi = 0$.

$$T_{s,m}(0, 0) = \left({}^1/_2 ls, m - s | jm\right) Y_l^{m-s}(0, 0) \, A_l \tag{IV.47}$$

As $Y_L^M(0, 0)$ is $\neq 0$ only for $M = 0$, we find that for a given s only 1 matrix element $T_{s,m}(0, 0)$ is $\neq 0$, namely

$$T_{s,s}(0, 0) = \left({}^1/_2 ls0 | js\right) Y_l^0(0, 0) \, A_l. \tag{IV.48}$$

From the tables of Clebsch-Gordan-coefficients one finds

$$\text{for} \quad j = l + \frac{1}{2} \qquad \left(\frac{1}{2} l, \pm\frac{1}{2} 0 \,\middle|\, j, \pm\frac{1}{2}\right) = + \sqrt{\frac{l+1}{2l+1}}$$

$$\text{and for } j = l - \frac{1}{2} \qquad \left(\frac{1}{2} l, \pm\frac{1}{2} 0 \,\middle|\, j, \pm\frac{1}{2}\right) = \pm \sqrt{\frac{l}{2l+1}}.$$

With $Y_l^0(0, 0) = \sqrt{\dfrac{1}{4\pi}} \sqrt{2l+1}$ (cf. Table 1) one obtains for a given j:

$$\begin{aligned} &1) \text{ for } l = j - \frac{1}{2}, \quad T_{\pm 1/2, \pm 1/2}(0, 0) = + \sqrt{\frac{1}{2}} \cdot \sqrt{\frac{2j+1}{4\pi}} \, A_l \\ &2) \text{ for } l = j + \frac{1}{2}, \quad T_{\pm 1/2, \pm 1/2}(0, 0) = \pm \sqrt{\frac{1}{2}} \cdot \sqrt{\frac{2j+1}{4\pi}} \, A_l \end{aligned} \tag{IV.49}$$

All $T_{s,m}(0, 0)$ with other indices are 0.

Generally we can write

$$T_{s,s}(0, 0) = \sqrt{\frac{2j+1}{4\pi}} \, G_s; \quad s = -\frac{1}{2}, +\frac{1}{2}. \tag{IV.50}$$

For fixed l one has

$$G_{\pm 1/2}(l = j - \tfrac{1}{2}) = +\sqrt{\tfrac{1}{2}}\,A_l$$

$$G_{\pm 1/2}(l = j + \tfrac{1}{2}) = \pm\sqrt{\tfrac{1}{2}}\,A_l$$

The quantities G_s characterize the dynamics of the decay, for instance they define the orbital angular momentum; they also might describe a parity violating decay involving both angular momenta $l = j - \frac{1}{2}$ and $l = j + \frac{1}{2}$. We call the G_s helicity amplitudes and assume them to be normalized to 1

$$\sum_s |G_s|^2 = 1. \tag{IV.51}$$

For parity conserving decays, $G_{1/2}$ and $G_{-1/2}$ are relatively real and equal in magnitude as seen from Eq. (IV.49). Their relative sign defines the orbital angular momentum. If the decay is parity violating involving the 2 decay amplitudes

$$a = A(l = j - \tfrac{1}{2}), \quad b = A(l = j + \tfrac{1}{2}), \tag{IV.52}$$

with $|a|^2 + |b|^2 = 1$, we have from Eq. (IV.49)

$$\begin{aligned} G_{1/2} &= +\sqrt{\tfrac{1}{2}}\,a + \sqrt{\tfrac{1}{2}}\,b \\ G_{-1/2} &= +\sqrt{\tfrac{1}{2}}\,a - \sqrt{\tfrac{1}{2}}\,b \end{aligned} \tag{IV.53}$$

With (IV.53) one may express the decay parameters in terms of G's. It is clear that the G's are complex quantities in this case:

$$\begin{aligned} \alpha &= 2\,\mathrm{Re}\,a^*b = |G_{+1/2}|^2 - |G_{-1/2}|^2 \\ \beta &= 2\,\mathrm{Im}\,a^*b = 2\,\mathrm{Im}\,G_{+1/2}G^*_{-1/2} \\ \gamma &= |a|^2 - |b|^2 = 2\,\mathrm{Re}\,G_{+1/2}G^*_{-1/2} \end{aligned} \tag{IV.54}$$

We shall now go from the conventional coordinate system S which is fixed in space or fixed to the production geometry of the Y^* to a coordinate system $S'(\theta, \phi)$ which depends on the decay angles. Figure 10 shows how this new coordinate system is obtained. For every Λ decay direction $\hat{\Lambda}(\theta, \phi)$, S goes into S' by

1) a rotation by θ about y: $R_y(\theta)$
2) a rotation by ϕ about z: $R_z(\phi)$

According to previous definitions we write

$$R_z(\phi)\, R_y(\theta) = R(\phi, \theta, 0)$$

and have

$$S \to S' = R(\phi, \theta, 0)\, S.$$

The new z' axis now coincides with the Λ emission direction $\hat{\Lambda}(\theta, \phi)$. So in S' the emission angles θ', ϕ' of the Λ are both 0.

Assume $|jn\rangle_{z'}$ is a Y^* eigenstate with respect to the z' *axis*. Then a general pure Y^* state in the frame S' is

$$\psi'_{Y^*} = \sum_n a'_n |jn\rangle_{z'} \tag{IV.55}$$

Now the spin state of a Λ *emitted in z' direction*

$$\psi'_\Lambda = \sum_\lambda b'_\lambda |\tfrac{1}{2}\lambda\rangle_{z'} \tag{IV.56}$$

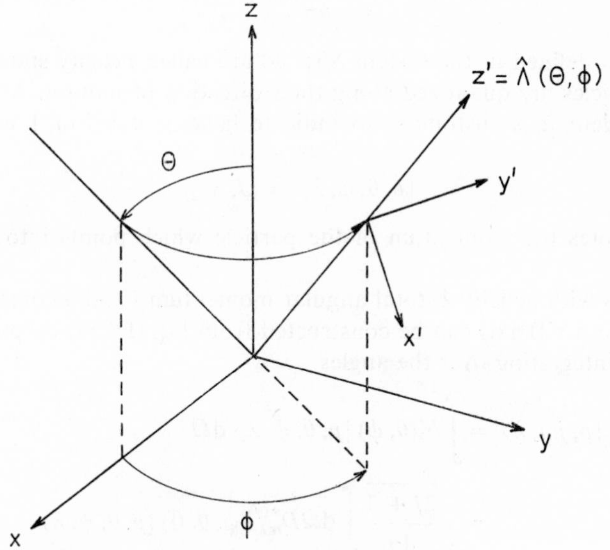

Fig. 10

is obtained by application of the transition matrix $T_{\lambda n}(\theta' = 0, \phi' = 0)$ to ψ'_{Y*} which gives

$$b'_\lambda = \sum_n T_{\lambda,n}(0, 0)\, a'_n = \sqrt{\frac{2j+1}{4\pi}}\, G_\lambda a'_\lambda \tag{IV.57}$$

If in the original system S the Y^* is in the spin state

$$\psi_{Y*} = \sum a_m |jm\rangle_z$$

then this spin state appears in the system S' as the state which results from ψ_{Y*} by a *passive rotation* $R_p(\phi, \theta, 0)$.

$$\psi_{Y*} \to \psi'_{Y*} = R_p(\phi, \theta, 0)\, \psi_{Y*} \tag{IV.58}$$

or

$$a'_n = \sum_m D^{(j)*}_{mn}(\phi, \theta, 0)\, a_m$$

Inserting this into (IV.57) gives the spin state of the Λ in the angle dependent system S'

$$b_\lambda(\theta, \phi) = \sqrt{\frac{2j+1}{4\pi}}\, G_\lambda \sum_m D^{(j)*}_{m\lambda}(\phi, \theta, 0)\, a_m \tag{IV.59}$$

The new transition matrix element between a Y^* eigenstate $|jm\rangle$ in the system S and a Λ eigenstate $|\frac{1}{2}, \lambda\rangle_{z'}$ in the system $S'(\theta, \phi)$ is

$$M_{\lambda m}(\theta, \phi) = \sqrt{\frac{2j+1}{4\pi}}\, G_\lambda \sum_m D^{(J)*}_{m\lambda}(\phi, \theta, 0) \tag{IV.60}$$

States $|J, \lambda\rangle_{z'}$ defined in the system $S'(\theta, \phi)$ are called helicity states because the spins of particles are quantized along their direction of motion. As the z' axis is angle dependent it is customary to indicate helicity states of 1 particle by the symbol

$$|p, \theta, \phi, \lambda\rangle = |J, \lambda\rangle_{z'} \tag{IV.61}$$

where p denotes the momentum of the particle which points into the direction (θ, ϕ).[1,22]

Eigenstates with helicity λ, total angular momentum j and a component $j_z = m$ along the z (not z'!) axis can be constructed from Eq. (IV.59) by putting $a_m = 1$, $G_\lambda = 1$ and integrating over the angles

$$|p, jm, \lambda\rangle = \int b'_\lambda(\theta, \phi)\, |p, \theta, \phi, \lambda\rangle \, \mathrm{d}\Omega$$

$$= \sqrt{\frac{2j+1}{4\pi}} \int \mathrm{d}\Omega D^{*(J)}_{m\lambda}(\phi, \theta, 0)\, |p, \theta, \phi, \lambda\rangle \tag{IV.62}$$

Linear combinations of these eigenstates will describe states with fixed j, m and orbital angular momentum l, i.e. the decay state of the Y^*

$$\psi(j, m, l) = \sum_\lambda G_\lambda |p, jm, \lambda\rangle. \tag{IV.63}$$

The formalism of helicity states is described in detail in an article by M. Jacob and G. C. Wick[22].

Now back to our problem, the Y^* decay. From Eq. (IV.59) we obtain immediately the decay angular distribution for a pure initial state:

$$I(\theta, \phi) = \sum_{\lambda=-1/2}^{1/2} |b'_\lambda(\theta, \phi)|^2 \tag{IV.64}$$

$$= \frac{2j+1}{4\pi} \sum_\lambda |G_\lambda|^2 \sum_{mn} a_m a_n^* D^{(J)*}_{m\lambda}(\phi, \theta, 0)\, D^{(J)}_{n\lambda}(\phi, \theta, 0)$$

Knowing the orthonormality relation of the D matrices [compare (I.56)]

$$\int D^{(J_1)*}_{m_1 m'_1}(\phi, \theta, 0)\, D^{(J_2)}_{m_2 m'_2}(\phi, \theta, 0)\, \mathrm{d}\Omega = \delta_{m_1 m_2}\, \delta_{m'_1 m'_2}\, \delta_{j_1 j_2} \frac{4\pi}{2j_1 + 1} \tag{IV.65}$$

one verifies immediately that the angular distribution is correctly normalized to 1. $\int I(\theta\, \phi)\, \mathrm{d}\Omega = 1$ if the a_m and G_λ are normalized to 1. Furthermore Eq. (IV.64)

where

$$D_{M,0}^{(L)*}(\phi, \theta, 0) = \sqrt{\frac{4\pi}{2L+1}}\, Y_L^M(\theta, \phi)$$

From the relation [cf. (I.36)]

$$(jj\,{}^1\!/_2, -{}^1\!/_2|L0) = (-1)^{2j+L}(jj, -{}^1\!/_2\,{}^1\!/_2|L0)$$

follows

$$(-1)^{j+1/2}(jj, -{}^1\!/_2\,{}^1\!/_2|L0) = (-1)^L(-1)^{j-1/2}(jj\,{}^1\!/_2, -{}^1\!/_2|L0)$$

So the angular distribution can be split into 2 sums over even and odd L respectively:

$$I(\theta, \phi) = \frac{2j+1}{\sqrt{4\pi}}(-1)^{j-1/2}$$

$$\times \Bigg\{ \sum_{L_{\text{even}}, M} (|G_{1/2}|^2 + |G_{-1/2}|^2)\, q_L^{M*}(jj\,{}^1\!/_2, -{}^1\!/_2|L0) \frac{1}{\sqrt{2L+1}} Y_L^M(\theta, \phi)$$

$$+ \sum_{L_{\text{odd}}, M} (|G_{1/2}|^2 - |G_{-1/2}|^2)\, q_L^{M*}(jj\,{}^1\!/_2, -{}^1\!/_2|L0) \frac{1}{\sqrt{2L+1}} Y_L^M(\theta, \phi) \Bigg\}$$

With the normalization

$$|G_{1/2}|^2 + |G_{-1/2}|^2 = 1$$

and the definitions

$$|G_{+1/2}|^2 - |G_{-1/2}|^2 = 2\,\mathrm{Re}\,[A^*(l = j - {}^1\!/_2)\, A(l = j + {}^1\!/_2)] \tag{IV.78}$$

$= \alpha$ decay parameter cf. Eq. (IV.54)

$= 0$ if only strong decays are considered

$$n_{L0} = (-1)^{j-1/2} \sqrt{\frac{2j+1}{4\pi}}\,(jj\,{}^1\!/_2, -{}^1\!/_2|L0) \tag{IV.79}$$

$$t_L^M = \sqrt{\frac{2j+1}{2L+1}}\, q_L^M \tag{IV.80}$$

one obtains in the notation of Byers and Fenster

$$I(\theta, \phi) = \sum_{L_{\text{even}}, M} n_{L0} t_L^{M*} Y_L^M(\theta, \phi) + \alpha \sum_{L_{\text{odd}}, M} n_{L0} t_L^{M*} Y_L^M(\theta, \phi) \tag{IV.81}$$

In terms of moments

$$\langle Y_L^M \rangle = \int I(\theta, \phi)\, Y_L^M(\theta, \phi)\, d\Omega$$

we have

$$\begin{aligned} n_{L0} t_L^M &= \langle Y_L^M \rangle \quad \text{for } L \text{ even} \\ \alpha n_{L0} t_L^M &= \langle Y_L^M \rangle \quad \text{for } L \text{ odd.} \end{aligned} \tag{IV.82}$$

The Y^* density matrix can be reconstructed from the t_L^M:

$$\varrho_{mm'} = \sum_{L,M} q_L^{M*} Q_L^M = \sum_{L,M} t_L^{M*} \sqrt{\frac{2L+1}{2j+1}} (-1)^{j-m'} (jjm, -m'|LM) \tag{IV.83}$$

(One verifies easily that this yields exactly the expression found for the density matrix of bosons decaying into 2 spinless particles, Eq. (IV.19), if in n_{Lo} one replaces $\lambda = \pm\frac{1}{2}$ by 0 and takes into account the different definition of the t_L^M).

Let us ask now for the polarization of the Λ coming from the Y^* decay. The spin $\frac{1}{2}$ density matrix can be expressed in terms of polarization according to Eq. (III.7)

$$\varrho = \tfrac{1}{2} I(\theta, \phi) \begin{bmatrix} 1 + P_z & P_x - iP_y \\ P_x + iP_y & 1 - P_z \end{bmatrix} \tag{I\_.84}$$

So the longitudinal polarization of the Λ will be

$$I(\theta, \phi)\,(\mathbf{P}_\Lambda(\theta, \phi) \cdot \hat{\Lambda}) = \varrho^{\text{fin}}_{1/2\,1/2}(\theta, \phi) - \varrho^{\text{fin}}_{-1/2-1/2}(\theta, \phi)$$

$$= \sum_{L_{\text{odd}},M} n_{Lo} t_L^{M*} Y_L^M(\theta, \phi) - \alpha \sum_{L_{\text{even}},M} n_{Lo} t_L^{M*} Y_L^M(\theta, \phi) \tag{IV.85}$$

where $\hat{\Lambda}$ is a unit vector along the Λ emission direction (θ, ϕ).

$$n_{Lo} t_L^M = \langle (\boldsymbol{P}_\Lambda \cdot \hat{\Lambda})\, Y_L^M(\theta, \phi) \rangle \quad \text{for } L \text{ odd}$$

and

$$\alpha n_{Lo} t_L^M = \langle (\boldsymbol{P}_\Lambda \cdot \hat{\Lambda})\, Y_L^M(\theta, \phi) \rangle \quad \text{for } L \text{ even.} \tag{IV.86}$$

According to relation (II.26) the moment $\langle (\mathbf{P}_\Lambda \cdot \hat{\Lambda})\, Y_L^M \rangle$ is found experimentally e.g. by calculating the sample average of N events ($k = 1, N$):

$$\langle (\boldsymbol{P}_\Lambda \cdot \hat{\Lambda})\, Y_L^M \rangle = \frac{3}{\alpha_\Lambda} \cdot \frac{1}{N} \sum_{k=1}^{N} Y_L^M(\theta_k \cdot \phi_k)\, (\hat{\Lambda}_k \cdot \hat{p}_k) \tag{IV.87}$$

where α_Λ is the α decay parameter of the Λ and $\hat{\mathbf{p}}$ is the proton emission direction in the Λ rest frame.

The transverse components of the polarization are contained in the off diagonal elements of the density matrix. Using (IV.76) one obtains for $\varrho^{\text{fin}}_{1/2,-1/2}$

$$\varrho^{\text{fin}}_{1/2,-1/2} = \frac{2j+1}{4\pi} G_{1/2} G^*_{-1/2} \sum_{LM} \sqrt{\frac{2L+1}{2j+1}}$$

$$\times\, t_L^{M*} (-1)^{j+1/2} (jj\tfrac{1}{2}, \tfrac{1}{2}|L1)\, D^{(L)*}_{M,1}(\phi, \theta, 0) \tag{IV.88}$$

With the definition

$$n_{L1} = (-1)^{j-1/2} \sqrt{\frac{2j+1}{4\pi}} (jj\tfrac{1}{2}, \tfrac{1}{2}|L1), \quad (= 0 \text{ for } L \text{ even})$$

one has

$$\varrho^{\text{fin}}_{1/2,-1/2} = -G_{1/2}G^*_{-1/2} \sum_{L,M} n_{L1} \sqrt{\frac{2L+1}{4\pi}}\, t_L^{M*} D^{(L)*}_{M,1}(\phi,\theta,0) \tag{IV.90}$$

With Eq. (IV.54) this becomes

$$\varrho^{\text{fin}}_{1/2,-1/2} = -\frac{1}{2}(\gamma+i\beta) \sum_{L,M} n_{L1} \sqrt{\frac{2L+1}{4\pi}}\, t_L^{M*} D^{(L)*}_{M,1}(\phi,\theta,0) \tag{IV.91}$$

From Eq. (IV.84) we know that

$$\varrho^{\text{fin}}_{1/2,-1/2} = \tfrac{1}{2}I(\theta,\phi)(P'_x - iP'_y).$$

The prime denotes that P is defined in the rotated system S'. Introducing spherical polarization vectors P_m with relation (IV.38) we obtain

$$\begin{aligned} P_{+1} &= -\sqrt{\tfrac{1}{2}}(P_x + iP_y) \\ P_{-1} &= \sqrt{\tfrac{1}{2}}(P_x - iP_y) \\ P_0 &= P_z \end{aligned} \tag{IV.92a}$$

and

$$\varrho^{\text{fin}}_{1/2,-1/2} = \sqrt{\tfrac{1}{2}}\, I(\theta,\phi)\, P'_{-1} \tag{IV.92b}$$

Between P in the frame S and P' in the frame S' we have the relation

$$\begin{aligned} P'_{+1} &= \sum_m D^{(1)}_{m,1}(\phi,\theta,0)\, P_m \\ P'_{-1} = -P'^*_{+1} &= -\sum_m D^{(1)*}_{m,1}(\phi,\theta,0)\, P^*_m \end{aligned} \tag{IV.93}$$

With (IV.92) and (IV.93), Eq. (IV.91) becomes

$$I(\theta,\phi)\sum_m D^{(1)*}_{m,1}P^*_m = \sqrt{\frac{1}{2}}(\gamma+i\beta)\sum_{L,M} n_{L1}\sqrt{\frac{2L+1}{4\pi}}\, t_L^{M*}D^{(L)*}_{M,1}(\phi,\theta,0) \tag{IV.94}$$

Multiplying both sides with $D^{(L')}_{M',1}$ and integrating over θ, ϕ gives with relation (IV.65) and complex conjugation

$$\sum_m \left\{ \iint \mathrm{d}\Omega\, I(\theta,\phi)\, P_m D^{(1)}_{m,1} D^{(L)*}_{M,1} \right\} = \sqrt{\frac{1}{2}}(\gamma - i\beta)\, n_{L1} \sqrt{\frac{4\pi}{2L+1}}\, t_L^M \tag{IV.95}$$

The product of D matrices on the left side can be expanded with Eq. (IV.75)

$$D^{(L)*}_{M,1}D^{(1)}_{m,1} = \sum_l D^{(l)*}_{M-m,0}(L1M,-m|l,M-m)(L11,-1|l0)(-1)^{m-1} \tag{IV.96}$$

With

$$(j_1 j_2 - m_1 - m_2 | j - m) = (-1)^{j_1+j_2-j}(j_1 j_2 m_1 m_2 | jm) \quad \text{(IV.97)} = \text{(I.36d)}$$

$$(j_1 j_2 m_1 m_2 | jm) = (-1)^{j_1+j_2-j}(j_2 j_1 m_2 m_1 | jm) \quad \text{(IV.98)} = \text{(I.36c)}$$

$$(1L,-mM|l,M-m) = (-1)^{L+l-m}\sqrt{\frac{2l+1}{L+1}}(1lm,M-m|LM) \tag{IV.99}$$

and

$$D^{(l)*}_{n,0}(\phi, \theta, 0) = \sqrt{\frac{4\pi}{2l+1}}\, Y^n_l(\theta, \phi)$$

one obtains

$$(\gamma - i\beta)\, n_{L1} t^M_L = \sqrt{2} \sum_{l,m} \langle P_m Y^{M-m}_l \rangle\, (1lm, M-m|LM)\, (1L1, -1|l0) \qquad \text{(IV.100)}$$

Applying relation (IV.97) and

$$t^{M*}_L = (-1)^M t^{-M}_L, \quad P^*_m = (-1)^m P_{-m}$$

complex conjugation of (IV.100) gives

$$(\gamma + i\beta)\, n_{L1} t^M_L$$
$$= \sqrt{2} \sum_{l,m} \langle P_m Y^{M-m}_l \rangle\, (1lm, M-m|LM)\, (1L1, -1|l0)\, (-1)^{1+l-L} \qquad \text{(IV.101)}$$

With

$$(1L1, -1|L-1, 0) = \sqrt{\frac{L+1}{2(2L+1)}}$$

$$(1L1, -1|L, 0) = \sqrt{\frac{1}{2}}$$

$$(1L1, -1|L+1, 0) = \sqrt{\frac{L}{2(2L+1)}}$$

one obtains from addition and subtraction of (IV.100) and (IV.101)

$$\gamma n_{L1} t^M_L = \sqrt{\frac{L+1}{2L+1}} \sum_m \langle P_m Y^{M-m}_{L-1} \rangle\, (1, L-1, m, M-m|LM)$$
$$+ \sqrt{\frac{L}{2L+1}} \sum_m \langle P_m Y^{M-m}_{L+1} \rangle\, (1, L+1, m, M-m|LM) \qquad \text{(IV.102)}$$

(for L odd only)

and

$$\beta n_{L1} t^M_L = i \sum_m \langle P_m Y^{M-m}_L \rangle\, (1, L, m, M-m|LM) \qquad \text{(IV.103)}$$

(for L odd only)

Recall that the spherical polarization vector P_m is defined in the original system S and that only polarization components perpendicular to the Λ direction of flight in the Y^* rest system are projected out by Eq. (IV.102) and (IV.103). β is different from 0 only in weak decays with final state interactions or if time reversal invariance is violated.

(The moments $\langle P_m(\theta, \phi)\, Y^{M-m}_L(\theta, \phi) \rangle$ are evaluated by replacing in Eq. (IV.87) the unit vector $\hat{\Lambda}$ by the unit vectors $\hat{x}, \hat{y}, \hat{z}$, which will give the 3 Cartesian components of the Λ polarization from which the spherical components P_m are obtained with relation (IV.92a). As discussed in the appendix for the practical application of Eq. (IV.87) it is important that the decay proton from the Λ is first Lorentz-transformed into the Y^* rest frame and only from there into the Λ rest frame.)

In strong decays γ determines the parity of the Y^*. If j is the spin of the Y^* and l the orbital angular momentum of the decay one has

$$\gamma = 1 \quad \text{for} \quad l = j - \tfrac{1}{2}$$

$$\gamma = -1 \quad \text{for} \quad l = j + \tfrac{1}{2} \qquad \text{(IV.104)}$$

Assuming parity conserving decays the density matrix can be entirely reconstructed with Eq. (IV.72) from the t_L^M obtained from the angular distribution (even L) and the longitudinal polarization (odd L). Recall that a complete determination of the density matrix was not possible for the decay of a boson into 2 spinless besons. A certain spin hypothesis can be tested with the well known restriction to the density matrix as discussed in section III.

Furthermore for spin j no moments with $L > 2j$ should occur. The parity *and the spin* of the Y^* are determined by the quantity $(2j + 1)\gamma$ which can be obtained from the measured values of $n_{L0}t_L^M$ and $n_{L1}t_L^M$ for odd L. The latter result from the longitudinal and transverse polarization of the Λ with the help of Eq. (IV.86) and (IV.102). To obtain $(2j + 1)\gamma$ one uses the relation

$$\frac{n_{L1}}{n_{L0}} = \frac{(jj\tfrac{1}{2}\tfrac{1}{2}|L1)}{(jj\tfrac{1}{2}, -\tfrac{1}{2}|L0)} = \frac{2j+1}{\sqrt{L(L+1)}} \quad \text{for } L \text{ odd} \qquad \text{(IV.105)}$$

n_{L1} being $= 0$ for L even.

From the arguments of section IVa one concludes that, for parity conserving 2 body production, $t_L^M = 0$ for M odd if z is the production normal. Similarly, if the y axis is the production normal even and odd M are allowed but the t_L^M are real.

An experimental application of the method of Byers and Fenster can be found e.g. in the work by Schlein *et al.*[15]

A similar spin analysis method was proposed by Ademollo and Gatto[23].

J. Button-Shafer[24] has extended the analysis of Byers and Fenster to fermion decays into a spin 0 and a spin $^3/_2$ particle.

d) Decay of a Boson into a Boson of Spin 1 plus a Spinless Boson

In this section we consider the decay

$$B_1(j) \to B_2(1) + B_3(0) \qquad \text{(IV.106)}$$

The analysis method applied is due to S. U. Chung[27] and is closely analogous to that of Byers and Fenster so that we can use many relations derived in the last section.

A spin eigenstate $|jm\rangle$ of B_1 leads, by simple angular momentum decomposition, to the final state ψ^{fin}

$$|jm\rangle_{B_1} \rightarrow \psi^{\text{fin}} = \sum_s (1ls, m-s|jm)\, Y_l^{m-s}(\theta,\phi)\, |1,s\rangle_{B_2}$$

So the transition matrix is

$$T_{sm}(\theta,\phi) = (1ls, m-s|jm)\, Y_l^{m-s}(\theta,\phi)\, A_l \qquad \text{(IV.107)}$$

where l is the orbital angular momentum between B_2 and B_3. The amplitude A_l is 1 if only one angular momentum wave is present. At $\theta = 0$, $\phi = 0$ we have as only matrix elements different from 0:

$$T_{s,s}(0,0) = (1ls0|js)\, Y_l^0(0,0)\, A_l \qquad \text{(IV.108)}$$

With

$$Y_l^0(0,0) = \sqrt{\frac{2l+1}{4\pi}}\,.$$

$T_{s,s}(0,0)$ can be written in the form

$$T_{s,s}(0,0) = \sqrt{\frac{2l+1}{4\pi}}\,(1ls0|js)\, A_l \qquad \text{(IV.109)}$$

and from the table of Clebsch-Gordan coefficients:

$$T_{s,s}(0,0) = \sqrt{\frac{2j+1}{4\pi}}\, K_{jls} A_l \qquad \text{(IV.110)}$$

where the quantities K_{jls} are listed in the scheme below.

s	1	0	−1
$l = j-1$	$\sqrt{\frac{j+1}{2(2j+1)}}$	$\sqrt{\frac{j}{2j+1}}$	$\sqrt{\frac{j+1}{2(2j+1)}}$
$l = j$	$\sqrt{\frac{1}{2}}$	0	$-\sqrt{\frac{1}{2}}$
$l = j+1$	$\sqrt{\frac{j}{2(2j+1)}}$	$-\sqrt{\frac{j+1}{2j+1}}$	$\sqrt{\frac{j}{2(2j+1)}}$

(IV.111)

Generally we can write

$$T_{s,s}(0,0) = \sqrt{\frac{2j+1}{4\pi}}\, G_s \qquad \text{(IV.112)}$$

where G_s may contain contributions from different angular momenta l:

$$G_s = \sum_l A_l K_{jls} \qquad \text{(IV.113)}$$

The A_l are complex decay amplitudes describing the dynamics of the decay. We shall confine ourselves to parity conserving decays where, for a given j, 2 cases are possible corresponding to different parity of B_1:

1) $l = j$

2) $l = j - 1$ and $l = j + 1$

From the requirement of time reversal invariance it follows for case 2) that the amplitudes A_{j-1} and A_{j+1} are relatively real, i.e. A_{j-1}/A_{j+1} is real. In parity conserving decays where $l = j$ and $l = j \pm 1$ cannot be present simultaneously one verifies immediately from (IV.113) and the table of K_{jls} that

$$|G_s| = |G_{-s}| \qquad \text{(IV.114)}$$

For the parity case $l = j$, one has $G_0 = 0$.

If the decay boson B_2 is a photon, special restrictions apply to the G_S. It is well known that the photon can have only spin projections $s = \pm 1$ in its direction of flight, $s = 0$ is forbidden.[39]

So the parity case $j = l$ causes no trouble because $G_0 = 0$ anyway. For the other parity case, however, both angular momenta $l = j - 1$ and $l = j + 1$ must be present in a certain relative proportion in order to make $G_0 = 0$. As is easily seen from the K_{jls} for photons with $l = j \pm 1$ one has to require

$$A_{j-1}\sqrt{\frac{j}{2j+1}} - A_{j+1}\sqrt{\frac{j+1}{2j+1}} = 0$$

or

$$A_{j+1} = \sqrt{\frac{j}{j+1}}\, A_{j-1} \qquad \text{(IV.115)}$$

leading to

$$G_1 = \sqrt{\tfrac{1}{2}}A, \quad G_{-1} = \sqrt{\tfrac{1}{2}}A, \quad G_0 = 0. \qquad \text{(IV.116)}$$

We shall always assume the G_S to be normalized to 1:

$$\sum |G_s|^2 = 1 \qquad \text{(IV.117)}$$

Now we proceed in complete analogy to the method of Byers and Fenster. A pure state of the decaying boson $B_1(j)$ described by the column vector a_m is first rotated into the system S' which results from the original one by a rotation $R(\phi, \theta, 0)$. The new spin state is

$$a'_\lambda = \sum_m D^{(j)*}_{m\lambda}(\phi, \theta, 0)\, a_m \qquad \text{(IV.118)}$$

Applying to a'_λ the transition matrix (IV.112) now in the system S' leads to the spin state b'_λ of the boson $B_2(1)$:

$$b'_\lambda = T_{\lambda\lambda}(0, 0)\, a'_\lambda$$

$$b'_\lambda = \sqrt{\frac{2j+1}{4\pi}}\, G_\lambda \sum_m D^{(j)*}_{m\lambda}(\phi, \theta, 0)\, a_m \tag{IV.119}$$

$$\lambda = -1, 0, 1$$

This defines a transition matrix between a_m in S and b'_λ in S'

$$M_{\lambda m}(\theta, \phi) = \sqrt{\frac{2j+1}{4\pi}}\, G_\lambda \sum_m D^{(j)*}_{m\lambda}(\theta, \phi) \tag{IV.120}$$

In analogy to the last section we find for the density matrices

$$\varrho^{\text{fin}}_{\lambda\lambda'}(\theta, \phi) = \frac{2j+1}{4\pi}\, G_\lambda G^*_\lambda \sum_{mm'} D^{(j)*}_{m\lambda}\, \varrho_{mm'} D^{(j)}_{m'\lambda'} \tag{IV.121}$$

$\varrho_{mm'}$ of $B_1(j)$ is expanded in spherical tensor operators:

$$\varrho_{mm'} = \sum_{LM} q^{M*}_L (-1)^{j-m'}\, (jjm, -m'|L, m-m') \tag{IV.122}$$

leading after application of some algebra to

$$\varrho^{\text{fin}}_{\lambda\lambda'}(\theta, \phi) = \frac{2j+1}{4\pi}\, G_\lambda G^*_{\lambda'} \sum_{LM} q^{M*}_L (-1)^{j-\lambda'}\, (jj\lambda, -\lambda'|L, \lambda-\lambda')\, D^{(L)*}_{M,\lambda-\lambda'} \tag{IV.123}$$

The decay angular distribution is

$$I(\theta, \phi) = \sum_\lambda \varrho^{\text{fin}}_{\lambda\lambda}(\theta, \phi)$$

$$= \frac{2j+1}{4\pi} \sum_\lambda |G_\lambda|^2 \left\{ \sum_{LM} q^{M*}_L (-1)^{j-\lambda}\, (jj\lambda, -\lambda|L0) \sqrt{\frac{4\pi}{2L+1}}\, Y^M_L(\theta, \phi) \right\} \tag{IV.124}$$

As we have assumed a parity conserving decay, only even L terms appear. The maximum possible L is $L_{max} = 2j$. If, however, the decay proceeds only over $l = j - 1$ the highest detectable L in the angular distribution is, of course, only $2j - 2$. From this one concludes that from the decay angular distribution alone a spin determination is impossible. On the other hand, if $l = j + 1$, the highest L is, nevertheless, only $2j$ and not $2j + 2$ as one might think naively.

There is, however, further information available from the polarization or alignment of the boson $B_2(1)$. In the following we shall assume that the decay product B_2 undergoes a subsequent decay into 2 spinless bosons.

$$B_2(1) \rightarrow B_3(0) + B_4(0). \tag{IV.125}$$

We will now look at the decay angular distribution of (IV.125) in rest frame of B_2. As coordinate system we choose the system S' (Lorentz transformed to the B_2 rest frame) i.e. the z' axis is the B_2 direction of flight in the B_1 rest frame. Averaging over the azimuth φ in the decay angular distribution we need consider only the diagonal density matrix elements of B_2 in the system S'. From (IV.121) one easily shows that the diagonal density matrix elements of B_2 summed over the whole decay angular distribution of B_1 are

$$\int \varrho_{\lambda\lambda}^{\mathrm{fin}}(\theta, \phi)\, \mathrm{d}\Omega = |G_\lambda|^2 \tag{IV.122}$$

With this result and (IV.113) and (IV.111) one can immediately write down the decay angular distribution of B_2 for various spin-parity assignments:

$$j = 0 \qquad l = 1 \quad I(\vartheta') = 3\cos^2\vartheta' \tag{IV.123}$$

$$j = 1 \qquad \begin{cases} l = 0 & I(\vartheta') = 1 \\ l = 1 & I(\vartheta') = \frac{3}{2}\sin^2\vartheta' \\ l = 2 & I(\vartheta') = \frac{1}{2}\sin^2\vartheta' + \frac{4}{2}\cos^2\vartheta' \end{cases}$$

$$j = 2 \qquad \begin{cases} l = 1 & I(\vartheta') = \frac{9}{10}\sin^2\vartheta' + \frac{12}{10}\cos^2\vartheta' \\ l = 2 & I(\vartheta') = \frac{3}{2}\sin^2\vartheta' \\ l = 3 & I(\vartheta') = \frac{3}{5}\sin^2\vartheta' + \frac{9}{5}\cos^2\vartheta' \end{cases}$$

If one observes a pure $\sin^2\vartheta$ distribution, all one can say is that $l = j$. In general the decay distribution of B_2 alone will not give a unique spin parity assignment for B_1 because also in the other parity case ($l = j \pm 1$) there exist ambiguities due to the 2 possible angular momentum states. Only the assignments ($j = 0$, $l = 1$) and ($j = 1$, $l = 0$) are unique, at least theoretically.

As neither the decay angular distribution of B_1 nor of B_2 gives an unambiguous spin determination we shall consider combined distributions now.

First we expand the density matrix of B_2 (1) defined in the rotated system S' in terms of tensor operators taking into account that $\varrho_{\lambda\lambda'}^{\mathrm{fin}}(\theta, \phi)$, as given by Eq. (IV.123), is normalized to $I(\theta, \phi)$.

$$\varrho_{\lambda\lambda'}^{\mathrm{fin}}(\theta, \phi) = \left\{\sum_{kn} r_k^{n*}(\theta, \phi)\,(11\lambda, -\lambda'|kn)\,(-1)^{1-\lambda'}\right\} I(\theta, \phi) \tag{IV.124}$$

where r_k^n are spherical tensor operators in S'.

Inserting this into Eq. (IV.123), multiplying both sides by $D^{(L)}_{M,\lambda-\lambda'}$ and integrating gives

$$\sum_{kn}(-1)^{1-\lambda'}(11\lambda,-\lambda'|kn)\int r_k^{n*}(\theta,\phi)\,I(\theta,\phi)\,D^{(L)}_{M,\lambda-\lambda'}(\phi,\theta,0)\,\mathrm{d}\Omega =$$

$$=\frac{2j+1}{4\pi}\,\frac{4\pi}{2L+1}\,G_\lambda G^*_{\lambda'}q_L^{M*}(-1)^{j-\lambda'}(jj\lambda,-\lambda'|L,\lambda-\lambda') \qquad \text{(IV.125)}$$

or

$$\sum_{kn}(11\lambda,-\lambda'|kn)\left\{\int \mathrm{d}\Omega I(\theta,\phi)\,r_k^n(\theta,\phi)\,D^{(L)*}_{M,\lambda-\lambda'}(\phi,\theta,0)\right\}$$

$$=(-1)^{j+1}\frac{2j+1}{2L+1}\,q_L^M(jj\lambda,-\lambda'|L,\lambda-\lambda')\,G^*_\lambda G_{\lambda'} \qquad \text{(IV.126)}$$

The expression in the bracket { } is an experimentally determinable quantity which we shall call $F(kn; LM)$

$$F(kn;LM)=\int \mathrm{d}\Omega I(\theta,\phi)\,r_k^n(\theta,\phi)\,D^{(L)*}_{M,n}(\phi,\theta,0). \qquad \text{(IV.127)}$$

It is more convenient to evaluate F in the original system S. Therefore we express the expansion coefficients r_k^n by R_k^N defined in S (precisely in that rest frame of B_2 which results from S by a mere Lorentz translation along the B_2 direction of flight in S).

$$r_k^n=\sum_N D^{(k)}_{Nn}(\phi,\theta,0)\,R_k^N \qquad \text{(IV.128)}$$

$$F(kn;LM)=\int \mathrm{d}\Omega I(\theta,\phi)\sum_N R_k^N D^{(L)*}_{Mn}D^{(k)}_{Nn}$$

$$\uparrow$$

With

$$D^{(L)*}_{Mn}D^{(k)}_{Nn}=\sum_K D^{(K)*}_{M-N,0}(LkM,-N|K,M-N)(Lkn,-n|K0)(-1)^{N-n}$$

and

$$D^{(K)*}_{\alpha 0}(\phi,\theta,0)=\sqrt{\frac{4\pi}{2K+1}}\,Y_K^\alpha(\theta,\phi)$$

we have

$$F(kn;LM)=\sqrt{4\pi}\sum_{K,N}\sqrt{\frac{1}{2K+1}}\,(-1)^{N-n}(LkM,-N|K,M-N)(Lkn,-n|K0)$$

$$\times\,\langle R_k^N(\theta,\phi)\,Y_K^{M-N}(\theta,\phi)\rangle \qquad \text{(IV.129)}$$

where $R_k^N(\theta,\phi)$ is found from the decay angular distribution (ϑ,φ) of B_2 in its rest frame with axes parallel to those of S. From the expansion of the B_2 density matrix

$$\varrho_{ss'}=\sum_{kN}R_k^{N*}(-1)^{1-s'}(11s,-s'|kN) \qquad \text{(IV.130)}$$

one obtains by comparison with Eq. (IV.20)

$$R_k^N = -\frac{\sqrt{4\pi}\sqrt{2k+1}}{3(1100|k0)}\langle Y_k^N(\vartheta,\varphi)\rangle \tag{IV.131}$$

for even k only.

So with the experimental averages

$$\langle R_k^N(\theta,\phi)\, Y_K^{M-N}(\theta,\phi)\rangle = -\frac{\sqrt{4\pi}\sqrt{2k+1}}{3(1100|k0)}\langle Y_k^N(\vartheta,\varphi)\, Y_K^{M-N}(\theta,\phi)\rangle \tag{IV.132}$$

where

$$(1100|k0) = -\sqrt{\frac{1}{3}} \quad \text{for} \quad k=0, \quad \sqrt{\frac{2}{3}} \quad \text{for} \quad k=2,$$

the $F(kn; LM)$ are determined and can be inserted into Eq. (IV.126) which we write down again

$$\sum_k (11\lambda, -\lambda'|kn)\, F(kn; LM) = (-1)^{j+1}\frac{2j+1}{2L+1} q_L^M(jj\lambda, -\lambda'|Ln)\, G_\lambda^* G_{\lambda'} \tag{IV.133}$$

Multiplying both sides by $(11\lambda, -\lambda'|k'n')$ and summing over λ, λ' gives

$$F(kn; LM) = (-1)^{j+1}\frac{2j+1}{2L+1} q_L^M \sum_{\lambda\lambda'} (jj\lambda, -\lambda'|Ln)\,(11\lambda, -\lambda'|kn)\, G_\lambda^* G_{\lambda'} \tag{IV.134}$$

$F(kn; LM)$ is defined only for even k because the decay of B_2 into 2 spinless particles permits only the determination of the multipole parameters r_k^n with k even. For k even one has from the symmetry of Clebsch-Gordan-coefficients in (I.36d)

$$F(k\,-n; LM) = (-1)^L F(kn; LM) \tag{IV.135}$$

so that only F's with $n \geqq 0$ need be considered. For the relevant (k, n)-values Eq. (IV.134) reads with

$$f = (-1)^{j+1}\frac{2j+1}{2L+1} \tag{IV.136}$$

$$F(22; LM) = f q_L^M(jj11|L2)\, G_1^* G_{-1} \tag{IV.137}$$

$$F(21; LM) = f q_L^M(jj10|L1)\sqrt{\tfrac{1}{2}}\,[G_1^* G_0 + G_0^* G_{-1}] \tag{IV.138}$$

$$F(20; LM) = f q_L^M\sqrt{\tfrac{3}{2}}\,[(jj1, -1|L0)\,|G_1|^2 + (jj00|L0)\,|G_0|^2] \tag{IV.139}$$

$$F(00; LM) = f q_L^M\sqrt{\tfrac{1}{3}}\,[2(jj1, -1|L0)\,|G_1|^2 - (jj00|L0)\,|G_0|^2] \tag{IV.140}$$

for even L only.

Relations (IV.139) and (IV.140) use $|G_{+1}| = |G_{-1}|$ as already stated in (IV.114). We shall assume time reversal invariance which implies that the G's can be considered as real quantities.

Instead of Eq. (IV.139) and (IV.140) we will use linear combinations of them. Adding and subtracting (IV.139) and (IV.140) gives

$$\sqrt{2}\,F(00;LM) + F(20;LM) = fq_L^M\sqrt{6}\,(jj1,-1|L0)\,|G_1|^2 \quad \text{(IV.141)}$$

$$-F(00;LM) + \sqrt{2}\,F(20;LM) = fq_L^M\sqrt{3}\,(jj00|L0)\,|G_0|^2 \quad \text{(IV.142)}$$

Assume the spin of B_1 is known. Then with the normalization

$$|G_0|^2 = 1 - 2\,|G_1|^2 \quad \text{(IV.143)}$$

one can determine from (IV.141) and (IV.142) first the quantities $|G_0|^2$, $|G_1|^2$ and q_L^M and then, with the q_L^M the density matrix of B_1. Only even L are allowed. Equations (IV.137) and (IV.138) give another independent determination of q_L^M and G_0, G_1 which we assume to be real. Remember that according to (IV.113) we have for the parity case

$$l = j: \qquad G_1 = \sqrt{\tfrac{1}{2}},\quad G_0 = 0,\quad G_{-1} = -\sqrt{\tfrac{1}{2}} \quad \text{(IV.144)}$$

and for

$$l = j \pm 1: \quad G_1 = G_{-1} \quad \text{(IV.145)}$$

If spin and parity of B_1 are unknown they can, in principle, be determined from the measured quantities $F(kn; LM)$. For this purpose we first substitute in (IV.141) and (IV.137) the Clebsch-Gordan coefficients by the relations[28]

$$(jj1,-1|L0) = \left[\frac{L(L+1)}{2j(j+1)} - 1\right](jj00|L0) \quad \text{(IV.146)}$$

and

$$(jj11|L2) = \sqrt{\frac{L(L+1)}{(L-1)(L+2)}}\,(jj00|L0) \quad \text{(IV.147)}$$

which hold for even L.

Then substitution of $fq_L^M(jj00|L0)$ in Eq. (IV.141) by the corresponding expression obtained from Eq. (IV.137) yields for the spin of B_1:

$$j(j+1) = \frac{L(L+1)\,c}{\varepsilon\sqrt{\frac{2}{3}}\sqrt{\frac{L(L+1)}{(L-1)(L+2)}}\,(\sqrt{2}a + b) + 2c} \quad \text{(IV.148)}$$

where

$$\begin{aligned} a &= \text{Re or Im } F(00;LM) \\ b &= \text{Re or Im } F(20;LM) \\ c &= \text{Re or Im } F(22;LM) \end{aligned} \quad \text{(IV.149)}$$

and

$$\varepsilon = \frac{G_1^* G_{-1}}{|G_1|^2}$$

According to (IV.144) and (IV.145)

$$\varepsilon = 1 \quad \text{for} \quad l = j \pm 1 \qquad \text{(IV.150)}$$
$$\varepsilon = -1 \quad \text{for} \quad l = j.$$

Relation (IV.148) gives for all allowed values of L, M independent determinations of the quantity $j(j+1)$ if the parity ε is known. As $G_0 = 0$ for the parity case $l = j$ we obtain from (IV.138) and (IV.142) relations

$$\left.\begin{aligned} F(21; LM) &= 0 \\ F(00; LM) &= \sqrt{2}\, F(20; LM) \end{aligned}\right\} \text{for} \quad l = j \qquad \text{(IV.151)}$$

which allow us to determine the parity ε. Equations (IV.148) then fix the spin j of B_1.

Berman[29] proposed a spin test which is closely related to a particular case of Eq. (IV.148), namely

$$\frac{2\,\mathrm{Re}\, F(22; 20)}{\sqrt{2}\, F(00; 20) + F(20; 20)} = \varepsilon \frac{j(j+1)}{3 - j(j+1)}$$

which follows directly from (IV.137) and (IV.141).

With the previously derived relations:

$$F(kn; LM) = \int d\Omega\, I(\theta, \phi)\, r_k^n(\theta, \phi)\, D_{M,n}^{(L)*}(\phi, \theta, 0)$$

and

$$r_k^n = -\frac{\sqrt{4\pi}\sqrt{2k+1}}{3(1100|k0)} \langle Y_k^n(\vartheta', \varphi') \rangle$$

where ϑ', φ' are the CM decay angles of B_2 in the rotated coordinate system $S'(\theta, \phi)$ and with

$$D_{0,2}^{(2)}(\phi, \theta, 0) = \frac{\sqrt{6}}{4} \sin^2 \theta$$

$$D_{0,0}^{(2)}(\phi, \theta, 0) = \frac{3}{2} \cos^2 \theta - \frac{1}{2}$$

one obtains from the explicit B_2 decay angular distribution (IV.13) Berman's relation

$$\frac{\int 2\,\mathrm{Re}\, \varrho_{1-1}^{\mathrm{fin}}(\theta, \phi) \sin^2 \theta\, d\Omega}{\int [\varrho_{11}^{\mathrm{fin}}(\theta, \phi) + \varrho_{-1-1}^{\mathrm{fin}}(\theta, \phi)]\,(3\cos^2\theta - 1)\, d\Omega} = \varepsilon \frac{j(j+1)}{3 - j(j+1)} \qquad \text{(IV.152)}$$

with

$$2\,\mathrm{Re}\, \varrho_{1-1}^{\mathrm{fin}}(\theta, \phi) = -{}^5/_2 \int I(\theta\phi\vartheta'\varphi') \sin^2 \vartheta' \cos 2\varphi'\, d\omega'$$

$$\varrho_{11}^{\mathrm{fin}}(\theta, \phi) + \varrho_{-1-1}^{\mathrm{fin}}(\theta, \phi) = \tfrac{1}{2} \int I(\theta\phi\vartheta'\varphi')\,(3 - 5\cos^2 \vartheta')\, d\omega'$$

where $I(\theta\phi\vartheta'\varphi')$ is the combined decay distribution with the normalization

$$\int I(\theta\phi\vartheta'\varphi') \underbrace{\mathrm{d}\cos\vartheta'\,\mathrm{d}\varphi'}_{d\omega'} = I(\theta, \phi)$$

Thus in terms of moments we can write

$$\frac{-5\langle\sin^2\vartheta'\cos 2\varphi'\sin^2\theta\rangle}{\langle(3-5\cos^2\vartheta')(3\cos^2\theta-1)\rangle} = \varepsilon\,\frac{j(j+1)}{3-j(j+1)} \tag{IV.153}$$

In the practical application it should be borne in mind that these methods are strictly valid only for the case that the two successive decays of B_1 and B_2 are well separated, i.e. if the spin 0 particle of the B_1 decay does not interfere with the decay products of the vector meson B_2. This interference is certainly in the Dalitz plot region with overlapping vector meson bands as in the decay $A \to \varrho + \pi$, $\varrho \to \pi\pi$. In this case the problem has to be treated as 3 particle decay with proper symmetrization of the 3π wave function in the final state.[19,30]

e) Photons as Decay Products

The decay of a boson of spin j into a γ and a spin zero particle can be described entirely by the formalism developed in the last section. The only additional restriction for the decay into a photon is the requirement that the photon does not occur with spin projection $m = 0$ along its direction of flight. In other words the helicity amplitude G_λ with $\lambda = 0$ has to be 0:[39]

$$G_0 = 0$$

In the type of decay considered

$$B_1(j) \to \gamma(1^-) + B_2(0) \tag{IV.154}$$

j denotes the spin of the parent boson B_1 as well as the total angular momentum (including orbital angular momentum 1) which is carried away by the photon. In the following j has always the latter meaning when general properties of the multipole radiation are discussed. As shown in the last section $G_0 = 0$ is automatically fulfilled for the parity case

1) $l = j$, *i.e. magnetic* $2j$ *pole emission* (Mj)

with

$$G_1 = \sqrt{1/2}, \quad G_0 = 0, \quad G_{-1} = -\sqrt{1/2} \tag{IV.155a}$$

Taking into account the negative intrinsic parity of the photon the overall parity of the magnetic $2j$ pole is

$$P_M(j) = (-1)^{j+1} \tag{IV.155b}$$

For the other parity case

2) $l = j \pm 1$, *i.e. electric* $2j$ *pole emission*, (Ej)

two orbital angular momentum waves A_{j-1} and A_{j+1} are possible which have to be superimposed in the right proportion in order to make $G_0 = 0$. As demonstrated in the previous section one has to require

$$A_{j+1} = \sqrt{\frac{j}{j+1}}\, A_{j-1}$$

or with normalization to 1:

$$A_{j-1} = \sqrt{\frac{j+1}{2j+1}} \qquad A_{j+1} = \sqrt{\frac{j}{2j+1}} \tag{IV.156}$$

which leads to the helicity amplitudes

$$G_1 = \sqrt{1/2}, \quad G_0 = 0, \quad G_{-1} = \sqrt{1/2} \tag{IV.157a}$$

The overall parity of the electric $2j$-pole is

$$P_E(j) = (-1)^j \tag{IV.157b}$$

The case $j = 0$ does not exist for electromagnetic radiation. We shall treat 2 examples in some detail:

a) $$V(1^-) \to P(0^-) + \gamma(1^-)$$

where V stands for any vector meson and P for a pseudosclar meson. From the spins and parities involved it follows immediately that the photon is emitted as a magnetic dipole, i.e. $j = l = 1$ and $P_M(1) = 1$.

Assume V to be in the eigenstate $|1, m\rangle$. Then angular momentum decomposition gives

$$|1, m\rangle_V \to \sum_s (11s, m - s|1m)\, Y_1^{m-s}(\theta, \phi)\, |1, s\rangle_\gamma \tag{IV.158}$$

For the eigenstate $|1, 1\rangle_V$

$$|1, 1\rangle_V \to -\sqrt{\tfrac{1}{2}}\, Y_1^1(\theta, \phi)\, |1, 0\rangle_\gamma + \sqrt{\tfrac{1}{2}}\, Y_1^0 |1, 1\rangle_\gamma \tag{IV.159}$$

Summing over the photon spin states yields the angular distribution

$$|1, 1\rangle_V \to I(\theta, \phi) = \frac{1}{2}|Y_1^1|^2 + \frac{1}{2}|Y_1^0|^2$$

$$= \frac{1}{4\pi} \cdot \frac{3}{4}(1 + \cos^2\theta) \tag{IV.160}$$

and similarly

$$|1, 0\rangle_V \to I(\theta, \phi) = \frac{1}{4\pi} \cdot \frac{3}{2} \sin^2\theta \tag{IV.161}$$

It is straightforward to show that the angular distribution in terms of the V density matrix elements is, with $x = \cos\theta$,

$$\begin{aligned}4\pi I(V \to P\gamma) = 1 & \\ & - {}^1/_2(\varrho_{00} - \varrho_{11})(3x^2 - 1) \\ & + {}^3/_2\varrho_{1-1}(1 - x^2)\cos 2\varphi \\ & + 3\sqrt{2}\,\mathrm{Re}\,\varrho_{10}x\sqrt{1 - x^2} \\ = {}^1/_2(3 - 4\pi I(V \to P_-))\end{aligned} \tag{IV. 162}$$

where $I(V \to PP)$ stands for the corresponding decay distribution when V decays into 2 spinless bosons. (Distribution of decay normal in case of $\omega \to 3\pi$). The symmetry structure (III.11) was assumed for the density matrix.

b) $$A(1^+) \to P(0^-) + \gamma(1^-)$$

where A stands for any axial vector meson. The decay has to proceed over electric dipole emission with $l = 0, 2$; $P_E(1) = -1$. An eigenstate of A, $|1, m\rangle_A$, leads with (IV.156) to the decay state

$$|1, m\rangle_A \to \sqrt{\frac{2}{3}}\, Y_0^0(\theta, \phi)\, |1, m\rangle_\gamma + \\ + \sqrt{\frac{1}{3}} \sum_s (12s, m - s|1m)\, Y_2^{m-s}(\theta, \phi)\, |1, s\rangle_\gamma \tag{IV.163}$$

e.g.

$$|1, 1\rangle_A \to \sqrt{\frac{2}{3}}\, Y_0^0|1, 1\rangle_\gamma \\ + \sqrt{\frac{1}{3}}\left\{\sqrt{\frac{3}{5}}\, Y_2^2|1, -1\rangle_\gamma - \sqrt{\frac{3}{10}}\, Y_2^1|1, 0\rangle_\gamma + \sqrt{\frac{1}{10}}\, Y_0^0|11\rangle\right\} \tag{IV.164}$$

Calculating the decay angular distributions one finds that it is identical to the vector meson decay distribution

$$I(A \to P\gamma) = I(V \to P\gamma)$$

Generally it can be shown that the electric $2j$ pole angular distribution is the same as the corresponding magnetic $2j$ pole distribution (analogy to Minami ambiguity for $F(j) \to B(0) + F(\tfrac{1}{2})$). This follows directly from the fact that $|G_\lambda|^2$ is the same for electric and magnetic multipoles and from relation (IV.124) of the last section which is of the form

$$I(\theta, \phi) = \sum_\lambda \varrho_{\lambda\lambda}^{\mathrm{fin}}(\theta, \phi) = \sum_\lambda |G_\lambda|^2 f_\lambda(\theta, \phi) \tag{IV.165}$$

It is interesting to note that the angular distribution of a vector meson decay into a lepton pair ($V^0 \to l^+l^-$) is for vanishing lepton mass the same as $I(V \to P\gamma)$. [31]

By rotation of the coordinate system it can be verified in the particular examples (IV.159) and (IV.164) that the γ is in fact emitted only in the eigenstates $\lambda = \pm 1$ with respect to its direction of flight. The eigenstates $\lambda = \pm 1$ correspond to right and left circularly polarized light. The postulate that $\lambda = 0$ is forbidden ($G_0 = 0$) implies that the electric polarization vector is alway perpendicular to the γ direction of flight.

To obtain from the spin state of the γ

$$\psi = b_1|1, 1\rangle + b_0|1, 0\rangle + b_{-1}|1, -1\rangle$$

its electric polarization, one has to go from the spherical vector b_m to the Cartesian vector ε_α by the transformation (IV.38)

$$\begin{aligned} b_1 &= \sqrt{{}^1/_2}\,(-\varepsilon_x - i\varepsilon_y) \\ b_{-1} &= \sqrt{{}^1/_2}\,(\varepsilon_x - i\varepsilon_y) \\ b_0 &= \varepsilon_z \end{aligned} \tag{IV.166}$$

One verifies immediately that the electric polarization vector ε_α is perpendicular to the γ direction of flight for the case that the γ is emitted in z direction with $b_0 = 0$.

We shall discuss the γ polarization in greater detail for dipole emission. Assume the total spin (intrinsic γ spin + orbital angular momentum) the γ carries away is 1 and is in the pure state

$$\psi = \sum a_m|1, m\rangle$$

Then the spin state of the emitted γ in the system S' (z' axis along emission direction) is given by the vector $b'_\lambda(\theta, \phi)$ which is obtained from rel. (IV.119) of the last section

$$b'_\lambda(\theta, \phi) = \sqrt{\frac{2j+1}{4\pi}}\, G_\lambda \sum_m D^{(J)*}_{m\lambda}(\phi, \theta, 0)\, a_m$$

where the b_λ are normalized to $I(\theta, \phi)$. With the rotation matrices

$$D^{(J)}_{m'm}(\alpha\beta\gamma) = \mathrm{e}^{-i(\alpha m' + \gamma m)}\, \mathrm{d}^{(J)}_{m'm}(\beta)$$

we obtain in detail:

$$\begin{aligned} b'_1(\theta, \phi) &= \sqrt{\frac{3}{4\pi}}\, G_1 \left\{a_1\, \mathrm{e}^{i\phi}\, \frac{1 + \cos\theta}{2} + a_0\, \frac{\sin\theta}{\sqrt{2}} + a_{-1}\, \mathrm{e}^{-i\phi}\, \frac{1 - \cos\theta}{2}\right\} \\ b'_0(\theta, \phi) &= 0 \\ b'_{-1}(\theta, \phi) &= \sqrt{\frac{3}{4\pi}}\, G_{-1} \left\{a_1\, \mathrm{e}^{i\phi}\, \frac{1 - \cos\theta}{2} - a_0\, \frac{\sin\theta}{\sqrt{2}} + a_{-1}\, \mathrm{e}^{-i\phi}\, \frac{1 + \cos\theta}{2}\right\} \end{aligned} \tag{IV.167}$$

with

$$G_1 = \sqrt{{}^1/_2}, \quad G_{-1} = \sqrt{{}^1/_2} \qquad \text{for electric dipole}$$

$$G_1 = \sqrt{{}^1/_2}, \quad G_{-1} = -\sqrt{{}^1/_2} \quad \text{for magnetic dipole.}$$

Thus, if for an electric multipole the γ is in the helicity spin state

$$\psi_E = b_1|1, 1\rangle + b_{-1}|1, -1\rangle \tag{IV.168a}$$

the corresponding magnetic multipole γ has

$$\psi_M = b_1|1, 1\rangle - b_{-1}|1, -1\rangle \tag{IV.168b}$$

In terms of polarization unit vectors $\hat{e}_x, \hat{e}_y, \hat{e}_z$ with components (c.f. IV.166)

$$\begin{aligned} \varepsilon_x &= \sqrt{{}^1/_2}\,(-b_1 + b_{-1}) \\ \varepsilon_y &= \sqrt{{}^1/_2}\, i(b_1 + b_{-1}) \\ \varepsilon_z &= b_0 \end{aligned} \tag{IV.169}$$

one has correspondingly

$$\psi_E = \varepsilon_x\hat{e}_x + \varepsilon_y\hat{e}_y \tag{IV.170a}$$

$$\psi_M = i\varepsilon_y\hat{e}_x - i\varepsilon_x\hat{e}_y \tag{IV.170b}$$

(IV.168a) or (IV.170a) is the most general discription of a photon in a pure spin state propagating along the z axis. The complex numbers ε_x and ε_y are normalized to 1. A common phase factor $e^{i\varphi}$ is arbitrary so that one can in principle always choose ε_x as real.

Thus the most general pure photon spin (or polarization) state depends on 2 real parameters like the pure spin ${}^1/_2$ state. Calling these parameters α and β it is convenient to define

$$\varepsilon_x = \cos\alpha; \quad \varepsilon_y = \sin\alpha\, e^{i\beta}$$

or

$$\psi = \cos\alpha\,\hat{e}_x + \sin\alpha\, e^{i\beta}\,\hat{e}_y \tag{IV.171}$$

Compare (I.56) for spin ${}^1/_2$!

We distinguish the following cases:

1) $\beta = 0$: Linear polarization at an angle α with the x-axis.

2) $\cos\alpha = \sin\alpha = \sqrt{\frac{1}{2}}; \quad \beta = \pm\frac{\pi}{2}$:

Left and right circular polarization.

3) α, β arbitrary: elliptic polarization.

As example we assume an axial vector particle A in the spin eigenstate $|1, 1\rangle_A$. As stated before, the decay into a π and a γ proceeds over an electric dipole transition. From (IV.167) and (IV.170a) one calculates the polarization state of the emitted γ as a function of the emission angle θ

$$\psi(\theta) = \frac{1}{1 + \cos^2\theta}(-\cos\theta\, \hat{e}_{x'} + i\hat{e}_{y'}) \qquad \text{(IV.172)}$$

where the unit vectors (defined in the $\theta - \phi$ dependent system S') are perpendicular to the γ direction of flight. For $\theta = 0$ one finds right handed circular polarization and for $\theta = \pi/2$ linear polarization in y' dircetion (x, y plane), as one would expect in a classical picture for light emission from an electric charge moving on a circular orbit in the xy-plane.

As last example we shall discuss the decay

$$\Sigma^0 \to \Lambda^0 + \gamma$$

As the relative $\Sigma - \Lambda$ parity is even[32] the decay has to proceed over magnetic dipole emission ($M1$), otherwise it would be an electric dipole ($E1$). We assume the Σ^0 to be in the spin eigenstate $|\frac{1}{2}\,\frac{1}{2}\rangle$. Clebsch-Gordan decomposition into Λ spin states $|\frac{1}{2}s\rangle_\Lambda$ and photon total (orbital + intrinsic) angular momentum states $|1, m\rangle_{M1}$ gives

$$|\tfrac{1}{2}, \tfrac{1}{2}\rangle_{\Sigma^0} \to -\sqrt{\tfrac{1}{3}}\,|\tfrac{1}{2}, \tfrac{1}{2}\rangle_\Lambda\,|1,0\rangle_{M1} + \sqrt{\tfrac{2}{3}}\,|\tfrac{1}{2}, -\tfrac{1}{2}\rangle_\Lambda\,|1, 1\rangle_{M1} \qquad \text{(IV.173)}$$

When averaging over the dipole states (i.e. over angular distribution and photon polarization) we find that the average Λ polarization in z direction is $-\frac{1}{3}$ (also for $E1$). This provides a method to determine Σ^0 polarization. The actual decay state is obtained by further decomposition of the dipole states into orbital angular momentum Y_1^m and intrinsic photon spin $|1n\rangle_\gamma$. One obtains for $|\frac{1}{2}, \frac{1}{2}\rangle_{\Sigma^0}$ the decay state

$$\begin{aligned}\psi = &-\sqrt{\tfrac{1}{3}}\,|\tfrac{1}{2}, \tfrac{1}{2}\rangle_\Lambda \left\{\sqrt{\tfrac{1}{2}}\, Y_1^{-1}|1, 1\rangle_\gamma - \sqrt{\tfrac{1}{2}}\, Y_1^{1}|1, -1\rangle_\gamma\right\}\\ &+ \sqrt{\tfrac{2}{3}}\,|\tfrac{1}{2}, -\tfrac{1}{2}\rangle_\Lambda \left\{\sqrt{\tfrac{1}{2}}\, Y_1^{0}|1,1\rangle_\gamma - \sqrt{\tfrac{1}{2}}\, Y_1^{1}|1, 0\rangle_\gamma\right\}\end{aligned} \qquad \text{(IV.174)}$$

We shall now calculate the density matrix of the Λ in the original frame where the Σ^0 spin state is defined, as a function of the emission angles, θ, ϕ).

As we have to average over the γ spin we decompose ψ into 3 states ψ_1, ψ_2, ψ_3 each corresponding to a different γ spin eigenstate:

$$\psi_1 = \left\{-\sqrt{\tfrac{1}{6}}\, Y_1^{-1}|\tfrac{1}{2}, \tfrac{1}{2}\rangle_\Lambda + \sqrt{\tfrac{1}{3}}\, Y_1^{0}|\tfrac{1}{2}, -\tfrac{1}{2}\rangle_\Lambda\right\} |1, 1\rangle_\gamma$$

$$\psi_2 = \left\{-\sqrt{\tfrac{1}{3}}\, Y_1^{1}|\tfrac{1}{2}, -\tfrac{1}{2}\rangle_\Lambda\right\} |1, 0\rangle_\gamma$$

$$\psi_3 = \left\{\sqrt{\tfrac{1}{6}}\, Y_1^{1}|\tfrac{1}{2}, \tfrac{1}{2}\rangle_\Lambda\right\} |1, -1\rangle_\gamma$$

The averaging over the γ spin is done by adding the Λ density matrices of these 3 states. One obtains

$$\varrho_\Lambda(\theta, \phi) = \begin{bmatrix} \frac{1}{3}|Y_1^1|^2 & -\sqrt{\frac{1}{18}}\, Y_1^{-1} Y_1^0 \\ +\sqrt{\frac{1}{18}}\, Y_1^1 Y_1^0 & \frac{1}{3}(|Y_1^1|^2 + |Y_1^0|^2) \end{bmatrix} \tag{IV.175}$$

One sees that the angular distribution (= sum of diagonal elements) is isotropic.

If the Σ^0 is not in an eigenstate but in a state described by the density matrix elements $\varrho_{++}, \varrho_{--}, \varrho_{+-}, \varrho_{-+}$ the angle dependent density matrix of the Λ^0 is found to be with $x = \cos\theta$

$$\begin{aligned} \varrho^\Lambda_{1/2\,1/2}(\theta,\phi) &= \frac{1}{4\pi}\left\{\frac{1}{3}\varrho_{++} + \frac{2}{3}\varrho_{--} + \frac{1}{6}[\varrho_{--} - \varrho_{++}](3x^2 - 1) \right. \\ &\quad \left. - x\sqrt{1-x^2}\,\mathrm{Re}\,[\varrho_{+-}\,\mathrm{e}^{i\phi}]\right\} \\ \varrho^\Lambda_{-1/2\,-1/2}(\theta,\phi) &= \frac{1}{4\pi}\left\{\frac{1}{3}\varrho_{--} + \frac{2}{3}\varrho_{++} + \frac{1}{6}[\varrho_{++} - \varrho_{--}](3x^2 - 1) \right. \\ &\quad \left. + x\sqrt{1-x^2}\,\mathrm{Re}\,[\varrho_{+-}\,\mathrm{e}^{i\phi}]\right\} \\ \varrho^\Lambda_{1/2\,-1/2}(\theta,\phi) &= \frac{1}{4\pi}\left\{-\frac{1}{3}\varrho_{+-} + \frac{1}{6}\varrho_{+-}(3x^2 - 1) \right. \\ &\quad \left. - \frac{1}{2}[\varrho_{++} - \varrho_{--}]\,x\sqrt{1-x^2}\,\mathrm{e}^{-i\phi} - \frac{1}{2}\varrho^*_{+-}(1-x^2)\,\mathrm{e}^{-2i\phi}\right\} \end{aligned} \tag{IV.176}$$

Averaging the Λ density matrix over the emission angles, θ, ϕ yields

$$\begin{aligned} \langle\varrho^\Lambda_{1/2\,1/2}\rangle &= \tfrac{1}{3}\varrho_{++} + \tfrac{2}{3}\varrho_{--} \\ \langle\varrho^\Lambda_{-1/2\,-1/2}\rangle &= \tfrac{2}{3}\varrho_{++} + \tfrac{1}{3}\varrho_{--} \\ \langle\varrho^\Lambda_{1/2\,-1/2}\rangle &= -\tfrac{1}{3}\varrho_{+-} \end{aligned} \tag{IV.177}$$

which completely determines the Σ^0 density matrix.

In an analogous way one could calculate the γ polarization averaging over the Λ spin. In contrast to the angular and Λ polarization distributions which are the same for $M1$ and $E1$ transitions, the γ polarization is different for the two cases as pointed out previously and could in principle serve to determine the relative $\Sigma - \Lambda$ parity. This parity determination was done however with Dalitz pairs coming from virtual γ rays which show different invariant mass distributions for electric and magnetic dipole emission.[32,33]

APPENDIX

RELATIVISTIC GENERALIZATION OF THE SPIN ANALYSIS

For the discussion of relativistic spin problems we choose as an example the Ξ decay $\Xi^- \to \Lambda\pi^-$ which was treated in section IIc.

When calculating the Λ spin state as a function of the emission angles θ, ϕ in the Ξ rest frame

$$\psi_\Lambda = a(\theta, \phi) \begin{pmatrix} 1 \\ 0 \end{pmatrix} + b(\theta, \phi) \begin{pmatrix} 0 \\ 1 \end{pmatrix}$$

we tacitly assumed that the Λ spin function ψ_Λ refers to the Λ *rest frame*. In fact the spin has a simple physical meaning only in the rest frame of a particle where the eigenfunctions $|j, m\rangle$ are defined. In the spin description, we did not distinguish between the Ξ system, where the decay orbital angular momentum is strictly defined, and the Λ rest system, where the Λ spin is strictly defined. It is clear therefore that our treatment is typically non-relativistic.

Let us now try to find a relativistic generalization.

For this purpose it is necessary to construct spin states for particles in motion.

The relativistic decay state of the Ξ in its rest system can be written as a linear superposition of states

$$|L, M, s, m\rangle = \int d\Omega_p Y_L^M(\Omega_p)\, \varphi_p \Gamma_p \chi_s^m \tag{A.1}$$

where the quantities on the right side are defined as follows:

Ω_p — angles θ_p, ϕ_p, denoting the direction of the Λ momentum $\boldsymbol{p}$ in the Ξ rest system.

$d\Omega_p$ — $d\cos\theta_p\, d\phi_p$.

$Y_L^M(\Omega_p)$ — decay orbital angular momentum state with angular momentum L and z component M.

φ_p — plane wave state $e^{i\mathbf{px}}$ for Λ (and π) in Ξ rest system where Λ has momentum $\mathbf{p}$ and π has $-\mathbf{p}$.

χ_s^m — spin eigenstate of Λ *in its own rest system* which is so defined that its coordinate axes are parallel to those in the Ξ rest system. s denotes the Λ spin, m its z component.

If for example the Λ spin is $\frac{1}{2}$, $\chi_{1/2}^{1/2}$ and $\chi_{1/2}^{-1/2}$ can be described by the Dirac spinors in the particle rest system

$$\chi_{1/2}^{1/2} = \begin{bmatrix} 1 \\ 0 \\ 0 \\ 0 \end{bmatrix} \qquad \chi_{1/2}^{-1/2} = \begin{bmatrix} 0 \\ 1 \\ 0 \\ 0 \end{bmatrix}$$

Γ_p — is a matrix that transforms the Λ spin state from the Λ rest system to the Ξ rest system. It corresponds to the Lorentz transformation L_p

which brings the Λ rest system to the Ξ rest system:

$$L_{\mathbf{p}}: \begin{cases} \mathbf{x}' = \mathbf{x} + \boldsymbol{\beta}\gamma\left[\dfrac{\gamma}{\gamma+1}\,\boldsymbol{\beta}\mathbf{x} - t\right] \\ t' = \gamma[t - \boldsymbol{\beta}\mathbf{x}] \quad \text{with} \quad \gamma = \dfrac{1}{\sqrt{1-\beta^2}} \end{cases} \tag{A.2}$$

where $\boldsymbol{\beta}$ is the velocity of the Λ in the Ξ rest system. $\Gamma_{\mathbf{p}}$ reduces to the unit matrix in the non-relativistic case.

In the following we shall show that the rotation properties of the relativistic states $|L, M, s, m\rangle$ are independent of the Λ momentum $\boldsymbol{p}$, i.e. they transform under rotations in the Ξ rest system as the corresponding non-relativistic states. Once this is proved, one may argue as follows: All angular momentum operators J_x, J_y, J_z are proportional to operators of infinitesimal rotations about the x, y, z axes. The commutation relations between J_x, J_y, J_z define the entire spin-angular momentum algebra. As in our problem the relativistic states Eq. (A.1) transform under rotations as the corresponding non-relativistic states, our non-relativistic treatment of the Ξ decay, which considers only angular momentum in the Ξ rest system is formally identical to the relativistic treatment when expressing the Ξ decay state as a linear superposition of the states $|L, M, s, m\rangle$ in Eq. (A.1). So it remains to show that the rotation transformations of these states are independent of the Λ momentum $\boldsymbol{p}$.

Apply a rotation R in the Ξ rest system to the state Eq. (A.1)

$$R|L, M, s, m\rangle = \int R\, d\Omega_{\mathbf{p}}(RY_L^M(\Omega_{\mathbf{p}})\,\varphi_{\mathbf{p}})\,(R\Gamma_{\mathbf{p}}\chi_s^m).$$

The factor $Y_L^M(\Omega_{\mathbf{p}})\,\varphi_{\mathbf{p}}$ is a plane wave of amplitude $Y_L^M(\Omega_{\mathbf{p}})$ running in the direction of $\boldsymbol{p}$. Rotating this configuration gives another plane wave $\varphi_{R\mathbf{p}}$ of the same amplitude but running in the direction of $R\boldsymbol{p}$, i.e. $Y_L^M(\Omega_{\mathbf{p}})\,\varphi_{R\mathbf{p}}$. Therefore we have

$$R|L, M, s, m\rangle = \int d\Omega_{R\mathbf{p}} Y_L^M(\Omega_{\mathbf{p}})\,\varphi_{R\mathbf{p}}(R\Gamma_{\mathbf{p}}\chi_s^m)$$

where we have replaced $d\Omega_{\mathbf{p}}$ by $d\Omega_{R\mathbf{p}}$ (one has $d\Omega_{\mathbf{p}} = d\Omega_{R\mathbf{p}}$).

Below we show that

$$R\Gamma_{\mathbf{p}} = \Gamma_{R\mathbf{p}}R \tag{A.3}$$

i.e. instead of first transforming the Λ spin state to the Ξ system and then rotating it, one can first rotate the Λ spin state in the Λ rest system and then transform it to the Ξ rest system along the rotated direction $R\boldsymbol{p}$. With Eq. (A.3) one can write

$$R|L, M, s, m\rangle = \int d\Omega_{R\mathbf{p}} Y_L^M(\Omega_{\mathbf{p}})\,\varphi_{R\mathbf{p}}\Gamma_{R\mathbf{p}}R\chi_s^m.$$

Substituting $\boldsymbol{p}$ for $R\boldsymbol{p}$ gives

$$R|L, M, s, m\rangle = \int d\Omega_{\mathbf{p}} Y_L^M(\Omega_{R^{-1}\mathbf{p}})\,\varphi_{\mathbf{p}}\Gamma_{\mathbf{p}}R\chi_s^m.$$

In terms of the D matrices for finite rotations of non-relativistic spin states one can write

$$Y_L^M(\Omega_{R^{-1}\mathbf{p}}) = \sum_{M'} D_{MM'}^{(L)}(R)\, Y_L^{M'}(\Omega_\mathbf{p})$$

and

$$R\chi_s^m = \sum_{m'} D_{mm'}^{(s)}(R)\, \chi_s^{m'}$$

and consequently:

$$R|L, M, s, m\rangle = \sum_{M'm'} D_{MM'}^{(L)}(R)\, D_{mm'}^{(s)}(R)\, |L, M', s, m'\rangle, \tag{A.4}$$

just as in the non-relativistic case. So it is shown that the relativistic states transform under rotations in the Ξ rest system as non-relativistic spin states.

We still have to prove the relation

$$R\Gamma_\mathbf{p} = \Gamma_{R\mathbf{p}}R \tag{A.3}$$

which is essential for the simple transformation property Eq. (A.4) of the states $|L, M, s, m\rangle$. Equation (A.3) is equivalent to the relation

$$RL_\mathbf{p} = L_{R\mathbf{p}}R \tag{A.5}$$

where $L_\mathbf{p}$ is the Lorentz transformation Eq. (A.2)

$$RL_\mathbf{p} \text{ is } \begin{cases} \mathbf{x}' = R\mathbf{x} + R\boldsymbol{\beta}\gamma\left[\dfrac{1}{\gamma+1}(\boldsymbol{\beta}\mathbf{x}) - t\right] \\ t' = \gamma[t - (\boldsymbol{\beta}\mathbf{x})] \end{cases}$$

$$L_{R\mathbf{p}}R \text{ is } \begin{cases} \mathbf{x}' = R\mathbf{x} + R\boldsymbol{\beta}\gamma\left[\dfrac{1}{\gamma+1}(R\boldsymbol{\beta}\cdot R\mathbf{x}) - t\right] \\ t' = \gamma[t - (R\boldsymbol{\beta}\cdot R\mathbf{x})] \end{cases}$$

Hence

$$RL_\mathbf{p} = L_{R\mathbf{p}}R$$

follows from $(R\boldsymbol{\beta}\cdot R\mathbf{x}) = (\boldsymbol{\beta}\mathbf{x})$.

Although we have now proved that our original treatment of the Ξ decay is formally correct for the relativistic case also, we have still to re-interpret the results in terms of the relativistic decay states, Eq. (A.1). According to the definition of these states the Λ spin eigenstates χ_s^m refer to that Λ rest system which results from the Ξ rest system by applying a Lorentz transformation $L_{-\mathbf{p}}$ [defined in Eq. (A.2)] to the Ξ rest system. Therefore to every Λ emission direction there corresponds a different Λ rest system, in which the Λ polarization and its decay angular distribution are exactly described by the non-relativistic formulae derived in this paper.

In this connection it has to be stressed that in the relativistic case the Λ rest system defined as above by a Lorentz translation applied to the Ξ c.m. system is only one among an infinite number of possible rest systems, differing from each other by rotations of the coordinate system. For instance if one transforms the Λ

from the Ξ c.m. first to the laboratory system and from there by a translation to its rest system, this rest system will, in general, be different from the rest system defined above, by a rotation which tends to zero for decreasing relative velocities. This rotation is a purely kinematical effect known as "Thomas precession". It comes from the fact that translations are not a subgroup of the Lorentz group in contrast to the Galilei group. That means the product of two Lorentz translations is in general a translation coupled with a rotation.

To compare experiment with theory one has to transform experimental quantities such as polarization or angular distribution, to the system in which they have been calculated theoretically. In our problem of the decay parameters, we are, for instance, interested in the angular distribution of the protons from the Λ decay with respect to the Λ direction of flight *measured in that Λ rest frame which is defined by the Ξ rest frame and the Λ momentum* $\mathbf{p}_\Lambda$ *in this system.* Experimentally everything is observed in the laboratory, so to compare with the theoretical angular or polarization distribution, one has first to transform the Λ *and the decay proton* to the Ξ rest frame, and from there, the proton to the Λ rest frame defined as above.

Let us finally calculate the rotation which results from two successive Lorentz translations.

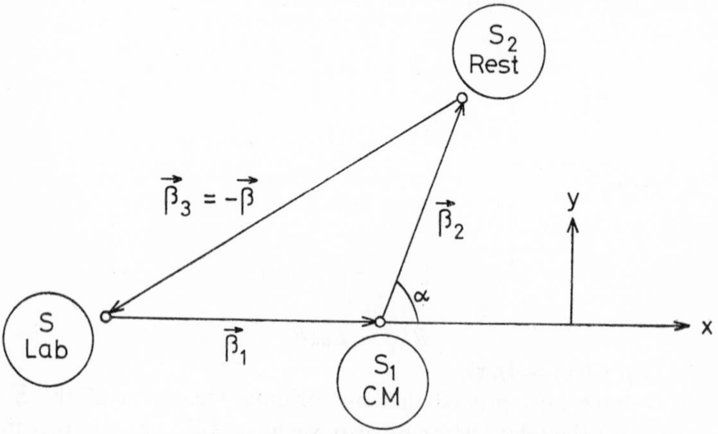

Fig. 11

Assume system S_1 moves relative to system S with a velocity β_1 in x direction. System S_2 moves relative to system S_1 with a velocity $\boldsymbol{\beta}_2$ lying in the x-y plane and including an angle α with the x axis. System S moves with the velocity $\boldsymbol{\beta}_3 = -\boldsymbol{\beta}$ relative to S_2 where $\boldsymbol{\beta}$ is the velocity resulting from the addition of $\boldsymbol{\beta}_1$ and $\boldsymbol{\beta}_2$

$$\boldsymbol{\beta} = \frac{\boldsymbol{\beta}_1 + \boldsymbol{\beta}_2\gamma_2\left[\dfrac{\gamma_2}{\gamma_2 + 1}(\boldsymbol{\beta}_1\boldsymbol{\beta}_2) + 1\right]}{\gamma_2[1 + \boldsymbol{\beta}_1\boldsymbol{\beta}_2]} \tag{A.6}$$

In connection with our problem, systems S, S_1 and S_2 can be identified with the laboratory system, the Ξ c.m. system, and the Λ rest system respectively.

The Lorentz translation

$$T(\beta_1) \text{ transforms } S \text{ into } S_1$$

$$T(\beta_2) \text{ transforms } S_1 \text{ into } S_2$$

so the product transformation

$$L = T(\beta_2)\,T(\beta_1) \text{ transforms } S \text{ into } S_2.$$

What we wish to show is that

$$L = T(\beta_2)\,T(\beta_1)$$

can be written as the product of a Lorentz translation $T(\beta)$ and a rotation $R(\omega)$:

$$R(\omega)\,T(\beta) = T(\beta_2)\,T(\beta_1)$$

or

$$R(\omega) = T(\beta)^{-1}\,T(\beta_2)\,T(\beta_1)$$

or, as

$$\beta = -\beta_3$$

$$R(\omega) = T(\beta_3)\,T(\beta_2)\,T(\beta_1). \tag{A.7}$$

Let us represent the T's as matrices operating on four vectors:

$$T(\beta_1) = \begin{bmatrix} \gamma_1 & 0 & 0 & i\beta_1\gamma_1 \\ 0 & 1 & 0 & 0 \\ 0 & 0 & 1 & 0 \\ -i\beta_1\gamma_1 & 0 & 0 & \gamma_1 \end{bmatrix}$$

$$T(\beta_2) = \left[\begin{array}{c|c|c|c} 1 + (\gamma_2 - 1)\cos^2\alpha & (\gamma_2 - 1)\sin\alpha\cos\alpha & 0 & i\beta_2\gamma_2\cos\alpha \\ (\gamma_2 - 1)\sin\alpha\cos\alpha & 1 + (\gamma_2 - 1)\sin^2\alpha & 0 & i\beta_2\gamma_2\sin\alpha \\ 0 & 0 & 1 & 0 \\ -i\beta_2\gamma_2\cos\alpha & -i\beta_2\gamma_2\sin\alpha & 0 & \gamma_2 \end{array}\right]$$

$T(\beta_3)$ is a matrix corresponding to $T(\beta_2)$ but containing instead of β_2, γ_2

$$\beta_3 = \frac{1}{\gamma_3}\sqrt{\gamma_3^2 - 1}$$

$$\gamma_3 = \gamma_1\gamma_2[1 + \beta_1\beta_2\cos\alpha]$$

and according to Eq. (A.6) instead of $\sin\alpha$, $\cos\alpha$

$$\sin\varphi = -\gamma_1 \frac{\beta_2\gamma_2 \sin\alpha\left[\frac{\gamma_2}{\gamma_2+1}\beta_1\beta_2\cos\alpha + 1\right]}{\sqrt{\gamma_3^2 - 1}}$$

$$\cos\varphi = -\gamma_1 \frac{\beta_1 + \beta_2\gamma_2 \cos\alpha\left[\frac{\gamma_2}{\gamma_2+1}\beta_1\beta_2\cos\alpha + 1\right]}{\sqrt{\gamma_3^2 - 1}}$$

Working out the product matrix

$$R(\omega) = T(\beta_3)\,T(\beta_2)\,T(\beta_1)$$

one finds that it has the structure

$$R(\omega) = \begin{bmatrix} a_{11} & a_{12} & 0 & 0 \\ a_{21} & a_{22} & 0 & 0 \\ 0 & 0 & 0 & 0 \\ 0 & 0 & 0 & 1 \end{bmatrix}$$

This Lorentz matrix can only effect a rotation about the z axis by an angle ω with

$$a_{11} = \cos\omega \quad a_{12} = -\sin\omega$$

$$a_{21} = \sin\omega \quad a_{22} = \cos\omega\,.$$

The element a_{12} can be written in the form

$$a_{21} = \sin\omega = \beta_1\beta_2 \sin\alpha\gamma_1\gamma_2 \frac{1+\gamma_1+\gamma_2+\gamma_3}{(1+\gamma_1)(1+\gamma_2)(1+\gamma_3)}; \quad \gamma_3 = \gamma$$

or in an arbitrary coordinate system

$$\sin\omega = \boldsymbol{\beta}_1 \times \boldsymbol{\beta}_2\gamma_1\gamma_2 \frac{1+\gamma_1+\gamma_2+\gamma}{(1+\gamma_1)(1+\gamma_2)(1+\gamma)} \tag{A.8}$$

Applied to our special case, $\boldsymbol{\beta}_1$ is the Ξ velocity in the laboratory, $\boldsymbol{\beta}_2$ is the Λ velocity in the Ξ system and $\boldsymbol{\beta}$ is the Λ velocity in the laboratory. The result means the following: When transforming the decay proton directly from the laboratory to the Λ rest system one has afterwards to rotate the proton momentum vector by an angle ω defined by Eq. (A.8) in the right-handed sense around the axis $\boldsymbol{\beta}_1 \times \boldsymbol{\beta}_2$ in order to make it coincide with the proton momentum vector which was transformed *via the Ξ system* to the Λ rest frame.

Generalized treatments of the relativistic spin problem can be found in articles by H. P. Stapp, M. I. Shirokov[26], M. Jacob and G. C. Wick[22] and M. Jacob[22].

REFERENCES

1. N. E. Rose, Elementary Theory of Angular Mometnum, John Wiley and Sons, Inc., New York (1957).
2. R. Hagedorn, Angular Momentum, Lectures at the Max-Planck-Institut für Physik, München (1963).
3. A. Messiah, Quantum Mechanics, North Holland Publishing Company (1965).
4. L. I. Schiff, Quantum Mechanics, Mc Graw-Hill (1955).
5. E. U. Condon, and G. H. Shortley, The Theory of Atomic Spectra, Cambridge University Press, Cambridge (1951).
6. A. R. Edmonds, Angular Momentum in Quantum Mechanics, Princeton University Press (1957).
7. J. B. Shafer, J. J. Murray, and D. O. Howe, *Phys. Rev. Letters* **10**, 179 (1963).
8. R. K. Adair, *Phys. Rev.* **100**, 1540 (1955).
9. F. Eisler *et al.*, *Nuovo Cimento* **7**, 222 (1958).
10. C. Alff *et al.*, *Phys. Rev. Letters* **11**, 90 (1963).
11. L. Stodolsky, and J. J. Sakurai, *Phys. Rev. Letters* **11**, 90 (1963).
12. W. B. Teutsch, S. Okubo, and E. C. G. Sudarshan, *Phys. Rev.* **114**, 1148 (1959).
13. A. H. Rosenfeld *et al.*, Data on Particles and Resonant States, UCRL-8030 (1967).
14. R. H. Capps, *Phys. Rev.* **122** 929 (1961).
15. P. E. Schlein *et al.*, *Phys. Rev. Letters* **11**, 167 (1963).
16. G. F. Wolters, *Physics Letters* **3**, 41 (1962), and *Nuovo Cimento* **28**, 843 (1963).
17. K. Gottfried, and J. D. Jackson, *Nuovo Cimento* **33**, 309 (1964).
18. K. Gottfried and J. D. Jackson, *Nuovo Cimento* **34**, 735 (1964).
19. C. Zemach, *Phys. Rev.* **133**, B 1201 (1964).
20. M. Hamermesh, Group Theory, Addison-Wesley Publishing Company (1962).
21. N. Byers, and S. Fenster, *Phys. Rev. Letters* **11**, (1963) 52 Ashkin, Varenna Summer School 1964.
22. M. Jacob, and G. C. Wick, *Ann. of Phys.* **7**, 404 (1959); M. Jacob, Summer Meeting of Nuclear Physicists 1961, Herceg Novi.
23. M. Ademollo, and R. Gatto, *Phys. Rev.* **133**, B 531 (1964); M. Ademollo, R. Gatto, and G. Preparata, *Phys. Rev. Letters* **12**, 462 (1964); M. Ademollo, R. Gatto, and G. Preparata, *Phys. Rev.* **139**, B 1608 (1965); M. Ademollo, R. Gatto, and G. Preparata, *Phys. Rev.* **140**, B 192 (1965).
24. J. Button-Shafer, *Phys. Rev.* **139**, B 607 (1965).
25. G. Szegö, Orthogonal Polynomials, *Amer. Math. Soc.*, 1939 (Colloquium Publications Vol. 23).
26. H. P. Stapp, *Phys. Rev.* **103**, 425 (1956); M. I. Shirokov, *JETP* **5**, 835 (1957).
27. S. U. Chung, *Phys. Rev.* **138**, B 1541 (1965).
28. Ref. 3., page 1057.
29. S. M. Berman, and M. Jacob, SLAC — report Wo. 43 (unpublished).
30. S. M. Berman, and M. Jacob, *Phys. Rev.* **139**, B 1023 (1965); C. Zemach, *Nuovo Cimento* **32**, 1605 (1964a); C. Zemach, *Phys. Rev.* **140**, B 97, B 109 (1965).
31. R. J. Oakes, *Nuovo Cimento* **44**, 440 (1966).
32. H. Courant *et al.*, *Phys. Rev. Letters* **10**, 409 (1963).
33. G. Feinberg, *Phys. Rev.* **109**, 1019 (1958); G. Feldman, and T. Fulton, *Nucl. Phys.* **8**, 106 (1958).
34. U. Fano, *Rev. Mod. Phys.* **29**, 74 (1957).
35. R. Hagedorn, CERN 58-7.
36. J. von Neumann, *Göttinger Nachrichten* **245** and **273** (1927).
37. U. Fano, and G. Raçah, Irreducible Tensorial Sets, Academic Press N.Y. (1959).
38. M. Peshkin, *Phys. Rev.* **133** B 428 (1964).
39. A. I. Achieser, und W. B. Berestezki, Quantenelektrodynamik, Harri Deutsch, Frankfurt/Main 1962.
40. J. D. Jackson, High Energy Physics Les Houches 1965, Gordon and Breach Science Publishers New York.
41. E. R. Cohen, Tables of Clebsch-Gordan Coefficients, Atomics International NAA-SR-2123.
42. Proceedings of the 1964 Easter School for Physicists, Herceg-Novi, CERN 64-13.
43. T. D. Lee, and C. N. Yang, *Phys. Rev.* **109**, 1755 (1958).